PEARSON   ALWAYS LEARNING

Theodore R. Bosela

Electrical Systems Design

Custom Edition

Taken from:
Electrical Systems Design
by Theodore R. Bosela

ISBN 10: 1-256-92345-1
ISBN 13: 978-1-256-92345-9

This book is dedicated to my wife, Christine,
and to my children, Stephen and Emily,
for their love and understanding
during the preparation of this text.

Preface

This text focuses primarily on the design of electrical power systems commonly found in residential, commercial, and industrial occupancies. While the text is not meant to be an interpretation of the *National Electrical Code®* (*NEC*)[1], it emphasizes the design of electrical systems in accordance with the *NEC*. Requirements of the *NEC* are explained as needed to provide the student with an appreciation of the *Code* as well as to ensure that electrical systems are designed with regard to public safety and well-being. It is strongly suggested that students obtain a copy of the *NEC* to reference the *Code* sections specified throughout the text.

The text is suitable for use in a sophomore-level course in electrical power distribution systems commonly taught at community colleges. In addition, the text may be suitable for electrical apprentice and industrial training programs. The necessary prerequisites include courses in basic electrical circuits, college algebra, and trigonometry. Readers should be familiar with the concepts of complex algebra and power relationships in single-phase and three-phase alternating current circuits. Prerequisite courses in electrical machinery are not required because sufficient background information is given in the chapters dealing with transformers and motors. Mathematics requirements are intentionally kept at the college algebra and trigonometry level, and calculus has been kept to a minimum.

Introduction

Chapter 1 provides an overview of electrical power distribution systems commonly encountered in residential, commercial, and industrial occupancies. Representation of electrical power systems through the use of one-line and riser diagrams is discussed. Common system voltages, as well as applicable codes and standards are introduced. In addition, a design team consisting of architects, civil/structural engineers, mechanical engineers, and electrical engineers is introduced to give the reader an appreciation of the interaction that must occur among these disciplines if a design project is to be successful.

Chapter 2 introduces the concept of an electrical load, which is fundamental in understanding the calculation of load current, power, and power factor. Estimates of electrical load based on the *NEC* requirements are discussed, as well as the application of load demand factors. These elements provide the basis for which branch circuit, feeder, and service entrance conductors are sized.

---

[1] *National Electrical Code®* and *NEC®* are registered trademarks of the National Fire Protection Association, Inc., Quincy, MA 02269.

Chapter 3 discusses the method used to estimate the electrical load in various occupancies. Included in the discussion are rates and billing calculations and the application of appropriate demand factors.

Different types of wiring devices are discussed in Chapter 4. The characteristics, ratings, and applications of toggle or "snap" switches commonly used to control lighting, receptacles, and small motor loads are discussed. Also discussed are the characteristics and applications of general-purpose receptacles, isolated ground receptacles, and hospital-grade receptacles. A discussion of the different NEMA pin configurations for separable connectors is presented, and the application and rating of disconnect switches used to isolate certain types of equipment from the power supply are discussed.

Chapter 5 presents a discussion of the various types of overcurrent and short circuit protection devices used in electrical system design. Current-limiting, non-current-limiting and other fuse types are discussed, as are fuse classifications according to UL Standards. Fixed trip, adjustable trip, and electronic circuit breakers are covered, as well. Standard ratings and applications in accordance with the *NEC* are included in the chapter.

Chapter 6 focuses on the different types of conductor, insulation, and cables commonly used in electrical construction. The determination of conductor ampacity as a function of ambient temperature, conductor type, and insulation is presented. In addition, the derating of conductor ampacity as a function of ambient temperature and number of current-carrying conductors in a raceway is discussed. The temperature limitations of device terminals and the effect of this limitation on the conductor ampacity are also discussed.

Chapter 7 discusses the specific *NEC* requirements for switch, receptacle, lighting outlet location, and branch circuit requirements for various occupancies. Ground fault and arcing fault protection requirements are also discussed. The development of cabling diagrams as a design element for residential and commercial locations is presented.

The use of conduit, wireways, and cable tray as a means of supporting and protecting conductors is discussed in Chapter 8. Various types of metallic and nonmetallic conduit are presented. Sizing of conduit, cable tray, and boxes based on allowable *NEC* conduit fill requirements is discussed in detail. Conduit fittings, supports, and cable tray systems are also discussed.

Chapter 9 discusses the important subject of grounding. Reasons for grounding equipment and raceways are discussed along with the concept of ground fault protection. Proper sizing of equipment ground conductors, service grounding requirements, grounding of separately derived systems and instrument transformer grounding are presented.

The design of service entrance equipment in accordance with the *NEC* is presented in Chapter 10. The maximum number of service entrance disconnects, ground fault circuit interruption requirements, service entrance conductor sizing, service entrance grounding, main overcurrent protective device location, and estimated service load are discussed in detail.

The use of panelboards and switchboards as a means of distributing power is discussed in Chapter 11. The definition of lighting and appliance branch circuit panelboards is presented as well as several common panelboard arrangements and schematics. Clearances required around switchgear and panelboards, the development of panelboard schedules, balancing, and grounding of panelboards and switchboards are presented.

Chapter 12 provides an introduction to interior and exterior lighting fundamentals. Various types of lamps and ballasts are presented, followed by a discussion of required lighting levels in accordance with the standards of the Illuminating Engineering Society of North America. Direct and indirect lighting, the lumen method, and zonal cavity method for interior lighting are presented. A discussion on depreciation factors due to aging, accumulation of dirt, and lamp burnout is presented. The use of isofootcandle characteristic curves for outdoor lighting design is presented.

Chapter 13 discusses *NEC* requirements for motor power circuits. A brief discussion of alternating current motor theory and schematic connection diagrams is presented to give the reader an understanding of motor operation and of the terminology used in the subsequent discussion. Motor and controller disconnect requirements are presented, followed by a discussion of motor starters, overload, and short circuit protection. The sizing of motor feeder conductors in accordance with the *NEC* is presented.

The use of transformers to supply power systems of different voltage levels is discussed in Chapter 14. As in the case of motors, a brief discussion of basic transformer theory is included to provide the necessary background. Included in this discussion is a description of transformer ratings, connections, transformer taps, and winding voltage designations. The sizing of transformers to supply a given load is also presented and discussed. The sizing of transformer overcurrent protection and feeder conductor sizing in accordance with the *NEC* are presented.

Chapter 15 discusses the application of power factor correction capacitors to electrical power distribution systems. The concept of power factor is reviewed, followed by the procedure for sizing and specifying power factor correction capacitors. Fixed, switched, and multistep switched capacitor applications are discussed. Switching transients during capacitor energization are briefly discussed. The correct sizing of overcurrent protection devices and conductor sizing in accordance with the *NEC* are presented.

The subjects of short circuit and voltage drop calculations and selective coordination are covered in Chapters 16, 17, and 18, respectively. The need for performing these types of calculations is presented followed by a discussion of the calculation procedure. An example of each type of study is included at the end of each chapter to illustrate the concept.

Chapter 19 introduces the subject of harmonics and power quality. This subject has received increased attention in recent years due to the increased use of power electronic energy conversion devices such as variable-speed motor drives, rectifiers, and switched-mode power supplies found in personal computers. The coverage begins with a definition of harmonics as applied to both current and voltage waveforms. Resonance problems and the use of detuned capacitor harmonic filters is discussed.

Ancillaries

An Instructor's Manual (ISBN 0-13-060792-4) contains answers to selected problems presented in each chapter.

Acknowledgments

I would like to express my thanks to Donald R. Slanina, Youngstown State University, Youngstown, OH; Youakim Al Kalaani, Northeastern Illinois University, Chicago, IL; Dennis O. Wiitanen, Michigan Technological University, Houghton, MI; and Greg Harstine, Stark State College of Technology, Canton, OH, for their thorough review, valued suggestions, and constructive criticism of the manuscript.

Contents

Preface

1 Introduction to Electrical Systems Design 1

Introduction, 1
Objectives, 1
1–1 Overview of Power Distribution Systems, 1
1–2 Riser Diagrams, 2
1–3 System Voltages, 8
1–4 The National Electrical Code, 11
1–5 The Design Team, 11
Problems, 14

2 Review of Electrical Circuit Concepts 15

Introduction, 15
Objectives, 15
2–1 Phasor Representation, 15
2–2 Complex Algebra, 20
2–3 Ohm's Law and Complex Impedances, 23
2–4 Power and Power Factor, 28
2–5 Leading and Lagging Power Factor, 30
2–6 Kirchoff's Voltage and Current Laws, 32
2–7 Calculating Load Current, 34
Problems, 35

3 Load Characteristics 38

Introduction, 38
Objectives, 38
3–1 Minimum Estimated Demand Load, 38
3–2 Demand Factors, 47
3–3 Rates and Billing, 51
Problems, 53

4 Wiring Devices 55

Introduction, 55
Objectives, 55
4–1 Toggle Switches, 55
4–2 Receptacles, 61
4–3 Disconnects, 73
Problems, 77

5 Overcurrent Protection Devices 79

Introduction, 79
Objectives, 79
5–1 Need for Overcurrent Protection, 79
5–2 Fuse Characteristics, 80
5–3 Circuit Breaker Characteristics, 90
5–4 Standard Ratings and Classifications, 98
Problems, 100

6 Conductors and Overcurrent Protection 102

Introduction, 102
Objectives, 102
6–1 Conductor Sizes and Types, 102
6–2 Cable Construction and Insulation Types, 105
6–3 Conductor Ampacities, 110
6–4 Derating Based on Ambient Temperature, 116
6–5 Derating Based on Number of Current-Carrying Conductors, 117
6–6 Temperature Limitations on Device Terminals, 120
6–7 Conductor and Overcurrent Protection Device (OCPD) Selection, 122
6–8 Parallel Conductors, 131
Problems, 138

7 Branch Circuit and Feeder Design 140

Introduction, 140
Objectives, 140
7–1 Branch Circuit Outlet Device Ratings, 140
7–2 Receptacle and Circuit Loading, 142
7–3 Required Receptacle Locations, 143
7–4 Required Lighting Outlets, 145
7–5 Ground Fault Circuit Interruption Requirements, 148
7–6 Arc Fault Circuit Interruption Requirements, 149
7–7 Determining the Number of Branch Circuits Required, 150

7–8 Multiwire Branch Circuits, 153
7–9 Development of Cabling Diagrams, 155
Problems, 160

8 Conduit and Raceway Systems 162

Introduction, 162
Objectives, 162
8–1 Conduit Types, 162
8–2 Conduit Sizing, 173
8–3 Expansion Characteristics, 177
8–4 Cable Tray, 179
8–5 Pull, Junction, Device, and Outlet Boxes, 179
8–6 Wireways and Auxiliary Gutters, 186
8–7 Wiring Methods, 189
8–8 Cable Pulling Calculations, 192
8–9 Cable and Conduit Schedule, 200
Problems, 200

9 Grounding 203

Introduction, 203
Objectives, 203
9–1 Reasons for Grounding, 204
9–2 System Grounding, 207
9–3 Grounding Electrode System, 209
9–4 Service Grounding Requirements, 213
9–5 Grounding of Separately Derived Systems, 220
9–6 Equipment Grounding, 224
9–7 Ground Fault Circuit Interruption, 230
9–8 Grounding of Instrument Transformers, 232
Problems, 233

10 Services 236

Introduction, 236
Objectives, 236
10–1 Service Drop and Service Lateral General Requirements, 236
10–2 Service Entrance Conductors, 244
10–3 Service Disconnect Requirements, 248
10–4 Service Overcurrent Protection Device, 251
10–5 Examples of Service Entrance Calculations, 253
10–6 Metering, 257
Problems, 266

11   Panelboards and Switchboards   268

Introduction,   268
Objectives,   268
11–1 Panelboard Busbar Arrangements,   268
11–2 Classification and Ratings of Panelboards,   273
11–3 Overcurrent Protection of Panelboards,   275
11–4 Panel Schedules,   278
11–5 Panel Balancing,   282
11–6 Main Distribution Panel Schedules,   283
11–7 Medium-Voltage Switchgear and Unit Substations,   284
11–8 Clearances Around Panelboards and Switchgear,   289
Problems,   293

12   Lighting Fundamentals   295

Introduction,   295
Objectives,   295
12–1 Light Sources,   295
12–2 Ballasts,   300
12–3 Lighting Fixtures,   303
12–4 Photometrics,   305
12–5 Indoor Lighting Design,   314
12–6 Outdoor Lighting Design,   332
12–7 Light Fixture Schedule,   339
Problems,   339

13   Motor Circuits   342

Introduction,   342
Objectives,   342
13–1 Basic Induction Motor Operation,   342
13–2 Motor Ratings,   345
13–3 Terminal Connections,   346
13–4 Locked-Rotor Current,   346
13–5 Basic Motor Circuit,   349
13–6 Multiple Motor Circuit,   359
Problems,   364

14   Transformers   366

Introduction,   366
Objectives,   366
14–1 Basic Theory of Operation,   366
14–2 Service Transformers,   370
14–3 Low-Voltage Transformers,   376

14–4 Connections and Winding Voltage Designations,   377
14–5 Standard Ratings,   382
14–6 Loading Calculations and Sizing,   386
14–7 Transformer Voltage Taps,   394
14–8 Transformer Impedances,   397
14–9 Transformer Rated Line Currents,   399
14–10 Transformer Circuit Design,   401
Problems,   408

15 Capacitor Applications   410

Introduction,   410
Objectives,   410
15–1 Construction and Ratings,   410
15–2 Power Factor Improvement,   411
15–3 Voltage Improvement,   414
15–4 Switching Considerations,   415
15–5 Controls,   418
15–6 Conductor Sizing,   419
Problems,   420

16 Voltage Drop Calculations   422

Introduction,   422
Objectives,   422
16–1 Voltage Ranges,   423
16–2 Voltage Drop Defined,   424
16–3 Cable Impedances,   425
16–4 Transformer Voltage Drop,   430
16–5 Transformer Taps,   434
16–6 Voltage Drop Due to Motor Starting,   434
16–7 Examples of Voltage Drop Studies,   438
Problems,   444

17 Short Circuit Calculations   447

Introduction,   447
Objectives,   447
17–1 Symmetrical and Asymmetrical Fault Currents,   448
17–2 Equivalent System Impedance,   451
17–3 Transformer Impedances,   454
17–4 Reflecting Impedances Through the Transformer,   455
17–5 Cable Impedances,   456
17–6 Motor Contribution,   460
17–7 Three-Phase Systems,   460
17–8 Single-Phase Systems,   465
Problems,   470

18 Coordination and Equipment Protection 472

Introduction, 472
Objectives, 472
18–1 Overcurrent Device Coordination, 472
18–2 Cable Protection, 481
18–3 Motor Circuits, 482
18–4 Transformer Protection, 484
18–5 Time–Overcurrent Relays, 494
18–6 Reflecting OCPD Characteristics, 496
Problems, 505

19 Power System Harmonics 507

Introduction, 507
Objectives, 507
19–1 Sources of Harmonics, 508
19–2 Resonance Problems, 512
19–3 Detuned Capacitor Harmonic Filter Design, 521
19–4 IEEE Standard 519, 530
19–5 Summary of Detuned Harmonic Filter Design and Analysis, 533
Problems, 533

Index 537

1

Introduction to Electrical Systems Design

INTRODUCTION

Chapter 1 provides an overview of electrical power distribution systems commonly encountered in residential, commercial, and industrial buildings. It discusses the representation of electrical power systems through the use of one-line and riser diagrams and introduces the history and use of the *National Electrical Code*® to give the reader an insight into this important document.[1] The chapter describes common system voltages used in electrical power distribution systems and the connection of electrical loads and grounding. In addition, the chapter introduces the design team, consisting of architects, civil/structural engineers, mechanical engineers, and electrical engineers, to give the reader an appreciation of the interaction that must occur among these disciplines if a design project is to be successful.

OBJECTIVES

At the end of this chapter, you will:

- Understand the overall function of the electrical power distribution system in a building
- Understand the basic philosophy behind the development of power distribution systems
- Have knowledge of the more common system voltages used for power distribution
- Have an appreciation of the *National Electrical Code*
- Appreciate the need for interaction and communication among the various professional disciplines involved in a design project

1–1 OVERVIEW OF POWER DISTRIBUTION SYSTEMS

Before attempting to design the electrical power distribution system for a building, you must understand the basic elements that make up the overall power distribution system. The overall layout of the major components of a power distribution system is often the first

---

[1] *National Electric Code*® and *NEC*® are registered trademarks of the National Fire Protection Association, Inc., Quincy, MA 02269.

1

step in the design process. It is at this beginning stage that the designer develops a general idea as to the nature of the distribution system. For example, in this early stage the designer will probably establish the location of the service entrance, inquire as to the service voltage(s) available from the local utility company, determine the location of electrical closets and vaults, determine approximate locations for distribution panelboards and switchboards, and so forth. With experience comes the ability to determine more accurately these design parameters in the early stages of a project. Please be aware that these elements are only a first approximation in the overall design process. Designing any system or component is an iterative process, one that will need to be repeated several times before the design is finished.

1–2   RISER DIAGRAMS

The interconnection among the main components that comprise a power distribution system are easily shown on what is referred to as a *power riser diagram.* The actual riser diagram for a particular building will have its own unique characteristics depending on the type of occupancy—residential, commercial, institutional, or industrial. The riser diagram for any occupancy will typically show only the major electrical equipment, such as utility transformer, metering, service entrance, subpanels, large motors, HVAC equipment, emergency generator system, elevator equipment, and so on. The individual branch circuits, general-purpose convenience receptacles, and lighting are generally not shown on the riser diagram to keep it from becoming too cluttered. Keep in mind that the purpose of the riser diagram is to show the general location of the major electrical equipment and the main feeders connecting this equipment.

Residential Riser Diagram

In order to develop an understanding of the components that comprise a power distribution system, consider the riser diagram shown in Figure 1–1, which is representative of a diagram for a simple residential occupancy. The service entrance cable runs from the point of connection with the local utility company to the meter socket. The power meter used in most residential applications is referred to as self-contained, which means that the current element of the meter is rated to carry the full load current of the load to be served. Generally, services rated below 400 amps will use self-contained power meters.

The service entrance cable then proceeds from the meter socket to the main service entrance panelboard. The main service panelboard will typically have a main service disconnect, which is used to deenergize the entire electrical system in the residence. In some applications, the main service disconnect will be located in a separate enclosure between the point of entrance of the service cable into the building and the main service panel. As discussed in a later chapter, the main service disconnect may consist of up to six separate disconnects grouped together.

Note that there is a feeder from the main service panelboard to a subpanel. This subpanel may be necessary to supply a group of loads that are remote from the main service panelboard. An example would be a subpanel installed in a garage or workshop area. All

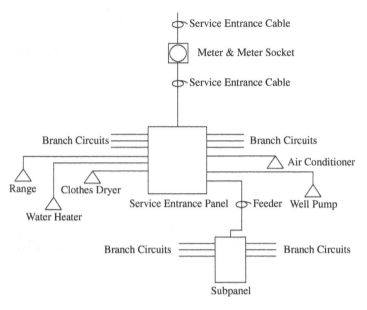

FIGURE 1–1
Riser Diagram of Residential System

loads in these areas could be supplied from the subpanel if necessary. It may also be necessary to use a subpanel if the main panel does not have sufficient space to accommodate the number of branch circuits required to supply the entire building.

Branch circuits may originate from the main or subpanel to supply the final utilization equipment. Typically, these branch circuits are rated at either 15 or 20 amps and may supply lighting and receptacle loads. Branch circuits for general lighting and appliance branch circuits are usually not shown individually on a riser diagram in order to keep the diagram from becoming too cluttered. Note also that there are several other feeders or branch circuits that supply major equipment such as the well pump, water heater, clothes dryer, range, and air conditioner.

Commercial Riser Diagram

The riser diagram shown in Figure 1–2 is for a simple commercial office building. In Figure 1–2, note that the service entrance location is shown in the lower left-hand corner of the drawing. In most instances, the electric utility company providing the service owns and maintains the main service transformer. However, in some instances this transformer may be owned and maintained by the owner of the building. The service entrance conductors originate at the transformer and pass underground through a set of conduits into a current transformer or CT cabinet. The CT cabinet contains the metering class current transformers necessary to step the load current down to a level that can be carried by the current elements of the meter. Since the equipment inside the CT cabinet is considered to be part of

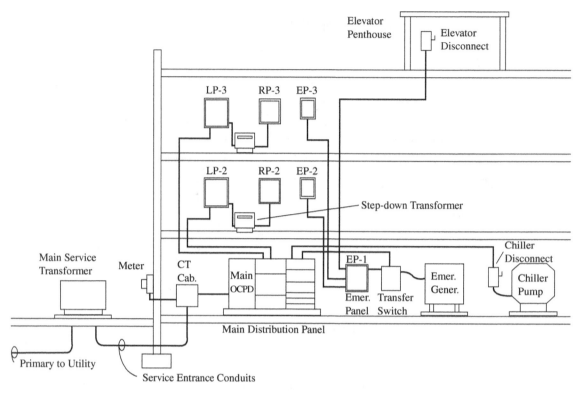

FIGURE 1–2
Riser Diagram of Commercial System

the metering equipment, the CT cabinet will also have a meter seal attached to prevent unauthorized tampering with the metering equipment. Conductors carrying the secondary current from the current transformers and conductors supplying the voltage potential to the meter are contained in a separate conduit between the CT cabinet and the meter socket. In some applications, the CTs are mounted on the secondary bushings of the pad-mount utility supply transformer, thereby eliminating the need for a CT cabinet. Keep in mind that all metering and supply issues must be coordinated with the local utility company.

From the CT cabinet, the service entrance conductors continue on to the main service equipment. As in the case of the residential building, the main service equipment will have a main disconnect switch or switches. This main service equipment may also have other feeder overcurrent devices, such as fuses or circuit breakers, installed. In this particular example, the service is 480 V, three phase, although other service voltages may be available for commercial occupancies.

Note in Figure 1–2 that there are several 480 V feeders originating from the main service equipment to other electrical equipment, such as the chiller pump, which is part of the HVAC equipment of this building. Note also that there are several 480 V feeders from the main service equipment to lighting subpanels, designated LP-1, LP-2, etc., located on each floor of the building. It is common in commercial buildings supplied by 480 V, three-phase service, to use 277 V lighting circuits. From each of these lighting subpanels, a feeder is used to connect to the primary of a step-down transformer, which transforms the voltage from 480 V to 208Y/120 V. The low-voltage side of the transformer is connected to a receptacle panelboard, designated RP-1, RP-2, etc., and are used to supply 120 V branch circuits for receptacle loads and other loads requiring 120 V supply.

In some instances, it is necessary to provide for emergency power. In this facility, the emergency power requirements are met by the emergency generator, transfer switch, and emergency panel. The emergency panel has two sources of supply: the emergency generator and the feeder from the main service equipment. The transfer switch provides the means of switching from the normal supply (main service) to the emergency supply. In the event of loss of voltage on the utility system, the transfer switch logic will signal the emergency generator to start. After the generator starts and comes up to rated speed, the transfer switch will switch the emergency panelboard over to the generator supply. When utility power is restored, there will be a time delay before the transfer switch switches back over to the normal utility supply. This time delay is necessary to ensure that the utility service has been restored on a permanent, not momentary, basis. The emergency generator will then go into a cool-down mode before shutting down.

Note that there are several emergency circuits originating from the emergency panel board in the lower level to emergency panelboards on each floor of the building. Emergency lighting and receptacle circuits may be connected to these emergency panelboards as required. Also, note that there is a feeder for the elevator equipment that is supplied from the emergency panelboard. This is to ensure continuous operation of the elevator equipment in the event of a power failure on the utility supply.

One-Line Diagram of Commercial Building

As discussed in the previous section, the power riser diagram will show the layout of the electrical system of a building with some detail as to the actual physical location of the electrical equipment. This level of detail is often not needed, particularly when performing short-circuit studies, coordination studies, voltage-drop studies, or other system studies. A shorthand version of the power riser diagram is the one-line diagram. The one-line diagram shows only the electrical connection of the electrical system components, the ratings and types of overcurrent protection devices, the type and sometimes length of cables for major feeders, etc. The individual branch circuits are generally not shown. A representative one-line diagram for the commercial building whose power riser diagram was shown in Figure 1–2 is shown in Figure 1–3.

Notice in Figure 1–3 that the electrical connection of the components follows the physical layout of the components, a correlation that can be observed by comparing Figures 1–2 and 1–3. The main service transformer is shown, along with its respective voltage and apparent power ratings: 12,470–480Y/277 V, 750 kVA. Note that this information may or may not be found on the riser diagram. The CT cabinet and metering are also shown on the one-line diagram. In this instance, the cable type, size, and length are not

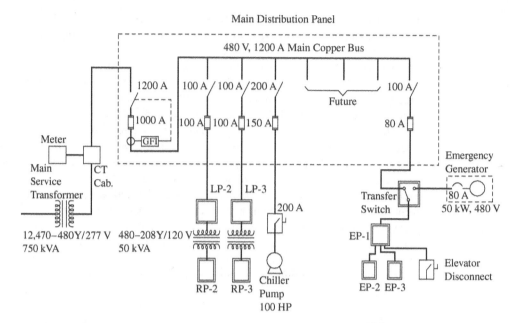

FIGURE 1–3

One-Line Diagram for Commercial System

shown for purposes of clarity. However, on most one-lines this cable information would be shown. When the cable sizes, types, and lengths are not shown on the one-line diagram, they would typically be shown on a cable and conduit schedule.

Figure 1–3 shows the main distribution panel with the rating of the main bus indicated: 480 V, 1200 amp main copper bus. The main 1200 amp disconnect switch is also shown, along with the 1000 amp fuse and ground fault protection, or GFI. All of the 480 V feeders originating from the main distribution panel and their respective disconnect rating and fuse ratings are shown. Note that the feeders supplying the lighting panels LP-2 and LP-3 are included, but that the individual lighting branch circuits originating from these panel boards are not. The step-down transformers, and, typically, their ratings, between the two lighting panels and receptacle panels RP-2 and RP-3 are also shown. Also, like the lighting branch circuits, the receptacle branch circuits are not shown on the one-line diagram. Instead, the branch circuits for lighting, receptacles, and other loads will be shown on the cabling diagram of the building floor plans. The location of the branch circuit breakers will typically be shown on the panel schedules for the building.

The 480 V feeder from the main distribution panel to the transfer switch is shown along with its rating: 100 A disconnect, 80 A fuse. Shown in the transfer switch is the internal switch mechanism for normal feed to the emergency panel EP-1. Panel EP-1 is clearly shown feeding emergency panels EP-2 and EP-3 on the second and third floors, respectively. Also, the feeder supplying the elevator disconnect is shown as are the ratings of the emergency generator and the generator breaker. Note that the generator, emergency circuits, and emergency panelboards are all 480 V. As such, the circuits originating from these panelboards will be either 277 V, suitable for lighting, or 480 V, suitable for critical three-phase 480 V loads only. If it is desired to supply receptacle or lighting loads at 120 V, additional step-down transformers would have to be installed and fed from the emergency panels EP-1, EP-2, or EP-3. The secondaries of these additional step-down transformers would feed emergency panelboards suitable for supplying branch circuits at 120 V.

Some of the more common electrical plan and one-line diagram symbols are shown in Figure 1–4. These symbols are a representative sampling of the hundreds of symbols encountered in electrical system design.

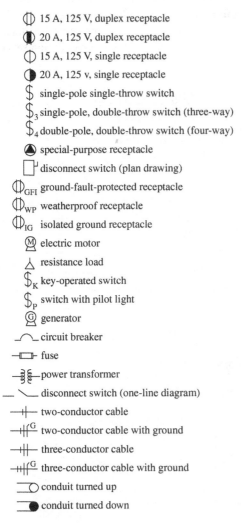

FIGURE 1–4
Common Electrical Plan Symbols

1–3   SYSTEM VOLTAGES

An understanding of the various system voltages used in electrical systems is of great importance in their design and maintenance. Knowing how the loads are connected between phases and between phase and neutral will enable the designer to properly design and specify the components of an electrical system and enable maintenance personnel to safely maintain and operate these systems.

There are several different system voltages that may be available for the power supply, and these must be determined from the utility supplying the electric service. Keep in mind that not all service voltages are available for any load. For example, three-phase service may not be available for residential buildings, minimum load requirements may be specified for supplying three-phase service, minimum service voltage may be specified for large loads, and so on. The designer is responsible for determining the service voltage requirements. Figure 1–5 is a schematic representation of some of the more common service voltages.

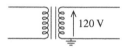
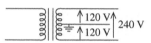

A. 120 V, Single-Phase,
Two-Wire System

B. 120/240 V, Single-Phase,
Three-Wire System

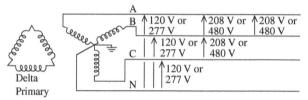

C. 208Y/120 V, or 480Y/277 V, Three-Phase, Four-Wire Wye System

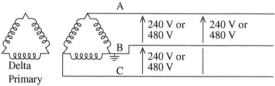

D. 240 V or 480 V, Three-Phase, Three-Wire Delta System

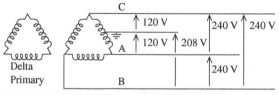

E. 240/120 V, Three-Phase, Four-Wire Delta System

FIGURE 1–5
Common Service Voltages

120 V, Single-Phase, Two-Wire System

The schematic diagram for the 120 V, single-phase, two-wire system is shown in Figure 1–5(A). One of the supply conductors is referred to as the *ungrounded conductor* or *hot conductor* and is fully insulated. The other supply conductor is grounded at the transformer secondary and is referred to as the *neutral* or *grounded conductor.* This conductor is connected to the transformer case and earth grounding system (typically, a ground rod) at the transformer location. At the service entrance location, the grounded conductor is again connected to an earth grounding system. However, on the load side of the main service disconnect, a separate equipment grounding conductor is present in addition to the grounded conductor. It is extremely important to note the distinction between the ground*ing* conductor and the ground*ed* conductor. The ground*ing* conductor serves as the safety ground for electrical apparatus, while the ground*ed* conductor provides a return path for load current back to the source. Under normal operating conditions, the grounding conductor carries no current and serves to maintain a zero volt potential for electrical apparatus case grounding. The only time the grounding conductor carries current is in the event of a short circuit between the ungrounded conductor (hot) and ground. Both the ungrounded conductor and the grounded conductor are fully insulated inside the premises. All electrical loads are connected between the ungrounded (hot) conductor and the grounded (neutral) conductor. Under no circumstances are loads permitted to be connected between the ungrounded conductor and the equipment grounding conductor.

120/240 V, Single Phase, Three Wire

The 120/240 V, single-phase, three-wire system is the most common system for single-phase loads. The three-wire system is derived by center tapping the transformer secondary, as shown in Figure 1–5(B). This center tap is connected to earth ground at the transformer location. The system-grounded conductor originates from this center tap. As in the previous system, the grounded conductor is also connected to earth ground at the service entrance. The grounding conductor and grounded conductor must be kept separate inside the building. Electrical loads are not permitted to be connected between any of the ungrounded conductors and the equipment grounding conductor.

The ungrounded supply conductors originate from the "outer" portion of the secondary transformer winding. Electrical loads requiring 120 volts are connected between either of the two ungrounded conductors and the grounded conductor. Likewise, electrical loads requiring 240 volts are connected between the ungrounded conductors. This is commonly referred to as the "220 volt" line. This system has an advantage over the 120 V, two-wire system in that large electrical loads such as ranges and hot water heaters can be designed and operated at 240 volts. Operation at this higher voltage results in less current draw for the same power rating.

208Y/120 V, Three Phase, Four Wire

The 208Y/120 V, three-phase, four-wire system is the preferred system for smaller three-phase load requirements. As shown in Figure 1–5(C), the transformer secondaries are connected in the form of a wye. As such, this system is commonly referred to as a *four-wire wye-connected system*. The common point of the three transformers is earth grounded and establishes connection for the grounded conductor. As in the previous systems, the grounded conductor is also connected to earth ground at the service entrance. The grounding conductor and grounded conductor must be kept separate inside the building. Electrical loads are not permitted to be connected between any of the ungrounded conductors and the equipment grounding conductor.

The voltage between any of the three phases—"a," "b," or "c"—is 208 volts. These three phases are the ungrounded conductors of the system. Large three-phase loads are connected between the three ungrounded phase conductors. Likewise, smaller, 120 volt, single-phase loads such as receptacles and lighting are connected between any of the three phase conductors and the neutral conductor. In this system, it is permitted to connect 208 volt, single-phase loads between any two of the three ungrounded phase conductors.

480Y/277 V, Three Phase, Four Wire

The 480Y/277 V, three-phase, four-wire system is also represented in Figure 1–5(C); it is preferred for larger three-phase load requirements and is very similar to the 208Y/120 V, three-phase, four-wire system previously discussed. Like the 208Y/120 V system, this system is also referred to as a four-wire wye-connected system. The common point of the three transformers is earth grounded and establishes connection for the grounded conductor. As in the previous systems, the grounded conductor is also connected to earth ground at the service entrance. The grounding conductor and grounded conductor must be kept separate inside the building. Electrical loads are not permitted to be connected between any of the ungrounded conductors and the equipment grounding conductor.

The voltage between any of the three phases—"a," "b," or "c"—is 480 volts, and they are the ungrounded conductors of the system. Large three-phase loads are connected between the three ungrounded phase conductors. Likewise, smaller, 277 volt, single-phase loads such as lighting are connected between any of the three phase conductors and the neutral conductor. In this system, it is permitted to connect 480 volt single-phase loads between any two of the three ungrounded phase conductors.

240 V, Three Phase, Three Wire

The 240 V, three-phase, three-wire system is shown in Figure 1–5(D). This three-phase system has one of the phases ("b" phase) grounded at the transformer location and at the service entrance. Phase "b" is the grounded conductor of the system, while phases "a" and "c" are the ungrounded conductors. This type of system is often referred to as a *corner-grounded system*, since one of the corners of the delta is grounded. As in the previous systems, the grounded conductor and grounding conductor are kept separate inside the premises. Loads requiring 240 V three phase may be connected between phases "a," "b," and "c." It is also possible to connect 240 V single-phase loads between any two of the three phases.

240/120 V, Three Phase, Four Wire

The 240/120 V, three-phase, four-wire system is shown in Figure 1–5(E). Note that there are three transformer secondary windings shown. The center tap of one of the transformers is connected to earth ground and serves as the connection for the grounded conductor. As in the previous systems, the grounded conductor is also connected to earth ground at the service entrance. The grounding conductor and grounded conductor must be kept separate inside the building, as with the other systems. Electrical loads are not permitted to be connected between any of the ungrounded conductors and the equipment grounding conductor.

There are three ungrounded conductors in this system, forming a 240 volt, three-phase delta connection. Large 240 volt, three-phase loads such as motors and resistance heat are connected between the three ungrounded conductors—"a," "b," and "c." Smaller, 120 volt, single-phase loads are connected between either phase "a" and the grounded conductor, or phase "c" and the grounded conductor. Larger 240 volt, single-phase loads are connected between phases "a" and "c." The voltage between phase "b" and the grounded conductor is 208 volts and is considered the high leg to ground. It is not permitted to connect any 208 volt single-phase loads between phase "b" and the grounded conductor in this system. Because of some unique operating problems that may arise from this type of system, its use is not recommended.

1–4 THE NATIONAL ELECTRICAL CODE

The National Fire Protection Agency (NFPA) is the organization responsible for publishing codes applicable to life safety. Included in the NFPA publications is the *National Electrical Code*. Initially developed in 1897, and taken under sponsorship by the National Fire Protection Agency in 1911, the *NEC* is updated every three years.

The primary purpose of the code is to establish provisions for the design, installation, and maintenance of electrical systems, with due regard for public safety and the protection of property. Although the *NEC* is the fundamental reference used in the design, installation, and maintenance of electrical systems, it is not a design guide in and of itself—it does not provide a set of guideline specifications, but establishes a general set of rules governing electrical power distribution systems.

Many agencies having jurisdiction over the installation of electrical systems have adopted the *NEC* as the appropriate standard. The "local authority having jurisdiction" is how the *NEC* frequently refers to the local inspection agency. This inspection agency may choose to adopt the code in its published form or may set additional rules and regulations that exceed the requirements of the *NEC*. The designer must check with the local authority to determine if there are additional regulations.

1–5 THE DESIGN TEAM

The design of any system requires coordination and interaction among many different engineering disciplines. Usually, there will be a project manager assigned to oversee the total project design. This individual will be selected from one of the disciplines involved in the project, and this discipline then becomes the lead discipline. The discipline that is expected to do the major portion of the work on a project is typically selected as the lead. As an example, the construction of a wastewater treatment plant will often be led by the environmental engineering group. Institutional projects such as schools, hospitals, and office buildings will have an architect as the lead discipline. The civil/structural group may be the lead discipline on a highway or bridge project that requires roadway lighting.

To successfully complete a design project, a complete set of plans and specifications is required. The production of these plans and specifications must be done under the supervision of licensed professional engineers of the respective disciplines. In addition to providing the design parameters of the facility, the plans and specifications are a form of communication between the designer and the contractor. Therefore, it is important that the plans and specifications be complete, concise, and accurate. In fact, the plans and specifications typically constitute what are referred to as *legal contract documents*. Errors and omissions on plans and specifications can be the cause of costly overruns and possible legal action.

Architectural Responsibilities

On many institutional and commercial projects, the architectural discipline is involved in the development of floor plans and elevation drawings, as well as some of the structural, electrical, and mechanical details. Architects, using standard design practices, are generally involved in the overall design of the building. Many architects will sub-out the mechanical, electrical, and civil/structural portions of a project. In addition, the architectural group is often responsible for the aesthetic aspects of a project, such as the selection of decorative lighting and wall and floor finishes.

Civil/Structural Engineering Responsibilities

Civil/structural engineers are typically involved in the site layout, surveying, and general structural aspects of a project. The establishment of benchmark and elevations for underground conduit banks and manholes would be the general responsibility of the civil group. The design of transformer vaults with a specified fire rating and oil-spill-containment requirements would also involve the civil group.

Structural engineers may be needed to determine special structural requirements for large electrical machinery such as generators and transformers, for example, the location of a transformer weighing several tons in the penthouse of a large office tower and the design of a concrete pad for a generator or transformer foundation.

Environmental Engineering Responsibilities

Environmental engineers are the primary lead discipline in the design of water and wastewater treatment facilities. The selection of pump motor sizes, the determination of emergency generator requirements, and the design of chemical dispensing systems are the responsibilities of the environmental engineering group. All of these systems require electrical power for operation and control.

In addition to the design of environmental systems, the environmental engineer may be involved in developing spill prevention, containment, and control plans for liquid-insulated transformers in accordance with Environmental Protection Agency (EPA) regulations. Site studies to determine compliance with wetland regulations is also the responsibility of the environmental engineer.

Mechanical Engineering Responsibilities

The mechanical engineering group is primarily responsible for the heating, ventilating, and air conditioning (HVAC) system design in the building. Associated with the HVAC system are control systems that may require the electrical group's expertise. Also, the HVAC system will have power requirements for operation and so the electrical group will need to know what type of loads the HVAC equipment will have on the system, which is particularly important if electric heat is being considered. Likewise, the mechanical group will need to know what the lighting load will be to properly size the air-conditioning equipment. Ventilation requirements for indoor transformer vaults and equipment rooms will also have to be conveyed to the mechanical group.

The mechanical group is also responsible for designing the water supply and wastewater system for the building. This is important to the electrical group in that the location of water coolers, water-conditioning equipment, instant hot water heaters, and so on must be known so that power can be provided. The mechanical group is also involved in the piping required for the fuel supply system of an emergency generator.

Electrical Engineering Responsibilities

The electrical engineering group is primarily responsible for the design of the power distribution and lighting systems in a building. In addition, this group is responsible for fire alarm systems, security systems, and public address and sound systems. While the piping design for a fire protection sprinkler system is the responsibility of the mechanical engineer, the specification of flow meters to detect system operation is the responsibility of the electrical engineer. The design of damper control systems, HVAC system selective shutdown, and elevator recall systems as part of a fire protection system are also the responsibility of the electrical engineer.

Need for Communication Among Disciplines

The preceding discussion was meant to convey some of the typical job duties and functions of the various disciplines involved in a project. While it is by no means an exhaustive account of the activities of a typical engineering office, it does show the importance of the need for communication among disciplines. Early in the design process, it is necessary to establish an effective dialogue. No one discipline can successfully complete its part of the project without input from the other disciplines, and many of the decisions that are made in the beginning stages of a project will affect the later stages of the design process. For example, the service entrance requirements must be established so that adequate physical space can be allowed for the installation of electrical equipment. Failure to do so early on may result in costly redesigns of portions of the building later.

PROBLEMS

1. Is it permissible to connect an electrical load between the ungrounded conductor and grounded conductor of an electrical system?

2. Is it permissible to connect an electrical load between the ungrounded conductor and grounding conductor of an electrical system?

3. Is it permissible to connect an electrical load between the "b" phase and the grounded conductor of a 240/120 V, three-phase, four-wire system?

4. Why is an equipment grounding conductor present in an electrical system?

5. Sketch the connections for a 120 V, single-phase load in a 120/240 V, single-phase, three-wire system.

6. Sketch the connections for a 240 V, single-phase load in a 120/240 V, single-phase, three-wire system.

7. Sketch the connections for a 120 V, single-phase load in a 240/120 V, three-phase, four-wire system.

8. Sketch the connections for a 120 V, single-phase load in a 208Y/120 V, three-phase, four-wire system.

9. Sketch the connections for a 208 V, single-phase load in a 208Y/120 V, three-phase, four-wire system.

10. Sketch the connections for a 277 V, single-phase load in a 480Y/277 V, three-phase, four-wire system.

11. Sketch the connections for a 480 V, single-phase load in a 480Y/277 V, three-phase, four-wire system.

12. State three areas of responsibility for a civil/structural engineer on a design project.

13. State three areas of responsibility for an environmental engineer on a design project.

14. State three areas of responsibility for a mechanical engineer on a design project.

15. State in your own words the importance of communication among the various disciplines on a project.

2

Review of Electrical Circuit Concepts

INTRODUCTION

Chapter 2 provides a review of some of the fundamental concepts of alternating current circuit analysis techniques. Of particular interest are the phasor representation of time-varying sinusoidal waveforms and phasor algebra techniques. In addition, the application of Ohm's law to alternating current circuits, and the calculation of complex apparent power are discussed. Kirchoff's voltage and current laws as applied to simple networks are also reviewed. The purpose of this review is to refresh the students' proficiency in the analysis of alternating current circuits prior to advancing to other topics.

OBJECTIVES

Upon completion of this chapter, you will be able to:

- Understand the method of phasor analysis of alternating current circuits
- Understand the concept of complex impedance
- Apply Ohm's law to alternating current circuits
- Understand the concepts of active, reactive, and apparent power
- Understand the concepts of power factor and reactive factor
- Understand the concepts of leading and lagging power factor
- Apply Kirchoff's voltage and current laws to simple circuits
- Calculate line current from load power specifications

2–1   PHASOR REPRESENTATION

In alternating current circuits and systems, the voltages and currents take on the form of time-varying sinusoids. These sinusoidal voltage waveforms are generated as a result of the physical construction of the generators in the generating plants of the utility companies. The placement of the stator windings and field construction dictate the waveform of the generated voltage. The construction is such that the voltage waveform produced is a very "clean" sine wave with little or no distortion. The mathematical expression for this waveform is given by

$$V(t) = V_m \sin(\omega t) \tag{2–1}$$

where:

V_m = peak instantaneous voltage magnitude in volts
ω = angular frequency in radians per second
t = time in seconds

The frequency is usually expressed in hertz. The relation between the frequency in radians per second and hertz is

$$f = \omega/(2\pi) \qquad\qquad (2\text{--}2)$$

Figure 2–1 shows representations of the time-varying sinusoidal voltage waveform.

When performing electrical calculations involving sinusoidal waveforms, it is much more convenient to express the voltage magnitude in terms of its root-mean-square or rms value rather than the instantaneous value. The rms value of an alternating current waveform essentially relates the sinusoidal waveform to an equivalent direct current value. In some instances, the rms value is referred to as the "effective dc" value. The voltage rating of all electrical power equipment is expressed in terms of rms voltage, not peak instantaneous voltage. For sinusoidal waveforms, the relation between the rms and peak instantaneous value is given by

$$V_{\text{rms}} = \frac{V_m}{\sqrt{2}} \qquad\qquad (2\text{--}3)$$

Note that although the previous discussion has been developed for a voltage waveform, Equations (2–1) and (2–3) apply to current waveforms as well.

EXAMPLE 2–1

A voltage waveform is given by the following expression:

$$V(t) = 170 \sin(377t) \text{ V}$$

Determine the rms value of voltage and the frequency in hertz

FIGURE 2–1
Sinusoidal Voltage Waveform

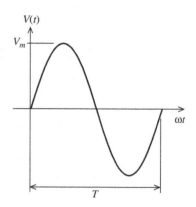

Solution: From Equation (2–3), the rms voltage is equal to: $V = 170 \div \sqrt{2} = 120$ V

The frequency is given by Equation (2–2): $f = 377 \div (2\pi) = 60$ Hz

When a sinusoidal voltage is applied to a passive linear load, a sinusoidal current will flow. This current waveform will either be in phase with, leading, or lagging the applied voltage, depending on the characteristic of the load. For a purely resistive load, the current and voltage will be in phase, as shown in Figure 2–2(A). In an inductive load, the current waveform will be shifted such that it lags the applied voltage by some angle θ. Voltage and current waveforms for an inductive load are shown in Figure 2–2(B). Likewise, in a capacitive load, the current waveform will be shifted in such a manner as to lead the applied voltage by some angle θ. Voltage and current waveforms for a capacitive load are shown in Figure 2–2(C). The amount of phase shift will depend on the nature of

FIGURE 2–2
Voltage and Current Relations for Resistor, Inductor, and Capacitor

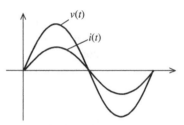

A. Resistive Load

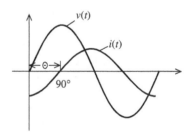

B. Inductive Load

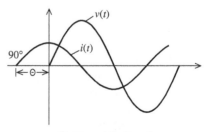

C. Capacitive Load

the load. If the current lags the applied voltage, the angle θ is negative; if the current leads the applied voltage, the angle θ is positive.

The mathematical expressions for the phase-shifted sinusoidal current waveforms shown in Figure 2–2 are given by

$$\text{Resistive load:} \qquad I(t) = I_m \sin(\omega t) \qquad \textbf{(2–4a)}$$

$$\text{Capacitive load:} \qquad I(t) = I_m \sin(\omega t + \theta) \qquad \textbf{(2–4b)}$$

$$\text{Inductive load:} \qquad I(t) = I_m \sin(\omega t - \theta) \qquad \textbf{(2–4c)}$$

where:

I_m = peak instantaneous current magnitude in amperes
ω = angular frequency in radians per second
t = time in seconds

Rather than working with the complicated expressions given in Equations (2–1) and (2–4), a method referred to as *phasor algebra* was developed in which, essentially, these time-varying sinusoidal waveforms are represented by vectors in a two-dimensional coordinate system, often referred to as the *complex plane*. In this two-dimensional system, the horizontal axis is referred to as the *real* axis and the vertical axis referred to as the *imaginary* axis. (The vertical axis is also referred to as the "*j*" axis, in reference to the "*j*" operator. The use of the *j* operator in complex algebra will be explained later.) Think of this phasor or vector representation as a "snapshot" of the time-varying waveforms. Bear in mind that this technique is nothing more than a mathematical method developed to make the calculations easier to manage.

In this two-dimensional coordinate system, the horizontal axis to the right of the origin is selected as the reference axis. All phasors have a magnitude expressed in terms of rms values and a displacement expressed in degrees with reference to the reference axis. The angular displacement is positive going in the counterclockwise direction from the reference axis. The waveforms of Figure 2–2 are shown in Figure 2–3 along with their respective phasor representation. Note that the voltage phasor is selected as the reference, the in-phase current phasor is drawn along the same line as the voltage phasor, the leading current phasor is drawn at an angle θ in the counterclockwise direction with respect to the voltage phasor, and the lagging current phasor is drawn at an angle θ in the clockwise direction with respect to the voltage phasor. Be aware that any phasor may be selected as a reference, with all other phasors expressed in relation to the selected reference.

EXAMPLE 2–2

Determine the phasor representation for the time-varying waveforms given by the following expressions:

a) $I(t) = 20 \sin(377t - 30°)$
b) $V(t) = 170 \sin(377t + 45°)$
c) $V(t) = 391.7 \sin(377t - 120°)$

FIGURE 2–3
Phasor Representation of
Waveforms

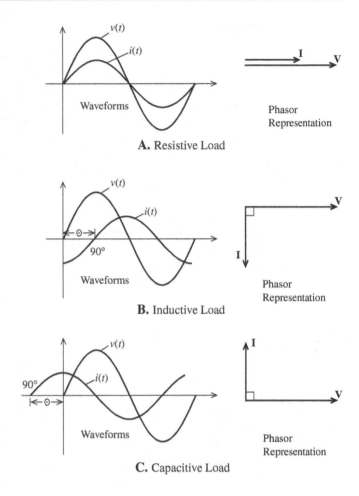

A. Resistive Load

B. Inductive Load

C. Capacitive Load

Solution: As previously stated, phasors are represented in terms of the rms quantity of the sinusoidal waveform. The phase angle is equal to the phase shift shown in the preceding equations.

a) $I_{rms} = 20 \div \sqrt{2} = 14.14$ A. The phase angle is $-30°$. Therefore, the phasor representation is

$$\mathbf{I} = 14.14 \angle -30° \text{ A}$$

b) $V_{rms} = 170 \div \sqrt{2} = 120$ V. The phase angle is $+45°$. Therefore, the phasor representation is

$$\mathbf{V} = 120 \angle +45° \text{ V}$$

c) $V_{rms} = 391.7 \div \sqrt{2} = 277$ V. The phase angle is $-120°$. Therefore, the phasor representation is

$$\mathbf{V} = 277 \angle -120° \text{ V}$$

2–2   COMPLEX ALGEBRA

A phasor can be represented in the complex plane in two different ways. The first representation is in rectangular form, in which the phasor is expressed in terms of real and imaginary components. The other representation is in polar form, in which a phasor is expressed in terms of magnitude and phase angle. The method used to represent a phasor quantity is a matter of convenience. In most situations, phasors will be expressed in polar form. However, in performing certain calculations, it is desirable to use rectangular form. Conversion from one form to the other is straightforward.

Consider, for example, a phasor expressed in rectangular form as

$$\mathbf{A} = \text{Re(A)} + j\,\text{Im(A)} \qquad (2\text{–}5)$$

In this expression for the phasor **A**, Re(**A**) represents the component of **A** along the real axis and is referred to as the *real component*. Likewise, Im(**A**) represents the component of **A** along the imaginary or "j" axis and is referred to as the *imaginary component*. The representation of this phasor in the complex plane is shown in Figure 2–4. This phasor can also be expressed in polar form as

$$\mathbf{A} = A \angle \theta° \qquad (2\text{–}6)$$

where:

$$A = \text{magnitude of phasor} = \sqrt{[\text{Re(A)}]^2 + [\text{Im(A)}]^2} \qquad (2\text{–}7)$$
$$\theta = \text{phase angle of phasor with respect to reference}$$

Extreme care must be taken when determining the phase angle of the phasor. Always sketch the phasor to determine which quadrant you are in. The complex plane has four quadrants, labeled I, II, III, and IV, as shown in Figure 2–4. The following equations can be used to determine the phase angle for the various quadrants:

$$\text{Quadrant I:}\quad \theta = \tan^{-1}[\text{Im(A)}/\text{Re(A)}] \qquad (2\text{–}8a)$$

$$\text{Quadrant II:}\quad \theta = 180° - \tan^{-1}[\text{Im(A)}/\text{Re(A)}] \qquad (2\text{–}8b)$$

$$\text{Quadrant III:}\quad \theta = 180° + 1\,\tan^{-1}[\text{Im(A)}/\text{Re(A)}] \qquad (2\text{–}8c)$$

$$\text{Quadrant IV:}\quad \theta = 360° - \tan^{-1}[\text{Im(A)}/\text{Re(A)}] \qquad (2\text{–}8d)$$

FIGURE 2–4
Phasor in Complex Plane

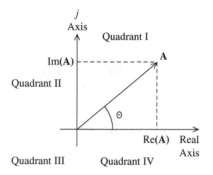

Many electronic calculators have polar-to-rectangular and rectangular-to-polar conversion function keys.

EXAMPLE 2–3

Determine the polar form of the following phasors:

a) $\mathbf{I} = -3.5 + j4.2$ A
b) $\mathbf{V} = -100 - j25$ V
c) $\mathbf{Z} = 35 + j20$ Ω
d) $\mathbf{S} = 100 - j50$ kilovoltamperes (kVA)

Solution:

a) The current magnitude is $\mathbf{I} = \sqrt{3.5^2 + 4.2^2} = 5.5$ A. Since this phasor lies in quadrant II, the phase angle is given by Equation (2–8b):

$$\theta = 180° - \tan^{-1}[4.2/3.5] = 129.8°$$

b) The voltage magnitude is $\mathbf{V} = \sqrt{100^2 + 25^2} = 103.1$ V. Since this phasor lies in quadrant III, the phase angle is given by Equation (2–8c):

$$\theta = 180° + \tan^{-1}[25/100] = 194°$$

c) The impedance magnitude is $\mathbf{Z} = \sqrt{35^2 + 20^2} = 40.3$ Ω. Since this phasor lies in quadrant I, the phase angle is given by Equation (2–8a):

$$\theta = \tan^{-1}[20/35] = 29.7°$$

d) The apparent power magnitude is $\mathbf{S} = \sqrt{100^2 + 50^2} = 111.8$ kVA. Since this phasor lies in quadrant IV, the phase angle is given by Equation (2–8d):

$$\theta = 360° - \tan^{-1}[50/100] = 333.4°$$

When converting from polar to rectangular, the following equations are useful:

$$\mathrm{Re}(\mathbf{A}) = |\mathbf{A}|\cos(\theta) \qquad\qquad (2\text{–}9a)$$
$$\mathrm{Im}(\mathbf{A}) = |\mathbf{A}|\sin(\theta) \qquad\qquad (2\text{–}9b)$$

EXAMPLE 2–4

Determine the rectangular form of the following phasors:

a) $\mathbf{I} = 100 \angle -25°$ A
b) $\mathbf{V} = 120 \angle +75°$ V
c) $\mathbf{Z} = 36 \angle +50°$ Ω
d) $\mathbf{S} = 750 \angle -25°$ VA

Solution:

a) The real component is given by Equation (2–9a):

$$\text{Re}(\mathbf{I}) = 100\cos(-25°) = 90.63 \text{ A}$$

The imaginary component is given by Equation (2–9b):

$$\text{Im}(\mathbf{I}) = 100\sin(-25°) = -42.3 \text{ A}$$

b) The real component is given by Equation (2–9a):

$$\text{Re}(\mathbf{V}) = 120\cos(75°) = 31.1 \text{ V}$$

The imaginary component is given by Equation (2–9b):

$$\text{Im}(\mathbf{V}) = 120\sin(75°) = 115.9 \text{ V}$$

c) The real component is given by Equation (2–9a):

$$\text{Re}(\mathbf{Z}) = 36\cos(50°) = 23.1 \text{ }\Omega$$

The imaginary component is given by Equation (2–9b):

$$\text{Im}(\mathbf{Z}) = 36\sin(50°) = 27.6 \text{ }\Omega$$

d) The real component is given by Equation (2–9a):

$$\text{Re}(\mathbf{S}) = 750\cos(-25°) = 679.7 \text{ VA}$$

The imaginary component is given by Equation (2–9b):

$$\text{Im}(\mathbf{S}) = 750\sin(-25°) = -317.0 \text{ VA}$$

When adding or subtracting complex numbers, it is necessary to express the numbers in rectangular form. The real components are added or subtracted, and the imaginary components are added or subtracted. To multiply two complex numbers, express them in polar form, multiply the magnitudes, and add the phase angles. For division, divide the magnitudes, and subtract the angle of the complex number in the denominator from the angle of the complex number in the numerator. The following example illustrates the procedures.

EXAMPLE 2–5

Perform the following operations:

a) $\mathbf{Z} = 12\angle-30° + 7\angle+25°$ Ω
b) $\mathbf{V} = 120\angle-120° - 120\angle0°$ V
c) $\mathbf{S} = (240 - j120°)(10\angle+45°)$ VA
d) $\mathbf{I} = (120\angle+30°) \div (7 + j5)$ A

Solution:

a) To add two complex numbers, it is necessary to convert to rectangular form, then perform the addition. The real components are added to each other, as are the imaginary components.

$$\mathbf{Z} = 12 \angle -30° + 7 \angle +25°$$
$$= 12 \cos(-30°) + j12 \sin(-30°) + 7 \cos(+25°) + j7 \sin(-25°)$$
$$= 10.39 + j(-6) + 6.34 + j(2.96)$$
$$= 16.73 + j(-3.04)$$
$$= 17.0 \angle 349.7° \ \Omega$$

b) To subtract one complex number from another, it is necessary to convert both numbers to rectangular form, then perform the subtraction.

$$\mathbf{V} = 120 \angle -120° - 120 \angle 0°$$
$$= 120 \cos(-120°) + j120 \sin(-120°) - [120 \cos(0°) + j120 \sin(0°)]$$
$$= -60 + j(-103.9) - [120 + j(0)]$$
$$= -180 + j(-103.9)$$
$$= 207.8 \angle 210° \ \text{V}$$

c) To multiply two complex numbers, it is necessary to convert both numbers to polar form. The magnitudes are multiplied and the phase angles added to achieve the result.

$$\mathbf{S} = (240 - j120°)(10 \angle +45°) = (268.3 \angle -26.6°)(10 \angle +45°) = 2683 \angle +18.4° \ \text{VA}$$

d) To divide one complex number into another, it is necessary to convert to polar form.

$$\mathbf{I} = (120 \angle +30°) \div (7 + j5) = (120 \angle +30°) \div (8.6 \angle 35.5°)$$
$$= 13.95 \angle -5.5°$$
$$= 13.89 + j(-1.34) \ \text{A}$$

2–3   OHM'S LAW AND COMPLEX IMPEDANCES

The relation between the current and voltage in a passive linear circuit element is given by Ohm's law. For direct current circuits, Ohm's law is relatively straightforward. This is because the voltage and current are constant and do not vary as a function of time. Ohm's law is given by

$$V = I R \tag{2–10}$$

where:

V = applied voltage in volts
I = current in amperes
R = resistance in ohms

Equation (2–10) can be solved for the current as follows:

$$I = V/R \qquad\qquad (2\text{–}11)$$

with all variables as defined in Equation (2–10). Equations (2–10) and (2–11) express the relationship between current and voltage in a resistance as applied to a direct current circuit. This resistance is a real quantity having a certain magnitude.

Application of Ohm's law to alternating current circuits requires consideration of the magnitude of the impedance and the phase shift that occurs between current and voltage. The phase shift that occurs can be modeled by introducing the concept of complex impedance. This complex impedance is designated Z and has both magnitude and phase angle associated with it. Ohm's law expressed for alternating current circuits is

$$\mathbf{V} = \mathbf{IZ} \qquad\qquad (2\text{–}12)$$

where:

$\mathbf{V}$ = applied voltage in volts
$\mathbf{I}$ = current in amperes
$\mathbf{Z}$ = complex impedance in ohms

Equation (2–12) can be solved for the current as follows:

$$\mathbf{I} = \mathbf{V/Z} \qquad\qquad (2\text{–}13)$$

with all variables as defined in Equation (2–12).

The complex impedances for resistance, inductance, and capacitance are shown in Figure 2–5. For the resistor shown in Figure 2–5(A), the complex impedance is given by

$$\mathbf{Z} = R \angle 0° \ \Omega \qquad\qquad (2\text{–}14)$$

where:

R = magnitude of the resistance in ohms

Note that the phase angle associated with the impedance for a resistor is 0° and that the magnitude is a constant equal to R.

The complex impedance for the inductor is shown in Figure 2–5(B). The impedance is given by

$$\mathbf{Z}_L = 2\pi f L \ \angle +90° \ \Omega$$
$$= j(2\pi f L) \qquad\qquad (2\text{–}15)$$

where:

L = magnitude of the inductance in henrys
f = frequency of the system in hertz
j = $1 \angle 90°$

Note that the phase angle associated with the impedance for an inductor is +90° and that the magnitude is equal to $2\pi f L$. The magnitude of the complex impedance for the inductor is designated $|\mathbf{Z}_L|$ and is referred to as the *inductive reactance*. Note that the inductive reactance is not a constant, but will vary as a function of frequency.

FIGURE 2–5
Complex Impedances

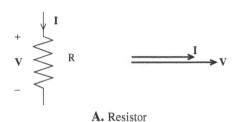

A. Resistor

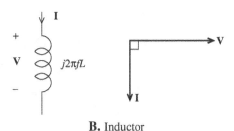

B. Inductor

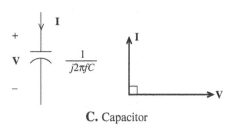

C. Capacitor

The complex impedance for the capacitor is shown in Figure 2–5(C). The impedance is given by

$$\mathbf{Z}_C = 1/(2\pi fC) \angle -90° \; \Omega \qquad\qquad (2\text{--}16)$$
$$= 1/(j2\pi fC)$$
$$= -j/(2\pi fC)$$

where:

   C = magnitude of the capacitance in farads
   f = frequency of the system in hertz

Note that the phase angle associated with the impedance for a capacitor is $-90°$ and that the magnitude is equal to $1/(2\pi fC)$. The magnitude of the complex impedance for the capacitor is referred to as the *capacitive reactance*. As with the inductive reactance, the capacitive reactance is not a constant, but will vary as a function of frequency.

EXAMPLE 2–6

Determine the complex impedance for the following elements at the specified frequency:

a) $R = 10.0 \, \Omega$ @ 60 Hz
b) $L = 1.0$ millihenry @ 60 Hz
c) $L = 1.0$ millihenry @ 300 Hz
d) $C = 5.0$ microfarad @ 60 Hz
e) $C = 5.0$ microfarad @ 300 Hz

Solution:

a) $R = 10.0 + j0.0 = 10.0 \angle 0° \, \Omega$
b) From Equation (2–15):

$$\mathbf{Z}_L = 2\pi (60)(1.0 \times 10^{-3}) \angle +90° = 0.377 \angle +90° = j0.377 \, \Omega$$

c) Again, from Equation (2–15):

$$\mathbf{Z}_L = 2\pi(300)(1.0 \times 10^{-3}) \angle +90° = 1.885 \angle +90° = j1.885 \, \Omega$$

Note the increase in the inductive reactance as compared to part (b). This is due to an increase in frequency. Note also that the phase angle remains the same as in part (b).
d) From Equation (2–16):

$$\mathbf{Z}_C = 1/[2\pi(60)(5 \times 10^{-6})] \angle -90° = 530.5 \angle -90° = -j530.5 \, \Omega$$

e) Again, from Equation (2–16):

$$\mathbf{Z}_C = 1/[2\pi(300)(5 \times 10^{-6})] \angle -90° = 106.1 \angle -90° = -j106.1 \, \Omega$$

Note the decrease in the capacitive reactance as compared to part (d). This is due to an increase in frequency. Note also that the phase angle remains the same as in part (d).

EXAMPLE 2–7

Determine the current (expressed in phasor notation) through each of the elements of Example 2–6. The applied voltage for all cases is equal to $\mathbf{V} = 120 \angle 0° \, V$

a) $\mathbf{I} = (120 \angle 0°) \div (10 \angle 0°) = 12 \angle 0° \, A$
b) $\mathbf{I} = (120 \angle 0°) \div (0.377 \angle 90°) = 318.3 \angle 90° \, A$
c) $\mathbf{I} = (120 \angle 0°) \div (1.885 \angle 90°) = 63.67 \angle 90° \, A$
d) $\mathbf{I} = (120 \angle 0°) \div (530.5 \angle -90°) = 0.226 \angle -90° \, A$
e) $\mathbf{I} = (120 \angle 0°) \div (106.1 \angle -90°) = 1.13 \angle -90° \, A$

EXAMPLE 2–8

Determine the total complex impedance by adding the following impedance elements:

a) $R = 10 \angle 0° \, \Omega$ and $X_L = 5 \angle 90° \, \Omega$
b) $R = 10 \angle 0° \, \Omega$ and $X_C = 5 \angle -90° \, \Omega$
c) $R = 10 \angle 0° \, \Omega$, $X_L = 5 \angle 90° \, \Omega$, and $X_C = 5 \angle -90° \, \Omega$

Solution:

a) $Z_T = 10 + j5 = 11.18 \angle 26.6° \ \Omega$
b) $Z_T = 10 - j5 = 11.18 \angle -26.6° \ \Omega$
c) $Z_T = 10 + j5 - j5 = 10 + j0 = 10 \angle 0° \ \Omega$

Note that in part (c), the imaginary or j terms canceled out. Please note that the imaginary parts will not always cancel.

EXAMPLE 2–9

Determine the current (expressed in phasor notation) through each of the elements of Example 2–8. The applied voltage for all cases is equal to $V = 120 \angle 0° \ V$

a) $I = (120 \angle 0°) \div (11.18 \angle 26.6°) = 10.73 \angle -26.6° \ A$
b) $I = (120 \angle 0°) \div (11.18 \angle -26.6°) = 10.73 \angle 26.6° \ A$
c) $I = (120 \angle 0°) \div (10 \angle 0°) = 12 \angle 0° \ A$

The complex conjugate of a complex number is of interest when determining the complex representation of the apparent power in an ac circuit. To find the complex conjugate of a complex number expressed in polar form, simply invert the sign of the angle of the number. If the complex number is expressed in rectangular form, invert the sign of the imaginary component of the number. Keep in mind that taking the complex conjugate of a complex number is purely a mathematical operation. The following example illustrates the operation.

EXAMPLE 2–10

Determine the complex conjugate of the following complex currents:

a) $I = 50 \angle 30° \ A$
b) $I = 75 \angle -20° \ A$
c) $I = 10 + j30 \ A$
d) $I = 25 - j15 \ A$

Solution:

a) $I^* = 50 \angle -30° \ A$

Note that the phase angle has been changed from $+30°$ to $-30°$ as a result of taking the complex conjugate.

b) $I^* = 75 \angle +20° \ A$

As in part (a), the phase angle has been changed from $-20°$ to $+20°$ as a result of taking the complex conjugate.

c) $I^* = 10 - j30 \ A$
d) $I^* = 25 + j15 \ A$

Notice that in both parts (c) and (d), the sign of the imaginary component of the complex number has changed sign. The designation for the complex conjugate is the superscript*.

2–4   POWER AND POWER FACTOR

The fundamental purpose of a building electrical system is to supply the necessary loads within the building. An understanding of load characteristics in electrical power systems involves the concept of power and power factor. The power consumed by a load will be comprised of several individual power components. These components are apparent power, reactive power, and active power or real power. All loads in electrical power systems are comprised of these individual components.

The active or real power component of the load is that portion of load that performs real work. Consider, for example, an electric motor. The electric motor is a device that converts electrical power to mechanical power. The relationship between mechanical power and electrical power is that one horsepower is equal to 746 watts. Another example would be a resistive heating element. A typical rating for a heating element might be 1500 W at 120 V. In both of these examples, it is evident that the power consumed by the load has a significant real power component.

The reactive power component of a load is used to supply energy that is stored in either a magnetic or electrical field. A good example of reactive power being used to supply a magnetic field is the magnetizing current consumed by an electric motor. This reactive power is used to produce the magnetic fields within the motor, thereby enabling the motor to perform real work. The motor is said to consume reactive power necessary for the motor to operate. An example of a device that supplies reactive power is the power factor correction capacitor.

Note in the previous two examples that reactive power is consumed by the motor, yet supplied by the capacitor. From this observation, it is evident that an electrical load may consume or supply reactive power. Whether or not a load consumes or supplies reactive power is a characteristic of the load itself.

The relationship between these electrical power quantities is best visualized by using the power triangle shown in Figure 2–6. The power triangle is a concept that was developed to allow easier calculations of these electrical quantities and to allow for easier visualization. Note that the triangle shown in Figure 2–6 is a right triangle. As such, right triangle trigonometry and the Pythagorean theorem apply.

In reference to Figure 2–6, it can be seen that the base of the power triangle represents the real power component, while the vertical component represents the reactive

FIGURE 2–6
Power Triangle Relationships

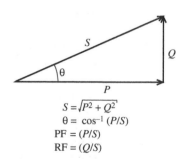

$$S = \sqrt{P^2 + Q^2}$$
$$\theta = \cos^{-1}(P/S)$$
$$PF = (P/S)$$
$$RF = (Q/S)$$

power component. The hypotenuse of the triangle represents the apparent power component. From this observation, the magnitude of the apparent power can be calculated using the Pythagorean theorem:

$$S = \sqrt{P^2 + Q^2} \tag{2–17}$$

where:

   S = magnitude of apparent power
   P = magnitude of real power
   Q = magnitude of reactive power

The ratio of real power to apparent power is also of interest to the electrical designer. This ratio is referred to as the *power factor* of the load and is given by

$$\text{PF} = \frac{P}{S} = \cos(\theta) \tag{2–18}$$

The power factor is essentially a measure of how well the load is converting the total power consumed into real work. A power factor equal to 1.0 indicates that the load is converting all of the power consumed into real work. On the other hand, a power factor of 0.0 indicates that the load is not producing any real work. In all cases, the power factor of a load will be between 1.0 and 0.0. For most typical loads, the power factor will be equal to or slightly less than unity, falling in the range of 1.0 to about 0.7. Electric motors may typically have a power factor at full load of between 0.5 and 0.95. Electric resistance heating will typically have a power factor of 0.95 to 1.0. Power factor correction capacitor banks typically have a power factor of 0.0 to 0.1. Note that in all cases, apparent power is consumed by the load, but the amount of real power can vary significantly.

The ratio of reactive power to apparent power is referred to as the *reactive factor* of the load and is given by

$$\text{RF} = \frac{Q}{S} = \sin(\theta) \tag{2–19}$$

Similar to the power factor, the reactive factor gives an indication of how much reactive power is consumed as a ratio to total apparent power. A reactive factor equal to 1.0 means that none of the power consumed by the load is being used to produce real work. For example, a power factor correction capacitor bank will have a reactive factor close to 1.0. This means that the capacitor is producing no real work. Electric resistance heating will have a reactive factor close to 0.0, meaning that the heating element does not consume a significant amount of reactive power. Again, it should be obvious that the heating element does produce useful energy. Electric motors will have a reactive factor at full load typically in the range of 0.3 to 0.9, depending on the size of the motor.

EXAMPLE 2–11

A three-phase load consumes 100 kW, and 50 kvar. Determine the apparent power, power factor, reactive factor, and the power factor angle for this load.

Solution: The apparent power is given by Equation (2–17):

$$S = \sqrt{100{,}000^2 + 50{,}000^2} = 111{,}803.4 \text{ VA} = 111.8 \text{ kVA}$$

The power factor is given by Equation (2–18):

$$\text{PF} = \frac{P}{S} = \frac{100{,}000}{111{,}803} = 0.8944$$

The reactive factor is given by Equation (2–19):

$$\text{RF} = \frac{Q}{S} = \frac{50{,}000}{111{,}803} = 0.4472$$

2–5   LEADING AND LAGGING POWER FACTOR

In addition to calculating the magnitude of the active, reactive, and apparent powers, it is necessary to understand the concepts of leading and lagging power factors. A load in which the current lags the applied voltage is said to have a *lagging* power factor. On the other hand, a load in which the current leads the applied voltage is said to have a *leading* power factor. As stated previously, the current in an inductive-type load will lag the applied voltage by some angle. Therefore, an inductive load will have a lagging power factor. The best example of a load having a lagging power factor is the induction motor.

A leading power factor load is one in which the current leads the applied voltage by some angle. An example of a leading power factor load is the power factor correction capacitor bank. Figure 2–7 shows the power triangle representations for both leading and lagging power factor loads. Note that in Figure 2–7 the reactive powers are shown in opposite directions for leading and lagging power factor loads. This is due to the fact that the current in a lagging power factor load lags the applied voltage, while the current in a

FIGURE 2–7
Power Triangle for Lagging and Leading Power Factors

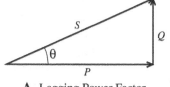

A. Lagging Power Factor

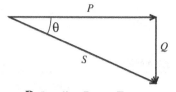

B. Leading Power Factor

leading power factor load leads the applied voltage. This is an important concept that will be used to perform power factor correction calculations.

EXAMPLE 2–12

A load consumes 500 kW at a power factor of 0.85 lagging. Determine the apparent power, reactive power, and power factor angle.

Solution: The apparent power is found by solving Equation (2–18) for S. The result is

$$S = \frac{P}{\text{PF}} = \frac{500,000}{0.85} = 588,235 \text{ VA} = 588.2 \text{ kVA}$$

The reactive power is determined by solving Equation (2–17) for Q. The result is

$$Q = \sqrt{S^2 - P^2} = \sqrt{588,200^2 - 500,000^2} = 309,872 \text{ var} = 309.9 \text{ kvar}$$

Last, the power factor angle is determined by solving Equation (2–18) for θ:

$$\theta = \cos^{-1}(\text{PF}) = \cos^{-1}(0.85) = 31.8°$$

The apparent power can also be determined if the voltage and current are known. If both the voltage and current are expressed as complex numbers, the apparent power can be determined from

$$\mathbf{S} = \mathbf{V} \times \mathbf{I}^* \qquad\qquad (2\text{–}20)$$

where:

$\mathbf{V}$ = complex phase voltage expressed in volts
$\mathbf{I}^*$ = complex conjugate of phase current expressed in amperes

The apparent power, as determined from Equation (2–20), has units of volt-amperes (VA) and will also be a complex number.

The real component of the complex apparent power as determined from Equation (2–20), referred to as the *real power,* has units of watts (W) and is given by

$$P = VI\cos(\alpha) \qquad\qquad (2\text{–}21)$$

where:

V = magnitude of the phase voltage
I = magnitude of the phase current
α = angle between the phase voltage and phase current

Likewise, the imaginary component of the complex apparent power, referred to as the *reactive power,* has units of volt-amperes-reactive (var) and is given by

$$Q = VI\sin(\alpha) \qquad\qquad (2\text{–}22)$$

with all variables as defined in Equation (2–21). If the current lags the voltage, the sign of the reactive power (Q) will be positive. Likewise, if the current leads the voltage, the sign of Q will be negative. This sign convention comes as a result of taking the complex conjugate of the current.

EXAMPLE 2–13

The phase voltage across a particular load is $120 \angle 30°$ V, and the phase current through the load is $7 \angle 10°$ A. Determine the complex apparent power, real power, and reactive power consumed by the load.

Solution: The phase angle between the voltage and current is $30° - 10° = 20°$. Direct application of Equations (2–20), (2–21), and (2–22) results in

$$\mathbf{S} = \mathbf{V} \times \mathbf{I^*} = (120 \angle 30°)(7 \angle 10°)^* = 840 \angle 20° = 789.3 + j287.3 \text{ VA}$$

$$P = VI\cos(\propto) = (120)(7)\cos(20°) = 789.3 \text{ W}$$

$$Q = VI\sin(\propto) = (120)(7)\sin(20°) = 287.3 \text{ var}$$

Note that the real and reactive components of the complex apparent power agree with the real and reactive powers as determined by applying Equations (2–21) and (2–22).

2–6   KIRCHOFF'S VOLTAGE AND CURRENT LAWS

When performing voltage drop calculations, it is necessary to understand the concept of voltage rise and voltage drop in a circuit. Consider, for example, the simple circuit shown in Figure 2–8(A). The source voltage is designated by $\mathbf{V_S}$, the load voltage is designated by

FIGURE 2–8
Kirchoff's Voltage and Current Laws

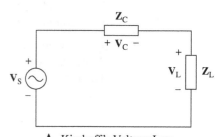

A. Kirchoff's Voltage Law

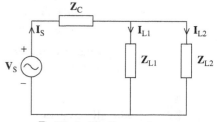

B. Kirchoff's Current Law

V_L, and the voltage drop across the cable impedance is designated V_C. Kirchoff's voltage law (KVL) states that the voltage drops must equal the voltage rises around any closed path in a circuit. Applying KVL to the circuit of Figure 2–8(A) results in the following:

$$\mathbf{V_S} = \mathbf{V_C} + \mathbf{V_L} \tag{2–23}$$

All voltages referenced in Equation (2–23) are complex numbers having both magnitude and phase angle.

EXAMPLE 2–14

Given a source voltage of $277 \angle 10°$ V and a load voltage of $270 \angle 5°$ V, determine the voltage drop across the cable impedance.

Solution: Equation (2–23) is solved for V_C, resulting in

$$
\begin{aligned}
\mathbf{V_C} &= \mathbf{V_S} - \mathbf{V_L} \\
&= 277 \angle 10° - 270 \angle 5° \\
&= (272.8 + j48.1) - (269.0 + j23.5) \\
&= 3.8 + j24.6 \\
&= 24.9 \angle 81.2° \text{ V}
\end{aligned}
$$

Kirchoff's current law (KCL) states that the summation of currents entering a node must equal the summation of the currents leaving a node. An example of the application of KCL is shown in Figure 2–8(B). The load currents of the two loads are designated I_{L1} and I_{L2}, respectively. The source current is designated I_S. Here, it is evident that the sum of the two load currents must equal the source current. Expressed as an equation:

$$\mathbf{I_S} = \mathbf{I_{L1}} + \mathbf{I_{L2}} \tag{2–24}$$

EXAMPLE 2–15

Two loads are connected in parallel to a 277 V branch circuit. Load #1 consumes a current of $5.7 \angle -25°$ A, and load #2 consumes a current of $6.2 \angle 10°$ A. Determine the source current.

Solution: Direct application of Equation (2–24) results in

$$
\begin{aligned}
\mathbf{I_S} = \mathbf{I_{L1}} + \mathbf{I_{L2}} &= 5.7 \angle -25° + 6.2 \angle 10° \\
&= (5.2 - j2.4) + (6.1 + j1.1) \\
&= 11.3 + j(-1.3) \\
&= 11.4 \angle -6.6° \text{ A}
\end{aligned}
$$

2–7   CALCULATING LOAD CURRENT

To properly size power conductors, it is necessary to determine the magnitude of the load current from the estimated load. It is the magnitude of the current that produces heat in the conductors due to the I^2R losses occurring in the conductor resistance.

For a single-phase load, the current magnitude is given by

$$I = \frac{VA}{V} = \frac{W \div PF}{V} \text{ (amps)} \qquad (2\text{--}25)$$

where:

VA = total apparent power of load in volt-amperes
W = total real power of load in watts
PF = power factor of load
V = magnitude of applied voltage

For three-phase loads, the current magnitude is given by

$$I = \frac{VA}{\sqrt{3}\ V_{LL}} = \frac{W \div PF}{\sqrt{3}\ V_{LL}} \text{ (amps)} \qquad (2\text{--}26)$$

where:

VA = total three-phase apparent power of load in volt-amperes
V_{LL} = line to line voltage magnitude

EXAMPLE 2–16

Calculate the magnitude of the line current for the specified loads:

a) 10 kVA, unity power factor, 120 V, single phase, two wire
b) 50 kW, 0.9 lagging power factor, 120/240 V, single phase, three wire
c) 150 kVA, 0.8 lagging power factor, 208Y/120 V, three phase, four wire
d) 200 kW, 0.85 lagging power factor, 480Y/277 V, three phase, four wire

Solution:

a) Application of Equation (2–25) results in

$$I = \frac{10{,}000 \text{ VA}}{120 \text{ V}} = 83.3 \text{ A}$$

b) Here it is assumed that the single-phase load is balanced. The result is that the neutral current is equal to zero. Therefore, the voltage is 240 V. Application of Equation (2–25) results in

$$I = \frac{50{,}000 \text{ W} \div 0.9}{240 \text{ V}} = 231.5 \text{ A}$$

c) The three-phase load is assumed to be balanced among all three phases. Application of Equation (2–26) results in

$$I = \frac{150,000 \text{ VA}}{\sqrt{3}\ 208 \text{ V}} = 416.4 \text{ A}$$

d) Again, the three-phase load is assumed to be balanced as in part (c). Application of Equation (2–26) results in

$$I = \frac{200,000 \text{ W} \div 0.85}{\sqrt{3}\ 480 \text{ V}} = 283 \text{ A}$$

PROBLEMS

1. Determine the rms voltage or current and the frequency in hertz for each of the following waveforms:
   a. $v(t) = 500 \sin (700t + 25°)$ V
   b. $i(t) = 320 \sin (950t - 30°)$ A

2. Determine the rms phasor representation for the waveforms of Problem 1.

3. Determine the polar form of the following complex numbers:
   a. $\mathbf{I} = 15 + j23$ A
   b. $\mathbf{I} = -25 + j50$ A
   c. $\mathbf{I} = -15 - j20$ A
   d. $\mathbf{I} = 30 - j30$ A

4. Determine the rectangular form of the following complex numbers:
   a. $\mathbf{V} = 120 \angle +45°$ V
   b. $\mathbf{I} = 40 \angle -25°$ A
   c. $\mathbf{V} = 480 \angle +210°$ V
   d. $\mathbf{Z} = 35 \angle -15°$ Ω

5. Given the complex numbers $\mathbf{A} = 15 - j25$, $\mathbf{B} = 12 \angle +45°$, perform the following operations:
   a. $\mathbf{A} + \mathbf{B}$
   b. $\mathbf{B} - \mathbf{A}$
   c. $\mathbf{A} * \mathbf{B}$
   d. $\mathbf{B} / \mathbf{A}$

6. Determine the complex impedance expressed in both polar form and rectangular form for the following circuit elements:
   a. $C = 25$ microfarad at 60 Hz
   b. $C = 25$ microfarad at 420 Hz
   c. $L = 535$ microhenry at 60 Hz
   d. $L = 535$ microhenry at 660 Hz
   e. $R = 10$ Ω at 60 Hz
   f. $R = 10$ Ω at 300 Hz

7. Determine the total complex impedance of the following series-connected elements:
   a. $R = 20\ \Omega$, $X_L = 10\ \Omega$
   b. $R = 10\ \Omega$, $X_C = 15\ \Omega$
   c. $R = 5\ \Omega$, $X_L = 10\ \Omega$, $X_C = 15\ \Omega$
   d. $R = 20\ \Omega$, $L = 300$ microhenry at 60 Hz

8. Determine the current through each of the impedance elements given below, assuming an applied voltage of $480\ \angle 30°$ V. Express your answers in polar form.
   a. $\mathbf{Z} = 50 + j0\ \Omega$
   b. $\mathbf{Z} = 20 + j15\ \Omega$
   c. $\mathbf{Z} = 30 - j25\ \Omega$

9. Determine the complex conjugate of the following:
   a. $\mathbf{V} = 100 + j50$ V
   b. $\mathbf{I} = 200 - j200$ A
   c. $\mathbf{V} = 277\ \angle 120°$ V
   d. $\mathbf{I} = 150\ \angle -45°$ A

10. Determine the real power, power factor, and reactive factor for a load that consumes 100 kVA and 90 kW.

11. Determine the apparent power, reactive power, and reactive factor for a load that consumes 500 kW at a power factor of 0.85 lagging.

12. Determine the apparent power, power factor, and reactive factor for a load that consumes 200 kW and 150 kvar.

13. Determine the real power, power factor, and reactive factor for a load that consumes 300 kVA and 190 kvar.

14. A load impedance of $5\ \angle +45°\ \Omega$ has an applied voltage of $120\ \angle -30°$ V. Determine the current through the impedance, complex apparent power, real power, reactive power, and power factor of this load. Specify whether the power factor is leading or lagging.

15. Given a simple series circuit similar to that shown in Figure 2–8(A), determine the voltage drop across the cable impedance if the source voltage is $\mathbf{V}_S = 120\ \angle 0°$ V and the load voltage is $\mathbf{V}_L = 117\ \angle -3°$ V.

16. Given a simple series circuit similar to that shown in Figure 2–8(A), determine the load voltage if the source voltage is $\mathbf{V}_S = 120\ \angle 0°$ V, the load current is $\mathbf{I}_L = 10\ \angle -30°$ A, and the cable impedance is $\mathbf{Z}_C = 0.5\ \angle +45°$.

17. Given a simple parallel circuit similar to that shown in Figure 2–8(B), determine the source current if the load currents are $\mathbf{I}_{L1} = 30\ \angle +45°$ A and $\mathbf{I}_{L2} = 20\ \angle -20°$ A.

18. A simple parallel circuit similar to that shown in Figure 2–8(B) has three loads connected to it. Determine the source current if the load currents are $\mathbf{I}_{L1} = 30\ \angle +45°$ A and $\mathbf{I}_{L2} = 20\ \angle -20°$ A, and $\mathbf{I}_{L3} = 10\ \angle -90°$ A.

19. A simple parallel circuit similar to that shown in Figure 2–8(B) has two loads connected to it. The load impedances are $\mathbf{Z}_{L1} = 10\ \angle +45°\ \Omega$ and $\mathbf{Z}_{L2} = 20\ \angle +90°\ \Omega$. The applied load voltage is $120\ \angle 0°$ V.
   Determine the current in each load impedance and the source current.

20. Determine the magnitude of the line current for each of the following specified loads:
   a. 100 kW, 0.8 lagging power factor, 480Y/277 V, three phase, four wire wye
   b. 200 kW, 0.7 lagging power factor, 208Y/120 V, three phase, four wire wye
   c. 75 kW, 0.85 lagging power factor, 240 V, three phase, three wire delta
   d. 100 kW, 0.8 lagging power factor, 120/240 V, single phase, three wire
   e. 50 kVA, 0.9 lagging power factor, 480Y/277 V, three-phase, three wire wye
   f. 50 kVA, 0.9 lagging power factor, 120/240 V, single phase, three wire.

3

Load Characteristics

INTRODUCTION

This chapter addresses the calculation of the electrical loads to be served in a given building. The concepts of unit loads, load tabulation, and demand factors are presented. Examples of load calculation to determine service entrance requirements for residential and commercial occupancies are also given.

OBJECTIVES

Upon completion of this chapter, you will be able to:

- Determine the estimated demand load for a given branch circuit, feeder, or service
- Apply demand factors to account for load diversity
- Understand the *NEC* minimum load requirements
- Determine the demand load for single-phase and three-phase motors
- Determine the demand load for household electric ranges, cooktops, and ovens
- Determine the demand load for household electric dryers
- Determine service entrance ampacity requirements

3–1   MINIMUM ESTIMATED DEMAND LOAD

An accurate estimate of the demand load on a particular branch circuit, feeder, or service is necessary to determine the required rating of these circuits. The actual number of branch circuits or feeders is also based on the determination of the estimated demand load. Branch circuit and feeder design is discussed in Chapter 7.

Article 220 of the *NEC* discusses the required rules for determining the minimum estimated demand load for branch circuits, feeders, and services. The basic rule is that the branch circuit, feeder, or service must have a rating sufficient to supply the demand load to be served. The demand load on a circuit is equal to the minimum estimated load as determined by applying *NEC* minimums, or the actual load, whichever is greater. What this means is that the designer will typically need to calculate the actual load to be served and the minimum required by the *NEC*. Design of the system will be based on the greater of the two.

Although the *NEC* does provide information necessary to determine the minimum estimated loads, the designer must exercise common sense and judgment when determining the load to be served. The quantity and location of receptacles and lighting fixtures will vary depending on the nature of the occupancy. For example, a restaurant will generally have decorative fixtures necessary to create a certain "ambiance." On the other hand, general office areas may require only functional lighting to provide a certain level of illumination. From these examples it should be evident that the load will be related to the type of occupancy to be served.

General Lighting Load

The general lighting load that shall be applied to a particular occupancy is based on a certain unit load per square foot of floor space. This value is expressed in terms of volt-amperes per square foot. The total minimum estimated lighting load can be determined by multiplying the unit load by the total square foot area of the occupancy. The unit loads for various occupancies are shown in Table 220.3(A) of the *NEC*. This table is shown in Table 3–1.

If the type of occupancy you are designing for is not listed in Table 220.3(A), the load is determined based on the actual connected equipment. In addition, only the habitable areas of dwelling units are used in the square-footage determination. Unfinished basements, garages, or porches are not considered habitable areas and should not be included in the square-footage determination.

EXAMPLE 3–1

Determine the estimated lighting load for an office area that measures 50 ft × 100 ft. The office contains 20 fluorescent lighting fixtures, each having a ballast input of 277 V, 0.7 A.

Solution: The lighting load must be calculated based on the application of the unit load from the *NEC* and by determining the actual load based on the connected lighting equipment. The estimated demand load is the greater of the two loads calculated. The branch circuit and feeder design will be based on this estimated demand load. From Table 3–1, the unit load for lighting in an office area is 31/2 volt-amperes per square foot. The total square foot area is equal to 50 ft × 100 ft = 5000 sq ft. Therefore, the total lighting load is

$$S = (5000 \text{ sq ft}) \times (31/2 \text{ VA per sq ft}) = 17,500 \text{ VA}$$

The lighting load based on the connected equipment is determined by calculating the volt-ampere load of each lighting fixture and multiplying by the number of fixtures. Therefore, the actual connected lighting load is equal to

$$S = (20 \text{ fixtures}) \times (277 \text{ V}) \times (0.7 \text{ A}) = 3878 \text{ VA}$$

Note that although the actual connected lighting load is 3878 VA, the estimated demand load will be 17,500 VA based on the *NEC* minimum requirements. The number of branch circuits required for general lighting in this area must be based on an estimated load of 17,500 VA, not 3878 VA. Again, the greater of the two values applies.

The footnotes to Table 220.3(A) require some explanation. First, although Table 220.3(a) applies to general lighting loads, the load from general-purpose receptacle outlets

TABLE 3–1
NEC **Table 220.3(A) General Lighting Loads by Occupancy**

Type of Occupancy	Unit Load	
	Volt-Amperes per Square Meter	Volt-Amperes per Square Foot
Armories and auditoriums	11	1
Banks	39[b]	3½[b]
Barber shops and beauty parlors	33	3
Churches	11	1
Clubs	22	2
Court rooms	22	2
Dwelling units[a]	33	3
Garages—commercial (storage)	6	½
Hospitals	22	2
Hotels and motels, including apartment houses without provision for cooking by tenants[a]	22	2
Industrial commercial (loft) buildings	22	2
Lodge rooms	17	1½
Office buildings	39	3½[b]
Restaurants	22	2
Schools	33	3
Stores	33	3
Warehouses (storage)	3	¼
In any of the preceding occupancies except one-family dwellings and individual dwelling units of two-family and multifamily dwellings:		
Assembly halls and auditoriums	11	1
Halls, corridors, closets, stairways	6	½
Storage spaces	3	¼

[a]See 220.3(B)(10).

[b]In addition, a unit load of 11 volt-amperes/m^2 or 1 volt-ampere/ft^2 shall be included for general-purpose receptacle outlets where the actual number of general-purpose receptacle outlets is unknown.

Reprinted with permission from NFPA 70 *The National Electric Code* © 2002, National Fire Protection Association, Quincy, MA 02269. This reprinted material is not the referenced subject which is represented only by the standard in its entirety.

in habitable areas of dwelling units, hotels, and motels is permitted to be included with the general lighting load for the purposes of load estimation. In dwelling units, these general-purpose receptacle outlets will supply various cord- and plug-connected equipment in bedrooms, family rooms, living rooms, etc. In fact, many of these outlets will have table or floor lamps plugged in. The load from these receptacles is included in the unit lighting load from Table 220.3(A).

Also, for office buildings and banks, an additional load of 1 VA per square foot shall be included if the actual number of general-purpose receptacles is unknown. This is due to the fact that in many office-type occupancies, the final furniture layout is not known. The office space may consist of a large open area initially, with final layout of furniture and partitions to occur as the space is leased. This arrangement allows for maximum flexibility in locating desks, filing cabinets, partitions, etc. In these instances, power poles or office partitions containing wireways are used to distribute power in these areas. Since the designer may not know at the time of design what the final layout will be, this extra provision for load must be included.

Dedicated Branch Circuit Loads

The *NEC* requires that certain branch circuits in dwelling units be provided for receptacle outlets only. The connection of lighting outlets to these dedicated branch circuits is prohibited. Included in these required branch circuits are a minimum of two 20 A branch circuits to supply the small-appliance loads in the kitchen areas and one 20 A branch circuit to supply the laundry equipment in dwelling units. Section 220.16 of the *NEC* requires the computed loading on these dedicated branch circuits to be 1500 volt-amperes per circuit. Note that this load is in addition to the unit volt-amperes per square foot for general lighting.

General-Purpose Receptacle Load

Section 220.3(B)(9) of the *NEC* requires that a minimum load of 180 volt-amperes be assigned to other general-use receptacle outlets that are not located in habitable areas or connected to a dedicated branch circuit. The 180 volt-amperes applies to a device located on a single yoke or mounting strap. For example, a duplex receptacle consists of two outlets mounted on a single strap. The load is 180 volt-amperes for both receptacles on the strap. Bear in mind that the *NEC* minimum is 180 VA per receptacle. The estimated load can always be greater than the required *NEC* minimum. An example of this situation would be a dedicated branch circuit supplying two duplex receptacles in the workshop area of a residence. The *NEC* minimum load on this branch circuit could be estimated as 180 VA per receptacle × 2 receptacles = 360 VA. In reality, the load on this circuit could be expected to be much higher than 360 VA. A typical circular saw rated at 11 A @ 115 V would have a load of 1265 VA. A better estimate of the load on this particular circuit might be 1500 VA. You can always exceed *NEC* minimum requirements. Use common sense and judgment when estimating loads on circuits where you suspect large loads might be connected.

Other Loads

In addition to lighting and receptacle loads, there are other loads that will be present in a given occupancy. These loads, to name a few, may consist of electric heating, electric hot water tanks, motors, and other general-use receptacle outlets. For non-motor-operated appliances, the volt-ampere rating as calculated from the actual current and voltage ratings of the device is used as the load. Motor loads are also calculated based on the full load current of the motor, with 25% added to allow for slight overload conditions on the motor. For load estimating purposes, the full load current of various motors can be found in

Tables 430-147, 430-148, 430-149, and 430-150 of the *NEC,* which are reproduced in Chapter 13 of this text. In addition, for feeders or branch circuits supplying multiple motor loads, 25% of the load of the largest motor in the group must be added to the total motor load.

EXAMPLE 3–2

Determine the estimated demand load expressed in amperes and in volt-amperes for the following individual motors. Each of these motors is supplied by a dedicated branch circuit.

a) 1/3 hp, 115 V, single phase
b) 2 hp, 230 V, single phase
c) 40 hp, 460 V, three phase
d) 20 hp, 200 V, three phase

Solution:

a) The full load current from Table 430-148 is 7.2 A. The load expressed in volt-amperes is

$$S = (115 \text{ V}) \times (7.2 \text{ A}) = 828 \text{ VA}$$

b) The full load current from Table 430-148 is 12 A. The load expressed in volt-amperes is

$$S = (230 \text{ V}) \times (12 \text{ A}) = 2760 \text{ VA}$$

c) The full load current from Table 430-150 is 52 A. The load expressed in volt-amperes is

$$S = \sqrt{3} \, (460 \text{ V}) \times (52 \text{ A}) = 41{,}429 \text{ VA}$$

d) The full load current from Table 430-150 is 62.1 A. The load expressed in volt-amperes is

$$S = \sqrt{3} \, (200 \text{ V}) \times (62.1 \text{ A}) = 21{,}511 \text{ VA}$$

EXAMPLE 3–3

Determine the estimated demand load and load current for a 25 kW, 230 V, single-phase electric furnace containing a resistive heating element.

Solution: Electric resistance heating elements are assumed to have unity power factor. Therefore, the estimated demand load is 25,000 volt-amperes. The full load current is

$$I = (25{,}000 \text{ VA}) \div (230 \text{ V}) = 108.7 \text{ A}$$

EXAMPLE 3–4

Determine the estimated demand load and load current for an electric hot water tank that contains a 5.0 kW, 115 V, resistance heating element.

Solution: Again, resistive heating elements have a power factor of unity. Therefore, the estimated demand load is 5000 VA. The load current is

$$I = (5000 \text{ VA}) \div (115 \text{ V}) = 43.5 \text{ A}$$

EXAMPLE 3–5

A motor control center supplies the following motor loads: 20 hp, 460 V; 40 hp, 460 V; and 60 hp, 460 V. The motor control center is supplied by a 480 V feeder. Determine the estimated demand load on the feeder.

Solution: This is an example of multiple motors connected to a feeder. The estimated demand load on the feeder is equal to the sum of the full-load current of the motors plus 25% of the full-load current of the largest motor in the group. The individual motor full-load currents are determined from Table 430-150 as follows:

20 hp, 460 V: Full load current	= 27 A
40 hp, 460 V: Full load current	= 52 A
60 hp, 460 V: Full load current	= 77 A
Subtotal	= 156 A
+25% of largest motor = 0.25 × 77 A	= 19.3 A
Total estimated demand load	= 175.3 A

In terms of volt-amperes, the load is: $S = \sqrt{3} \times 175.3 \text{ A} \times 460 \text{ V} = 139{,}665 \text{ VA}$

Household Electric Cooking Equipment

Household electric cooking equipment may consist of free-standing electric ranges, counter-mounted cooktops, or wall-mounted electric ovens. The free-standing electric range will have both a cooktop and an oven built in as one complete unit and would therefore be supplied from a single branch circuit. On the other hand, the counter-mounted cooktop and wall-mounted oven are separate units. Although it is permitted to supply counter-mounted cooktops and wall-mounted ovens from the same branch circuit, it is preferable to supply these units from individual branch circuits. One branch circuit would supply the counter-mounted cooktop, while another circuit would supply the wall-mounted oven. In the case of the free-standing electric range, the branch circuit rating may be determined based on the estimated load. The ratings for branch circuits supplying counter-mounted cooktops or wall-mounted ovens must be based on the ratings of the individual units.

For the purposes of load estimation, electric ranges are considered individually. A counter-mounted cooktop and not more than two wall-mounted ovens all supplied from the same branch circuit may be considered as a single unit for the purpose of load estimation. In this case, the ratings of the units are added together to determine the equivalent rating. The demand load for household electric cooking appliances is taken from Table 220.19 of the *NEC,* as shown in Table 3–2. For household electric ranges (or equivalent cooktop/oven) individually rated at not over 12 kW, the estimated demand may be determined from column A of Table 220.19. If the range (or equivalent cooktop/oven) has a rating over 12 kW, but not exceeding 27 kW, the demand from column A must be increased by 5% for each kW in excess of 12 kW. The following examples illustrate the procedure.

EXAMPLE 3–6

Determine the estimated branch circuit demand load for the following household electric cooking equipment. Each of these units is supplied from an individual branch circuit.

a) 10 kW range
b) 15 kW range
c) 19 kW range
d) 6 kW cooktop
e) 8 kW oven

Solution:

a) Since this range has a rating less than 12 kW, the load is 8 kW, as read from Table 220.19.
b) For this 15 kW range, there are 3 kW in excess of 12 kW. The percentage increase is therefore equal to 3 kW × 5% per kW, or 15%. The result is

$$\text{Demand load} = 8 \text{ kW} \times 115\% = 9.2 \text{ kW}$$

c) For the 19 kW range, there are 7 kW in excess of 12 kW. The percentage increase is therefore equal to 7 kW × 5% per kW, or 35%. The result is

$$\text{Demand load} = 8 \text{ kW} \times 135\% = 10.8 \text{ kW}$$

d) The branch circuit demand load is equal to the rating of the cooktop, or 6 kW. The branch circuit supplying the cooktop must have a rating sufficient to supply this demand load.
e) The branch circuit demand load is equal to the rating of the oven, or 8 kW. The branch circuit supplying the oven must have a rating sufficient to supply this demand load.

EXAMPLE 3–7

Determine the estimated demand load for a branch circuit supplying both a counter-mounted cooktop unit having a rating of 5 kW and a wall-mounted oven rated at 6 kW.

Solution: It is permitted to consider one counter-mounted cooktop and one wall-mounted oven as a single range for the purposes of determining the estimated demand load on the branch circuit supplying the units. The combined rating of the units is 5 kW + 6 kW = 11 kW. Treating this as a single range with an equivalent rating of 11 kW, column A of Table 220.19 can be used directly. From the table, the estimated demand load is 8 kW.

EXAMPLE 3–8

Determine the estimated demand load for a branch circuit supplying both a counter-mounted cooktop unit having a rating of 7 kW and a wall-mounted oven rated at 8 kW.

Solution: As in the previous example, it is permitted to consider one counter-mounted cooktop and one wall-mounted oven as a single range for the purposes of determining the estimated load of the units. The combined rating of the units is 7 kW + 8 kW = 15 kW. Treating this as a single range with an equivalent rating of 15 kW, column A of Table

TABLE 3–2
NEC **Table 220.19 Demand Loads for Household Electric Ranges, Wall-Mounted Ovens, Counter-Mounted Cooking Units, and Other Household Cooking Appliances over 1¾ kW Rating (Column C to be used in all cases except as otherwise permitted in Note 3.)**

Number of Appliances	Demand Factor (Percent) (See Notes)		Column C Maximum Demand (kW) (See Notes) (Not over 12 kW Rating)
	Column A (Less than 3½ kW Rating)	**Column B** (3½ kW to 8¾ kW Rating)	
1	80	80	8
2	75	65	11
3	70	55	14
4	66	50	17
5	62	45	20
6	59	43	21
7	56	40	23
8	53	36	23
9	51	35	24
10	49	34	25
11	47	32	26
12	45	32	27
13	43	32	28
14	41	32	29
15	40	32	30
16	39	28	31
17	38	28	32
18	37	28	33
19	36	28	34
20	25	28	35
21	34	26	36
22	33	26	37
23	32	26	38
24	31	26	39
25	30	26	40

TABLE 3–2
Continued

Number of Appliances	DEMAND FACTOR (PERCENT) (See Notes)		Column C Maximum Demand (kW) (See Notes) (Not over 12 kW Rating)
	Column A (Less than 3½ kW Rating)	Column B (3½ kW to 8¾ kW Rating)	
26–30	30	24	15 kW + 1 kW
31–40	30	22	for each range
41–50	30	20	25 kW + ¾ kW
51–60	30	18	for each range
61 and over	30	16	

1. Over 12 kW through 27 kW ranges all of same rating. For ranges individually rated more than 12 kW but not more than 27 kW, the maximum demand in Column C shall be increased 5 percent for each additional kilowatt of rating or major fraction thereof by which the rating of individual ranges exceeds 12 kW.

2. Over 8¾ kW through 27 kW ranges of unequal ratings. For ranges individually rated more than 8¾ kW and of different ratings, but none exceeding 27 kW, an average value of rating shall be computed by adding together the ratings of all ranges to obtain the total connected load (using 12 kW for any range rated less than 12 kW) and dividing by the total number of ranges. Then the maximum demand in Column C shall be increased 5 percent for each kilowatt or major fraction thereof by which this average value exceeds 12 kW.

3. Over 1¾ kW through 8¾ kW. In lieu of the method provided in Column C, it shall be permissible to add the nameplate ratings of all household cooking appliances rated more than 1¾ kW but not more than 8¾ kW and multiply the sum by the demand factors specified in Column A or B for the given number of appliances. Where the rating of cooking appliances falls under both Column A and Column B, the demand factors for each column shall be applied to the appliances for that column, and the results added together.

4. Branch-Circuit Load. It shall be permissible to compute the branch-circuit load for one range in accordance with Table 220.19. The branch-circuit load for one wall-mounted oven or one counter-mounted cooking unit shall be the nameplate rating of the appliance. The branch-circuit load for a counter-mounted cooking unit and no more than two wall-mounted ovens, all supplied from a single branch circuit and located in the same room, shall be computed by adding the nameplate rating of the individual appliances and treating this total as equivalent to one range.

5. This table also applies to household cooking appliances rated over 1¾ kW and used in instructional programs. Reprinted with permission from NFPA 70 *The National Electric Code* © 2002, National Fire Protection Association, Quincy, MA 02269. This reprinted material is not the referenced subject which is represented only by the standard in its entirety.

220.19 can be used. Note, however, that the demand from column A must be adjusted since the combined rating is more than 12 kW. The combined rating of 15 kW exceeds 12 kW by 3 kW. The correction factor is 3 kW × 5% per kW in excess of 12 kW = 15%. The estimated demand load is therefore 8 kW × 115% = 9.2 kW for the units.

Electric Clothes Dryers

Section 220.18 of the *NEC* requires that the demand load for electric household clothes dryers be computed as being equal to 5000 VA or the nameplate rating, whichever is larger. The branch circuit supplying the dryer must have a rating sufficient to supply the demand load of the dryer. Demand factors for more than one dryer connected to a given feeder or service are shown in Table 220.18 of the *NEC*.

EXAMPLE 3–9

Determine the estimated demand load for the following household electric dryers:

a) 3.5 kW
b) 7 kW

Solution:

a) The minimum demand of 5 kW applies even though the actual rating is 3.5 kW. Therefore, the estimated demand load is 5 kW.
b) The actual rating of the dryer applies in this case since it exceeds 5 kW. The demand load is 7 kW for this case.

3–2   DEMAND FACTORS

The actual demand load for a particular occupancy will be less than the sum of all connected loads due to the diversity of equipment use. Not all equipment will be running at any given time. Sizing a feeder or service equal to the sum of the connected loads would result in excessive sizing of these elements. These oversized services and feeders would, of course, be able to carry the connected load, but would not be economical.

To understand the concept of load diversity, consider the simple riser diagram shown in Figure 3–1. Assume that this is the riser diagram for a 2000-square-foot residence. Note that there are four circuits for general lighting and receptacles, four circuits for dedicated small-appliance branch circuits, and one dedicated laundry circuit. In addition, there are three circuits supplying general-use receptacle outlets in unfinished areas of the dwelling. Dedicated circuits supply the microwave, overhead door operator, electric range, footer sump pump, laundry sump pump, dishwasher, air-conditioning unit, electric dryer, refrigerator, garbage disposal, deep freeze, and electric hot water heater. The ratings of these large appliances are shown on the riser diagram. Adding up the individual demand loads for these circuits will result in a total connected load of 47,673 volt-amperes. However, the actual demand load will be less than the connected load due to the fact that not all loads will be on at the same time.

Demand factors may be applied to portions of the total load due to the diversity of use that typically occurs in a particular occupancy. Demand factors for general lighting loads are given in *NEC* Tables 220.11 and 220.13. These tables are shown in Table 3–3. Note that the use of these tables is not permitted when determining the required number of branch circuits for general lighting. These demand factors are only to be used to determine the total load that would typically apply only to services or feeders.

The lighting load that may be subjected to the demand factors shown in Table 220.11 is comprised of the following individual loads:

1. Lighting load determined from Table 220.3(A)
2. Small-appliance branch circuit load (1500 VA each)

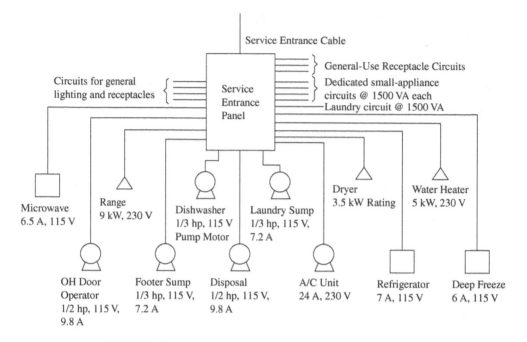

FIGURE 3–1
Riser Diagram for Load Calculation in Residential Example

    3. Laundry circuit load (1500 VA each)
    4. Miscellaneous general-use receptacles that were calculated at 180 VA each

Note that even though Table 220.11 applies to lighting loads, it is permissible to include the small-appliance branch circuit loads, laundry circuit load, and other miscellaneous receptacle loads in the application of these demand factors.

EXAMPLE 3–10

A residential building has a living area of 2000 square feet. There are four small-appliance branch circuits supplying the kitchen and dining areas and one laundry circuit. In addition, there are a total of 20 duplex receptacles for miscellaneous use in the unfinished areas of the residence. Determine the estimated demand for this portion of the dwelling load.

Solution: The load tabulation for this portion of the load is shown below.

General illumination: 2000 sq ft @ 3 VA per sq ft   = 6,000 VA
Small-appliance branch circuits: 4 @ 1500 VA per circuit   = 6,000 VA
Laundry circuit: 1 @ 1500 VA   = 1,500 VA
Misc. general-use receptacles: 20 @ 180 VA per receptacle = 3,600 VA
                                                       Total = 17,100 VA

Next, the demand factors of Table 220.11 are applied:

First 3,000 VA @ 100%:   (3,000 VA) × 100%   = 3,000 VA

Next 3,001 VA to 120,000 VA @ 35%: (17,100 VA − 3,000 VA) × 35% = 4,935 VA

Total = 7,935 VA

Note in this example that although the total estimated connected load was 17,100 VA, the estimated demand load was 7,935 VA, a little less than half of the estimated connected load.

If the total load consists of loads that are prevented from operating simultaneously, only the larger of the two needs to be considered in the total load calculation. A good example of this is electric heating and central air-conditioning equipment. Obviously, the electric heating element will not be on at the same time as the air-conditioning unit. Another example is duplex pumping systems where only one pump motor is permitted to run at any given time.

TABLE 3–3
NEC **Table 220.11 Lighting Load Demand Factors**

Type of Occupancy	Portion of Lighting Load to Which Demand Factor Applies (Volt-Amperes)	Demand Factor (Percent)
Dwelling units	First 3000 or less at	100
	From 3001 to 120,000 at	35
	Remainder over 120,000 at	25
Hospitals*	First 50,000 or less at	40
	Remainder over 50,000 at	20
Hotels and motels, including apartment	First 20,000 or less at	50
houses without provision for cooking	From 20,001 to 100,000 at	40
by tenants*	Remainder over 100,000 at	30
Warehouses	First 12,500 or less at	100
(storage)	Remainder over 12,500 at	50
All other	Total volt-amperes	100

*The demand factors of this table shall not apply to the computed load of feeders or services supplying areas in hospitals, hotels, and motels where the entire lighting is likely to be used at one time, as in operating rooms, ballrooms, or dining rooms.

NEC **Table 220.13 Demand Factors for Nondwelling Receptacle Loads**

Portion of Receptacle Load to Which Demand Factor Applies (Volt-Amperes)	Demand Factor (Percent)
First 10 kVA or less at	100
Remainder over 10 kVA at	50

Reprinted with permission from NFPA 70 *The National Electric Code* © 2002, National Fire Protection Association, Quincy, MA 02269. This reprinted material is not the referenced subject which is represented only by the standard in its entirety.

EXAMPLE 3–11

Determine the load expressed in volt-amperes and amperes for a dishwasher that contains a 1/3 hp, 115 V, pump motor and a 900 W resistive heating (dryer) element.

Solution: This is an example of noncoincident loads. In other words, the pump motor will not operate at the same time as the dryer element. The two devices are prevented from operating simultaneously by the electrical control circuitry. The estimated load is the larger of the two individual loads. The motor load is 7.2 A, corresponding to 828 VA @ 115 V. The dryer element has a rating of 900 W, or 900 VA, assuming unity power factor. Thus, the load of the dryer element exceeds that of the motor, resulting in a load of 900 VA for this device.

If four or more fastened-in-place appliances are present, Section 210.17 of the *NEC* permits a demand factor of 75% to be applied to the sum of the full-load current ratings of these appliances. This demand factor shall not apply to electric ranges, clothes dryers, space heating, or air-conditioning equipment. Examples of fastened-in-place appliances that may be subjected to this demand factor are sump pumps, garage door operators, garbage disposals, refrigerators, microwave ovens, deep freezes, dishwashers, etc. Even though many of these appliances may be cord-and-plug connected, they can be considered fastened in place—not easily movable.

EXAMPLE 3–12

The residence of Example 3–10 has the following fastened-in-place appliances. Determine the estimated demand load for these appliances.

Solution:

Footer sump pump:	⅓ hp, 115 V, 7.2 A	= 828 VA
Laundry sump pump:	⅓ hp, 115 V, 7.2 A	= 828 VA
Overhead door operator:	½ hp, 115 V, 9.8 A	= 1127 VA
Refrigerator:	7.0 A, 115 V	= 805 VA
Deep freeze:	6.0 A, 115 V	= 690 VA
Microwave hood:	6.5 A, 115 V	= 748 VA
Garbage disposal:	½ hp, 115 V, 9.8 A	= 1127 VA
Dishwasher:	900 W dryer (Ex. 3.11)	= 900 VA
	Total connected load	= 7053 VA

Applying the 75% demand factor to the connected load for these appliances results in

Estimated demand load: 7053 VA × 75% = 5290 VA

As in the previous example, note that although the total connected appliance load was 7053 VA, the estimated demand load is 5290 VA. Again, this is due to the diversity of the load.

EXAMPLE 3–13

Determine the total estimated demand load for the residence discussed in Examples 3–10, 3–11, and 3–12. In addition to the loads specified in these examples, the residence has an electric hot water tank rated at 5 kW, 230 V; an air-conditioning unit rated at 230 V, 24 A; and an electric range rated at 10 kW. Use this estimated demand load to determine the required service entrance ampacity.

Solution: From Example 3–10, the subtotal for general illumination was 7935 VA. From Example 3–12, the subtotal for the appliance demand load was 5290 VA. The remaining items are the electric range, air-conditioning unit, and electric hot water heater. In addition, since the demand load on the service is being determined, it is necessary to add 25% of the largest motor load to the calculation. The largest motor load will most likely be the air-conditioning compressor unit. Therefore, 25% of the full-load current rating of the A/C unit will be added to the calculations. All loads are tabulated next.

General illumination:	= 7,935 VA
Fastened-in-place appliances:	= 5,290 VA
Electric range (refer to Ex. 3.6):	= 8,000 VA
Hot water tank (actual rating):	= 5,000 VA
Air-conditioning unit (volts × amps):	= 5,520 VA
25% of largest motor (A/C unit)	= 1,380 VA
Total service demand load	= 33,125 VA

This demand load of 33,125 VA corresponds to a load current of 138 A @ 240 V. Therefore, the service entrance rating must be based on an estimated demand of 138 A. In this example, a 200 ampere service would be appropriate to supply the load and allow for load growth.

3–3   RATES AND BILLING

In many instances, the electrical designer must estimate the monthly cost of electricity for a particular occupancy. For example, the estimated monthly electric bill must often be calculated to determine the economic benefits of energy management systems, power-factor-correction capacitor application, or selection of different rate structures. With electrical utility deregulation, it is possible to select from several different power suppliers in order to achieve maximum economic benefits. Thus, a basic knowledge of rates and billing is required.

Utility rate schedules will vary considerably among utilities nationwide. The rates will generally vary depending on the type of generation, geographic location, size, and service voltage of the load being served, customer class, and other factors. All rate schedules include a cost per kilowatt hour (kWh) of energy consumption. (Recall that one kWh is equal to 1 kW of power being consumed for a one-hour period and has units related to demand multiplied by time.) Other rate schedules may incorporate charges relating to peak demand, power factor, time-of-day usage, interruptible service riders, and so forth. Special rates are sometimes offered by utilities for street lighting, water heating, private outdoor lighting, traffic signals, and other types of specialized services.

The cost of generating power is directly related to the type of energy source used to drive the prime mover in the generating plant. Geographic location of the generating facilities will have a direct impact on the type of prime mover used. For example, hydroelectric power generating plants constitute a large percentage of the total generating capacity for electric utilities in the northwestern United States and Canada. Oil- and natural-gas-fired steam power plants constitute a larger percentage of total generation capacity for electric utilities in the eastern portion of the United States. In the midwestern region of the United States, coal-fired steam power plants make up the largest percentage of total generation capacity.

Most electric utilities separate the customer base into three major billing classes: residential, commercial, and industrial. The ampacity and service voltage rating of the load generally determine in which class the customer would be billed. For example, it would be impossible (and not economical) for a large steel mill to be billed at a residential rate. Nor is it possible for the residential customer to be billed at the industrial rates. The determination of customer classification is prescribed by rules and regulations usually approved by the state utilities commissions.

Within each billing class there may be several rate structures or schedules. A rate schedule is simply the method by which the electric power bill is calculated. For example, within the residential class, there may be a rate schedule based solely on kWh energy consumption, as well as a schedule based on kWh consumption and kW load demand. Customers within the billing class will sometimes have a choice among several different schedules.

The following example illustrates the rate calculation for a small commercial establishment. The rate schedule shown in the example has been derived for the purposes of illustration. Rate schedules for your area can be obtained from the local electric utility company.

EXAMPLE 3–14

Load data for a commercial establishment indicate a peak demand of 167 kW and a usage of 45,890 kWh for the previous month. Using the following rate schedule, determine the monthly billing.

	Rate Schedule
Demand charge:	$17.32 per kW for first 100 kW
	$13.56 per kW for remaining kW
Energy charge:	$0.0856 for first 200 kWh per kW of billing demand
	$0.0474 for all kWh over 200 kWh per kW of billing demand
Fuel Cost Adjustment:	$0.0035 per kWh

Solution:

Demand:	100 kW $\times$ $17.32 per kW =	$1,732.00
	67 kW $\times$ $13.56 per kW =	$ 908.52

Energy: 200 kWh per kW of demand is
                                 167 kW × 200 kWh per kW = 33,400 kWh
                                 33,400 kWh @ $0.0856 per kWh = $2,859.04
                                 The remaining kWh is
                                 45,890 − 33,400 = 12,490 kWh
                                 12,490 kWh @ $0.0474 per kWh = $ 592.02
Fuel Cost Adjustment: 45,890 kWh × $0.0035 per kWh = $ 160.62
                                                                        Total $6,252.20

Note that this rate schedule included a fuel cost adjustment charge of $0.0035 per kWh. Many utilities will assess this charge to account for large fluctuations in the price they pay for fuel.

PROBLEMS

1. Determine the minimum estimated lighting load for a school building that has a total floor area of 25,000 sq ft. The area in question is to be illuminated with 125 fluorescent light fixtures, each having a ballast input of 277 V, 0.8 A.

2. Determine the estimated lighting load for an office area that is 100 ft by 200 ft. The area is illuminated with 100 fluorescent light fixtures, each having a ballast input of 277 V, 0.8 A. In addition, the actual number of receptacle outlets is unknown.

3. An electric hot water heater is rated 230 V, 5 kW. Determine the estimated demand load in volt-amperes and the rated current of the water heater.

4. Determine the demand load expressed in volt-amperes for the following motors:
   a. 10 hp, 230 V, single-phase induction motor
   b. 1 hp, 115 V, single-phase induction motor
   c. 100 hp, 460 V, three-phase induction motor
   d. 100 hp, 460 V, three-phase synchronous motor, 80% leading power factor

5. Determine the loading on a 120 V, 20 A branch circuit that has seven general use duplex receptacles connected to it.

6. Determine the estimated demand load on a feeder supplying a motor control center that supplies the following motors:

10 hp, 460 V, three phase
10 hp, 460 V, three phase
25 hp, 460 V, three phase
75 hp, 460 V, three phase
50 hp, 460 V, three phase

7. Determine the estimated branch circuit demand load for the following household electric ranges:
   a. 12 kW
   b. 16 kW
   c. 7 kW
   d. 17 kW

8. Determine the estimated load for a branch circuit supplying both a counter-mounted cooktop unit having a rating of 4 kW and a wall-mounted oven having a rating of 7 kW.

9. Determine the estimated load for a branch circuit supplying both a counter-mounted cooktop unit having a rating of 6 kW and a wall-mounted oven having a rating of 8 kW.

10. Determine the estimated service demand load in volt-amperes and amperes @ 240 V for a residence having the following characteristics:

2500 sq ft living space
25 general-use receptacle outlets in unfinished areas
4 small-appliance branch circuits supplying the kitchen areas
1 laundry circuit
1 dedicated branch circuit supplying outside receptacles
OH door operators: 2 @ $\frac{1}{2}$ hp, 115 V each
Sump pump: $\frac{1}{3}$ hp, 115 V
Dishwasher: $\frac{1}{3}$ hp pump motor, 1000 W dryer element
Garbage disposal: $\frac{1}{2}$ hp, 115 V
Microwave hood: 8 A, 115 V
Refrigerator: 9 A, 115 V
Counter-mounted cooktop: 6 kW, 230 V
Wall-mounted oven: 8 kW, 230 V (supplied from same circuit as cooktop)
Air-conditioning unit: 24 A, 230 V

11. Determine the estimated demand load in volt-amperes and amperes @ 240 V for an office area containing 5000 sq ft of floor space and the following connected equipment:

Fluorescent light fixtures: 50 @ 1.3 A, 115 V each
Air-conditioning unit: 48 A, 230 V
Computer stations: 10 @ 5 A, 115 V each
30 general-use duplex receptacles
Electric hand dryers in restrooms: 2 @ 10 A, 230 V each
Electric hot water heater: 6 kW, 230 V
Two small-appliance branch circuits supplying lunchroom area
Copy machine: 13 A, 115 V

12. Using the rate schedule shown in Example 3–14, determine the monthly billing for the following commercial loads. Comment on how much can be saved by reducing the peak demand.
    a. Demand of 95 kW, usage of 27,500 kWh.
    b. Demand of 135 kW, usage of 27,500 kWh.

4

Wiring Devices

INTRODUCTION

This chapter describes the various types of wiring devices used in electrical power distribution systems. These devices typically include switches, receptacles, and disconnects. Generally, these devices are used to control the flow of electrical current and to allow for the desired operation of other devices or equipment. The various types and ratings of wiring devices are discussed to allow the designer to properly specify these devices. The use of disconnect switches to control and isolate electric equipment is also discussed.

OBJECTIVES

Upon completion of this chapter, you will be able to:

- Understand the operation and application of standard toggle switches, including three-way and four-way switches
- Understand the various rating of switches, receptacles, and disconnect switches
- Understand the characteristics of single and duplex receptacles
- Understand the grounding requirements of receptacles
- Understand the operation of ground fault receptacles
- Specify the proper NEMA configuration of receptacles
- Specify and apply isolated ground receptacles
- Understand the ratings and types of various disconnect switches
- Specify and apply disconnect switches

4–1   TOGGLE SWITCHES

The switches used in most residential and commercial applications generally are toggle switches. These switches are commonly used to control light fixtures, although they may be used to control small motor loads as well. Most of these switches have two positions, and several have markings indicating the OFF and ON positions. Figure 4–1 shows examples of typical toggle switches rated for residential applications.

Contact Arrangements

The contact arrangement of toggle switches refers to the internal switching arrangement that is accomplished by the switch. Various contact and switching arrangements for toggle

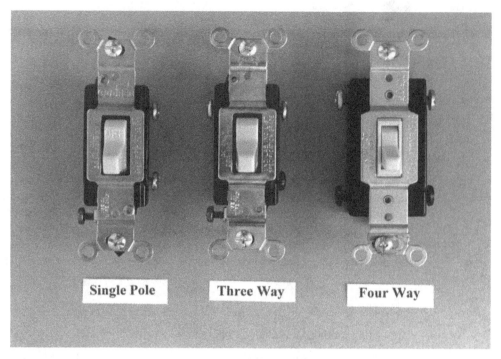

FIGURE 4–1
Examples of Toggle Switches

switches are shown in Figure 4–2. (Do not confuse the switch contacts as shown in Figure 4–2 as being of the knifeblade type. Many toggle switches are self-contained with no externally visible switch contacts. The exception to this is the disconnect switch to be discussed in a later section. The use of the knifeblade symbols is meant to enhance understanding of the switch contact arrangements.) The switching arrangement is commonly specified by the number of poles and by the number of throws. The number of poles refers to the number of inputs to the switch. The number of throws can be thought of as the number of outputs affected by the switching operation.

The single pole–single throw, or SPST, switching arrangement is shown in Figure 4–2(A). This is the most common switching arrangement for toggle switches. Note that there is a single conductor entering the switch and a single conductor leaving the switch. The switch has two states: ON or OFF. With the switch in the ON position, the input is connected directly to the output. Likewise, with the switch in the OFF position, the input is not connected to the output. Single-pole–single-throw switches are commonly used to control the switching operation of light fixtures from a single location.

The double-pole–single-throw, or DPST, switching arrangement is shown in Figure 4–2(B). Note that this arrangement is very similar to the SPST switch with the exception that two separate inputs are switched to two separate outputs by switch operation. Thus, two separate outputs can be switched OFF or ON from two separate inputs. This type of

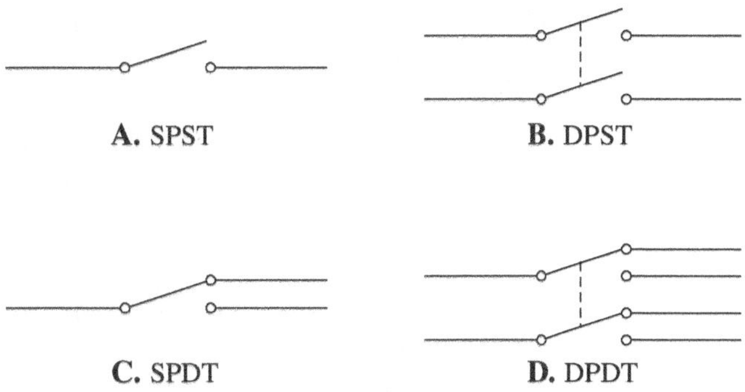

FIGURE 4–2
Contact and Switching
Configurations of Toggle
Switches

A. SPST   **B.** DPST

C. SPDT   **D.** DPDT

switch is commonly used to switch two ungrounded (or "hot") conductors in a circuit. For example, in the switching of a 230 V electric motor, both ungrounded circuit conductors are switched. It is also permissible to switch both the ungrounded (hot) and grounded conductor (neutral) in a circuit as long as both are switched simultaneously. For example, in certain hazardous locations, both the ungrounded and grounded circuit conductors are required to be switched simultaneously. The DPST switch can be used for this purpose.

In general, the term *double throw* refers to the ability of the switch to connect a single input to two outputs. The single-pole–double-throw (SPDT) switching arrangement is shown in Figure 4–2(C). Note that the input may be switched to one of two distinct outputs. This type of switch is commonly referred to as a *three-way switch.* SPDT switches are generally not marked with ON and OFF designations, since one of the two outputs will be energized at a given time. Thus, there is no true OFF position. One possible application of the SPDT switch would be the switching of the ungrounded conductor supplying two separate loads in an alternating fashion, with only one of the loads energized at any given time.

The double-pole–double-throw (DPDT) switch arrangement is shown in Figure 4–2(D). Note that in this arrangement, two distinct inputs are connected to two distinct outputs. This arrangement is similar to having two separate SPDT switches controlled by a single operating lever. Like the SPDT switch, the DPDT switch could be used to switch two ungrounded conductors supplying separate loads in an alternating fashion with one of the loads energized at any given time. Likewise, it would be possible to switch the ungrounded conductor and grounded conductors simultaneously.

Toggle Switch Applications

The most common application of the SPST switch is shown in Figure 4–3(A). Note that the source is connected to the load through the switch. Typically, loads connected between the ungrounded and grounded conductors are switched in this fashion. In this simple arrangement, the load can be energized or deenergized by operating the switch. Electrically, switching of either the ungrounded conductor or the grounded conductor will cause the load to be energized or deenergized. However, it is a violation of the *NEC* to switch only the grounded conductor. If the grounded conductor were to be opened by the

FIGURE 4–3
Common Applications of
Toggle Switches

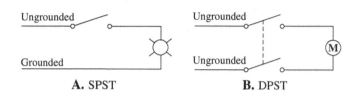

A. SPST   **B.** DPST

switch, the ungrounded (or hot) conductor would remain connected to the load, presenting a possible hazard.

The DPST switch can be used to energize or deenergize a load connected between two ungrounded conductors or between the ungrounded and grounded conductors of a system, as shown in Figure 4–3(B). Note that it is permissible to switch a load connected between the ungrounded and grounded conductor of a system provided both the ungrounded and grounded conductors are switched simultaneously. This means that the same operating mechanism or handle must cause both conductors to be switched at the same time.

The most common use of the SPDT switch is as a three-way switch, as shown in Figure 4–4(A). This application requires two three-way switches connected in series to control the switching operation of a lighting outlet. The common terminal of SW #1 is

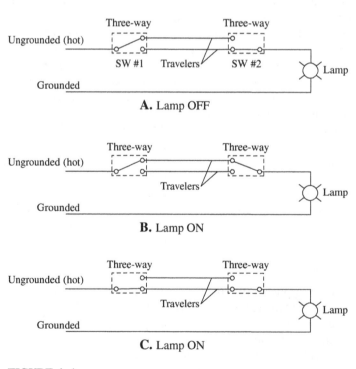

FIGURE 4–4
Three-Way Switch Application

connected to the source, and the common terminal of SW #2 is connected to the load. The common terminal on a three-way switch will be darker in appearance than the other two terminals. The conductors connecting the other two terminals of each three-way switch are referred to as the *travelers*. The circuits shown in Figures 4–4(B) and 4–4(C) indicate the switch positions required for the lighting outlet to be energized. Thus, the lighting outlet can be controlled from two separate locations, such as from each end of a hallway.

A modification of the DPDT switch is commonly used in conjunction with two three-way switches to control a lighting outlet from three or more locations. The modified DPDT switch as used for control of lighting outlets is commonly referred to as a *four-way switch*. While the internal switching arrangement of the four-way is the same as that of the DPDT switch, there are two internal connections that connect two pairs of output terminals together, as shown in Figure 4–5(A). Note that these connections are built into the switch and cannot be accessed externally. As a result of these modifications, the four-way switch will have two terminal connections on the source side and two terminal connections on the load side.

Inspection of Figure 4–5(A) reveals that with the switch in one position, terminal a is connected to c, and terminal b is connected to d. Likewise, with the switch in the other position, terminal a is connected to d, and terminal b is connected to c. Thus, one of the travelers is energized at a given time.

The use of the four-way switch to control lighting outlets is shown in Figure 4–5(B). Note that there are two three-way switches—one closest to the source and one closest to the load. The four-way switch is placed "in between." Again, the conductors between the

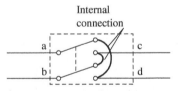

A. Internal Contact Arrangement

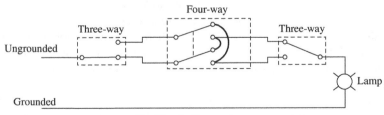

B. Circuit Connection

FIGURE 4–5
Four-Way Switch Application

switches are referred to as *travelers*. The lighting outlet can be controlled from three separate locations. If it is desired to control the lighting outlet from more than three locations, additional four-way switches can be placed "in between" the three-way switches.

Switch Ratings

Switches are rated in terms of their continuous current capability and voltage rating. The continuous current rating of most toggle switches is 15 A, 20 A, or 30 A. The voltage rating is either a straight voltage, such as 120 V, or a dual voltage rating, such as 120/277 V. The straight voltage rating means that the switch is capable of operating satisfactorily at the given voltage. The dual or slash rating means that the switch can operate at either 120 V or 277 V. The 277 V rating is required when connecting lighting outlets between the ungrounded and grounded conductors on a 480Y/277 V system.

In addition to the voltage and current ratings, toggle switches are rated for either ac operation only or ac/dc. If rated for ac only, Section 404.14(A) of the *NEC* specifies that the switch is capable of carrying rated current for resistance and inductive loads, tungsten-filament lamp loads not exceeding the ampere rating of the switch at 120 V, and motor loads not exceeding 80% of the ampere rating of the switch at rated voltage.

Section 404.14(B) of the *NEC* specifies that switches rated "ac/dc" can carry the load current of resistive loads not exceeding the ampere rating of the switch at rated voltage, the load current of inductive loads not exceeding 50% of the switch rating at rated voltage, and the load current of tungsten-filament lamp loads not exceeding the ampere rating of the switch at the rated voltage if "T" rated. Motor-rated switches can switch up to rated hp at rated voltage.

Special Switches

In addition to the standard toggle switches previously described, there are several specialty switches available. The key-operated switch is used in areas where the operation is to be done only by authorized personnel, such as public areas, restrooms, and so on. Switch operation on emergency circuits is sometimes done only with key-operated switches. The pilot light switch has an illuminated handle that lights up when power to the load is on. This type of switch would be used in areas where it is necessary to know whether or not the circuit was energized. The lighted handle switch has an illuminated handle that glows when power to the load is off, making it easy to locate the switch in darkened rooms.

Momentary contact toggle switches are also available. These types of switches are typically used in control-type applications where momentary application of power to the load is desired. Power is supplied to the load only when the switch is held in its operating position. When the operating force is removed, the contacts return to their nonoperating state.

Manual motor-starting switches are available for the starting and stopping of alternating current and direct current motors. Available for both single-phase and three-phase motors, these motor-starting switches would typically be horsepower and voltage rated. Generally, separate overload protection is required when using these types of manual motor-starting switches, since the switch itself does not have built-in overload protection.

4–2   RECEPTACLES

Receptacles are wiring devices that are used to allow connection of portable appliances or other equipment to a source of power. Typically, these appliances are referred to as *cord-and-plug-connected equipment*. The function of the receptacle is to allow connection of the ungrounded circuit conductors, grounded circuit conductor, and equipment grounding conductor of the equipment to the supply. Requirements for receptacles are covered in Section 406 of the *NEC*. Figure 4–6 shows typical examples of receptacle outlets.

The connection of the load to the source is done through a variety of receptacle configurations. Consider the 15 amp, 125 volt, duplex receptacle and plug shown in Figure 4–7. The ungrounded, or hot, circuit conductor is electrically connected to the shorter slot on the receptacle face. The grounded, or neutral, conductor is connected to the longer slot, and the equipment grounding conductor to the semicircular slot. The plug that connects to the receptacle obviously has to have the same type of configuration as that of the receptacle. Examination of the plug would indicate that the prong connecting the equipment grounding conductor is longer than either the ungrounded conductor blade or the grounded conductor blade. This design allows for the grounding conductor to make contact before the other conductors when inserting the plug into the receptacle. Likewise, when removing

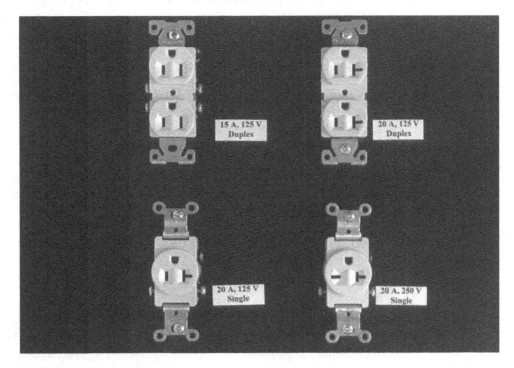

FIGURE 4–6
Single and Duplex Receptacles

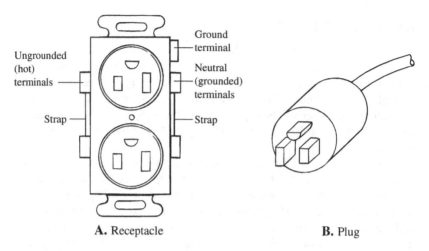

A. Receptacle   B. Plug

FIGURE 4–7
15 A, 125 V, Duplex Receptacle

the plug from the receptacle, the equipment grounding conductor prong is the last to break. This is done to ensure safety in the appliance. (Note: The use of ungrounded receptacles is not permitted except under special circumstances.)

The connections to the receptacle are typically made by screw terminal connections on the sides of the receptacle. Note that there are two screw terminals on each side of the receptacle connected by a strap—two terminals for the ungrounded conductor and two terminals for the grounded conductor. This arrangement allows for feed-through wiring of the receptacle. Generally, the ungrounded conductor terminals are bronze in color, and the grounded conductor terminals silver in color. The equipment-grounding conductor terminal is green in color and is located near the top or bottom of the receptacle.

Figure 4–8 shows a 20 amp, 125 volt receptacle and plug. Note the similarity to the 15 amp, 125 volt receptacle shown in Figure 4–7. The only difference in the slot configuration between the 15 A and 20 A receptacles is the shape of the slot for the grounded circuit conductor. The blade for the grounded conductor is at a right angle with respect to the blade for the ungrounded circuit conductor. Configuring the blades and slots in this manner makes it impossible to insert a 20 A plug into a 15 A receptacle. It is possible, however, to insert a 15 A plug into a 20 A receptacle.

NEMA Configurations

The National Electrical Manufacturers Association (NEMA) has established standard slot and prong configurations for various ampere- and voltage-rated receptacles and plugs. These configurations are shown in Figure 4–9 for nonlocking-type receptacles. Locking-type receptacles and plugs allow for the plug to be inserted into the receptacle, then twisted slightly to lock into place. This prevents accidental disconnecting of the plug from the

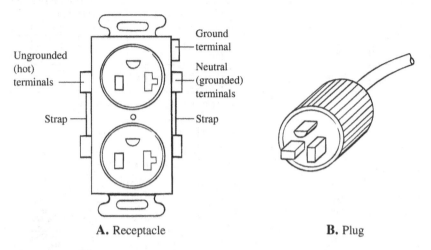

Ungrounded
(hot)
terminals

Ground
terminal

Neutral
(grounded)
terminals

Strap   Strap

A. Receptacle   **B.** Plug

FIGURE 4–8
20 A, 125 V, Duplex Receptacle

receptacle. The plug is removed by twisting in the opposite direction, then removing. Figure 4–10 shows NEMA standard configurations for locking-type receptacles.

Ground Fault Circuit Interrupting Receptacle

A special type of receptacle used to minimize electrical shock hazards is the ground fault circuit interrupter receptacle or GFCI. To understand the operation of the GFCI receptacle, consider the schematic shown in Figure 4–11. The majority of GFCI receptacles have feed-through capability, allowing standard receptacles to be used downstream and still have GFCI protection. A typical rating for a GFCI receptacle is 20 amp feed-through and 15 amp through its own terminals.

The major component of the GFCI is the ground fault sensor. This sensor monitors the flow of current through the ungrounded and grounded circuit conductors. It does not monitor the current through the equipment grounding conductor. Under normal conditions, all of the current flowing out through the ungrounded conductor to the load returns through the grounded conductor back to the source. This current is designated as I in Figure 4–11. Thus, the net current through the sensor is zero, and the sensor does not operate.

Now consider the situation in which a fault occurs between the ungrounded conductor and ground. Under these conditions, some of the current will return to the source through the equipment ground, bypassing the ground fault sensor. The current through the sensor is now unbalanced, resulting in an opening of the GFCI contacts and subsequent deenergization of the load. Note that the GFCI receptacle will only respond to faults on the load side of the receptacle. Also, the GFCI receptacle will generally not respond to short circuits between the ungrounded and grounded circuit conductor, only to short circuits involving ground. A typical GFCI will trip at a current of 5 mA in approximately 25 ms.

NEMA CONFIGURATIONS FOR GENERAL-PURPOSE NONLOCKING PLUGS AND RECEPTACLES

WIRING/VOLTAGE			15 AMPERE		20 AMPERE		30 AMPERE		50 AMPERE		60 AMPERE	
			RECEPTACLE	PLUG	RECEPTACLE	PLUG	RECEPTACLE	PLUG	RECEPTACLE	PLUG	RECEPTACLE	PLUG
2-POLE 2-WIRE	125V	1	1-15R	1-15P								
	250V	2		2-15P	2-20R	2-20P	2-30R	2-30P				
	277V AC	3	RESERVED FOR FUTURE CONFIGURATIONS									
	600V	4	RESERVED FOR FUTURE CONFIGURATIONS									
2-POLE 3-WIRE GROUNDING	125V	5	5-15R	5-15P	5-20R	5-20P	5-30R	5-30P	5-50R	5-50P		
	250V	6	6-15R	6-15P	6-20R	6-20P	6-30R	6-30P	6-50R	6-50P		
	277V AC	7	7-15R	7-15P	7-20R	7-20P	7-30R	7-30P	7-50R	7-50P		
	347V AC	24	24-15R	24-15P	24-20R	24-20P	24-30R	24-30P	24-50R	24-50P		
	480V AC	8	RESERVED FOR FUTURE CONFIGURATIONS									
	600V	9	RESERVED FOR FUTURE CONFIGURATIONS									
3-POLE 3-WIRE	125/250V	10			10-20R	10-20P	10-30R	10-30P	10-50R	10-50P		
	3Ø 250V	11	11-15R	11-15P	11-20R	11-20P	11-30R	11-30P	11-50R	11-50P		
	3Ø 480V	12	RESERVED FOR FUTURE CONFIGURATIONS									
	3Ø 600V	13	RESERVED FOR FUTURE CONFIGURATIONS									
3-POLE 4-WIRE GROUNDING	125/250V	14	14-15R	14-15P	14-20R	14-20P	14-30R	14-30P	14-50R	14-50P	14-60R	14-60P
	3Ø 250V	15	15-15R	15-15P	15-20R	15-20P	15-30R	15-30P	15-50R	15-50P	15-60R	15-60P
	3Ø 480V	16	RESERVED FOR FUTURE CONFIGURATIONS									
	3Ø 600V	17	RESERVED FOR FUTURE CONFIGURATIONS									
4-POLE 4-WIRE	3ØY 120/208V	18	18-15R	18-15P	18-20R	18-20P	18-30R	18-30P	18-50R	18-50P	18-60R	18-60P
	3ØY 277/480V	19	RESERVED FOR FUTURE CONFIGURATIONS									
	3ØY 347/600V	20	RESERVED FOR FUTURE CONFIGURATIONS									
4-POLE 5-WIRE GROUNDING	3ØY 120/208V	21	RESERVED FOR FUTURE CONFIGURATIONS									
	3ØY 277/480V	22	RESERVED FOR FUTURE CONFIGURATIONS									
	3ØY 347/600V	23	RESERVED FOR FUTURE CONFIGURATIONS									

FIGURE 4–9

NEMA Configurations for Nonlocking-Type Receptacle and Plug *Source:* Leviton Manufacturing Company, Inc.

NEMA CONFIGURATIONS FOR LOCKING TYPE PLUGS AND RECEPTACLES

WIRING/VOLTAGE			15 AMPERE		20 AMPERE		30 AMPERE	
			RECEPTACLE	PLUG	RECEPTACLE	PLUG	RECEPTACLE	PLUG
2-POLE 2-WIRE	125V	L1	L1-15R	L1-15P				
	250V	L2			L2-20R	L2-20P		
	277V AC	L3	RESERVED FOR FUTURE CONFIGURATIONS					
	600V	L4	RESERVED FOR FUTURE CONFIGURATIONS					
2-POLE 3-WIRE GROUNDING	125V	L5	L5-15R	L5-15P	L5-20R	L5-20P	L5-30R	L5-30P
	250V	L6	L6-15R	L6-15P	L6-20R	L6-20P	L6-30R	L6-30P
	277V AC	L7	L7-15R	L7-15P	L7-20R	L7-20P	L7-30R	L7-30P
	347V AC	L24			L24-20R	L24-20P		
	480V AC	L8			L8-20R	L8-20P	L8-30R	L8-30P
	600V AC	L9			L9-20R	L9-20P	L9-30R	L9-30P
3-POLE 3-WIRE	125/250V	L10			L10-20R	L10-20P	L10-30R	L10-30P
	3Ø 250V	L11	L11-15R	L11-15P	L11-20R	L11-20P	L11-30R	L11-30P
	3Ø 480V	L12			L12-20R	L12-20P	L12-30R	L12-30P
	3Ø 600V	L13					L13-30R	L13-30P
3-POLE 4-WIRE GROUNDING	125/250V	L14			L14-20R	L14-20P	L14-30R	L14-30P
	3Ø 250V	L15			L15-20R	L15-20P	L15-30R	L15-30P
	3Ø 480V	L16			L16-20R	L16-20P	L16-30R	L16-30P
	3Ø 600V	L17					L17-30R	L17-30P
4-POLE 4-WIRE	3ØY 120/208V	L18			L18-20R	L18-20P	L18-30R	L18-30P
	3ØY 277/480V	L19			L19-20R	L19-20P	L19-30R	L19-30P
	3ØY 347/600V	L20			L20-20R	L20-20P	L20-30R	L20-30P
4-POLE 5-WIRE GROUNDING	3ØY 120/208V	L21			L21-20R	L21-20P	L21-30R	L21-30P
	3ØY 277/480V	L22			L22-20R	L22-20P	L22-30R	L22-30P
	3ØY 347/600V	L23			L23-20R	L23-20P	L23-30R	L23-30P

FIGURE 4–10

NEMA Configurations for Locking-Type Receptacle and Plug *Source:* Leviton Manufacturing Company, Inc. Downloaded from Leviton website.

FIGURE 4–11
Ground Fault Circuit
Interruption Receptacle
Operation

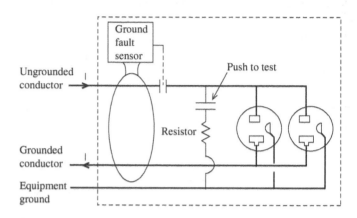

To test the GFCI, the PUSH TO TEST button is depressed, resulting in an intentional fault between the ungrounded conductor and the grounding conductor through a resistor. The purpose of the resistor is to limit the amount of fault current flowing during the testing of the GFCI. Note that this is a controlled short circuit intentionally introduced to test the operation of the receptacle. Once the GFCI has tripped either due to an accidental short circuit or testing, the device may be reset by pressing the RESET button. Figure 4–12 shows a typical GFCI receptacle.

Isolated Ground Receptacle

In areas supplying computer, data processing, and other sensitive electronic equipment, it is desirable to use a point ground system to eliminate ground loops. Ground loops are formed by the interconnection of various types of equipment grounding conductors. For example, in most cases, a bare ground wire is used for the equipment ground. This bare ground wire may come in contact with other metallic objects, such as metal conduit, structural steel, and so on. It is obvious that the ground current will flow through a myriad of paths back to the source, where it may form current loops and cause interference with the electronic equipment. This interference occurs as a result of small voltages being induced into the ground plane.

The use of a point ground as shown in Figure 4–13(A) provides a single connection of the electronic equipment to ground through an insulated equipment grounding conductor. This arrangement minimizes the possibility of interference and allows the electronic equipment to have a zero voltage ground for satisfactory operation. In essence, two ground connections are formed, one for the electronic equipment and one for the metal conduit, structural steel, and so on.

The connection of the isolated ground conductor to the electronic equipment is accomplished through the use of an isolated ground receptacle, as shown in Figure 4–13(B). The connections are essentially the same as those of the duplex receptacle, except that the insulated ground conductor is connected to the grounding terminal of the receptacle. Internally, this isolated ground is connected only to the semicircular grounding slot on the receptacle face. The isolated ground is not connected to the mounting strap of the receptacle

FIGURE 4–12
Typical GFCI Receptacle

as in the case of the standard receptacle. The receptacle mounting strap, metal boxes, and metal faceplate (if used) must be grounded either through the raceway system or by use of a separate bare or insulated ground. The isolated ground receptacle will be identified by an orange triangle on the faceplate.

Hospital-Grade Receptacles

Hospital-grade receptacles are heavy-duty receptacles designed for use in areas where the receptacle may be subjected to impact and sudden cord removal or insertion. The internal contact action usually provides for multiple levels of wiping action between the plug prongs and the receptacle contacts. This improves the conductivity between the receptacle

FIGURE 4-13
Operation of Isolated Ground
Receptacle

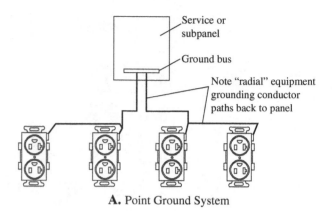

A. Point Ground System

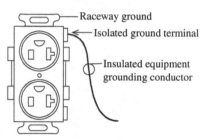

B. Isolated Ground Receptacle

and plug and typically results in longer service life. The receptacle is identified by a green dot on the faceplate. Figure 4–14 shows a combination isolated ground/hospital-grade receptacle.

Tamper-Resistant Receptacles

Tamper-resistant receptacles are designed to make the insertion of small objects such as paper clips, pins, wire, and so on, into the receptacle difficult. Typically, some form of sliding barrier is incorporated into the design of the receptacle, and only a properly rated plug can be easily inserted. These types of receptacles may be installed in pediatric care areas of health care facilities, day care centers, or any other area where limiting the danger of accidental insertion is desirable. Be aware that these receptacles only limit improper access to energized contacts; the receptacle may not prevent contact in extreme cases.

Transient Voltage Surge Suppressor Receptacles

Transient voltage surge suppressor receptacles are used to protect sensitive electronic equipment from transient overvoltage conditions. Equipment such as personal computers, medical equipment, fax machines, and photocopy machines, should be protected from

FIGURE 4–14
Hospital-Grade/Isolated Ground Receptacle

overvoltage. Transient overvoltages are typically the result of lightning strikes to power lines or switching surges.

These receptacles come in a variety of forms but most typically use metal oxide varistors (MOV) that absorb the transient energy from the surge. In effect, the MOV will clip off the voltage transient by discharging the transient to ground. The amount of discharge energy the receptacle can dissipate is expressed in terms of joules. Recall that 1 joule is equal to 1 watt second. Thus, the amount of energy that can be dissipated will be a function of both power and time.

Some versions of this receptacle have indicating lamps to show when the surge suppression feature is functional. Others have an alarm that sounds when the surge suppression is no longer functioning. Transient voltage surge suppressor receptacles are available in standard duplex, isolated ground, hospital grade, and isolated ground hospital grade.

Wiring of Receptacles

Receptacles are wired in such a manner as to permit connection of electrical loads in parallel. As a result of the parallel connection, rated voltage will be applied across each load. Figure 4–15(A) shows the typical wiring connection of a single 15 A, 125 V, duplex receptacle. Note that the ungrounded, or hot, conductor is connected to the terminals on one side of the receptacle, while the grounded or neutral conductor is connected to the other set of terminals. The grounding conductor is connected to the green grounding terminal.

Figure 4–15(B) shows the connection for several receptacles (or other loads) connected on the same circuit. Note that in this instance, the grounding conductor is pigtailed for connection to the grounding terminal of the receptacle. The hot conductor is fed through to the other loads by connecting to the other terminal on the same side of the receptacle. The neutral conductor is fed through in a manner similar to the hot conductor. Note the parallel connection of each receptacle to the source.

FIGURE 4–15
Wiring of Receptacles

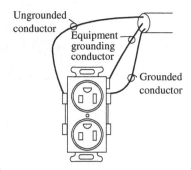

A. Single 15 A, 125 V Duplex Receptacle

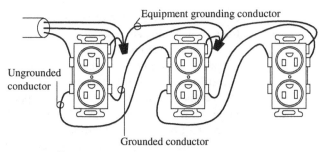

B. Several 15 A, 125 V Duplex Receptacles

Duplex receptacles may be split-wired to allow for a division of load between two circuits supplying the receptacles. The connections for split-wiring of receptacles are shown in Figure 4–16. Note that the receptacles are supplied by two circuits from a two-pole breaker, with the top receptacle slot supplied from one circuit and the bottom receptacle slot supplied by the other circuit. The use of a two-pole breaker ensures that both hot conductors will be deenergized in the event of a short circuit on either of the two circuits supplying the receptacles. The strap connecting the two hot terminals of each receptacle must be removed to allow for the connection of the two circuits to each receptacle. Failure to remove the strap will result in a short circuit between the two ungrounded conductors of the system. The voltage potential between the two hot terminals of split-wired receptacles is 240 V for a single-phase, three-wire system. Typically, the hot conductors would be pigtailed to the receptacle terminals as shown. Removal of the pigtail from either hot terminal will result in the disconnection of the receptacle from that particular circuit. The grounding conductor is pigtailed to the grounding terminal of each receptacle in a similar manner.

The connection of the grounded (neutral) conductor to split-wired receptacles must be pigtailed to each of the receptacles as shown. If one of the receptacles must be removed,

FIGURE 4–16

Wiring of Split-Wired Receptacles

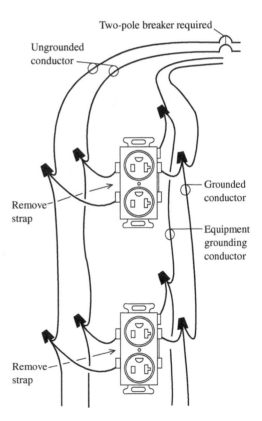

To other receptacles

the pigtail would be disconnected from the receptacle terminal only, with continuity of the grounded conductor maintained to other receptacles in the group. If the continuity of the grounded conductor is broken, the potential voltage of the grounded conductor terminal (neutral) will float between 0 V and 240 V, with the actual voltage determined by the load impedance. The following example illustrates this point.

EXAMPLE 4–1

Two 120 V loads are supplied from opposite legs of a 120/240 V, single-phase, three-wire system. Load #1 is represented by a 10 Ω resistance, and load #2 is represented by a 5 Ω resistance. Determine the voltage across each leg if the grounded conductor is disconnected between the source and load.

Solution: The resulting system can be represented as shown in Figure 4–17. Note that the two halves of the 120/240 V system are connected in series, resulting in 240 V placed across the two loads in series. The current I is given by:

$$I = \frac{120\ V + 120\ V}{10\ \Omega + 5\ \Omega} = 16\ A$$

The voltage V_1 is given by

$$V_1 = (16\ A)(10\ \Omega) = 160\ V$$

Likewise, the voltage V_2 is calculated as

$$V_2 = (16\ A)(5\ \Omega) = 80\ V$$

Therefore, the voltage across the 10 Ω resistance is (160 V) ÷ (120 V) or 133% of normal, while the voltage across the 5 Ω resistance is (80 V) ÷ (120 V) or 67% of normal. The leg with the higher resistance will have the higher voltage impressed across it. Loads connected across either leg will experience a voltage far out of the normal operating range. Voltages of these magnitudes will result in failure of equipment.

FIGURE 4–17
Problem of Open Neutral on Split-Wired
Receptacles

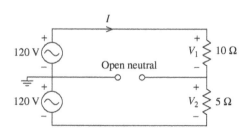

4–3 DISCONNECTS

Construction and Ratings

Like toggle switches, disconnect switches are used to provide a means of disconnecting a load from the electrical supply. However, these switches differ from standard toggle switches by virtue of their heavy-duty construction. In addition, the ratings of disconnect switches are much higher than those of toggle switches. The most common application of a disconnect switch is in motor circuits where a physical means of disconnecting and deenergizing the motor is desired. Figure 4–18 shows a three-pole disconnect installation.

FIGURE 4–18
Disconnect Switch Installation *Source:* Courtesy of Youngstown State University.

Disconnect switches are usually enclosed in a metal housing, with an operating handle located on the right-hand side of the enclosure. The operating handle is usually equipped with a provision for padlocking in the OFF position. The switch contacts are usually of a knifeblade-type construction, with both a movable and stationary contact assembly. When operating the switch, a wiping action takes place between the movable and stationary contacts. This wiping action tends to keep the contacts clean, thereby promoting good electrical connection. The switch contact operating mechanism allows for a quick-make, quick-break operation to minimize arcing. Extreme care must be exercised when operating a disconnect switch. Never stand directly in front of the disconnect switch when operating the switch; stand to the side of the switch and turn your head away from the switch. Move the operating handle with a forceful continuous motion.

The two most common types of enclosures are the NEMA 1, designed for indoor use only; and the NEMA 3R, designed for general outdoor use. The NEMA 1 enclosure protects against physical contact with the internal energized parts of the switch as well as against dirt falling into the enclosure. The NEMA 3R provides essentially the same protection as the NEMA 1 enclosure, but in addition is weatherproof and will resist water penetration under normal rainfall conditions. However, the NEMA 3R enclosure is not watertight, and may be unsuitable for applications where water spray resulting from a wash-down or pressure hose may force entry of water into the enclosure. Other types of enclosures include the following:

- NEMA 4: Protects against physical contact with internal energized switch parts, falling dirt, dust, and wash-down with noncorrosive elements. Usually has gasketed doors. May be used for indoor or outdoor applications.
- NEMA 4X: Same protection as NEMA 4 but also protects against corrosive elements. Usually has gasketed doors. May be used for indoor or outdoor applications.
- NEMA 12: Protects against physical contact with internal energized switch parts, falling dirt, dust, and oil seepage. Usually has gasketed doors. Generally used for indoor applications.
- NEMA 13: Protects against physical contact with internal energized switch parts, falling dirt, dust, oil seepage, and oil spray. Usually has gasketed doors. Generally used for indoor applications.

Disconnect switches are available as either fused or unfused. The fused-type switch will have a fuseholder in addition to the main switch contacts. This fuseholder allows the switch to accommodate an appropriately rated fuse for overcurrent and short circuit protection of the downstream equipment. A Class R rejection kit is available from some manufacturers to allow the installation of current-limiting fuses only. These current-limiting fuses act to limit the let-through fault current in the event of a short circuit. The physical construction of a current-limiting fuse differs from that of a standard non-current-limiting fuse, which makes it impossible to install a non-current-limiting fuse in a fuseholder having the rejection feature. Standard, non-current-limiting fuses will not fit into the fuseholder if the rejection kit is installed.

Disconnect switches are typically rated at either 240 V for general duty or 600 V for heavy-duty applications. The voltage rating of the switch must equal or exceed the line-to-line system voltage. The ampere ratings of disconnect switches are 30 A, 60 A, 100 A, 200 A,

400 A, 600 A, 800 A, 1200 A, 1600 A, 2000 A, 3000 A, 4000 A, and 6000 A. The rating of the fuse installed in a disconnect must be equal to or less than the rating of the switch. The physical dimensions of the fuse make it impossible to insert a fuse into the fuseholder of a disconnect switch having a rating lower than that of the fuse. Thus, a 125 A fuse will not physically fit into a 100 A disconnect; a 200 A disconnect would be required in this instance. Some manufacturers offer fuse reducers to allow fuses of smaller physical size and rating to be inserted into a disconnect of higher rating. For example, a reducer is required to install a 90 amp fuse in a 200 amp disconnect. In addition to their ampere ratings, disconnect switches typically have a horsepower rating as well. The horsepower rating of the disconnect switch must exceed the horsepower rating of any motor connected to the load side of the switch.

Contact Switching Arrangements

The three-pole–single-throw (3PST) and four-pole–single-throw (4PST) switch arrangements are shown in Figures 4–19(A) and 4–19(B). Similar to the SPST and DPST switch arrangements, there are separate or distinct inputs and outputs affected by the switching operation. Thus, the 3PST and 4PST switching arrangements can be used to connect three or four distinct outputs to three or four distinct inputs. An example of the use of a 3PST switch would be the simultaneous disconnecting of the ungrounded circuit conductors of a

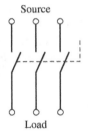

A. Three-Pole–Single-Throw

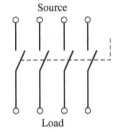

B. Four-Pole–Single-Throw

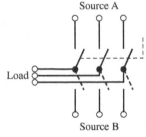

C. Three-Pole–Double-Throw

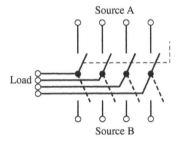

D. Four-Pole–Double-Throw

FIGURE 4–19
Disconnect Switch Contact Arrangements

three-phase system supplying a three-phase motor or other load. A 4PST switch may be used to disconnect the three ungrounded circuit conductors (hot) and the grounded conductor (neutral) simultaneously.

The three-pole–double-throw (3PDT) and four-pole–double-throw (4PDT) switching arrangements are shown in Figures 4–19(C) and 4–19(D). With the 3PDT and 4PDT switching arrangements, either three or four distinct inputs are switched to three or four distinct outputs. Typically, the 3PDT switch would be used to switch the three ungrounded conductors of a three-phase system simultaneously. Likewise, the 4PDT switch could be used to switch all three ungrounded conductors and the grounded conductor of a three-phase system simultaneously.

The most common application of the 3PST and 4PST switches is the switching control of three-phase loads. As shown in Figure 4–20(A), the 3PST switch is used to energize and deenergize the three ungrounded conductors of a three-phase system. A typical application would be a three-phase load such as a motor or HVAC equipment. The 4PST switch in Figure 4–20(B) is shown switching all three ungrounded phase conductors and the grounded conductor supplying the load. Again, it is permissible to switch the grounded conductor as long as all ungrounded conductors are switched simultaneously by the same switch. This type of switching arrangement may be required in certain hazardous locations. Another application of the 4PST switch would be in a two-phase, four-wire system. This voltage system is obsolete and is not likely to be encountered in practice.

As previously discussed, one of the more common applications of the 3PDT and 4PDT switches is the switching of ungrounded and grounded conductors of a three-phase system. Figure 4–21(A) shows the use of a 3PDT switch as a transfer switch. This type of switching arrangement is commonly used in conjunction with an emergency generator to switch from the normal utility power supply to the generator supply. The switching is often done automatically by the transfer switch control logic. With the 3PDT switch, only the three ungrounded conductors are switched. The use of the 4PDT switch, as shown in Figure 4–21(B), allows the grounded conductor (neutral) to be switched as well as the ungrounded conductors. The 4PDT switch is often used in transfer switches applied to systems having ground fault protection.

FIGURE 4–20
Applications of Single-Throw
Disconnect Switches

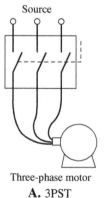

Three-phase motor
A. 3PST

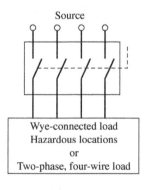

Wye-connected load
Hazardous locations
or
Two-phase, four-wire load
B. 4PST

FIGURE 4–21
Applications of Double-Throw
Disconnect Switches

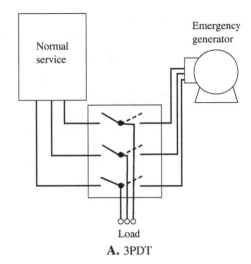

A. 3PDT

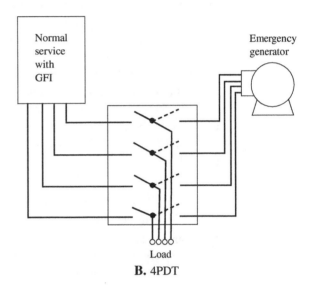

B. 4PDT

PROBLEMS

For Problems 4.1 through 4.10, sketch a schematic wiring diagram showing the connection of the ungrounded, grounded, and equipment grounding conductors to the wiring devices. Where switching is specified, designate the contact switching arrangement for each device (SPST, DPST, etc.).

1. Two lighting outlets controlled by a single switch.
2. Single lighting outlet controlled by two switches.

3. Single lighting outlet controlled by three switches.

4. Single lighting outlet controlled by four switches.

5. Two lighting outlets controlled by two switches.

6. A single lighting outlet controlled by a single switch and a duplex receptacle (always hot) fed from the same branch circuit.

7. A duplex receptacle with one receptacle outlet always hot and the other outlet switched from a single switch (split-wired receptacle)

8. Three duplex receptacles with one receptacle outlet on each duplex hot and the other receptacle outlet on each duplex switched together from a single location (three split-wired receptacles)

9. A duplex receptacle with one receptacle outlet always hot and the other outlet switched from two switch locations

10. Two duplex receptacles with one receptacle outlet on each duplex hot and the other receptacle outlet on each duplex switched together from two switch locations

11. Explain what may happen if the neutral conductor is not pigtailed in a circuit containing split-wired receptacles.

12. Explain the operation of the GFCI receptacle. Will the GFCI operate for a short circuit between the ungrounded and grounded conductors? Why might a GFCI falsely trip if supplying long cable lengths?

13. List three applications (locations) where isolated ground receptacles might be found. How does the point ground system minimize ground loops?

14. What is the maximum motor load in amperes permitted on a 15 A, 125 V toggle switch? A 20 A, 125 V switch?

15. A toggle switch has a voltage rating of 120 V. Is it permissible to use this switch on a 277 V lighting circuit?

16. Is it possible to insert a 70 amp fuse in a 60 amp disconnect?

17. Under what condition might it be possible to insert a 50 A fuse in a 100 A disconnect?

18. Obtain data on toggle switches, receptacles, and disconnect switches from three manufacturers by referring to their published catalogs or by searching the Internet Web sites of several manufacturers.

19. Calculate the voltage across each leg of a 120/240 V, single-phase, three-wire system in the event of an open in the grounded (neutral) conductor. The loads are represented by a 50 ohm resistance and a 10 ohm resistance. Express the resulting voltage in actual volts and as a percentage of nominal.

20. Will a NEMA 3R enclosure protect the internal energized components against splashing or wash-down? What type of enclosure would be more suitable in this instance?

5

Overcurrent Protection Devices

INTRODUCTION

This chapter discusses the construction, operation, rating, characteristics, and application of fuses and circuit breakers used as overcurrent protection devices. Overcurrent protection is necessary to ensure that the various components that comprise an electrical power distribution system are operating within their prescribed ratings. Operation of electrical equipment above rated current produces excessive heat and will result in damage to the equipment. The basic function of overcurrent protection devices is to deenergize, or disconnect from the supply, that portion of the electrical distribution system before any damage occurs.

OBJECTIVES

Upon completion of this chapter, you will be able to:

- Understand the need for overcurrent protection
- Differentiate between overloads and short circuits
- Have knowledge of the construction of fuses and circuit breakers
- Understand the time–current characteristics of fuses and circuit breakers
- Understand the peak let-through characteristics of current-limiting fuses
- Understand the operation of current-limiting circuit breakers
- Understand the operating characteristics of fuses and circuit breakers
- Have knowledge of the classifications and ratings of fuses and circuit breakers

5-1   NEED FOR OVERCURRENT PROTECTION

Under normal operating conditions, the current drawn by a particular load is within the rating of the system components, if properly designed. Transformers, circuit conductors, panelboards, and so on are examples of electrical equipment that carry the current required to supply the load. However, in certain instances, overcurrents can occur on branch circuits and feeders in an electrical power distribution system. These overcurrents can occur as overloads or short circuits.

An overload is a situation in which a particular device such as a motor draws more than rated current for an extended period of time. Another example is a branch circuit supplying multipurpose receptacle and lighting outlets in which the total connected load exceeds the rating of the branch circuit conductors. These overloads produce an overcurrent that exceeds the rating of the circuit conductors supplying the load. Overloads generally result in a current level exceeding the rated level for a long period of time.

A short circuit or fault condition is the direct result of an ungrouded or hot conductor coming in contact with either another ungrounded conductor, the grounded conductor, or the equipment grounding conductor. The most severe level of short circuit current occurs when there is a zero impedance connection between the faulted conductors. This is commonly referred to as a *bolted fault*. Under short circuit conditions, a current level several times rated flows through the circuit conductors and other supply equipment such as transformers, panelboards, and so on. It is not uncommon to have short circuit current levels equal to 20 to 30 times rated. (Calculation of short circuit current is done in a later chapter.) Currents of this magnitude cannot be allowed to flow for a long period of time. Cable insulation, conductors, busbars in panelboards, and the internal windings of transformers would melt due to the extreme heat produced. As a result, interruption of the short circuit current is usually required within one cycle after occurrence of the fault.

In addition to extreme heat, short circuit current levels produce large mechanical forces between conductors and busbars due to the high levels of magnetic flux produced. The amount of force produced is proportional to the current squared. Thus, a current equal to 30 times rated will produce a mechanical force equal to 900 times rated! These extreme mechanical forces can literally dislodge busbars from panelboards, and windings in transformers. Generally, these devices are braced to withstand the high levels of mechanical forces produced for a short period of time (milliseconds). If the high magnitude of short circuit current persists for a longer period of time, the equipment may be destroyed.

Overload and short circuit current will flow until the overcurrent protection device operates to disconnect the circuit conductors from the source or supply. Thus, it is the speed at which the overcurrent device opens that determines how long the overcurrent will persist. In addition, the overcurrent protection device must be able to interrupt the high level of short circuit current under fault conditions.

5–2   FUSE CHARACTERISTICS

A fuse is a device connected in series with the conductors that carries the full-load current supplied to the load. Since the fuse carries the load current, it will respond to changes in load current and also any short circuit current that flows on the load side of the fuse. In its simplest form, a fuse consists of a fusible link element enclosed in some sort of tube. Under normal conditions, the load current is less than the ampere rating of the fuse. As long as the load current is less than the ampere rating of the fuse, no damage occurs to the fuse link, and the fuse link remains intact to connect the load to the source. When an overload or short circuit occurs, the current through the link will also increase. This increase in current produces additional heating effects in the link, thereby causing the link to melt. Once the link is totally melted, an open circuit exists in the fuse, thereby disconnecting the load from the source. Once the fuse has operated to disconnect the load from the source, it must be replaced. Fuses are "one-time" devices.

As previously mentioned, a certain amount of time is required for a fuse or circuit breaker to operate. Generally, under short circuit conditions, the fuse must operate as quickly as possible to interrupt the current. However, under certain overload conditions, it is desirable to have a certain time delay occur before the fuse operates. This time delay will allow momentary overloads (such as that due to motor starting and transformer inrush current) to subside before the fuse operates. The actual amount of time required for the fuse to operate is a function of the magnitude of the current passing through the fuse. For high levels of current, the time required to operate is very small. On the other hand, for values of current slightly above rated, the time required for the fuse to operate is much longer. This increased time is due to the time required for heat to build up in the fuse to begin melting the fuse link.

Generally, there are two major classifications of fuses available: non-time-delay and time-delay. The non-time-delay fuse is a fast-acting fuse that has no time delay intentionally built in. This does not mean that the current interruption takes place instantaneously in a non-time-delay fuse. It simply means that the design of the fuse does not intentionally introduce any additional time delay beyond what is normally required for the fuse to operate. The time-delay fuse does have an intentional time delay built in so that it will not operate for momentary overloads. The time-delay feature is usually accomplished by incorporating a separate overload section in the fuse.

Non-Time-Delay Fuse

The basic construction of a non-current-limiting, non-time-delay fuse is shown in Figure 5–1(A). The link is connected to the end blades of the fuse as shown. Smaller fuse ratings may have round ferrules rather than blades at each end of the fuse. The fuse would be inserted into a fuseholder suitable for the application. During normal operation, the load current passes through the link, including the areas of reduced cross section. As a result, the current density in the reduced cross section is larger. The smaller area of the link would therefore operate at a higher temperature than the other sections of the link. During a condition of current flow above the fuse rating, the smaller section of the link will overheat and eventually melt. As the link melts, an electrical arc is established between the ends of the smaller section of the link. The current will be interrupted at the first or second normal zero crossing of the sinusoidal current waveform.

The basic construction of a current-limiting non-time-delay fuse is shown in Figure 5–1(B). Notice that there are several links in series, as well as a filler material surrounding the link. The actual number of links may depend on the voltage and ampere rating of the fuse. As in the non-current-limiting fuse, a current that exceeds the fuse rating will cause the link to begin to melt in the area of reduced cross section. As the link melts back away from the smaller cross section, an arc is established that increases in length. The increased arc length causes an increase in the arc resistance that forces the current to drop to a low

FIGURE 5–1
Basic Fuse Construction

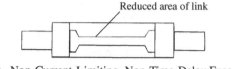

A. Non-Current-Limiting, Non-Time-Delay Fuse

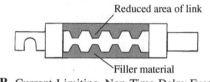

B. Current-Limiting, Non-Time-Delay Fuse

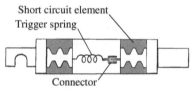

C. Current-Limiting, Time-Delay Fuse

value. With this low value of current, the arcing cannot be sustained, and current flow is interrupted. The filler material is designed to accelerate the quenching effect on the arc. When the arcing stops, the fuse link is open, and the current flow is interrupted.

Non-time-delay fuses are very fast acting and are not suitable for overload protection of circuits subject to inrush current or transient surges. Nuisance fuse blowing would result if these types of fuses are applied to circuits having high inrush conditions. However, the fast response of these fuses does make them suitable for short circuit protection of electronic circuits and other sensitive equipment.

Time-Delay Fuse

The time-delay fuse is usually referred to as a *dual-element fuse* because it has both a short circuit element and an overload element. The basic construction of a dual-element time-delay fuse is shown in Figure 5–1(C). Notice that the short circuit element is similar in construction to the non-time-delay fuse. The short circuit element of the time-delay fuse operates in a manner similar to the non-time-delay fuse and is usually current limiting. The short circuit element in a time-delay fuse is responsive to short circuit currents, while the overload element provides overload protection for loads that are subject to temporary overloads and inrush and surge currents. As shown, the short circuit and overload elements are connected in series.

The operation of the overload element is as follows. When the fuse is subjected to a current above rated current, heating of the short circuit link occurs. This heat is transferred to the heat absorber in the overload section of the fuse. If the overload continues, heat continues to build up and causes the trigger spring to pull back the connector from the short circuit link, thereby opening the circuit.

Time–Current Characteristics

The time required for a fuse to operate can be determined from the time–current characteristics of the fuse. These characteristics are a plot of time as a function of current magnitude. These characteristics are typically plotted on a logarithmic scale. Time–current characteristics are useful when performing overcurrent device coordination studies. The topic of overcurrent coordination is addressed in a later chapter. A typical time–current characteristic is shown in Figure 5–2.

Note that there are two characteristic curves shown in the figure. The first curve is referred to as the *minimum melt characteristic*. The minimum melt characteristic shows the time–current relationship required to initiate melting of the fuse link. This type of relationship is commonly referred to as an *inverse time relationship*. Note that at low levels of current, a long time is required to begin melting of the fuse link. At higher levels of current, a shorter time interval is required to begin melting. At extremely high levels of current in the short circuit region, the melting time is practically instantaneous.

The upper curve is referred to as the *total clear characteristic*. The total clear characteristic shows the time–current relationship required for the fuse to totally clear and interrupt the circuit. The time interval in between the minimum melt and total clear characteristics is the time required for the fuse link to melt, arcing to take place, quenching of the arc, and subsequent current interruption. Note that at high levels of current, particularly in the short circuit region, a minimum amount of time is required to clear the fault, as indicated on the total clear characteristic. For the purposes of this discussion, a minimum total clearing time of 0.0167 second, corresponding to 1 electrical cycle at 60 hertz, is assumed.

As previously discussed, the fuse time–current characteristics can be represented with the minimum melt and total clearing characteristics. Frequently, fuse characteristics are displayed showing the average melting characteristic. The average melting characteristic lies between the minimum melt and total clearing characteristics of the fuse. Time–current curves are readily obtained from the fuse manufacturer.

EXAMPLE 5–1

Using the time–current curve shown in Figure 5–2, determine the minimum melt and total clearing time for the following current levels:

a) 100 A
b) 500 A
c) 1000 A
d) 10,000 A

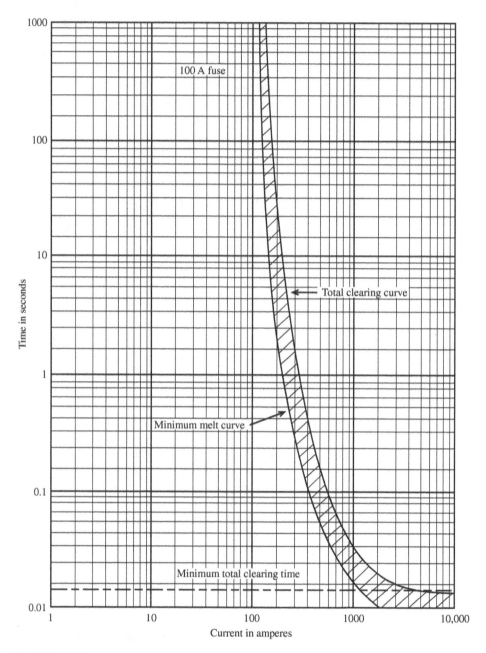

FIGURE 5–2
Time–Current Characteristic of Fuse

Solution: The minimum melt and total clearing times are determined from the time–current characteristic:

a) Since a current level of 100 A is equal to the fuse rating, the fuse should take an extremely long time to melt. Therefore, the minimum melt and total clearing times are not defined.

b) Minimum melt time = 0.05 s,　　　Total clear time = 0.17 s

c) Minimum melt time = 0.018 s,　　　Total clear time = 0.03 s

d) At this level of current, there is no significant time delay required to initiate fuse melting. Therefore, the minimum melt time is instantaneous. Total clearing time is approximately 0.0167 s.

The fuse time–current characteristic curves are plotted assuming a certain ambient temperature. For fuse application in ambient temperatures other than the reference, a derating curve must be used. These curves are generally available from the manufacturer. A typical fuse derating curve is shown in Figure 5–3. Note that there are two curves on the derating characteristic. One curve shows the effect of ambient temperature on the fuse rating, while the other curve shows the effect of ambient temperature on the fuse opening time. Note that both curves have an inverse relationship, in that both the fuse rating and opening time are decreased as the ambient temperature increases.

EXAMPLE 5–2

Given the derating curve of Figure 5–3 and the fuse curve of Figure 5–2, determine the fuse rating and total clearing times for a current level of 300 A, at the following ambient temperatures:

a) 0°C

b) 30°C

c) 40°C

d) 50°C

Solution: The fuse rating is 100 A, as shown in Figure 5–2. The derating factors are read directly from Figure 5–3, and the total clearing time at 300 A is read from Figure 5–2 as approximately 2 s.

a) Derating factor on fuse rating = 110%　　Fuse rating: 1.1 × 100 A = 110 A
　　Derating factor on opening time = 120%　　Total clearing time: 1.2 × 2 s = 2.4 s

b) Derating factor on fuse rating = 100%　　Fuse rating: 1.0 × 100 A = 100 A
　　Derating factor on opening time = 100%　　Total clearing time: 1.0 × 2 s = 2 s

c) Derating factor on fuse rating = 95%　　Fuse rating: 0.95 × 100 A = 95 A
　　Derating factor on opening time = 90%　　Total clearing time: 0.9 × 2 s = 1.8 s

d) Derating factor on fuse rating = 90%　　Fuse rating: 0.9 × 100 A = 90 A
　　Derating factor on opening time = 80%　　Total clearing time: 0.8 × 2 s = 1.6 s

FIGURE 5–3
Fuse Derating Curve
Source: Cooper Bussmann.

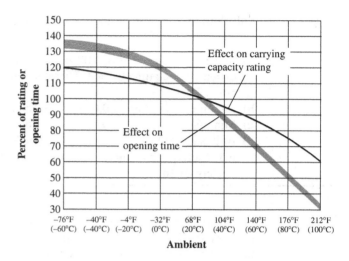

Peak Let-Through Characteristic

The ability of a current-limiting fuse to limit the peak magnitude of short circuit current can be understood by examining the waveform of the short circuit current that flows through the fuse. A typical short circuit current waveform is shown in Figure 5–4. The short circuit is assumed to occur at time $t = 0$ in the figure. Note that this waveform has the appearance of a sinusoidal waveform but is displaced or offset from the *x*-axis due to the presence of inductance in the circuit. The amount of offset in the waveform is a function of the ratio of inductive reactance to resistance in the circuit. This ratio is referred to as the *X/R* ratio of the circuit. A high *X/R* ratio results in a large offset and a corresponding high

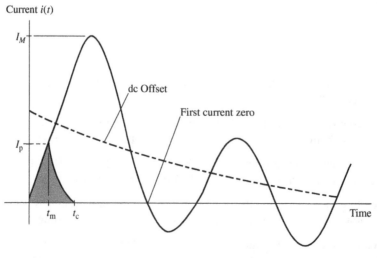

FIGURE 5–4
Short Circuit Current Waveform

value of maximum instantaneous current. The maximum instantaneous current that would flow if there were no current interruption is designated as I_M. The maximum instantaneous current can be determined by multiplying the rms symmetrical short circuit current by a multiplier. This multiplier is referred to as the *asymmetrical factor* and is a function of the X/R ratio of the system. The asymmetrical factor becomes larger as the X/R ratio increases. The calculation of short circuit currents is discussed in more detail in a later chapter.

If a non-current-limiting fuse were employed in this circuit, the fuse would likely interrupt the current at the first current zero, as shown. This would allow the full available short circuit current to flow during the first half-cycle of the waveform. Thus, the peak short circuit current would be equal to the maximum instantaneous current, I_M as shown. This high level of peak short circuit current may be high enough to cause significant damage to electrical equipment.

For sufficiently high levels of short circuit current, application of a current-limiting fuse would force the current to zero before the first current zero, usually within a half-cycle, as shown in the shaded area of Figure 5–4. The total clearing time and melting time of the fuse are designated as t_c, and t_m, respectively. This limitation of short circuit current also causes the maximum instantaneous current to be limited to the value designated by I_p in the figure. This value of current is referred to as the *peak let-through current* of the fuse. Bear in mind, however, that the current-limiting effect of a current-limiting fuse will occur only for high levels of current. The current level at which current limitation begins is referred to as the *threshold current* of the fuse. Current limiting will not occur at current levels below the threshold current level. Below the threshold current level, the maximum instantaneous current that flows will be equal to the rms symmetrical short circuit current multiplied by the asymmetrical factor.

At current levels above the threshold level, current limiting takes place, and the peak let-through current can be obtained from the peak let-through curve of the fuse. A typical let-through curve for a current-limiting fuse is shown in Figure 5–5. The line designated as $A–B$ in Figure 5–5 represents a constant asymmetrical factor for a given circuit X/R ratio. Typically, line $A–B$ is plotted for an asymmetrical factor of 2.3, corresponding to an X/R ratio of 6.6. The instantaneous peak let-through current without current limiting can be obtained by entering the graph at the level of prospective rms symmetrical short circuit current and projecting upward to line $A–B$. The value of peak current is determined by projecting horizontally over to the vertical axis. The threshold current level occurs at the intersection of line $A–B$ and the current-limitation portion of the curve. The instantaneous peak let-through current with current limiting is obtained by projecting upward to the current-limiting portion of the curve. It can be seen from the peak let-through curve that current limitation occurs only at short circuit current levels exceeding the threshold level.

EXAMPLE 5–3

Using the peak let-through curve shown in Figure 5–5, determine the peak let-through current with and without current-limiting effects for the following rms symmetrical short circuit current levels:

a) 3,000 A
b) 10,000 A
c) 100,000 A

FIGURE 5–5
Example of Peak Let-Through Curve of
Current-Limiting Fuse

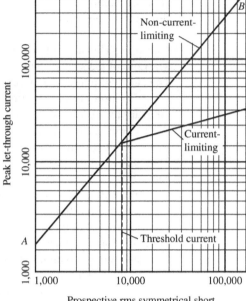

Solution:

a) Current below threshold level, thus no current limiting taking place. $I_p = 5,000$ A
b) With current limiting, $I_p \approx 20,500$ A; without current limiting, $I_p = 28,000$ A.
c) With current limiting, $I_p \approx 34,000$ A; without current limiting, $I_p = 280,000$ A

Physical Construction and Dimensions

The physical size of a fuse is dictated primarily by the voltage and current ratings of the fuse. Higher-ampere-rated fuses generally have a larger physical size than lower-rated fuses. The physical sizes of fuses are standardized and grouped into certain ampere ranges. For example, 250 V fuses in the $\frac{1}{10}$ A to 30 A range all have the same physical dimensions. Likewise, 250 V fuses in the 35 A to 60 A range have the same dimensions. Thus, a 250 V, 40 A fuse would have the same physical dimensions as a 250 V, 50 A fuse. Both fuses can be inserted into the same 250 V, 60 A fuseholder. The fuseholder dimensions differ between the ranges to make it impossible to overfuse a particular application. For example, it is impossible to insert a 250 V, 60 A fuse into a 250 V, 30 A fuseholder. It would also be impossible to insert a 250 V, 30 A fuse into a 600 V fuseholder, and so forth.

In addition to the difference in physical dimensions, the method in which the fuse is connected to the circuit differs as well. Figure 5–6 shows several of the different types of fuse construction available. Figure 5–6(A). shows a ferrule-type fuse. This type of fuse is commonly found in the lower ampere ratings, typically up to 60 A. Notice also that there is

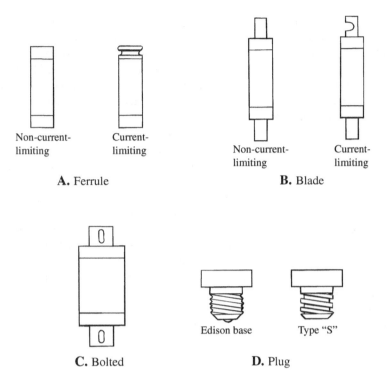

Non-current-limiting   Current-limiting

A. Ferrule

Non-current-limiting   Current-limiting

B. Blade

C. Bolted

Edison base   Type "S"

D. Plug

FIGURE 5–6
Physical Construction of Fuses

a difference between the non-current-limiting and current-limiting types of fuses. The current-limiting fuse has a slot cut into the end cap, while the non-current-limiting fuse does not. This is commonly referred to as the *rejection slot*. The fuseholder designed to accept this type of fuse will have a pin located in one of the fuse clips to allow insertion of a current-limiting fuse only. It is impossible to insert a non-current-limiting fuse into a fuseholder equipped with the rejection pin. Note, however, that it is possible to insert a current-limiting fuse into a fuseholder that does not have the rejection feature.

The construction shown in Figure 5–6(B) is a blade-type construction. Again, both the non-current-limiting and current-limiting types of fuse are shown. This type of construction is typical in fuses rated above 70 A up to 600 A. As with the cartridge-type fuses, the physical size is the same for certain ampere and voltage ratings. Note that the current-limiting fuse has a slot cut into one of the blades. The fuseholder for this type of fuse construction has a pin inserted into one end of the fuse clips to ensure that a non-current-limiting fuse cannot be installed. As with the cartridge-type fuse, it is possible to insert a current-limiting fuse into a fuseholder that does not have the rejection feature.

The bolted type of construction is shown in Figure 5–6(C). This type of fuse would be physically bolted to the busbars in the switchgear or panelboard. Generally, this type of bolted construction is found on the higher-ampere-rated fuses. The bolt pattern as well as the physical dimensions of these fuses differs for the various ranges of ratings.

Plug fuses are 125 V fuses, commonly available in ratings from ¼ amp to 30 amps. These fuses have a screw shell base that screws directly into the fuseholder. There are two basic types of plug fuse construction, as shown in Figure 5–6(D). The first type is referred to as the *Edison base* fuse. The screw shell of the Edison base fuse has the same physical dimensions regardless of ampere rating. Unfortunately, this arrangement allows for a fuse of a higher ampere rating to be used in a circuit with a lower ampere rating, for example, a 20 A fuse protecting a circuit conductor with an ampacity of 15 A. This is commonly referred to as *overfusing* and is a violation of the *NEC*. The use of Edison base fuses in new construction is prohibited.

The other type of plug fuse shown in Figure 5–6(D) has a rejection base and is generally referred to as a type *S* fuse. The type S fuse base prevents overfusing by arranging the threads of the fuse so that only a fuse of the proper rating and classification can be installed. Classifications are made in the following ranges: 0 A to 15 A, 16 A to 20 A, and 21 A to 30 A. Fuses within these classifications have the same thread patterns. Thus, it would be impossible to insert a 20 A type S fuse into a 15 A type S fuseholder. An Edison base fuseholder may be converted to a type S fuseholder by inserting an adapter of the appropriate rating. The adapters are constructed such that once installed, they are impossible to remove. It is highly recommended that Edison base fuseholders be converted to type S whenever possible. Figure 5–7 shows examples of various fuse types.

5–3   CIRCUIT BREAKER CHARACTERISTICS

Unlike fuses, which are one-time devices, circuit breakers are reuseable devices that may be reset after operation. Circuit breakers are used to protect circuits and equipment from overcurrents resulting from overloads and short circuits. In addition, breakers may also be used as a switch to energize and deenergize a circuit. It is also possible to operate a breaker from a remote location and to provide for circuit deenergization in the event of low voltage. These features are covered in more detail in a later section.

Electrically, circuit breakers are connected in series with the load and carry load current under normal conditions. For some high-current applications, current transformers may be used to transform the load current to a lower value suitable for use in a protective relay scheme. Circuit breakers in which the tripping mechanism, breaker contacts, and operating handle are all contained in one enclosed unit are referred to as *molded case breakers*. This discussion will involve only molded case breakers.

Circuit breakers have three operating conditions: ON (contacts closed), OFF (contacts open), or TRIPPED. In the ON position, the breaker contacts are closed, allowing load current to flow through the breaker. In the OFF position, the breaker contacts are open and the circuit is deenergized. The ON and OFF condition is typically the result of operating the breaker handle. The TRIPPED condition occurs when the breaker contacts have opened due to the operation of the breaker trip mechanism resulting from an overload or short circuit or by the operation of the shunt trip or undervoltage trip coil if so equipped. Typically, once tripped, manual resetting of the breaker is required.

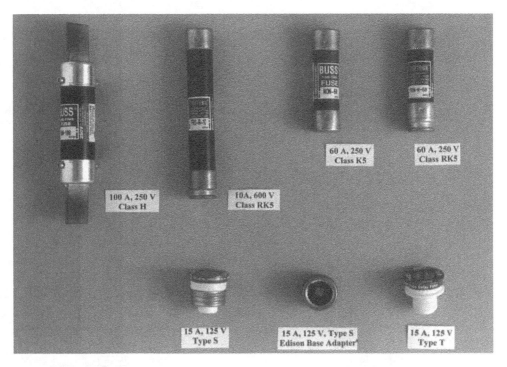

FIGURE 5–7
Examples of Various Fuse Types

Trip Mechanisms

Circuit breakers are generally classified according to the method in which they trip, or operate. Three types of tripping mechanisms are used in circuit breakers: thermal, magnetic, and electronic. Each tripping mechanism has unique characteristics, and may be adjustable in some breakers. Several breaker designs employ a combination of thermal and magnetic trip mechanisms and are referred to as *thermal-magnetic breakers.* Electronic trip mechanisms may be designed to model the thermal and/or magnetic characteristic.

The basic operation of the thermal trip mechanism is shown in Figure 5–8(A). With the breaker contacts closed, load current flows through the breaker, causing heating of the bimetallic element. Heating of the bimetal causes the bimetal strip to bend to the right due to the differences in coefficient of thermal expansion between the two metals making up the element. For current flow within rated conditions, the heating effect is not sufficient to cause the bimetal to move any significant amount. Load current exceeding the breaker rating causes the bimetal to expand and move to the right, thus releasing the latch mechanism. The breaker contacts are then forced open due to the spring force. Since the operation is dependent on the heating produced due to current flow, the element responds to the rms value of the current. Resetting of the trip mechanism is accomplished by manually moving the breaker handle to the OFF, then ON positions. Internally, this will reset the latch and

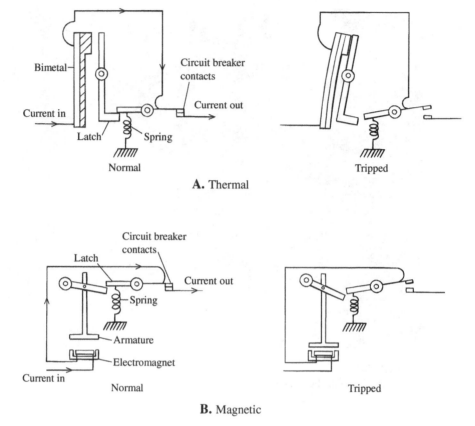

A. Thermal

B. Magnetic

FIGURE 5–8
Circuit Breaker Trip Mechanisms

spring mechanisms, provided the bimetal element has returned to its normal position. The thermal element typically responds to overload conditions from 1 to 10 times the breaker rating.

The magnetic trip mechanism is shown in Figure 5–8(B). This mechanism responds only to high current levels, typically 5 to 10 times the breaker rating. With the breaker contacts closed, load current flows through the electromagnetic coil in the trip mechanism. When the pick-up current level is reached, the armature is pulled into the electromagnet, thereby releasing the latch mechanism. The breaker contacts are then forced open due to the spring force. As with the thermal trip, resetting is accomplished by moving the breaker handle to the OFF, then ON positions.

The electronic trip mechanism employs the use of a current-sensing device located in the breaker housing. This sensor monitors the current waveform and supplies a solid-state digital trip system. The trip system computes the rms equivalent of the current waveform to determine if tripping of the breaker is required. Generally, there are no thermal or magnetic trip mechanisms in this type of breaker. Thermal and magnetic characteristics are modeled by the electronic trip system to achieve desired results. The ampere rating of the breaker is typically established by use of a rating plug inserted into the front of the breaker housing. Adjustable parameters often include the instantaneous trip current level, long time delay, and short time delay.

Current Interruption

When the tripping mechanism of a circuit breaker operates, the main breaker contacts begin to open. Upon opening, an arc will be established, similar to the arcing that occurs when a fuse operates. The current is interrupted once the arc is extinguished. This arc must be extinguished as quickly as possible to prevent damage not only to the electrical equipment on the load side of the breaker but also to the breaker itself. Smaller-ampere-rated breakers simply rely on the parting breaker contacts to stretch and cool the arc. The arc is extinguished and the current interrupted when the current waveform passes through the next current zero, usually within one cycle of the ac current. For higher levels of current interruption, some method must be employed to cool and extinguish the arc.

The most common method of stretching and cooling the arc is by use of deionizing plates or arc chutes, shown in Figure 5–9(A). In reference to Figure 5–9(A), when an arc is established, the heat from the arc causes the arc to rise into the deionizing plates. The arc is then elongated within the plates and subsequently cooled. The current would be interrupted at the next current zero. The current interruption method shown in Figure 5–9(A) is not current limiting. It is important to note that if the arc is not completely deionized, a restrike may occur. The overcurrent would continue to flow until the next current zero. The excessive heat and energy produced by the overcurrent may be enough to cause severe damage to the breaker or load equipment. Modern circuit breakers are designed to prevent this restrike from occurring.

The general method used in a circuit breaker to achieve some degree of current limitation is to force the arc into the deionizing plates quicker than would normally be possible. One such method is to use a reverse current loop, as shown in Figure 5–9(B). This method utilizes the principle that current flowing in two parallel conductors in opposite directions causes a magnetic flux that tends to produce a force of repulsion between the two conductors. The interrupting mechanism is designed such that one of the two conductors is the movable breaker contact arm. The force of repulsion increases the speed at which the breaker contacts open, thereby producing some degree of current limitation.

Another method used to force the overcurrent to zero before the normal zero crossing is to use an O-shaped magnet to surround the reverse current loop produced by the stationary and movable breaker contact arms, as shown in Figure 5–9(C). This magnet increases the amount of force produced on the movable contact arm, resulting in increased opening speed. In addition, the magnetic force produced by the magnet tends to push the arc into the deionizing plates very quickly. Circuit breakers with this type of construction are often classified as current limiting. Many current-limiting breakers have interrupting ratings of 200,000 amperes.

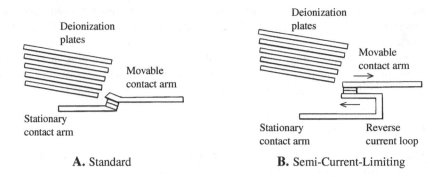

A. Standard   **B.** Semi-Current-Limiting

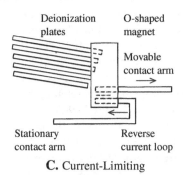

C. Current-Limiting

FIGURE 5–9
Current-Limiting Circuit Breaker

Common Accessories

Circuit breakers are available with several additional accessories not available on fuses. Some of the more common accessories are described next. Please note that not all accessories are available on all breakers. It is necessary to consult the manufacturer's application data for the availability of specific features.

In addition to tripping due to overcurrent, circuit breakers may be tripped due to several other system disturbances as well. The shunt trip accessory allows the breaker to be tripped remotely by applying voltage to the shunt trip coil. Ground fault shunt trip is available to provide circuit interruption in the event of a fault involving the equipment ground. Undervoltage trip is available to allow the breaker to trip in the event that the system voltage drops to a predetermined value for a certain period of time. This feature can be used to protect voltage-sensitive equipment.

In many modern energy management systems, it is necessary for the central controller to have information regarding the status of a breaker: ON, OFF, or tripped. Status indication may be provided in the form of auxiliary and alarm contacts. The auxiliary contact monitors the status of the main circuit breaker contacts and changes state when the main breaker contacts change state. The alarm contacts typically are designed to change state only when the breaker has tripped due to overcurrent, ground fault, or undervoltage. Other breaker features may include handle locks, manual push to trip, handle padlock attachments, handle ties, and so on.

Time–Current Characteristics

The time–current characteristic curve of a typical thermal-magnetic molded case circuit breaker is shown in Figure 5–10. Notice that there are two distinct regions of operation shown: thermal and magnetic. Typically, the current axis is shown with current as a

FIGURE 5–10
Time–Current Characteristic
of Circuit Breaker

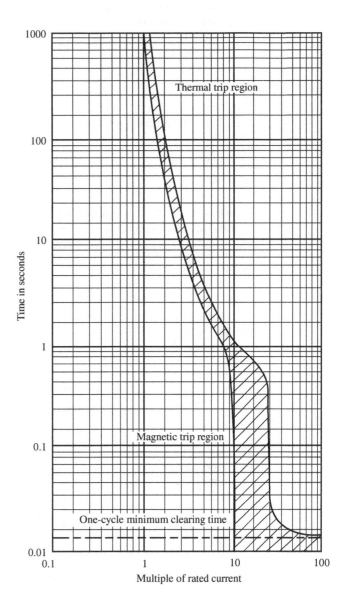

multiple of rated. Therefore, one curve may apply for several different breaker ratings within a given class. The time axis is delineated in seconds, as shown. The circuit breaker time–current characteristic is represented as a band between minimum and maximum total clearing times, due to manufacturing tolerances.

The thermal tripping region is typically in the range of from 1 to 10 times the ampere rating of the breaker. In this region, the breaker exhibits an inverse time characteristic responsive to overload conditions. In the thermal region, a longer time is required to trip the breaker to allow momentary overloads time to cease. The lower line indicates the time required for the trip mechanism to operate, and the upper line indicates the total clearing time.

The magnetic tripping region is essentially an instantaneous tripping region, with no intentional time delay built in. Breaker operation in this region is basically responsive to short circuit current levels and acts to interrupt the current as quickly as possible. The one-cycle minimum clearing time is shown for current levels in the short circuit region.

EXAMPLE 5–4

Given the time–current characteristic shown in Figure 5–10, determine the minimum and maximum total clearing time for a 100 A breaker at the following current levels:

a) 200 A
b) 600 A
c) 2000 A

Solution: It is first necessary to convert the actual currents into multiples of rated. The required time in seconds can then be read from the curve.

a) 200 A = 2 × rated. Minimum clearing time = 50 s; maximum clearing time = 100 s.
b) 600 A = 6 × rated. Minimum clearing time = 2 s; maximum clearing time = 3.2 s.
c) 2000 A = 20 × rated. Tripping time is instantaneous; maximum clearing time = 0.8 s.

Basic Construction

Molded case circuit breakers are typically available in a single-pole, two-pole, or three-pole configuration, as shown in Figure 5–11. The single-pole breaker is the most common and is installed to protect single-phase loads connected between the ungrounded and grounded conductors of a system. Typical load voltages for loads protected by a single-pole

FIGURE 5–11
Physical Construction of
Circuit Breakers

 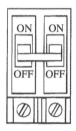 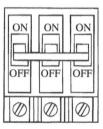

A. Single-Pole   **B.** Two-Pole   **C.** Three-Pole

breaker would be 120 V, or 277 V. The two-pole breaker is installed to protect single-phase loads connected between two ungrounded conductors in a system. Typical load voltages for loads protected by a two-pole breaker would be 208 V, 240 V, and 480 V. The three-pole breaker is used to protect three-phase loads connected between the three ungrounded conductors of a system. Typical load voltages for three-phase loads protected by a three-pole breaker are 208 V, 240 V, and 480 V.

In addition to the basic pole configuration, breakers are of either the plug-on or bolt-on type. Plug-on breakers have a spring clip assembly that attaches the breaker to the busbar in the panelboard. These breakers are generally of the lower ampere ratings. Bolt-on breakers have bolted attachments for connection of the breaker to the panelboard or enclosure in which it is mounted. Bolt-on breakers are generally found in higher ampere ratings. Both plug-on and bolt-on breakers have terminal lugs for connection of the load conductors to the breaker. These terminals must be tightened to the manufacturer's specification.

Manufacturers have also standardized the physical dimensions of their respective breakers into several classifications of frame size. Circuit breakers within a certain range of ampere ratings all have the same frame size. For example, a breaker rated 15 A may have the same frame size as a 20 A breaker. This arrangement allows breakers of several different ampere ratings to be installed in the same panelboard. Figure 5–12 shows examples of various molded case circuit breakers.

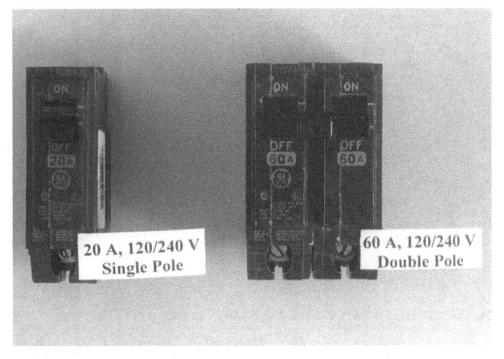

FIGURE 5–12
Examples of Circuit Breakers

TABLE 5–1
Standard Breaker Voltage Ratings

Grounded Neutral System Only	Grounded or Ungrounded Systems
120/240 V	120 V
480Y/277 V	240 V
	277 V
	480 V
	600 V

5–4   STANDARD RATINGS AND CLASSIFICATIONS

Voltage Ratings

The voltage ratings of circuit breakers have been standardized by the industry to ensure conformity among various manufacturers. Standard voltage ratings for breakers are shown in Table 5–1. Breakers with a "slash" voltage rating are designed for application on a grounded neutral system only, where the voltage between the ungrounded and grounded conductors does not exceed the lower voltage rating. The voltage between the ungrounded conductors must not exceed the higher of the two voltage designations. A single voltage designation indicates that the breaker may be applied on a system where the nominal voltage between conductors is equal to or less than the breaker rating. Single-voltage-rated breakers may be applied on grounded or ungrounded systems.

Standard voltage ratings for power fuses are 250 V, 300 V, 480 V, and 600 V. The general application rule is that fuses may be applied to a system whose voltage between conductors does not exceed the voltage rating of the fuse. For example, the voltage rating of a fuse applied on a 480 V corner-grounded delta system must be 480 V or 600 V. The exception to the rule applies to single-phase circuits supplied from a solidly grounded system where the line-to-neutral voltage does not exceed 300 V. This exception would allow the use of a 300 V fuse to protect a 277 V single-phase circuit supplied from a 480Y/277 V system, where there is no possibility of a short circuit between two ungrounded conductors. Plug-type fuses have a standard voltage rating of 125 V.

Ampere Ratings

The ampere ratings of fuses and circuit breakers have also been standardized according to industry standards. The standard ratings for fuses and fixed trip circuit breakers are shown in Table 5–2. In addition to the standard ratings, fuse manufacturers offer several sizes

TABLE 5–2
Standard Ratings for Fuses and Fixed Trip Circuit Breakers

15	20	25	30	35	40	45	50	60	70	80	90	100
110	125	150	175	200	225	250	300	350	400	450	500	600
700	800	1000	1200	1600	2000	2500	3000	4000	5000	6000		

between $\frac{1}{10}$ A and 30 A as well. These smaller fuse sizes allow a closer match to motor starting and running characteristics for optimum protection.

Interrupting Ratings

The interrupting rating of a fuse or circuit breaker is expressed in terms of the rms available short circuit current. To determine the interrupting rating, breakers and fuses are tested at industry-standard circuit power factors (circuit X/R ratio) to produce the desired dc offset. These tests are designed to represent the worst-case possible short circuit current offset. Generally, the standard interrupting rating for non-current-limiting fuses and non-current-limiting circuit breakers is 10,000 A. Interrupting ratings for current-limiting fuses and current-limiting breakers is typically 200,000 A. In addition, current-limiting fuses having an interrupting rating of 300,000 A are also available from several manufacturers. It is important to note that the interrupting rating of a current-limiting fuse or current-limiting breaker does not imply that the fuse or breaker can open and successfully interrupt a short circuit current of 200,000 A. The interrupting rating specifies the ability of the fuse to interrupt an available short circuit current of 200,000 A. The current-limiting device is able to do this by forcing the current to a level much lower than what is actually available. Refer to manufacturers' data for other interrupting ratings.

TABLE 5–3
Fuse Class Designations

Fuse Class	Voltage Ratings	Current Ratings	Interrupting Rating	General Notes
H	250 V 600 V	1 A to 600 A	10 kA	Non-current-limiting; do not have rejection feature.
R	250 V 600 V	1/10 A to 600 A	200 kA	Current-limiting; have rejection feature. Same physical dimensions as Class H; can be used in class H fuseholder.
K (K1, K5, K9)	250 V 600 V	1/10 A to 600 A	50, 100 and 200 kA	Are current-limiting but not marked as such. Same dimensions as Class H and R. Do not have rejection feature.
T	300 V 600 V	1 A to 1200 A	200 kA	Current-limiting; have rejection feature. Smaller physical dimension than Class R.
G	480 V	1 A to 60 A	100 kA	Smaller dimension than 600 V fuses. Rejection feature incorporated by different physical size.
CC	600 V	$\frac{1}{10}$ A to 30 A	200 kA	Small dimension, 13/32″ × 1½″. Have rejection feature. Generally used for control circuits.
J	600 V	1 A to 600 A	200 kA	Dimensions unique to this class. Not interchangeable with other classes.
L	600 V	601 A to 6000 A	200 kA	Current-limiting fuse having bolted connections only.

Fuse Classifications

Fuses classes have been established based on rating, physical dimensions, and operating characteristics. A general description of the more common fuse classes is listed in Table 5–3. When applying a specific fuse, it is best to obtain actual manufacturer's data.

PROBLEMS

1. Explain the differences between an overload and a short circuit condition in a circuit.
2. List three reasons why overcurrent protection is needed in a system.
3. Explain the operation of the short circuit element in a current-limiting fuse.
4. Explain the operation of the overload element in a dual-element time-delay fuse.
5. Why is the time–current characteristic of a fuse often referred to as "inverse time"?
6. Using the derating curve shown in Figure 5–3, determine the fuse rating and total clearing time of a 50 A fuse at am ambient temperature of 35°C.
7. What effect does circuit inductance have on the short circuit current waveform?
8. Explain the operation of the thermal trip mechanism of a thermal-magnetic circuit breaker.
9. Explain the operation of the magnetic trip mechanism of a thermal-magnetic circuit breaker.
10. Is it acceptable to use a Class H fuse in a system that has an available short circuit current of 25,000 A? Explain. What class of fuse would you use?
11. What is meant by the rejection feature of a fuse?
12. What is restrike in a circuit breaker?
13. What is the function of deionizing plates in a breaker?
14. How is current limiting achieved in a circuit breaker?
15. Access the Bussmann fuse manufacturer's Web site at *www.bussmann.com* and obtain the following data for the FRS-R dual-element time-delay fuse. Download and print out data for a fuse rating of $\frac{1}{10}$ A to 60 A, and 65 A to 600 A.
    a. General information
    b. Time–current characteristic curve
    c. Peak let-through curve
16. Using the data obtained in the previous problem, determine the following:
    a. Average melt time of a 30 A, 600 V, fuse at 40 A, 100 A, and 10,000 A
    b. Threshold current level of a 200 A, 600 V fuse
    c. Peak let-through current at 3,000 A and 30,000 A.
    d. Length and diameter in inches of the following fuses: 20 A, 50 A, 80 A, 175 A, 300 A, and 500 A.
17. Access the Square D company Web site at *www.squared.com*. Enter its technical library section under circuit breakers, then molded case circuit breakers. Under the selection/specifications section, enter specifications, then the thermal-magnetic/

magnetic only section. Download and print out the section pertaining to Class 601, 400 A frame molded case circuit breakers. (It may take a bit of practice to navigate the Square D Web site.)

18. Using the information on Class 601, 400 A frame size circuit breakers, determine the following for the type LA, three-pole, 175 A, 480 V breaker:
   a. Interrupting rating
   b. Range of magnetic trip settings
   c. Time delay for current of 350 A
   d. Height and width in inches
   e. Standard lug wire size range

6

Conductors and Overcurrent Protection

INTRODUCTION

The specification of the proper size and insulation type for conductors supplying electrical loads is an important element of electrical system design. The most important factor in the selection of the conductor is that the conductor must be sized to safely carry the load current. Likewise, the overcurrent protection device must be rated to carry the load current and to protect the conductor. Undersizing of the conductor or overcurrent protection may result in nuisance tripping of circuit breakers, blowing of fuses, or damage to the conductor itself. This chapter addresses the proper sizing of conductors and overcurrent devices.

OBJECTIVES

Upon completion of this chapter, you will:

- Have knowledge of the different insulation types
- Have knowledge of cable construction
- Understand conductor ampacity ratings
- Be able to specify appropriate conductor size
- Be able to apply conductor adjustment and derating factors
- Be able to specify the appropriate overcurrent device rating
- Understand device terminal temperature ratings and limitations

6–1 CONDUCTOR SIZES AND TYPES

Conductors used in electrical power distribution cables are made of copper or aluminum. Aluminum alloy is permissible only in the larger sizes, provided it is of an approved alloy. Conductor sizes are specified in terms of the American Wire Gauge (AWG) or thousand circular mils (kcmil). The AWG designation is used for conductors from #14 up through #4/0. The kcmil designation is used for sizes from 250 kcmil up through 2000 kcmil. For power distribution circuits including feeders and branch circuits, wire sizes in the range from #14 AWG to 500 kcmil are the most commonly specified. Wire sizes larger than 500 kcmil are frequently avoided due to difficulty with installation. In addition, breaker and fuseholder terminal lugs rarely have provisions for larger than 750 kcmil conductor sizes. Typically, solid conductors are used in sizes up to #10 AWG. Stranded conductors are generally used for #8 AWG and larger to ease installation. The actual number of strands varies according to conductor size, with common values of 7, 19, 37, or 61 strands.

The smallest wire size used in power distribution circuits is #14 AWG. This is typically a solid conductor having an outside diameter of 0.0641 inches, or 64.1 mils. A mil is equal to 1/1000 of an inch; therefore, to convert from inches to mils, multiply inches by 1000. The next larger wire size is a #12 AWG, having a diameter of 0.072 inches or 72 mils. The largest AWG designation is a #4/0 AWG, having a diameter of approximately 0.522 inches or 522 mils for a seven-strand conductor. Each individual strand of a seven-strand #4/0 AWG conductor has a diameter of 173.9 mils.

The area of larger conductors is expressed in terms of circular mils. To find the area in circular mils, the diameter in mils is squared (multiplied by itself). For example, a #10 solid conductor with a diameter of 0.162 inches or 162 mils has an area of $(162 \text{ mils})^2 = 26{,}244$ circular mils, or 26.2 kcmil. To convert from square inches to circular mils, the following conversion is used:

$$\text{Area in sq in.} = (\pi/4) \times (\text{diam. in inches})^2 \qquad (6\text{--}1)$$

$$\text{Area in mils} = (\text{diam. in inches} \times 1000)^2 = 1{,}000{,}000 \times (\text{diam. in inches})^2 \quad (6\text{--}2)$$

Solving Equation 6–2 for the diam. in inches squared, and substituting into Equation 6–1, results in the following:

$$\text{Area in sq in.} = \text{Area in mils} \times (\pi/4) \div 1{,}000{,}000 \qquad (6\text{--}3)$$
$$= \text{Area in mils} \times 785.5 \times 10^{-9}$$

Likewise,

$$\text{Area in mils} = \text{Area in sq in.} \div 785.5 \times 10^{-9} \qquad (6\text{--}4)$$
$$= \text{Area in sq in.} \times 1.273 \times 10^{6}$$

Equations (6–3) and (6–4) can be used to convert between square inches and circular mils as required.

The resistance of a conductor has an effect on the current-carrying capability of the conductor. Conductors with a high resistance will have higher power loss (I^2R loss) than a conductor with a lower resistance when carrying the same current. Higher power loss will result in a higher conductor temperature. In addition to increased power loss, higher resistance will result in larger voltage drop. The resistance of a conductor is a function of the conductor length, cross-sectional area, and material resistivity, as given by the following:

$$R = \frac{\rho \cdot L}{A} \qquad (6\text{--}5)$$

where:

ρ = conductor resistivity (ohms-cmil/ft)
L = conductor length (ft)
A = cross-sectional area (cmil)

Note that the resistance is directly related to conductor length and inversely related to area. Thus, a larger cross-sectional area results in a lower resistance. Typical resistivity values at

25°C are 10.571 ohms-cmil/ft for hard-drawn copper and 17.291 ohms-cmil/ft for hard-drawn aluminum.

EXAMPLE 6–1

Determine the resistance of a (a) hard-drawn copper and (b) hard-drawn aluminum conductor, 200 ft in length, having a diameter of 0.2043 in. at 25°C.

Solution: The cross-sectional area in cmil is: Area = $(204.3 \text{ mils})^2$ = 41,738 cmil.

a) The resistivity of hard-drawn copper is 10.571 ohms-cmil/ft. Equation (6–5) applies.

$$R = \frac{(10.571 \text{ ohms-cmil/ft})(200 \text{ ft})}{41,738 \text{ cmil}} = 0.0507 \ \Omega$$

b) The resistivity of hard-drawn aluminum is 17.291 ohms-cmil/ft. Again, Equation (6–5) applies.

$$R = \frac{(17.291 \text{ ohms-cmil/ft})(200 \text{ ft})}{41,738 \text{ cmil}} = 0.0829 \ \Omega$$

The resistivity of a conductor material varies as a function of temperature. Therefore, the resistance of a conductor will vary as a function of temperature as well. At temperatures within the normal expected operating range, the resistance will vary according to the following equation:

$$R = R_{25} \left[1 + \alpha \left(T_2 - T_1\right)\right] \tag{6–6}$$

where:

R = resistance at the new temperature
R_{25} = resistance at 25°C
T_2 = new temperature, °C
T_1 = reference temperature, 25°C
α = temperature coefficient of resistance, 0.00385 for copper and 0.00395 for aluminum

Equation (6–6) assumes a linear relationship between resistance and temperature and that the temperature coefficient of resistance remains constant. These are valid assumptions for normal operating temperatures.

EXAMPLE 6–2

Determine the resistance at 40°C for the conductors of Example 6–1.

Solution: Equation (6–6) applies in both cases.

a) $R = 0.0507[1 + 0.00385(40 - 25)] = 0.0536 \ \Omega$
b) $R = 0.0829[1 + 0.00395(40 - 25)] = 0.0878 \ \Omega$

6–2   CABLE CONSTRUCTION AND INSULATION TYPES

Cable Construction

As discussed in the previous section, the conductor material is copper or aluminum, with copper being more common. The conductors may be solid or stranded, depending on the size and desired amount of flexibility. There are several different ways in which the conductors are packaged to form an electrical power cable. The most common type of cable construction used for low-voltage (600 V) power cables is the single-conductor cable shown in Figure 6–1. Figure 6–1(A) gives an example of a single-conductor cable covered by a single layer of insulation. The cable shown in Figure 6–1(B) is a single-conductor cable covered by an outer nylon jacket. These cables would typically be installed in conduit or other suitable raceway system. The insulating material is extruded around the electrical conductors to provide electrical isolation between conductors. The thickness of the insulating material is generally determined by the voltage rating of the cable. For example, a cable rated for 5 kV will have a thicker insulation than a 600 V cable. Common voltage classes for cables are 600 V, 2 kV, 5 kV, 15 kV, 25 kV, and 35 kV. In addition, various insulation thicknesses are permitted within a given voltage class. Some cables have an outer jacket applied to serve as a protection for the cable insulation. Figure 6–2 shows examples of single-conductor cable of various sizes.

A multiconductor cable is an assembly of two or more conductors having an outer jacket to physically hold the individual conductors in place for ease of installation. Service entrance cable and nonmetallic sheathed cable are common examples of multiconductor cable. Type AC, armored cable, consists of insulated conductors contained in a flexible metal raceway, as shown in Figure 6–3(A). Several different variations exist with respect to the number and size of the conductors in the armored cable assembly. Generally, armored cable is available with two, three, or four insulated conductors, either solid or stranded, in sizes from #14 AWG to #2 AWG. Article 320 of the *NEC* permits type AC cable to be used in dry locations, embedded in plaster or masonry, or run through the hollow core of masonry block where not exposed to damp or wet conditions. This type of cable may be used for fixture whips for connection to fluorescent lighting fixtures. The outer armor may be used as an equipment grounding conductor if suitable fittings are employed.

Type MC, metal-clad, cable is shown in Figure 6–3(B). Individual insulated conductors along with one or more grounding conductors are grouped together and enclosed in an outer sheath. Generally, type MC cable is available with three or four insulated conductors and three bare grounding conductors encased in a single sheath. Other variations include cable containing both power and control conductors in the same sheath and cable

FIGURE 6–1
Low-Voltage, Single-Conductor
Cable Construction

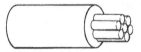 

A. Single Insulation Layer   **B.** Outer Nylon Jacket

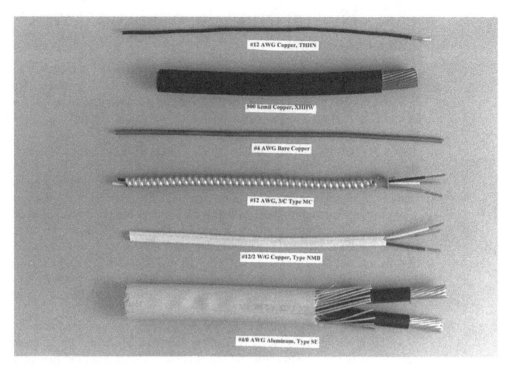

FIGURE 6–2
Cable Types

containing power conductors and fiber-optic cables in the same sheath. Fillers are used between the individual conductors to keep the conductors in place within the cable. The outer sheath may be a smooth metal sheath, corrugated metal sheath, or interlocked metal-tape armor sheath. The interlocking metal-tape armor sheath is not listed for use as an equipment grounding conductor, but may be used in conjunction with the enclosed grounding conductor to provide a suitable equipment ground. If the smooth or corrugated metal sheath is to be used as an equipment grounding conductor, it must be listed for this purpose. Article 330 of the *NEC* permits type MC cable to be installed indoors or outdoors, in wet (not submerged) or dry locations, as open runs of cable supported at intervals not exceeding 6 feet, in cable tray, in an approved raceway or conduit, or directly buried where listed for direct burial.

The most common type of cable used for residential branch circuits is type NM, nonmetallic, sheathed cable. This type of cable construction is shown in Figure 6–3(C). The cable is generally available with two or three insulated conductors, with or without a bare copper ground, and jacketed with an outer polyvinylchloride sheath, as shown. The conductor insulation is usually rated 90°C with a nylon jacket and is color-coded for identification purposes. Common conductor sizes are #14 AWG to # 2 AWG copper conductor. Article 334 of the *NEC* does not permit nonmetallic sheathed cable to be used in any

ITT Technical Institute

ET3480

Power Systems

PEARSON

WWW.PEARSONLEARNINGSOLUTIONS.COM

ISBN 1-256-29032-7

FIGURE 6–3
Low-Voltage Multiconductor Cable
Construction

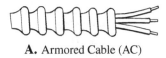

A. Armored Cable (AC)

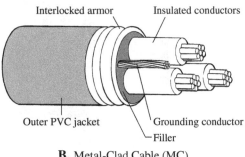

Interlocked armor   Insulated conductors

Outer PVC jacket   Grounding conductor
                         Filler

B. Metal-Clad Cable (MC)

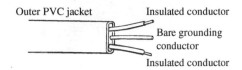

Outer PVC jacket   Insulated conductor

                         Bare grounding
                         conductor

                         Insulated conductor

C. Nonmetallic Sheathed Cable (NM)

structure more than three floors above grade, for service entrance cable, in commercial garages, or embedded in poured concrete or other aggregate. Other restrictions on the application of type NM cable can be found in Article 336 of the *NEC*. Type UF, underground feeder, cable has a construction similar in appearance to type NM but is listed for underground applications including direct burial. Type UF cable is commonly used in residential applications to supply lamp posts, pumps, and other similar outdoor equipment. Article 340 of the *NEC* discusses applications of type UF cable in more detail. Other variations of NM cable include NMC, which is permitted in dry, damp, moist, or corrosive locations. Type NMS cable is an assembly that contains power, signaling, and other communications conductors in a common sheath. NMS cable is typically installed in dry locations only. Figure 6–4 shows a typical nonmetallic sheathed cable installation in a residential dwelling.

Service entrance cables are typically identified as type SE or USE; two variations of type SE cable include type SEU and SER, as shown in Figure 6–5. Type SEU cable generally has two insulated conductors wrapped by a concentrically applied bare neutral, jacketed with a sunlight-resistant PVC outer covering. Type SER cable is used primarily as feeder conductor in dwelling units but may be used in other locations as well. Type SER cable is round in construction and is available in three or four conductor configurations.

FIGURE 6–4
Nonmetallic Sheathed Cable Installation

The three-conductor configuration would typically consist of two insulated phase conductors and an insulated neutral. The four-conductor configuration would consist of two insulated phase conductors, an insulated neutral, and a bare equipment grounding conductor. Type USE cable is designed to be installed underground, either in conduit or directly buried. Article 338 of the *NEC* describes type SE and USE cable. In addition, Article 230 of the *NEC* discusses service entrance requirements. Figure 6–6 shows a typical service cable installation supplying a 150 A residential service.

Insulation Types

The application will oftentimes dictate what type of insulation is required. Factors such as temperature, wet or dry location, exposure to sunlight, and so on all influence the type of insulation required. Some insulations are not suitable for installation in wet locations; others are not suited for installation where exposed to the direct rays of the sun. The environment in which a cable is applied has an effect on the life of the insulation. Improper application may cause a premature degradation of the cable insulation, with subsequent failure.

FIGURE 6–5
Service Entrance Cable

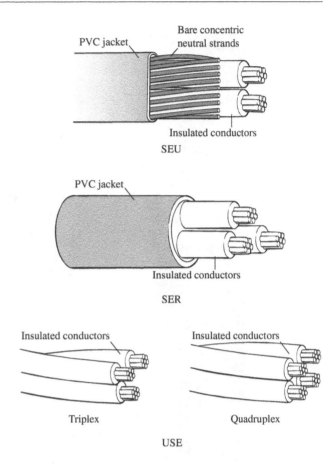

SEU

SER

Triplex   Quadruplex

USE

There are two major types of insulation typically used for building wire: thermoplastic and thermoset. Thermoplastic insulations will begin to melt at temperatures higher than rated. Polyethylene (PE) and polyvinylchloride (PVC) are examples of thermoplastic insulations. Thermosetting insulations will not melt at temperatures higher than rated, but will tend to deteriorate at a much quicker rate at these higher temperatures. Cross-linked polyethylene (XLPE) and rubber insulations are examples of thermoset insulations.

As previously discussed, when current flows through a conductor, heat is produced. This heat will obviously be transmitted to the conductor insulation. Thus, the conductor temperature will be about the same as the insulation temperature and vice versa. There are typically three temperature ratings assigned to conductor insulations: 60°C, 75°C, and 90°C. Operation of a conductor above its temperature rating will cause premature degradation of the conductor insulation.

Several different cable designations are used to describe building wire insulations. Factors such as insulation type, temperature rating, and suitability for application in wet or dry location influence the designation. Some of the more common cable designations are

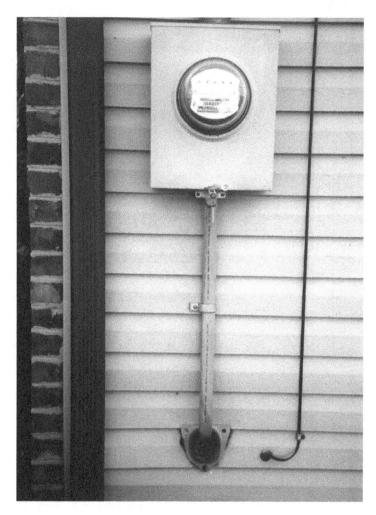

FIGURE 6–6
Service Cable Installation

shown in the Table 6–1. Note that insulations with a "-2" designation are suitable for operation at 90°C in wet or dry locations.

6–3   CONDUCTOR AMPACITIES

In the previous section, it was noted that the temperature of the conductor affects the temperature of the insulation. Higher current flow will mean higher conductor and insulation temperatures as a result of increased power losses in the conductor. Thus, one of the limiting factors in determining the conductor ampacity is the current flow required to bring the

TABLE 6–1
Cable Insulation Types

THW-2	<u>T</u>hermoplastic insulation (usually PVC), <u>H</u>eat resistant (90°C rating), suitable for <u>W</u>et locations.
THWN-2	Same as THW except <u>N</u>ylon jacket over reduced insulation thickness. Also rated THHN.
THHN	<u>T</u>hermoplastic insulation (usually PVC), <u>H</u>igh <u>H</u>eat resistant (90°C rating), dry locations only, <u>N</u>ylon jacket. Also rated THWN.
XHHW-2	Cross-linked polyethylene insulation (<u>X</u>), <u>H</u>igh <u>H</u>eat resistant (90°C rating), for wet and dry locations.
RHH	<u>R</u>ubber insulation. Most manufacturers use cross-linked polyethylene because it has the same properties as rubber. <u>H</u>igh <u>H</u>eat resistant (90°C rating), for dry locations only.
RHW-2	<u>R</u>ubber insulation (cross-linked polyethylene). <u>H</u>eat resistant (90°C rating), suitable for <u>W</u>et locations.
USE-2	<u>U</u>nderground <u>S</u>ervice <u>E</u>ntrance. Most utilize XLP for 90°C in direct burial applications. Product is usually triple rated: RHH-RHW-USE.
NM-B	<u>N</u>on<u>M</u>etallic sheathed cable. The "<u>B</u>" denotes that individual conductor insulation is rated 90°C; however, ampacity is limited to that of a 60°C conductor. Thermoplastic (PVC) conductor insulation, nylon jacketed, with overall PVC cable jacket.
SEU	<u>S</u>ervice <u>E</u>ntrance Cable, <u>U</u>narmored. Usually type XHHW insulated conductors with overall PVC jacket. As such, the cable is rated for 90°C dry, 75°C wet locations.
SER	<u>S</u>ervice <u>E</u>ntrance Cable, <u>R</u>ound. Same material construction as SEU but round construction.

Source: Southwire Power Cable Manual and Product Catalog, © Southwire Company.

conductor up to a certain temperature. Furthermore, different type designations on insulation reflect the ability of the insulation to withstand various temperatures, for example, 60°C, 75°C, or 90°C.

The heat generated internally as power loss in the conductor must be dissipated in order for the temperature to reach an equilibrium condition. The ability of a conductor to dissipate heat is affected by the ambient temperature in which the conductor is located and the proximity of other current-carrying conductors in the same raceway. Higher ambient temperatures will reduce the ability of the conductor to dissipate heat, thereby resulting in elevated conductor temperatures. Likewise, current-carrying conductors in close proximity to one another will generate heat that will likely raise the surface temperature of the conductors.

Tables 310.16, and 310.17 of the *NEC* are the most widely used tables for determining conductor ampacities. These tables are shown in Tables 6–2 and 6–3, both of which list conductor ampacities for copper and aluminum conductors in an ambient temperature of 30°C. Table 310.16 applies when there are not more than three current-carrying conductors

TABLE 6–2
Table 310.16 Allowable Ampacities of Insulated Conductors Rated 0 Through 2000 Volts, 60°C Through 90°C (140°F Through 194°F), Not More Than Three Current-Carrying Conductors in Raceway, Cable, or Earth (Directly Buried), Based on Ambient Temperature of 30°C (86°F)

	Temperature Rating of Conductor (See Table 310.13.)						
	60°C (140°F)	75°C (167°F)	90°C (194°F)	60°C (140°F)	75°C (167°F)	90°C (194°F)	
Size AWG or kcmil	Types TW, UF	Types RHW, THHW, THW, THWN, XHHW, USE, ZW	Types TBS, SA, SIS FEP, FEPB, MI, RHH, RHW-2, THHN, THHW, THW-2, THWN-2, USE-2, XHH, XHHW, XHHW-2 ZW-2	Types TW, UF	Types RHW, THHW, THW, THWN, XHHW, USE	Types TBS, SA, SIS, THHN, THHW, THW-2, THWN-2, RHH, RHW-2, USE-2, XHH, XHHW, XHHW-2, ZW-2	Size AWG or kcmil
	COPPER			ALUMINUM OR COPPER-CLAD ALUMINUM			
18	—	—	14	—	—	—	—
16	—	—	18	—	—	—	—
14*	20	20	25	—	—	—	—
12*	25	25	30	20	20	25	12*
10*	30	35	40	25	30	35	10*
8	40	50	55	30	40	45	8
6	55	65	75	40	50	60	6
4	70	85	95	55	65	75	4
3	85	100	110	65	75	85	3
2	95	115	130	75	90	100	2
1	110	130	150	85	100	115	1
1/0	125	150	170	100	120	135	1/0
2/0	145	175	195	115	135	150	2/0
3/0	165	200	225	130	155	175	3/0
4/0	195	230	260	150	180	205	4/0
250	215	255	290	170	205	230	250
300	240	285	320	190	230	255	300
350	260	310	350	210	250	280	350
400	280	335	380	225	270	305	400

Size							Size
500	320	380	430	260	310	350	500
600	355	420	475	285	340	385	600
700	385	460	520	310	375	420	700
750	400	475	535	320	385	435	750
800	410	490	555	330	395	450	800
900	435	520	585	355	425	480	900
1000	455	545	615	375	445	500	1000
1250	495	590	665	405	485	545	1250
1500	520	625	705	435	520	585	1500
1750	545	650	735	455	545	615	1750
2000	560	665	750	470	560	630	2000

CORRECTION FACTORS

For ambient temperatures other than 30°C (86°F), multiply the allowable ampacities shown above by the appropriate factor shown below

Ambient Temp. (°C)							Ambient Temp. (°F)
21–25	1.08	1.05	1.04	1.08	1.05	1.04	70–77
26–30	1.00	1.00	1.00	1.00	1.00	1.00	78–86
31–35	0.91	0.94	0.96	0.91	0.94	0.96	87–95
36–40	0.82	0.88	0.91	0.82	0.88	0.91	96–104
41–45	0.71	0.82	0.87	0.71	0.82	0.87	105–113
46–50	0.58	0.75	0.82	0.58	0.75	0.82	114–122
51–55	0.41	0.67	0.76	0.41	0.67	0.76	123–131
56–60	—	0.58	0.71	—	0.58	0.71	132–140
61–70	—	0.33	0.58	—	0.33	0.58	141–158
71–80	—	—	0.41	—	—	0.41	159–176

*See 240.4(D).

Source: Reprinted with permission from NFPA 70 *The National Electrical Code* © 2002, National Fire Protection Association, Quincy, MA 02269. This reprinted material is not the referenced subject which is represented only by the standard in its entirety.

TABLE 6–3
Table 310.17 Allowable Ampacities of Single-Insulated Conductors Rated 0 Through 2000 Volts in Free Air, Based on Ambient Air Temperature of 30°C (86°F)

Size AWG or kcmil	Temperature Rating of Conductor (See Table 310.13.)						Size AWG or kcmil
	COPPER			ALUMINUM OR COPPER-CLAD ALUMINUM			
	60°C (140°F)	75°C (167°F)	90°C (194°F)	60°C (140°F)	75°C (167°F)	90°C (194°F)	
	Types TW, UF	Types RHW, THHW, THW, THWN, XHHW, ZW	Types TBS, SA, SIS, FEP, FEPB, MI, RHH, RHW-2, THHN, THHW, THW-2, THWN-2, USE-2, XHH, XHHW, XHHW-2, ZW-2	Types TW, UF	Types RHW, THHW, THW, THWN, XHHW	Types TBS, SA, SIS, THHN, THHW, THW-2, THWN-2, RHH, RHW-2, USE-2, XHH, XHHW, XHHW-2, ZW-2	
18	—	—	18	—	—	—	—
16	—	—	24	—	—	—	—
14*	25	30	35				
12*	30	35	40	25	30	35	12*
10*	40	50	55	35	40	40	10*
8	60	70	80	45	55	60	8
6	80	95	105	60	75	80	6
4	105	125	140	80	100	110	4
3	120	145	165	95	115	130	3
2	140	170	190	110	135	150	2
1	165	195	220	130	155	175	1
1/0	195	230	260	150	180	205	1/0
2/0	225	265	300	175	210	235	2/0
3/0	260	310	350	200	240	275	3/0
4/0	300	360	405	235	280	315	4/0

250	340	405	455	265	315	355	250
300	375	445	505	290	350	395	300
350	420	505	570	330	395	445	350
400	455	545	615	355	425	480	400
500	515	620	700	405	485	545	500
600	575	690	780	455	540	615	600
700	630	755	855	500	595	675	700
750	655	785	885	515	620	700	750
800	680	815	920	535	645	725	800
900	730	870	985	580	700	785	900
1000	780	935	1055	625	750	845	1000
1250	890	1065	1200	710	855	960	1250
1500	980	1175	1325	795	950	1075	1500
1750	1070	1280	1445	875	1050	1185	1750
2000	1155	1385	1560	960	1150	1335	2000

Source: Reprinted with permission from NFPA 70 *The National Electrical Code* © 2002, National Protection Association, Quincy, MA 02269. This reprinted material is not the referenced subject which is represented only by the standard in its entirety.

in the raceway or conduit. Table 310.17 applies to a single conductor in free air. The temperature rating and insulation type letter designation is shown at the top of the tables, and the conductor size is shown in the left-hand column. For a conductor in a raceway containing no more than three current-carrying conductors in a 30°C ambient temperature, the ampacities are read directly from Table 310.16. Likewise, for a conductor in free air in a 30°C ambient temperature, the ampacity is read directly from Table 310.17.

EXAMPLE 6–3

Determine the ampacity of the following conductors. There are three current-carrying conductors in the raceway, and the ambient temperature is 30°C.

a) #10 TW copper, dry location
b) #4 THW copper, dry location
c) 500 kcmil THHW copper, wet location
d) 500 kcmil XHHW-2 copper, wet location

Solution:

a) Type TW is a 60°C insulation; therefore, the ampacity is 30 A.
b) Type THW is a 75°C insulation; therefore, the ampacity is 85 A.
c) Type THHW applied in a wet location requires the use of the 75°C rating. Therefore, the ampacity is 380 A. Note: If this conductor had been applied in a dry location, the ampacity would have been taken at the 90°C rating, 430 A.
d) Type XHHW-2 in a wet location is permitted to have an ampacity using the 90°C rating. Therefore, the ampacity is 430 A. Note: If this conductor insulation had been rated XHHW, the ampacity for application in a wet location would have been taken from the 75°C column, 380 A.

Selection of the proper conductor size requires knowledge of the load current to be supplied by the conductor. For applications involving a 30°C ambient temperature and no more than three current-carrying conductors in a raceway, the conductor ampacity must have a value equal to or greater than the load current to be served. For example, a load current of 70 A supplied by type THW copper conductors requires the use of a #4 conductor size. Note that the #4 THW copper conductor has a table-listed (75°C) ampacity of 85 A. The next smaller wire size, #6, has an ampacity of 65 A, which is too small for this application. The determination of load current is discussed in a subsequent section.

6–4   DERATING BASED ON AMBIENT TEMPERATURE

The conductor ampacities in the previous section were determined based on an ambient temperature of 30°C. In certain installations, the actual ambient temperature may be greater than 30°C. In such cases, an ambient temperature correction factor must be applied to the table-listed ampacity to determine the derated ampacity of the conductor. This correction factor is a function of both the ambient temperature and the conductor insulation type. The correction factors are found at the bottom of Tables 310.16 and 310.17. The derated conductor ampacity is calculated as:

$$\text{Derated ampacity} = \text{Table-listed ampacity} \times \text{Correction factor} \qquad (6\text{--}7)$$

The following example illustrates the use of the correction factor.

EXAMPLE 6–4

Determine the derated ampacities of the conductors in Example 6–3 if the ambient temperature is 37°C.

Solution:

a) The rated ampacity at 30°C ambient was 30 A. The derating factor for type TW at 37°C is 0.82. Therefore, the derated ampacity is (0.82)(30 A) = 24.6 A.
b) The rated ampacity at 30°C ambient was 85 A. The derating factor for type THW at 37°C is 0.88. Therefore, the derated ampacity is (0.88)(85 A) = 74.8 A.
c) The rated ampacity at 30°C ambient was 380 A. The derating factor for type THHW at 37°C in a wet location is 0.88. Therefore, the derated ampacity is (0.88)(380 A) = 334.4 A.
d) The rated ampacity at 30°C ambient was 430 A. The derating factor for type XHHW-2 at 37°C in a wet location is 0.91. Therefore, the derated ampacity is (0.91)(430 A) = 391.3 A.

6–5   DERATING BASED ON NUMBER OF CURRENT-CARRYING CONDUCTORS

A large number of current-carrying conductors in the same raceway restrict heat dissipation. Table 310.16 was developed based on no more than three current-carrying conductors in the raceway. This condition would apply to most three-phase balanced circuits, with load current flowing in the ungrounded conductors. If there are more than three current-carrying conductors in the raceway, a raceway fill adjustment factor must be applied. Similar to the temperature correction factor, the raceway fill adjustment factor reduces the table-listed ampacity of the conductor. Raceway fill adjustment factors are shown in Table 6–4. Note that these adjustment factors are in addition to any temperature correction factors that are applied. The derated conductor ampacity is calculated as

$$\text{Derated ampacity} = \text{Table-listed ampacity} \times \text{Adjustment factor} \qquad (6\text{--}8)$$

The following example illustrates the use of the raceway fill adjustment factor.

EXAMPLE 6–5

Determine the derated ampacity of a #1/0 THW copper conductor in a raceway containing four current-carrying conductors, at an ambient temperature of 30°C.

TABLE 6–4

Table 310.15(B)(2)(a) Adjustment Factors for More Than Three Current-Carrying Conductors in a Raceway or Cable

Number of Current-Carrying Conductors	Percent of Values in Tables 310.16 through 310.19 as Adjusted for Ambient Temperature if Necessary
4-6	80
7-9	70
10-20	50
21-30	45
31-40	40
41 and above	35

Source: Reprinted with permission from NFPA 70 *The National Electrical Code* © 2002, National Fire Protection Association, Quincy, MA 02269. This reprinted material is not the referenced subject which is represented only by the standard in its entirety.

Solution: The table-listed ampacity is 150 A. The raceway fill adjustment factor for four current-carrying conductors is 80%, or 0.8. Therefore, the derated ampacity is (150 A)(0.8) = 120 A.

The number of current-carrying conductors in a raceway is determined by counting all ungrounded (phase) conductors, plus any grounded (neutral) conductor that is considered to be carrying current under normal conditions. The neutral conductor of a single-phase, three-wire circuit is expected to carry only the unbalanced current in the circuit and is thus not considered to be a current-carrying conductor. Likewise, the neutral conductor of a three-phase, four-wire, wye-connected circuit supplying linear loads will carry only the unbalanced current in the circuit and need not be considered as a current-carrying conductor. Also, any equipment grounding conductors occupying the same raceway as the circuit conductors are not counted as a current-carrying conductor.

Neutral conductors considered to be current-carrying are identified in Section 310.15(B)(4) of the *NEC* and are shown in Figure 6–7. A single-phase circuit consisting of the ungrounded (phase) and grounded (neutral) conductor supplying a single-phase load is shown in Figure 6–7(A). Typical load voltages for this type of circuit would be 120 V, or 277 V. In this instance, the grounded conductor carries all of the return current from the load and would be considered a current-carrying conductor.

Figure 6–7(B) shows a circuit consisting of two-phase conductors and a neutral supplied from a three-phase, four-wire, wye-connected system. In this case, the neutral current will have a magnitude approximately equal to the two-phase conductors. Thus,

FIGURE 6–7

Counting the Grounded Conductor as
a Current-Carrying Conductor

A. Single-Phase Load Connected
Phase to Neutral

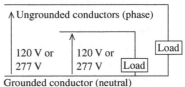

B. Two Single-Phase Loads Connected
Phase to Neutral

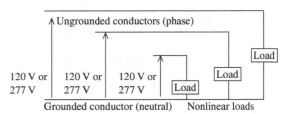

C. Three-Phase, Four-Wire Nonlinear Loads
Connected Phase to Neutral

the neutral must be counted as a current-carrying conductor. This type of circuit may consist of two-phase conductors and the neutral supplied from a 208Y/120 V, or 480Y/277 V system.

Lastly, Figure 6–7(C) shows a three-phase, four-wire circuit supplying nonlinear loads. Examples of nonlinear loads include fluorescent lighting, rectifiers, motor drives, personal computer power supplies, and so on. These nonlinear loads produce harmonics in the current waveform that add up in the neutral rather than canceling. The neutral current is therefore of sufficient magnitude to produce significant heating and must be counted as a current-carrying conductor. In extreme cases, the neutral current may actually exceed the phase current. This type of circuit may be comprised of all three-phase conductors and the neutral conductor supplied from a 208Y/120 V, or 480Y/277 V, three-phase, four-wire system.

When derating is required for both temperature and raceway fill, a total derating factor must be applied. This total derating factor is the product of the ambient temperature correction factor and the raceway fill adjustment factor. The total derating factor is therefore

$$\text{Total derating factor} = (\text{Correction factor}) \times (\text{Adjustment factor}) \qquad \textbf{(6–9)}$$

The derated conductor ampacity is

$$\text{Derated ampacity} = (\text{Table-listed ampacity}) \times (\text{Total derating factor}) \qquad \textbf{(6–10)}$$

EXAMPLE 6–6

Determine the total derating factor and derated conductor ampacity for a 350 kcmil THW copper conductor used in a three-phase, four-wire circuit supplying a nonlinear load in an ambient temperature of 40°C.

Solution: The table-listed ampacity is 310 A. The ambient temperature correction factor is 0.88. Since the load is nonlinear, the neutral is counted as a current-carrying conductor. Therefore, there are four current-carrying conductors in the raceway and the raceway fill adjustment factor is 0.8. The total derating factor is

$$(0.88)(0.8) = 0.704$$

The derated conductor ampacity is

$$\text{Derated ampacity} = (310 \text{ A})(0.704) = 218 \text{ A}$$

6–6   TEMPERATURE LIMITATIONS ON DEVICE TERMINALS

In general, the conductor temperature is dependent on the magnitude of the current flowing in the conductor, the ambient temperature, and the raceway fill. The previous sections dealt with conductor ampacity derating to account for ambient temperature correction and raceway fill adjustment. Both derating procedures were necessary due to the restriction of heat dissipation when conductors are placed in elevated temperatures or in close proximity to other current-carrying conductors. In particular, Tables 310.16 and 310.17 of the *NEC* listed the allowable ampacities of various conductor sizes for the various insulation temperature ratings. Specifically, conductor insulation temperature ratings of 60°C, 75°C, and 90°C are displayed in the tables. The data contained in Tables 310.16 and 310.17 can also be viewed as an indication of the expected temperature of a conductor for a certain current level. For example, if 75 A flows in a # 6 copper conductor, the temperature of the conductor would be 90°C. If 65 A were to flow in the same conductor, the temperature would be 75°C. Lastly, if 55 A were to flow in the conductor, the temperature would be 60°C. Thus, even if the conductor insulation were rated 90°C, the temperature would only be 75°C if 65 A were flowing, or 60°C if 55 A were flowing.

Branch circuit and feeder conductors will typically be terminated on the supply side by connection to a circuit breaker terminal lug or fuseblock terminal. On the load side, the conductors will typically be terminated on a device terminal such as the screw terminal of a receptacle or switch. By virtue of this connection, the heat produced in the conductor will be transmitted to the device terminals, thereby causing heating of the device terminals themselves. In cases where the conductor temperature is greater than that of the device terminals, the terminals will act as a heat sink. In this case, heat will be transferred from the conductor to the device terminal until an equilibrium condition is reached. It is generally assumed that the temperature of the device terminals will be the same as that of the conductor. If a sufficient amount of heat is transferred to the device, false tripping of circuit breakers, nuisance blowing of fuses, or equipment damage may result.

To minimize false tripping, nuisance fuse blowing, and possible damage to equipment and devices, the temperature rating of the device terminals cannot be exceeded. Section 110.14(C)(1) of the *NEC* discusses the selection of conductor temperature rating as related to the temperature limitations on device terminals. Typically, the maximum temperature rating of device terminals is 60°C for devices rated 100 A or less or designed to accommodate wire sizes #1 and smaller. However, several manufacturers list 75°C terminals for some devices less than 100 A. For devices rated greater than 100 A, or devices having terminals designed to accommodate wire sizes greater than #1, the maximum temperature rating of the device terminals is typically 75°C. Based on these restrictions, the maximum allowable current flow through a conductor cannot produce a temperature that exceeds the maximum permitted device terminal temperature rating. Therefore, if a 90°C rated conductor is used, the ampacity cannot exceed that shown in either the 60°C or 75°C column of Tables 310.16 or 310.17.

EXAMPLE 6–7

Determine the maximum allowable ampacity of a #2 THW-2 copper conductor connected to a breaker having a 60°C terminal rating.

Solution: In this instance, the #2 THW-2 conductor has a rating of 95 A, as taken from the 60°C column of Table 310.16. Note that the ampacity at 90°C is 130 A. However, the ampacity is limited to 95 A due to the device terminal temperature limitation.

EXAMPLE 6–8

Determine the maximum allowable ampacity of a 500 kcmil XHHW-2 copper conductor connected to a breaker having a 75°C terminal rating.

Solution: In this instance, the 500 kcmil XHHW-2 conductor has a rating of 380 A, as taken from the 75°C column of Table 310.16. Note that the ampacity at 90°C is 430 A. However, the ampacity is limited to 380 A due to the device terminal temperature limitation.

Based on the previous examples, one might wonder why it would be advantageous to use 90°C rated conductor insulation. The answer is that the use of higher-temperature conductor insulation is desirable when derating is required due to higher ambient temperature or raceway fill. Initially, the ampacity of the conductor can be selected from the 90°C column. The ambient temperature correction factor and/or raceway fill adjustment factors are then applied to the 90°C ampacity. This would result in a derated ampacity lower than that shown in the 90°C column. The resulting derated ampacity must then be compared to the ampacity listed in the 60°C or 75°C column, depending on the device terminal temperature limitation. The lower of the two values becomes the maximum permitted ampacity of the conductor. Using a higher-temperature-rated conductor when derating is required generally results in selection of a smaller conductor size to supply the load.

EXAMPLE 6–9

A three-phase, nonlinear load is to be supplied in a 35°C ambient. Determine the maximum allowable ampacity for the following conductors:

a) # 6 THW copper (75°C rating)
b) # 6 THW-2 copper (90°C rating)

Solution:

a) The adjustment factor for raceway fill is 0.8, and the ambient temperature correction is 0.94. The total derating factor is (0.8)(0.94) = 0.752. The table-listed ampacity at 75°C is 65 A. The derated ampacity is given by Equation (6–10):

$$\text{Derated ampacity} = (0.752)(65 \text{ A}) = 48.9 \text{ A}$$

It is now necessary to look up the table-listed ampacity of the #6 AWG conductor from the 60°C column to ensure that the device terminal temperature limitation is not exceeded. The table-listed ampacity at 60°C is found to be 55 A. Since the derated ampacity is less than the table-listed ampacity at 60°C, the maximum permitted ampacity is 48.9 A

b) The adjustment factor for raceway fill is 0.8, and the ambient temperature correction factor is 0.96. The total derating factor is (0.8)(0.96) = 0.768. The table-listed ampacity at 90°C is 75 A. The derated ampacity is given by Equation (6–10):

$$\text{Derated ampacity} = (0.768)(75 \text{ A}) = 57.6 \text{ A}$$

In this case, the derated ampacity of the conductor exceeds the 60°C table-listed ampacity of 55 A. However, due to device terminal temperature limitations, the maximum permitted ampacity is 55 A.

6–7   CONDUCTOR AND OVERCURRENT PROTECTION DEVICE (OCPD) SELECTION

Continuous and Noncontinuous Loads

To determine the minimum conductor size and OCPD rating required for a branch circuit or feeder to supply a certain load, it is necessary to determine the loading in amperes on the circuit. Generally, the load on a circuit will be comprised of continuous and noncontinuous loads. Article 100 of the *NEC* defines a continuous load as a load that is energized for three hours or more. Examples of continuous loads are lighting, computer terminals, copy machines, HVAC equipment, and other devices and equipment found in offices. Most processes in an industrial setting are also considered to be continuous loads. Noncontinuous loads are general-purpose receptacle outlets, residential lighting outlets, and so on. If there is a doubt as to whether or not a load should be continuous or noncontinuous, it is best to assume that the load is continuous.

Overcurrent Device Rating Selection

The overcurrent device selected to protect a feeder or branch circuit must be properly rated to supply the load and protect the circuit conductors. Section 210.20 and Section 215.3 of the *NEC* require that the rating of the overcurrent device must be at least equal to 125% of the continuous load plus 100% of the noncontinuous load. If an overcurrent device is rated for 100% continuous duty, then the design ampacity can be based on the sum of the continuous load and the noncontinuous load. Again, this increase in the load current for continuous loads is due to the fact that higher temperatures can be expected in the overcurrent device as a result of the continuous load current.

EXAMPLE 6–10

A three-phase feeder supplies a panelboard with connected loads of 30 A noncontinuous and 40 A continuous. Determine the minimum required overcurrent device rating for this feeder.

Solution: The design load current is equal to

$$\text{Design load current} = (1.25)(40 \text{ A}) + 1.0(30 \text{ A}) = 80 \text{ A}$$

Therefore, the feeder overcurrent device must be rated at least 80 A to supply this load. Note: It would also be permissible to take 125% of the sum of both the continuous and noncontinuous loads to determine the minimum overcurrent device rating. The result would be $(1.25)(30 \text{ A} + 40 \text{ A}) = 87.5 \text{ A}$. Therefore, a 90 A overcurrent device could be specified, resulting in a more conservative design that exceeds *NEC* requirements.

Conductor Size Selection

In the previous sections, the ampacity of a given conductor size was determined based on the table-listed ampacity for a given insulation temperature rating and device terminal temperature ratings. The application of ambient temperature correction and raceway fill adjustment factors was also discussed. The maximum permitted ampacity of a given conductor to protect the conductors and device terminals from overheating was established. It is now necessary to determine the conductor size required to supply a given load.

The next step in the conductor selection process involves application of Sections 210.19 and 215.2 of the *NEC*, which require the branch circuit or feeder conductors supplying a load to have an ampacity equal to or greater than 125% of the continuous load plus 100% of the noncontinuous load. This minimum conductor size is determined without the application of ambient temperature correction factors or raceway fill adjustment factors and is based on the 60°C or 75°C table-listed ampacity as dictated by the device terminal temperature rating. This requirement is due to the fact that a continuous load will produce a higher temperature in the circuit conductors along their length and that this higher temperature will be transferred to the device terminals. To account for this increase in temperature due to continuous load current, the value of the continuous load current is multiplied by 125%. In essence, the requirement of this section is meant to protect the device and device terminals from overheating by oversizing the conductors.

EXAMPLE 6–11

Determine the minimum required table-listed ampacity and THW-2 copper conductor size required to supply a continuous, nonlinear, three-phase load of 100 A with a three-phase, four-wire circuit at an ambient temperature of 35°C.

Solution: The minimum table-listed ampacity is based on 125% of the continuous load plus 100% of the noncontinuous load as follows:

$$\text{Minimum table-listed ampacity} = (1.25)(100\ \text{A}) + (1.0)(0\ \text{A}) = 125\ \text{A}$$

Therefore, the appropriate-size conductor will have a 75°C table-listed ampacity equal to or greater than 125 A. (Note that the 75°C ampacity is used since the device rating is greater than 100 A.) From Table 310.16, the appropriate-size conductor is a #1 AWG having a listed ampacity of 130 A.

Note: It is generally good design practice to use 125% as the basis for sizing overcurrent devices and circuit conductors. This results in a circuit load not exceeding 80% (the reciprocal of 125%) of its rating. If there is a question as to whether or not a load is continuous, always assume that it is continuous. This assumption results in a conservative design.

The next step in the conductor selection process involves the determination of the required minimum table-listed ampacity of a conductor to supply a certain load. This minimum table-listed ampacity is given by the following:

$$\text{Minimum table-listed ampacity} = \frac{\text{Load current to be supplied}}{\text{Total derating factor}} \qquad \textbf{(6–11)}$$

The total derating factor is given by Equation (6–9) and includes the ambient temperature correction and raceway fill adjustment factors. The load current to be supplied is based on 100% of the continuous load plus 100% of the noncontinuous load. The minimum required conductor size must have an ampacity equal to or greater than the minimum table-listed ampacity as determined from Equation (6–11).

EXAMPLE 6–12

Determine the minimum-size THW-2 conductor required to supply the load of Example 6–11.

Solution: The raceway fill adjustment factor is 0.8, since the grounded conductor must be treated as a current-carrying conductor due to the nonlinear load. The ambient temperature adjustment factor is 0.96 from the 90°C column for THW-2 insulation. The total derating factor is

$$\text{Total derating factor} = (0.8)(0.96) = 0.768$$

The load current to be supplied is taken as 100% of the continuous load plus 100% of the noncontinuous load, or 100 A. The minimum required table-listed ampacity is given by Equation (6–11):

$$\text{Minimum table-listed ampacity} = \frac{100\text{ A}}{0.768} = 130\text{ A}$$

Therefore, a #2 AWG THW-2 copper conductor, having a table-listed ampacity of 130 A, is initially selected for this application.

The minimum conductor size as determined based on the "125%" requirement must be compared to the conductor size as determined after the application of temperature and raceway fill derating. The larger of the two conductors so selected will become the minimum size required for the circuit. Comparing the results of Examples 6–11 and 6–12, the larger-size conductor is selected as #1 AWG THW-2.

Section 240.4 of the *NEC* requires that a conductor must be protected within its ampacity rating. Therefore, the trip rating of the overcurrent device must be less than or equal to the ampacity of the circuit conductor. Section 240.4(B) of the *NEC* allows the use of the next-higher-rated overcurrent device if the circuit is not a multioutlet branch circuit and the next-higher-rated device does not exceed 800 A. For example, a conductor having an ampacity of 55 A supplying a dedicated circuit can be protected by an overcurrent device with a 60 A trip rating (next-higher-standard-rated device). However, a conductor having an ampacity of 55 A supplying a multioutlet branch circuit must be protected by an overcurrent device with a rating not exceeding 55 A (conductor protected within its ampacity). Generally, multioutlet branch circuits are rated 15 A, 20 A, 30 A, 40 A, or 50 A. Multioutlet branch circuits supplying 15 A and 20 A receptacles are typically rated 15 A or 20 A. Essentially, the next-higher-rated device is permitted on dedicated circuits only, where the load is known. Other instances where the overcurrent device rating is permitted to exceed the conductor ampacity include circuits supplying motors, appliances, HVAC, and other similar equipment.

EXAMPLE 6–13

Determine the maximum permitted overcurrent device rating for the following conductors:

a) Conductor with an ampacity of 95 A supplying a dedicated load
b) Conductor with an ampacity of 35 A supplying a multioutlet branch circuit

Solution:

a) Since this is a dedicated circuit, the conductors may be protected at slightly above their ampacity. Therefore, an overcurrent device with a 100 A rating may be used.

b) For a multioutlet branch circuit, the conductor must be protected within its ampacity. Therefore, an overcurrent device with a standard rating of 30 A is the maximum permitted for this circuit.

A special note to Table 310–16 of the *NEC* indicates that the maximum overcurrent protection permitted for a #14 AWG copper conductor shall not exceed 15 A; for a #12 AWG copper conductor, 20 A; and for a #10 AWG copper conductor, 30 A. This restriction generally applies to multioutlet branch circuits. The exceptions to this rule include circuits supplying motor loads, transformers, and other such loads.

Summary of OCPD and the Conductor Selection Process

The following procedure summarizes the steps necessary to select overcurrent device rating and conductor size:

Step 1. Determine the design load current based on 125% of the continuous load plus 100% of the noncontinuous load.

Step 2. Determine the minimum overcurrent device rating required based on the design load current calculated in Step 1.

Step 3. Determine minimum required conductor size based on the design load current calculated in Step 1 and the temperature rating of the overcurrent device terminals. The required minimum conductor size is based on either the 60°C or 75°C ampacity, depending on the temperature rating of the device terminals.

Step 4. Determine the minimum required conductor size utilizing the actual load current and taking into account derating due to ambient temperature and raceway fill adjustment as required. (Note that the actual load current does not include the 125% factor applied to the continuous part of the load current for this part of the selection process.) This requires the application of Equation (6–11). Calculate the derated conductor ampacity according to Equation (6–10).

Step 5. Compare the conductor sizes from Steps 3 and 4 above. The larger of the two becomes the smallest conductor size permitted.

Step 6. Determine the maximum rating of the overcurrent device permitted based on the final selection of conductor size from Step 5. The maximum rating so selected must be high enough to supply 125% of the continuous load plus 100% of the noncontinuous load, as determined in Step 2.

The following examples illustrate the application of this step-by-step procedure.

EXAMPLE 6–14

Determine the required-size THW (75°C insulation rating) copper conductor and overcurrent device rating required for a dedicated feeder supplying a 70 A noncontinuous load. The ambient temperature is 35°C, and there are eight current-carrying conductors in the raceway.

Solution:

Step 1. Determine the design load current based on 125% of the continuous load plus 100% of the noncontinuous load:

$$\text{Design load current: } (1.0)(70 \text{ A}) = 70 \text{ A}$$

Step 2. Determine the minimum overcurrent device rating required based on the design load current:

$$\text{Overcurrent device rating} = 70 \text{ A}$$

Step 3. Determine the minimum required conductor size based on the design load current. The minimum required conductor size must be taken from the 60°C column since the device is rated less than 100 A. Therefore, a #4 AWG THW copper conductor, with a 60°C ampacity of 70 A, is specified as the required minimum.

Step 4. Determine the minimum required conductor size utilizing the actual load current and taking into account derating due to ambient temperature and raceway fill adjustment as required. The ambient temperature correction factor is 0.94, and the raceway fill adjustment factor is 0.7. Application of Equation (6–11) results in

$$\text{Minimum table-listed ampacity} = \frac{70 \text{ A}}{(0.7)(0.94)} = 106.4 \text{ A}$$

Therefore, a #2 AWG THW copper conductor, with a table-listed ampacity at 75°C of 115 A, is required based on this criterion. The derated ampacity is equal to (0.7)(0.94)(115 A) = 75.7 A.

Step 5. Compare the conductor sizes in Steps 3 and 4.

Conductor size from Step 3 = #4 AWG THW
Conductor size from Step 4 = #2 AWG THW

The larger of the two conductors, a #2 AWG THW copper conductor, having a derated ampacity of 75.7 A, is required for this load condition.

Step 6. Determine the maximum rating of the overcurrent device permitted based on the final selection of conductor size from Step 5. The maximum rating so selected must also be high enough to supply 125% of the continuous load plus 100% of the noncontinuous load. In this case, an 80 A overcurrent device is permitted since this is a dedicated feeder, and rounding up to the next-higher-standard-rated device is permitted.

Summary: 80 A overcurrent device, #2 AWG THW copper conductor.

EXAMPLE 6–15

Repeat Example 6–14 using THHN (90°C insulation rating) copper conductor.

Solution:

Step 1. Determine the design load current based on 125% of the continuous load plus 100% of the noncontinuous load:

Design load current: $(1.0)(70 \text{ A}) = 70 \text{ A}$

Step 2. Determine the minimum overcurrent device rating required based on the design load current:

Overcurrent device rating = 70 A

Step 3. Determine the minimum required conductor size based on the design load current. The minimum required conductor size must be taken from the 60°C column since the device is rated less than 100 A. Therefore, a #4 AWG THHN copper conductor, with a 60°C ampacity of 70 A, is specified as the required minimum.

Step 4. Determine the minimum required conductor size utilizing the actual load current and taking into account derating due to ambient temperature and raceway fill adjustment as required. The ambient temperature correction factor is 0.96, and the raceway fill adjustment factor is 0.7. Application of Equation (6–11) results in

$$\text{Minimum table-listed ampacity} = \frac{70 \text{ A}}{(0.7)(0.96)} = 104.2 \text{ A}$$

Therefore, a #3 AWG THHN copper conductor, having a table-listed ampacity at 90°C of 110 A, is required based on this criterion. The derated conductor ampacity is $(0.7)(0.96)(110 \text{ A}) = 74 \text{ A}$.

Step 5. Compare the conductor sizes in Steps 3 and 4.

Conductor size from Step 3 = #4 AWG THHN
Conductor size from Step 4 = #3 AWG THHN

Therefore, a #3 AWG THHN copper conductor having a derated ampacity of 74 A is required for this load condition.

Step 6. Determine the maximum rating of the overcurrent device permitted based on the final selection of conductor size from Step 5. The maximum rating so selected must also be high enough to supply 125% of the continuous load plus 100% of the noncontinuous load. As in the previous example, an 80 A overcurrent device rating is permitted since this is a dedicated feeder.

Summary: 80 A overcurrent device, #3 AWG THHN copper conductor. Comparing the results of the previous example with this example, the overcurrent device rating is the same. However, the smaller conductor size is permitted because of the higher insulation temperature rating combined with the use of the derating factors.

EXAMPLE 6–16

Determine the required-size THW (75°C insulation rating) copper conductor and overcurrent device rating required for a dedicated feeder supplying a 70 A continuous load. The ambient temperature is 35°C, and there are eight current carrying conductors in the raceway.

Solution:

Step 1. Determine the design load current based on 125% of the continuous load plus 100% of the noncontinuous load:

$$\text{Design load current: } (1.25)(70 \text{ A}) = 87.5 \text{ A}$$

Step 2. Determine the minimum overcurrent device rating required based on the design load current:

$$\text{Overcurrent device rating} = 90 \text{ A}$$

Step 3. Determine the minimum required conductor size based on the design load current. The minimum required conductor size must be taken from the 60°C column since the device is rated less than 100 A. Therefore, a #2 AWG THW copper conductor, with a 60°C ampacity of 95 A, is specified as the required minimum.

Step 4. Determine the minimum required conductor size utilizing the actual load current and taking into account derating due to ambient temperature and raceway fill adjustment as required. The ambient temperature correction factor is 0.94, and the raceway fill adjustment factor is 0.7. Application of Equation (6–11) results in

$$\text{Minimum table-listed ampacity} = \frac{70 \text{ A}}{(0.7)(0.94)} = 106.4 \text{ A}$$

Therefore, a #2 AWG THW copper conductor, having a table-listed ampacity at 75°C of 115 A, is required based on this criterion. The derated conductor ampacity is equal to $(0.7)(0.94)(115 \text{ A}) = 75.7 \text{ A}$.

Step 5. Compare the conductor sizes in Steps 3 and 4.

Conductor size from Step 3 = #2 AWG THW
Conductor size from Step 4 = #2 AWG THW

Therefore, a #2 AWG THW copper conductor is required for this load condition.

Step 6. Determine the maximum rating of the overcurrent device permitted based on the final selection of conductor size from Step 5. The maximum rating so selected must also be high enough to supply 125% of the continuous load plus 100% of the noncontinuous load. From Step 2, the minimum overcurrent device rating permitted is 90 A as required to supply the load. However, the derated ampacity of the #2 AWG THW copper conductor is 75.7 A from Step 4. Based on the derated ampacity of 75.7 A, the maximum overcurrent device rating permitted would be 80 A since this is a dedicated feeder and rounding up to the next-higher-standard rating is permitted. However, an 80 A OCPD is not sufficient to serve the design load of 87.5 A as calculated in Step 1. Therefore, the #2 AWG THW copper conductor is too small for this application. The next-larger-size conductor must be selected, and Step 4 repeated. The next-larger-size conductor is a #1 AWG THW copper conductor, having a table-listed ampacity of 130 A at 75°C. The derated conductor ampacity is $(0.7)(0.94)(130 \text{ A}) = 85.5 \text{ A}$. The next-higher-standard-rated device is permitted, which results in an overcurrent device with a 90 A rating. This is large enough to supply the load as required in Step 2.

Summary: 90 A overcurrent device, #1 AWG THW copper conductor.

EXAMPLE 6–17

Repeat Example 6–16 using THHN (90°C insulation rating) insulated copper conductor.

Solution:

Step 1. Determine the design load current based on 125% of the continuous load plus 100% of the noncontinuous load:

$$\text{Design load current: } (1.25)(70 \text{ A}) = 87.5 \text{ A}$$

Step 2. Determine the minimum overcurrent device rating required based on the design load current:

$$\text{Overcurrent device rating} = 90 \text{ A}$$

Step 3. Determine the minimum required conductor size based on the design load current. The minimum required conductor size must be taken from the 60°C column since the device is rated less than 100 A. Therefore, a #2 AWG THHN copper conductor with a 60°C ampacity of 95 A is specified as the required minimum.

Step 4. The ambient temperature correction factor is 0.96, and the raceway fill adjustment factor is 0.7. Application of Equation (6–11) results in

$$\text{Minimum table-listed ampacity} = \frac{70 \text{ A}}{(0.7)(0.96)} = 104.2 \text{ A}$$

Therefore, a #3 AWG THHN copper conductor, having a table-listed ampacity at 90°C of 110 A, is required based on this criterion. The derated conductor ampacity is equal to $(0.7)(0.96)(110 \text{ A}) = 74 \text{ A}$.

Step 5. Compare the conductor sizes in Steps 3 and 4.

Conductor size from Step 3 = #2 AWG THHN
Conductor size from Step 4 = #3 AWG THHN

Therefore, a #2 AWG THHN copper conductor having a table-listed 90°C ampacity of 130 A is required for this load condition. The derated ampacity of the #2 THHN copper conductor is $(0.7)(0.96)(130 \text{ A}) = 87.4 \text{ A}$.

Step 6. Determine the maximum rating of the overcurrent device permitted based on the final selection of conductor size from Step 5. The maximum rating so selected must also be high enough to supply 125% of the continuous load plus 100% of the noncontinuous load. From Step 2, the minimum overcurrent device rating permitted is 90 A as required to supply the load. Also, the derated ampacity of the #2 AWG THHN copper conductor is 87.4 A from Step 5. Based on this, the maximum over-current device rating permitted would be 90 A since this is a dedicated feeder and rounding up to the next-higher-standard rating is permitted.

Summary: 90 A overcurrent device, #2 AWG THHN copper conductor.

6–8   PARALLEL CONDUCTORS

Due to reasons of economics and installation considerations, the largest-size conductor is limited to 500 kcmil copper for most electrical power distribution systems. Cables larger than 500 kcmil become difficult to install. In addition, the ampacity rating of conductors larger than 500 kcmil does not increase in direct proportion to the conductor size. For example, the table-listed ampacity of a 500 kcmil copper conductor is 380 A; the table-listed ampacity of a 2000 kcmil copper conductor is 665 A. Thus, even though the 2000 kcmil conductor has 4 times the cross-sectional area as the 500 kcmil conductor, its ampacity is only $1\frac{1}{3}$ times as large. This is due to the fact that heat dissipation is more limited with the larger-size conductor, since the outside conductor surface area does not increase in the same proportion as the cross-sectional area. Another factor is that the current density in a conductor is not uniform across the cross section of the conductor. This phenomenon is referred to as *skin effect* in a conductor. Skin effect increases with an increase in frequency. The current density in the conductor tends to be higher toward the outer surface of the conductor. This results in higher power losses, with a corresponding increase in temperature.

A feeder circuit using 500 kcmil copper conductor would generally be protected by a 400 A overcurrent device, based on the table-listed ampacity. For feeders or services rated at more than 400 A, it is common practice to use parallel conductors as a practical means of supplying higher-ampere-rated feeders. For example, an 800 A feeder might have two or three conductors per phase and neutral. Paralleling of conductors involves making a physical electrical connection in each set of conductors at each end, as shown in Figure 6–8. For example, all conductors comprising phase A would be connected at each end, all phase B conductors at each end, and so on. Typically, the physical connection is made at the termination to the circuit breaker, fuseblock, or panelboard terminal lugs, as shown.

The rules for parallel installation of conductors are stated in Section 310.4 of the *NEC* and are designed to produce an even division of current in the conductors. Generally, conductors must have the same insulation type, temperature rating, conductor material, size, and length. The conductors must be terminated in the same manner. The raceway or conduit system must also be the same for each set of conductors. Also, parallel conductors must be #1/0 or larger.

FIGURE 6–8
Parallel Conductors

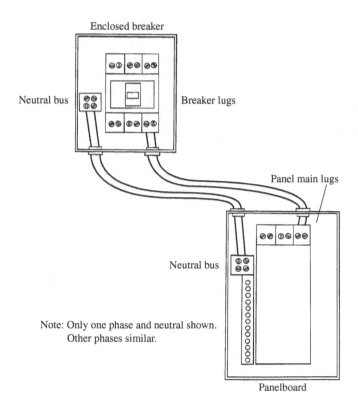

In addition to the requirements just stipulated, the parallel conductors must be grouped to minimize the effect of inductive heating. Inductive heating is the result of an alternating magnetic flux being induced in the wall of the conduit. Consider the example shown in Figure 6–9(A). This figure shows a single conductor carrying alternating current routed in a steel conduit. Recall that current flowing in an electrical conductor produces a magnetic flux around the conductor. This flux will be confined primarily to the conduit wall, since the conduit wall is a good magnetic conductor. The alternating flux produces hysteresis and eddy current losses in the conduit wall, much the same as in a transformer core. These losses are dissipated in the form of heat, resulting in heating of the raceway system itself.

To minimize inductive heating, magnetic flux must be cancelled or reduced. Consider the system in which two currents of equal magnitude but 180° phase displacement are flowing, as shown in Figure 6–9(B). The current flowing in each conductor does produce a magnetic flux as in the previous example; however, since the two currents are equal and opposite, the flux cancels out, thereby minimizing inductive heating effects.

For three-phase circuits, the conductors must be arranged as shown in Figure 6–9(C). Note that the conduit will contain a phase conductor from each phase and a neutral

FIGURE 6–9
Routing of Parallel Conductors to Minimize
Inductive Heating Effects

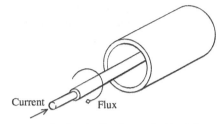

A. Single Conductor in Conduit

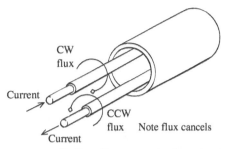

B. Two Conductors in Conduit with
Current Equal and Opposite

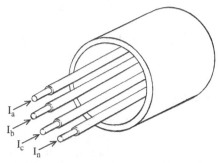

C. Three-Phase Conductors and Neutral

conductor. The currents that flow are generally assumed to be balanced, having the same magnitude and 120° phase displacement. Any unbalanced current is returned through the neutral. The net result is that the magnetic flux is again canceled out, minimizing inductive heating of the conduit. Figure 6–10 shows the terminal connections of a 1000 A breaker supplying a feeder comprised of three 400 kcmil THW copper conductors per phase and neutral.

The ampacity of the feeder conductors supplying a parallel circuit is determined in much the same way as for the single conductors in the previous sections. The total load

FIGURE 6–10
Terminal Connections of Parallel Feeder
Conductors

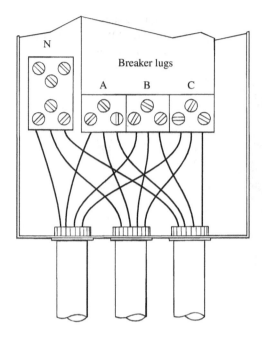

current to be supplied is divided by the number of anticipated parallel conductors per
phase. The ambient temperature correction factors and raceway fill adjustment factors are
applied as required. Device terminal temperature limitations are based on the size of each
conductor per phase. The following examples illustrate the procedure.

EXAMPLE 6–18

Determine the required THW copper conductor size and overcurrent device rating to supply a three-phase, four-wire feeder supplying a 500 A noncontinuous linear load. The
ambient temperature is 30°C.

Solution: Since this is a noncontinuous load, the design load current is equal to 500 A. If
a single conductor were used to supply this load, a 900 kcmil THW conductor would be
required. A conductor this large would be very difficult to install. In fact, it is unlikely that
the breaker or fuseblock lugs would accommodate such a large conductor. If two conductors per phase are used, the design would have to be based on 500 A ÷ 2 = 250 A per
conductor. The previous six-step procedure can now be used to determine the conductor
size.

Step 1. Design load current = (1.0)(500 A) = 500 A.

Step 2. Minimum overcurrent device rating = 500 A.

Step 3. Minimum conductor size based on 500 A ÷ 2 = 250 A per conductor. The minimum conductor size is 250 kcmil THW copper, having an ampacity of 255 A as taken from the 75°C column of Table 310–16.

Step 4. Since this is a linear load, the neutral will not be counted as a current-carrying conductor. Therefore, each conduit will contain three current-carrying conductors. There is no need to apply a raceway fill adjustment factor in this case. Also, since the specified ambient temperature is given as 30°C, there is no need to apply an ambient temperature correction factor in this situation. Since the minimum required table-listed ampacity was determined to be 250 A, a 250 kcmil THW copper conductor having a table-listed ampacity of 255 A is initially selected for this application.

Step 5. Conductor size from Step 3 = 250 kcmil THW
Conductor size from Step 4 = 250 kcmil THW

Step 6. The overcurrent device rating is based on the ampacity per conductor multiplied by the number of conductors per phase. In this case, the result is (2)(255 A) = 510 A. Note that since the overcurrent device rating does not exceed 800 A, rounding up to the next-higher-rated device would be permitted. However, in this case, a 500 A breaker would be appropriate.

Summary: 500 A overcurrent device, two 250 kcmil THW copper conductors per phase.

EXAMPLE 6–19

Determine the required THW copper conductor size and overcurrent device rating to supply a three-phase, four-wire feeder supplying a 700 A continuous nonlinear load. The ambient temperature is 35°C.

Solution: Since this is a continuous load, the factor of 125% must be applied. This results in a design load current of (1.25)(700 A) = 875 A. If two conductors per phase are used, the design would have to be based on (875 A) ÷ 2 = 437.5 A per conductor. This exceeds the maximum rating permitted for the 500 kcmil copper wire size. If three conductors per phase are used, the design would be based on 291.7 A per conductor. The previous six-step procedure can now be used to determine the conductor size.

Step 1. Design load current = (1.25)(700 A) = 875 A.

Step 2. Minimum overcurrent device rating = 1000 A.

Step 3. Minimum conductor size based on 875 A ÷ 3 = 291.7 A per conductor. The minimum conductor size is 350 kcmil THW copper, having an ampacity of 310 A as taken from the 75°C column of Table 310–16.

Step 4. Since this is a nonlinear load, the neutral must be counted as a current-carrying conductor. Therefore, each conduit will contain four current-carrying conductors—three phase wires and the neutral. The raceway fill adjustment factor is

0.8, and the ambient temperature correction factor is 0.94. Also, each conductor is expected to carry 700 A ÷ 3 = 233 A. From Equation (6–11) the minimum table-listed ampacity is

$$\text{Minimum table-listed ampacity} = \frac{233 \text{ A}}{(0.8)(0.94)} = 310 \text{ A}$$

Therefore, a 350 kcmil THW copper conductor having a table-listed ampacity of 310 A would be required to meet this criterion. The derated conductor ampacity is (310A) × (0.8) × (0.94) = 233.1 A.

Step 5. Conductor size from Step 3 = 350 kcmil THW
Conductor size from Step 4 = 350 kcmil THW

Step 6. The overcurrent device rating is based on the ampacity per conductor multiplied by the number of conductors per phase. In this case, the result is (3)(233.1 A) = 699.3 A. Note that since the minimum required overcurrent device rating (1000 A from Step 2) exceeds 800 A, rounding up to the next-higher-rated device is not permitted. Thus, the 350 kcmil conductor is not large enough to allow protection by the 1000 A OCPD required from Step 2.

To allow use of a 1000 A OCPD rating required to supply the load, the next-larger-size conductor must be selected. A 400 kcmil THW copper conductor has a table-listed ampacity of 335 A, as taken from the 75°C column of Table 310.16. The derated ampacity is (0.8)(0.94)(335 A) = 252 A. The resulting circuit ampacity, including all three conductors per phase, is (3)(252 A) = 756 A. Based on the derated conductor ampacity of 756 A, a maximum rating of 800 A would be permitted. This is less than the required 1000 A minimum rating as determined from Step 2. Selection of the next-larger-size conductor is required.

The next-larger conductor size is 500 kcmil, having a listed ampacity of 380 A as taken from the 75°C column of Table 310.16. The derated ampacity is (0.8)(0.94)(380 A) = 285.8 A. The resulting circuit ampacity including all three conductors per phase is (3)(285.8 A) = 857.3 A. Note that the use of 500 kcmil conductor size is still not adequate for the application.

To avoid the use of a conductor size larger than 500 kcmil, consideration will be given to the use of four conductors in parallel per phase. Based on a design load of 875 A and four conductors per phase, the current per conductor is based on 875 ÷ 4 = 219 A per conductor.

The six step procedure is repeated.

Step 1. Design load current = (1.25)(700 A) = 875 A.

Step 2. Minimum overcurrent device rating = 1000 A.

Step 3. Minimum conductor size based on 875 A ÷ 4 = 219 A per conductor. The minimum conductor size is #4/0 AWG THW copper, having an ampacity of 230 A as taken from the 75°C column of Table 310.16.

Step 4. Since this is a nonlinear load, the neutral must be counted as a current-carrying conductor. Therefore, each conduit will contain four current-carrying conductors—three-phase wires and the neutral. The raceway fill adjustment factor is 0.8, and the ambient temperature correction factor is 0.94. Also, each conductor is expected to carry 700 A ÷ 4 = 175 A. From Equation (6–11) the minimum table-listed ampacity is

$$\text{Minimum table-listed ampacity} = \frac{175 \text{ A}}{(0.8)(0.94)} = 232.7 \text{ A}$$

Therefore, a 250 kcmil THW copper conductor, having a table-listed ampacity of 255 A, would be required to meet this criterion. The derated conductor ampacity is (255A) × (0.8) × (0.94) = 191.8 A.

Step 5. Conductor size from Step 3 = #4/0 AWG THW
Conductor size from Step 4 = 250 kcmil THW

Step 6. The overcurrent device rating is based on the ampacity per conductor multiplied by the number of conductors per phase. In this case, the result is (4)(191.8 A) = 767.2 A. Note that since the minimum required overcurrent device rating (1000 A from Step 2) exceeds 800 A, rounding up to the next-higher-rated device is not permitted. Thus, the 250 kcmil conductor is not large enough to allow protection by the 1000 A OCPD required from Step 2.

To allow use of a 1000 A OCPD rating required to supply the load, the next-larger-size conductor must be selected. A 300 kcmil THW copper conductor has a table-listed ampacity of 285 A, as taken from the 75°C column of Table 310.16. The derated ampacity is (0.8)(0.94)(285 A) = 214.3 A. The resulting circuit ampacity, including all four conductors per phase, is (4)(214.3 A) = 857.3 A. Based on the derated conductor ampacity of 857.3 A, a maximum rating of 800 A would be permitted. This is less than the required 1000 A minimum rating as determined from Step 2. Selection of the next-larger-size conductor is again required.

A 350 kcmil THW copper conductor has a table-listed ampacity of 310 A, as taken from the 75°C column of Table 310–16. The derated ampacity is (0.8)(0.94)(310 A) = 233.1 A. The resulting circuit ampacity, including all four conductors per phase, is (4)(233.1 A) = 932.5 A. Based on the derated conductor ampacity of 932.5 A, a maximum rating of 800 A would be permitted. Selection of the next-larger-size conductor is again required.

A 400 kcmil THW copper conductor has a table-listed ampacity of 335 A, as taken from the 75°C column of Table 310.16. The derated ampacity is (0.8)(0.94)(335 A) = 251.9 A. The resulting circuit ampacity, including all four conductors per phase, is (4)(251.9 A) = 1007.7 A. Based on the derated conductor ampacity of 1007.7 A, a 1000 A OCPD would be permitted. Note: It is necessary to check on the breaker lug specifications to determine if four conductors per phase can be terminated.

Summary: 1000 A overcurrent device, four 400 kcmil THW copper conductors per phase.

PROBLEMS

1. Determine the resistance at 25°C of a copper conductor 175 feet in length, having a diameter of 0.5 in.

2. Repeat Problem 1 for an aluminum conductor.

3. Determine the resistance at 50°C for the conductor of Problem 1.

4. Determine the resistance at 50°C for the conductor of Problem 2.

5. Define *single-conductor cable.*

6. Define *multiconductor cable.*

7. Describe the construction of type AC cable and list typical applications.

8. Describe the construction of type MC cable and list typical applications.

9. Describe the construction of type NM cable and list typical applications.

10. How does UF cable differ from type NM cable?

11. What is the common designation for a service entrance cable?

12. How does THW insulation differ from THW-2?

13. What does the designator XHHW refer to?

14. What is the table-listed ampacity of a #3 AWG THW copper conductor in a raceway containing no more than three current-carrying conductors, 30°C, dry location?

15. What is the table-listed ampacity of a single #3 AWG THW copper conductor in free air?

16. What is the table-listed ampacity of a #2/0 AWG THHN copper conductor in a raceway containing no more than three current-carrying conductors, 30°C, wet location?

17. What is the table-listed ampacity of a #1 AWG THW copper conductor in a raceway containing no more than three current-carrying conductors, 40°C, dry location?

18. What is the ampacity of a #2 AWG THW copper conductor in a raceway containing four current-carrying conductors, 30°C, dry location?

19. What is the ampacity of a #2 AWG THW copper conductor in a raceway containing four current-carrying conductors, 40°C, dry location?

20. Specify all conditions in which the grounded conductor must be considered a current-carrying conductor for the purposes of ampacity adjustment.

21. What is the maximum allowable ampacity of a #2/0 AWG THHN copper conductor connected to a breaker having 75°C terminal ratings?

22. What is the maximum allowable ampacity of a #2 AWG THHN copper conductor connected to a breaker having 60°C terminal ratings?

23. A three-phase, nonlinear load is to be supplied by a #4 AWG THW-2 copper conductor. The ambient temperature is 37°C. Determine the maximum allowable ampacity for the conductor, taking into account raceway fill, ambient temperature, and device terminal temperature limitations.

24. Determine the required-size THW copper conductor and overcurrent device rating required for a dedicated feeder supplying a 250 A noncontinuous linear load. Assume an ambient temperature of 30°C.

25. Determine the required THW-2 copper conductor to supply a nonlinear, three-phase load of 145 A with a three-phase, four-wire circuit in an ambient temperature of 35°C. Remember to take into account raceway fill, ambient temperature, and device terminal temperature limitations.

26. Determine the required-size THW copper conductor and overcurrent device rating required for a dedicated feeder supplying an 85 A noncontinuous linear load. Assume an ambient temperature of 30°C.

27. Determine the required-size THW copper conductor and overcurrent device rating required for a dedicated feeder supplying an 85 A continuous nonlinear load. Assume an ambient temperature of 37°C.

28. Repeat Problem 26 using a THHN copper conductor.

29. How is inductive heating minimized when routing parallel conductors in multiple raceways?

30. Determine the required-size THW copper conductor and overcurrent device rating required for a dedicated feeder supplying a 600 A continuous linear load. Assume an ambient temperature of 30°C. Do not exceed a 600 kcmil conductor size.

7

Branch Circuit and Feeder Design

INTRODUCTION

An important aspect of electrical system design involves the design of branch circuits and feeders to supply the electrical loads in a given occupancy. The design information regarding branch circuit and feeder layout is often conveyed in the form of cabling diagrams. These diagrams present the design information to the electrical contractor, who will be responsible for the installation of the electrical system components. Cabling diagrams thus are an important communication tool between the designer and the electrician. In addition, these diagrams are part of the legal contract document package for a given project. To properly develop a cabling diagram, it is necessary to understand the *NEC* rules pertaining to receptacle location, lighting outlet location, switching requirements, receptacle loading, and so forth.

OBJECTIVES

Upon completion of this chapter, you will:

- Understand requirements for receptacle outlet ratings
- Understand requirements for receptacle location
- Understand requirements for lighting outlet location
- Understand lighting outlet switching requirements
- Understand requirements for ground fault circuit protection
- Understand arc fault circuit interruption
- Understand branch circuit and receptacle loading
- Be able to determine branch circuit requirements for a given occupancy
- Be able to develop cabling diagrams

7-1   BRANCH CIRCUIT OUTLET DEVICE RATINGS

Section 210.21(B) of the *NEC* specifies the receptacle ratings permitted on individual and multioutlet branch circuits. A single receptacle supplied by an individual branch circuit must have a rating greater than or equal to the overcurrent device rating. For the purpose of this discussion, a single receptacle is a device that will allow for the cord and plug connection of one piece of equipment. An individual branch circuit is a branch circuit that supplies a single device. For example, a 20 A single receptacle would typically be connected to a 20 A individual branch circuit. Likewise, a 15 A single receptacle would typically be supplied by a 15 A individual branch circuit. It would be a violation to connect a 15 A single receptacle to a 20 A individual branch circuit. These requirements are shown in Figure 7–1(A).

Where two or more receptacles are to be connected to a 15 A multioutlet branch circuit, the maximum permitted receptacle rating is 15 A. Recall that a multioutlet branch circuit is a circuit supplying two or more outlets. If two or more receptacles are to be connected to a 20 A multioutlet branch circuit, the receptacles may be rated 15 A or 20 A. It is common in residential applications to have 15 A duplex receptacles connected to a 20 A multioutlet branch circuit. However, in most commercial, industrial, and institutional applications, receptacles rated 20 A are typically specified for connection to 20 A multioutlet branch circuits. The requirements for receptacle outlets connected to a 15 A or a 20 A multioutlet branch circuit are shown in Figure 7–1(B).

In addition, Section 210.21(B)(3) of the *NEC* applies in situations where two or more receptacles are connected to a branch circuit rated more than 20 A:

 30 A multioutlet branch circuit: 30 A receptacle rating
 40 A multioutlet branch circuit: 40 A or 50 A receptacle rating
 50 A multioutlet branch circuit: 50 A receptacle rating

For branch circuits rated greater than 50 A, the receptacle rating must be equal to or greater than the branch circuit rating.

FIGURE 7–1
Branch Circuit Receptacle Ratings

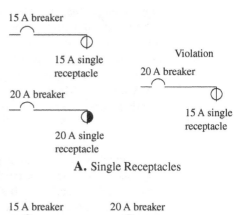

A. Single Receptacles

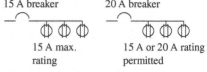

B. Multiple Receptacles

7–2   RECEPTACLE AND CIRCUIT LOADING

As specified in Table 210.21(B)(2) of the *NEC,* the maximum load permitted on a 15 A, 20 A, or 30 A receptacle is limited to 80% of the receptacle rating. This applies to 15 A, 20 A, and 30 A receptacles connected to a multioutlet branch circuit. Therefore, the maximum loading permitted is 12 A, 16 A, and 24 A, respectively. In addition, it is good design practice to limit the maximum load on 40 A and 50 A receptacles to 80% of their rating as well.

In accordance with Section 210.23(A)(1) of the *NEC,* the maximum rating of any one cord-and-plug-connected equipment supplied by a 15 A or 20 A branch circuit shall not exceed 80% of the branch circuit rating. Also, Section 210.23(A)(2) of the *NEC* specifies that the maximum rating of a single fastened-in-place piece of equipment shall not exceed 50% of the branch circuit rating if other equipment is connected to the circuit. The purpose of this requirement is to prevent a single piece of equipment from taking up too much of the circuit capacity. Also, the requirement of this section does not apply to lighting fixtures, which technically are considered to be fastened in place. Examples of other fastened-in-place equipment include wall-mounted water coolers, overhead door operators, and sump pumps. Note that even though this equipment is cord and plug connected, it is physically fastened in place.

EXAMPLE 7–1

An overhead door operator having a full-load current rating of 9.0 A is to be supplied from a multioutlet branch circuit in a residence. Determine the minimum branch circuit rating required to serve this equipment.

Solution: The overhead door operator is considered to be fastened in place. The maximum load for fastened-in-place equipment cannot exceed 50% of the branch circuit rating on a multioutlet circuit. The maximum rating of a single fastened-in-place piece of equipment connected to a 15 A circuit is 7.5 A (50% of 15 A). Likewise, the maximum rating of a single fastened-in-place piece of equipment connected to a 20 A circuit is 10 A. Therefore, a 20 A multioutlet branch circuit would be required in this case. Note that a 15 A individual branch circuit supplying a single receptacle may be used to supply the overhead door operator, although this is seldom done in practice.

In all occupancies, it is permissible to use 30 A, 40 A, or 50 A branch circuits to supply fastened-in-place, or cord-and-plug-connected equipment. In commercial and industrial locations, Sections 210.23(B) and 210.23(C) of the *NEC* permit the use of 30 A, 40 A, or 50 A branch circuits to supply lighting fixtures, provided the lampholders are of the heavy-duty type. A typical fluorescent lighting fixture does not have heavy-duty lampholders and therefore must be supplied from a 15 A or 20 A branch circuit. Fluorescent lighting fixtures installed for office lighting are commonly supplied by 20 A branch circuits. The maximum rating of any one piece of equipment connected to a 30 A branch circuit cannot exceed 80% of the circuit rating, or 24 A in this case. In any occupancy, only nonlighting loads may be supplied by branch circuits rated larger than 50 A. Again, it is good design practice to limit the load to 80% of the circuit rating.

7–3   REQUIRED RECEPTACLE LOCATIONS

Sections 210.52 through 210.63 of the *NEC* list the requirements for receptacle location. These sections apply to 125 V, 15 A and 20 A receptacle outlets required for cord-and-plug-connected equipment. Section 210.52 applies to residences, Section 210.60 to guest rooms in hotels and motels, Section 210.62 to show windows, and Section 210.63 to HVAC equipment. Although the *NEC* does stipulate the minimum required receptacle locations, good design will often dictate placing receptacles at other locations as well. The designer must use common sense and logic when determining receptacle location. In particular, the designer must develop an appreciation for the intended use of the room, furniture layout, and so on to properly locate receptacles. The requirements of Sections 210.52 through 210.63 of the *NEC* are summarized next:

- Section 210.52 (A)(1) states that in residences, a receptacle is to be installed in every habitable room, so that no point along the wall is more than 6 ft from a receptacle. Generally, this means that the receptacles are spaced no more than 12 ft apart. A habitable room does not include unfinished basement areas, porches, garages, and so forth. Section 210.52(A)(2) defines a wall space to include any wall that is 2 ft or more in width unbroken by doorways or other openings. The distance along the wall space is measured around corners and includes any fixed panels, room dividers, and counters. These requirements are shown in Figure 7–2.

FIGURE 7–2
Receptacle Location Requirements—
General

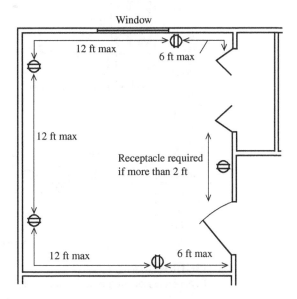

- Section 210.52(C)(1) states that in kitchen and dining room areas, receptacles are to be located on countertops along the wall or backsplash so that no point along the countertop is more than 2 ft from a receptacle. Therefore, the receptacle outlets must be spaced no more than 4 ft apart along the wall above the countertop. This provision applies to any unbroken countertop space 12 in. or more in length. Sections 210.52(C)(2) and 210.52(C)(3) require a receptacle to be installed at each island countertop and peninsula countertop more than 24 in. in length and 12 in. or more in width. Section 210.52(C)(5) specifies that where a wall or back-splash is available, the receptacle must be located no more than 20 in. above the countertop. It is permissible to mount the receptacle no more than 12 in. below the countertop where the construction is designed for the physically impaired or for island or peninsula countertops where no backsplash is available. It is not permissible to mount the receptacles in the work surface in a face-up position. These requirements for receptacle locations in kitchen and dining areas are shown in Figure 7–3. Note that the receptacles in the dinette area are to be located in accordance with the requirements for habitable living space as previously discussed.

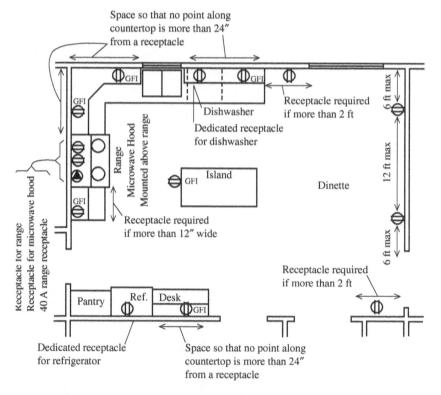

FIGURE 7–3
Receptacle Location Requirements—Kitchen and Dining Areas

Also, note that receptacle outlets are located to serve the island countertop. Dedicated receptacles are located behind the refrigerator and gas range and in the wall cabinet above the range to supply the microwave hood. Dedicated receptacles or junction boxes would also be installed to supply the dishwasher and garbage disposal. A 40 A receptacle outlet is shown to supply an electric range, if one is to be installed.

■ Section 210.52(D) requires a minimum of one receptacle to be installed in bathrooms within 36 in. of the washbasin. This receptacle is typically mounted in the wall space above the countertop. As with kitchen countertop receptacles, it is not permissible to mount this receptacle in the face-up position in the countertop.

■ Section 210.52(E) requires a minimum of one outdoor receptacle in the front and one in the back of a dwelling unit. These receptacles cannot be mounted more than 6½ ft above grade.

■ Section 210.52(F) requires at least one receptacle to supply laundry equipment. At least one receptacle in addition to the laundry receptacle is required in unfinished basements and garages. Therefore, at least two receptacles are required in unfinished basements containing laundry equipment, one for the laundry equipment itself and at least one other, general-purpose receptacle outlet.

■ Section 210.52(G) requires a receptacle to be located for general-purpose use in garages.

■ Section 210.52(H) requires a receptacle to be installed in hallways more than 10 ft in length. The length of a hallway is determined along the centerline of the hallway and includes any corners without passing through a doorway. Spacing of receptacles in hallways is not specifically addressed. Good design is 12 ft maximum spacing between receptacles in residential hallways and 25 ft between receptacles in commercial spaces.

■ Section 210.63 requires a 125 V, 15 A or 20 A receptacle to be located within 25 ft of any HVAC equipment that may require servicing. This includes HVAC equipment located in attics and in crawl spaces of residential occupancies. In addition, a 125 V, 15 A or 20 A receptacle is required to be located within 25 ft of rooftop equipment in other than one- and two-family residences.

■ In other than residential areas, particularly office spaces, it is good practice to locate receptacles so that no point along the wall is more than 6 ft from a receptacle. This spacing will allow for satisfactory supply of office equipment, computers, and so on. In commercial and industrial manufacturing areas, it is good practice to locate receptacles within 25 ft of any industrial equipment requiring service. This will provide a convenient location to connect portable power tools and supplemental lighting necessary to perform various maintenance activities.

7–4   REQUIRED LIGHTING OUTLETS

Section 210.70 of the *NEC* lists the requirements for lighting outlets. As with receptacle location requirements, the *NEC* can be used as a starting point to determine the required lighting outlet locations and switching arrangements. The actual design is one that will meet the *NEC* minimum requirements and provide an acceptable lighting arrangement. The design of lighting systems for commercial and industrial facilities is covered in a subsequent chapter. The following summarizes the *NEC* requirements for lighting outlets:

■ Section 210.70(A)(1) requires that at least one switched lighting outlet must be installed in every habitable room in residential occupancies. This lighting outlet is usually a ceiling-mounted light fixture. However, a switched receptacle may also be used in areas other than kitchens and bathrooms, which allows for the use of a table lamp connected to a switched receptacle. Figure 7–4(A) gives an example of

FIGURE 7–4
Switched Lighting Outlet Requirements

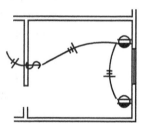

A. Switched Ceiling Lighting Outlets

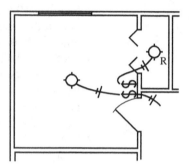

B. Switched Receptacle Outlets (Split-Wired)

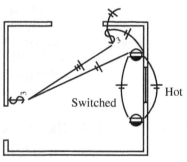

C. Split-Wired Receptacles Switched from Two Locations

a ceiling-mounted light fixture switched from one location. Note that one switch will control the fixture; the other switch controls the recessed fixture installed to provide illumination in the closet. Figure 7–4(B) gives an example of two split-wired receptacles controlled by a single switch. In this example, one of the receptacle outlets of a duplex receptacle is switched, while the other remains energized. A three-conductor cable is shown from the switch to the receptacles. One of the ungrounded conductors is switched, while the other remains hot to supply the receptacle outlets that are not switched. Figure 7–4(C) gives an example of two split-wired receptacles controlled by switches located at each entry point to the room. Note the separate cabling to supply the half of the receptacle outlets that are not switched. Wall switches would typically be located at each entry point to the room to control these fixtures, as shown in Figure 7–4(C).

■ Section 210.70(A)(2) requires at least one switched lighting outlet to provide illumination of hallways. Ceiling-mounted light fixtures are usually installed for this purpose. Wall switches for these lighting outlets are located at each end of the hallway and at other convenient points in between, which requires the use of three-way and four-way switches. An example of hallway lighting requirements is shown in Figure 7–5.

■ Section 210.70(A)(2) also requires at least one switched lighting outlet to provide illumination of stairways. Typically, ceiling-mounted fixtures are used. Wall-mounted switches to control these lighting fixtures must be located at each floor level for stairways consisting of more than six steps. Figure 7–6 shows an example of switched lighting requirements for stairways.

■ Section 210.70(A)(2) requires at least one switched lighting outlet in attached garages and detached garages where electrical power is available. Ceiling-mounted lighting fixtures are usually installed to meet this requirement. Wall-mounted switches to control these lighting fixtures are located at each entrance to such space. Other lighting fixtures may be of the pull-chain type if permitted.

■ Section 210.70(A)(2) requires a switched lighting outlet at all exterior entrances and exits. An exterior wall-mounted fixture would typically be installed to meet this requirement. A wall-mounted switch located inside at the point of exit is required to control this fixture. Additional switches may be installed at additional locations if desired.

FIGURE 7–5
Hallway Lighting Requirements

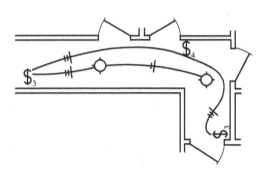

FIGURE 7–6

Stairway Lighting Requirements

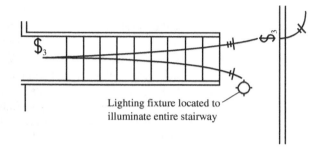

Lighting fixture located to
illuminate entire stairway

- Section 210.70(A)(3) requires a switched lighting outlet in basements, crawl spaces, attics, utility rooms, and so on used for storage. Ceiling-mounted fixtures would typically be installed to meet this requirement. At least one of these fixtures must be controlled by a wall-mounted switch located near the point of entry to such spaces. Other lighting fixtures may be of the pull-chain type if permitted.
- Section 210.70(C) requires switched lighting outlets near equipment requiring servicing in basements and garages. Ceiling-mounted fixtures would typically be installed to meet this requirement. At least one of these fixtures must be controlled by a wall-mounted switch located near the point of entry to the spaces containing this equipment.
- Section 210.70(C) requires a switched lighting outlet in attics and crawl spaces containing equipment that may require periodic servicing. Ceiling-mounted fixtures would typically be installed to meet this requirement. At least one of these fixtures must be controlled by a wall-mounted switch located near the point of entry to such spaces.
- Section 210.70(B) requires a switched lighting outlet in guest rooms of hotels. A ceiling-mounted fixture or switched receptacle would typically be installed to meet this requirement. A wall-mounted switch located at the entrance to the room would be installed to control these lighting outlets.
- Switched lighting is required in office spaces. Wall-mounted switches located at each entrance to the office space would be installed to control these lighting outlets. Supplemental task lighting located at each desk, table, or cubicle need not be switched at the point of entrance to the office space.

7–5   GROUND FAULT CIRCUIT INTERRUPTION REQUIREMENTS

Ground fault circuit interruption is required on 125 V, 15 A and 20 A receptacle outlets in certain locations as specified by Section 210.8 of the *NEC* to provide protection in the event of a ground fault. The locations are summarized next:

- Section 210.8(A)(1) applies to receptacles located in bathrooms.
- Section 210.8(A)(2) applies to receptacles located in garages. The exception to this rule is receptacles that are not readily accessible or receptacles installed to

supply a dedicated appliance. The exception generally applies to any appliance that is not easily moved, such as an overhead door operator, refrigerator, freezer, and so on. Ground fault protection is not recommended for receptacles supplying refrigerators or deep freezes since false tripping of the GFCI may occur during normal operation due to motor inrush current. It is important to note that this exception does not apply to receptacle locations in garages. Therefore, at least one GFCI-protected receptacle for general-purpose use is required in garage areas in addition to the dedicated or not readily accessible receptacle.

■ Section 210.8(A)(3) applies to receptacles located outdoors except for receptacles that are not readily accessible and supplied by a dedicated branch circuit for snow melting or other deicing equipment. Also, outdoor receptacles are required to be housed in a weatherproof enclosure.

■ Section 210.8(A)(4) applies to receptacles located in crawl spaces, at or below grade level.

■ Section 210.8(A)(5) applies to receptacles located in unfinished basements except for receptacles that are not readily accessible or receptacles installed to supply a dedicated appliance. The exception generally applies to any appliance that is not easily moved, such as a refrigerator, freezer, washer, dryer, sump pump, and so on. Note that if a receptacle is installed to supply a sump pump, washer, or dryer, GFCI is not required. Again, ground fault protection is not recommended for receptacles supplying refrigerators or deep freezes since false tripping of the GFCI may occur during normal operation due to motor inrush current. It is important to note that receptacle locations in unfinished basements are not covered by this exception. Therefore, at least one GFCI-protected receptacle for general-purpose use is required in unfinished basement areas in addition to the dedicated or not readily accessible receptacle.

■ Section 210.8(A)(6) applies to receptacles installed to serve kitchen countertops.

■ Section 210.8(A)(7) applies to receptacles installed to serve countertops within 6 ft of wet bar sinks

■ Section 210.8(B)(1) applies to receptacles installed in bathrooms of nonresidential occupancies.

■ Section 210.8(B)(2) applies to receptacles installed on rooftops of nonresidential occupancies. These receptacles are required to be housed in a weatherproof enclosure.

■ Section 210.8(B)(3) applies to receptacles installed in kitchen areas of nonresidential occupancies.

7–6   ARC FAULT CIRCUIT INTERRUPTION REQUIREMENTS

When an energized conductor comes in contact with another conductor or surface having a different electrical potential, an electrical arc will typically be established at the point of contact. This electrical arc will cause fault current to flow that contains harmonics due to the change in arc voltage and arc resistance. The resulting fault current waveform will not be sinusoidal, but will contain noise due to the arcing fault. Due to the high resistance of the arc, the actual fault current that flows may not be of sufficient magnitude to cause a standard circuit breaker to trip or fuse to blow. An arc fault circuit interrupter is a specially designed type of circuit breaker containing an electronic trip sensor that responds to the characteristics of the arc. This trip sensor will trip the breaker upon detection of a current waveform indicating the presence of an arcing fault, even if the rms current is below the trip rating of the breaker. Section 210.12(B) of the *NEC* requires arc fault circuit interruption of all 15 A and 20 A, 125 V, single-phase branch circuits supplying outlets in bedrooms of dwelling units.

7–7   DETERMINING THE NUMBER OF BRANCH CIRCUITS REQUIRED

Once the required receptacle and lighting outlets have been located, the branch circuiting of these outlets must be designed. Before proceeding to assign outlets to a specific branch circuit, it is necessary to determine the minimum number of branch circuits required to supply these outlets. The total number of branch circuits required includes the branch circuits supplying receptacle and lighting outlets for the general lighting load, small appliance branch circuits, the laundry branch circuit, the bathroom branch circuit, branch circuits supplying dedicated equipment loads, the outdoor receptacle branch circuit, and branch circuits supplying general-use receptacle outlets in unfinished areas. The actual number of branch circuits required will usually exceed the code minimum.

General Lighting

The minimum number of branch circuits required to supply the general lighting load is determined by using the unit load per square foot, as listed in Table 220.3(A) of the *NEC*. The unit lighting load is multiplied by the square foot area of the building unit to determine the total load to be served. Section 210.11(A) of the *NEC* requires that the minimum number of branch circuits required to supply a given occupancy must be determined before the application of any demand factors. The number of branch circuits required is determined by

$$\text{Minimum number of branch circuits} = \frac{\text{Total general lighting load (VA)}}{\text{Max. load per circuit (VA/circuit)}} \quad \textbf{(7–1)}$$

The maximum load per circuit is based on the rating of the branch circuit. Generally, for residential applications, 15 A or 20 A branch circuits may be used to supply the general lighting load. In commercial and industrial occupancies, 20 A branch circuits are generally used to supply the general lighting and receptacle loads. It is good design practice to limit the maximum load on a circuit to no more than 80% of the circuit rating. Therefore, the maximum load permitted on a 15 A circuit would be 12 A, and for a 20 A circuit the maximum load would be 16 A. These maximum ampere loadings correspond to $(120 \text{ V})(12 \text{ A}) = 1440 \text{ VA}$ for a 15 A circuit and $(120 \text{ V})(16 \text{ A}) = 1920 \text{ VA}$ for a 20 A circuit.

EXAMPLE 7–2

Determine the minimum number of branch circuits required to supply the general lighting load for the following occupancies:

a) 2200 sq ft residence, 15 A, 120 V circuits
b) 2200 sq ft residence, 20 A, 120 V circuits
c) 10,000 sq ft office, 20 A, 120 V circuits

Solution:

a) The unit load for general lighting is 3 VA per sq ft. The total general lighting load is (3 VA/sq ft)(2200 sq ft) = 6600 VA. The maximum VA loading for a 15 A circuit is 1440 VA. Therefore, the minimum required number of branch circuits for general lighting is

$$\text{Minimum number of branch circuits} = \frac{6600 \text{ VA}}{1440 \text{ VA/circuit}} = 4.6$$

Therefore, a minimum of five 15 A branch circuits would be required in this case.

b) Again, the unit load is 3 VA per sq ft, resulting in a total load of 6600 VA. The minimum number of branch circuits required is

$$\text{Minimum number of branch circuits} = \frac{6600 \text{ VA}}{1920 \text{ VA/circuit}} = 3.4$$

Therefore, a minimum of four 20 A circuits would be required.

c) The unit load is $3\frac{1}{2}$ VA per sq ft for general lighting plus 1 VA per sq ft for general-purpose receptacles. The total load is $(3\frac{1}{2}$ VA/sq ft $+$ 1 VA/sq ft)(10,000 sq ft) = 45,000 VA. The minimum number of branch circuits required is

$$\text{Minimum number of branch circuits} = \frac{45,000 \text{ VA}}{1920 \text{ VA/circuit}} = 23.4$$

Therefore, at least twenty-four 20 A branch circuits would be required.

An alternative approach is to determine the permitted maximum square foot area to be served by a branch circuit. This can be determined by dividing the maximum VA load permitted on a circuit by the unit load per square foot for the occupancy, as follows:

$$\text{Maximum sq ft per circuit} = \frac{\text{Maximum load per circuit (VA/circuit)}}{\text{Unit load (VA/sq ft)}} \qquad (7\text{–}2)$$

For example, in a residential occupancy, a 15 A 120 V circuit with a maximum load of 1440 VA would be permitted to supply (1440 VA/circuit)/ (3 VA/sq ft) = 480 sq ft of area. Likewise, a 20 A 120 V circuit would be permitted to supply a maximum of (1920 VA)/(3 VA/sq ft) = 640 sq ft of floor area. It is important to note that in some jurisdictions, limits are placed on the maximum allowable floor area to be served by a 15 A or 20 A circuit. For example, some jurisdictions require one 15 A 120 V circuit for every 300 sq ft of floor space or one 20 A 120 V circuit for every 500 sq ft of floor space.

Small Appliance Branch Circuits

Section 210.11(C)(1) of the *NEC* requires at least two 20 A branch circuits to supply the receptacle outlets in the kitchen, diningroom, pantry, and other similar areas of residential units. These circuits shall supply only receptacle outlets in these areas and may not extend to other areas of the dwelling. In addition, lighting outlets may not be connected to these small appliance branch circuits; separate circuits supplying only lighting outlets in these areas are required. It is generally good design practice to specify at least two 20 A circuits to supply the countertop receptacles only. Separate 20 A circuits are also recommended for the refrigerator, stove and microwave oven, dishwasher, garbage disposal, and other receptacle outlets in the kitchen and dining areas.

Laundry Circuit

Section 210.11(C)(2) of the *NEC* requires at least one 20 A branch circuit to supply the receptacles installed for laundry equipment. This circuit shall supply only the laundry receptacle outlets and no other outlets. It is not permissible to install lighting outlets on this circuit. Lighting outlets can be supplied from the branch circuit used for the general-purpose receptacle outlets in the area.

Bathroom Circuit

Section 210.11(C)(3) of the *NEC* requires at least one 20 A branch circuit to supply the receptacle outlets located in bathrooms, and this circuit may supply receptacle outlets in other bathrooms in the occupancy. If the circuit supplies receptacle outlets in more than one bathroom, then no other outlets, including lighting outlets, are permitted to be supplied from this circuit. However, if the circuit supplies a single bathroom, other outlets, including outlets for lighting and exhaust fans, located in the same bathroom are permitted to be supplied from this circuit. Thus it is possible to install a 20 A circuit to supply only the receptacle outlets in two bathrooms and perhaps a 15 A circuit to supply the lighting outlets in these two bathrooms. An alternative would be to install two 20 A circuits, one circuit to each bathroom, to supply receptacles, lighting, and other equipment in each bathroom.

Outdoor Receptacles

It is generally good design practice to supply the required outdoor receptacles from a separate branch circuit. This branch circuit may supply receptacles in the front and back of the residence. In some jurisdictions, a separate branch circuit may be required for outdoor receptacles.

General-Use Receptacles

General-use receptacles in unfinished areas such as basements and garages should be supplied from separate branch circuits. It is permissible to connect both lighting and receptacle outlets to these branch circuits, and it is common practice to do so. Generally, a separate branch circuit is used to supply the general-use receptacles and lighting outlets in the basement. Likewise, a separate branch circuit is usually installed to supply lighting and receptacles in the garage areas. In commercial and industrial occupancies, lighting and receptacle loads are usually kept on separate circuits.

Dedicated Equipment

As previously mentioned, separate 120 V branch circuits should be considered to supply the refrigerator, oven and microwave, garbage disposal, and other such equipment in the kitchen and dining areas of residential occupancies. In the basement, it is a good idea to supply the receptacles for cord-and-plug-connected sump pumps with a separate circuit. The furnace must be provided with a separate circuit. Essentially, a separate circuit should be considered for any large load even if it is not required by the *NEC*. Also, any 240 V equipment such as electric clothes dryers, electric hot water heaters, electric furnace, well pump, and so on must be supplied with its own dedicated circuit.

Maximum Number of Receptacles Permitted per Circuit

The *NEC* does not specifically limit the number of receptacle or lighting outlets permitted on 15 A or 20 A, 125 V branch circuits. The designer must determine based on experience and certain guidelines how many receptacle and lighting outlets can be connected to a circuit. Where the specific equipment rating is known, this value can be used to properly design the branch circuit. Where the specific equipment ratings are not available, a load of 180 VA can be assigned to each general-purpose receptacle mounted on a single strap. The maximum number of receptacles can then be determined by dividing the total permitted circuit load by 180 VA per receptacle. Recall that generally, the maximum load on a 125 V, 15 A branch circuit is 1440 VA, and for a 20 A branch circuit, 1920 VA. Thus, a maximum of eight outlets are permitted on a 15 A branch circuit, and a maximum of eleven on a 20 A branch circuit. Good design practice will limit this maximum number to no more than seven outlets on a 15 A circuit and no more than ten on a 20 A circuit.

In areas where heavier loads are anticipated, such as kitchen, dining, bathroom, and laundry areas, a higher load per receptacle may be assumed. For example, in the bathroom, a load of 1500 VA for a blow dryer is not unrealistic. Therefore, it is good practice to limit the number of outlets connected to the 20 A branch circuit supplying the bathroom to no more than three or four. For the laundry circuit, one duplex receptacle is usually installed to supply both a washer and a dryer. The small appliance branch circuits in the kitchen and dining areas are usually limited to four or five receptacles. The outdoor branch circuit is typically limited to two or three receptacles. The key point to remember is that a good design will provide for the connected load while being cost-effective.

7–8   MULTIWIRE BRANCH CIRCUITS

In some instances, it may be desirable to combine circuits into multiwire circuits to supply certain loads. By definition, a multiwire branch circuit is a circuit consisting of two or more ungrounded conductors and a grounded conductor. A 120 V or 277 V branch circuit consisting of a single ungrounded conductor and a grounded conductor is not considered a multiwire branch circuit. Likewise, a 208 V, 240 V, or 480 V branch circuit consisting of two ungrounded conductors is not considered a multiwire branch circuit. The voltage between each of the ungrounded conductors in a multiwire branch circuit is the same. Furthermore, the voltage between each ungrounded conductor and grounded conductor is also the same.

The loads in a multiwire branch circuit may be connected between the ungrounded conductors (line to line) or between the ungrounded and grounded conductors (line to neutral), with the grounded conductor used as a common connection to the loads. Only loads connected between the ungrounded and grounded conductors (line to neutral) are permitted unless a multipole breaker or single-pole breakers with a suitable handle tie are used. It is good design practice to specify a two-pole or three-pole breaker even if loads are only connected between the ungrounded and grounded conductors (line to neutral). Figure 7–7 shows examples of multiwire branch circuits.

The circuit shown in Figure 7–7(A) represents a multiwire branch circuit consisting of two ungrounded conductors and a grounded conductor. If supplied from a 120/240 V single-phase, three-wire system, the voltage between the ungrounded conductors is 240 V and the voltage between either ungrounded conductor and the grounded conductor is 120 V. For multiwire branch circuits supplied from a 208Y/120 V three-phase, four-wire

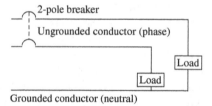

A. Two Single-Phase Loads Connected Between the
Ungrounded and Grounded Conductors (line to neutral)

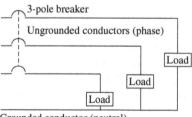

B. Three Single-Phase Loads Connected Between the
Ungrounded and Grounded Conductors (line to neutral)

FIGURE 7–7
Multiwire Branch Circuits

system, the voltage between the ungrounded conductors is 208 V and the voltage between either of the ungrounded conductors and the grounded conductors is 120 V. Lastly, for a multiwire branch circuit supplied from a 480Y/277 V three-phase, four-wire system, the voltage between the ungrounded conductors is 480 V and the voltage between either of the ungrounded conductors and the grounded conductors is 277 V. If the multiwire branch circuit as shown in Figure 7–7(A) is supplied from a three-phase, four-wire system, the current in the grounded conductor (neutral) will be approximately equal to the current flowing in the ungrounded conductor for balanced circuit load conditions. If supplied from a single-phase, three-wire system, the current in the grounded conductor is equal to the unbalanced current flowing to the loads, or zero for perfectly balanced load conditions.

The circuit shown in Figure 7–7(B) represents a multiwire circuit consisting of three ungrounded conductors and a grounded conductor. This multiwire circuit uses the grounded conductor as a common return for the load current and is typically supplied from a three-phase, four-wire, wye-connected system. If supplied from a three-phase, four-wire system, the current in the grounded conductor is equal to the unbalanced load current, provided only linear, nonharmonic-producing loads are supplied by the circuit. For perfectly balanced, nonharmonic-producing loads, the current in the grounded conductor is zero. If nonlinear, harmonic-producing loads, such as fluorescent lighting fixtures, are connected to a multiwire system, as shown in Figure 7–7(B), the resulting current in the grounded conductor can become significant and may even exceed the current in the ungrounded conductor.

For feeder circuits supplying lighting panelboards where the majority of lighting is fluorescent, it may be necessary to oversize the grounded conductor, which means that the grounded conductor will be larger in size than the ungrounded conductors. Several manufacturers of electrical equipment offer panelboards with provisions for termination of a neutral conductor rated at 200% for this purpose.

7–9   DEVELOPMENT OF CABLING DIAGRAMS

Typical information contained in a cabling diagram includes the physical location of receptacles and switches, switching arrangements for lighting and receptacle outlets, and the branch circuits to which these receptacle and lighting outlets are connected. The cabling connection between devices is usually shown on the drawing by a curved line. The actual branch circuit conductors may be nonmetallic sheathed cable, single conductor in conduit, or flexible metal conduit. Generally, cabling diagrams are used exclusively in residential and small commercial applications. For larger commercial, industrial, and institutional projects, the actual conduit system routing may be shown to scale in more detail. Often, a combination of cabling diagrams and conduit system layout is used in a project. It is also common in commercial, industrial, and institution design to separate all cabling diagrams for lighting from the cabling diagrams and conduit routing for receptacle and other power circuits. This prevents the drawings from becoming too cluttered.

The first step in developing a cabling diagram is to decide where to place receptacle and lighting outlets. This placement is done in accordance with *NEC* requirements and the functional requirements of the space, such as furniture layout, and so on. The location and rating of all known equipment must be determined, which is typically accomplished through discussions with the architectural and other engineering disciplines involved in the project. The branch circuit and switching requirements for all outlets are then developed, with dedicated branch circuits supplying all major equipment.

Figure 7–8 shows the completed cabling diagram for the bedroom area shown in Figures 7–2 and 7–4(A). Notice that this diagram shows the manner in which the receptacle and lighting outlets are connected to a particular branch circuit and that the lighting and receptacle outlets are placed on the same branch circuit. The switching of the lighting outlets for the bedroom and closet is also shown. Note that this branch circuit supplies the receptacle and lighting outlets in this bedroom only, although outlets in other areas may be supplied as well if permitted by the *NEC*. Some designers plan for at least two branch circuits to overlap coverage of a given area for reasons of reliability. If one branch circuit trips, there will be another available to supply power to the room.

The number of ungrounded conductors in the circuit is indicated by the number of short hash marks placed on the cable; the number of grounded conductors is indicated by the longer hash mark. The equipment grounding conductor may be designated by a long hash mark and the letter *G*. The home run arrow is used to indicate the connection back to the panelboard from the first device on the branch circuit. The branch circuit designation indicates which panel the branch circuit is supplied from as well as the number of the branch circuit within the panel. Designations such as LP-1, RP-1, and so on are used to indicate the panel and circuit number of the branch circuit. This circuit numbering information will be cross-referenced to the panel schedule, which will be discussed later.

FIGURE 7–8
Cabling Diagram of Bedroom Area

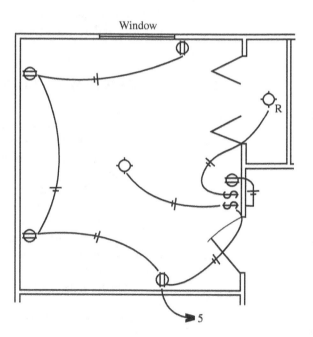

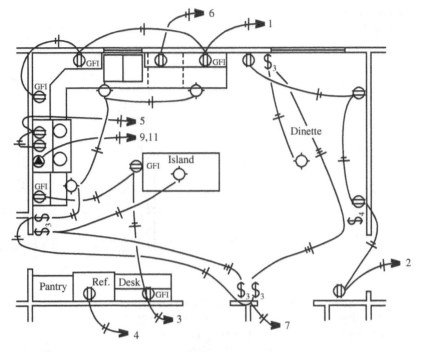

Note:
 - Circuit numbers shown next to home run arrows.
 - Circuit 9,11 is 240 V for electric range.
 - Separate lighting and receptacle circuits.

FIGURE 7–9
Cabling Diagram of Kitchen and Dining Area

The completed cabling diagram for the kitchen area shown in Figure 7–3 is shown in Figure 7–9. Note that the countertop receptacles are supplied by two branch circuits, as required by the *NEC*. There is also a separate circuit supplying the receptacle outlets in the dinette area. Receptacle outlets for the dishwasher, refrigerator, and range and microwave are also supplied from separate branch circuits. A 240 V, 40 A circuit is used to supply a 40 A receptacle to connect an electric range if desired. In accordance with the *NEC*, no lighting outlets are connected to any of the 120 V branch circuits supplying receptacle outlets in the kitchen and dining areas; these lighting outlets are supplied from a separate circuit and are switched as shown.

A cabling diagram for the bathroom is shown in Figure 7–10. All equipment in this bathroom is connected to the 120 V, 20 A branch circuit. Recall that it is permissible to connect other outlets to the bathroom circuit as long as the circuit supplies no other outlets on the premises.

A cabling diagram for a portion of the basement area is shown in Figure 7–11. A separate 240 V, 30 A individual branch circuit is provided for an electric clothes dryer. A

FIGURE 7–10
Cabling Diagram of Bathroom

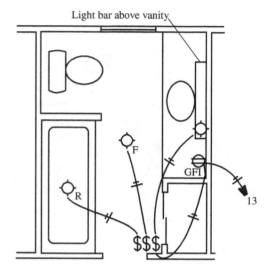

duplex receptacle is located between the washer and dryer and is connected to the dedicated laundry circuit, as required by the *NEC*. Note that lighting is not connected to the laundry circuit. The sump pump is supplied from a 125 V, 20 A single receptacle connected to an individual branch circuit. Since the receptacles supplying the laundry and sump pump are supplying dedicated equipment, GFI protection is not required. Note that an additional GFI-protected receptacle must be provided for general-purpose use, and the diagram shows a 125 V, 15 A GFI-protected receptacle. Lighting is permitted to be connected

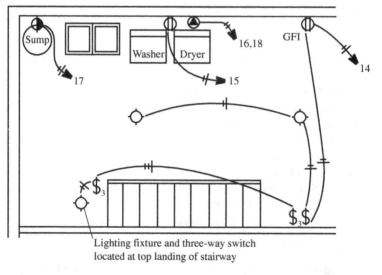

Lighting fixture and three-way switch
located at top landing of stairway

FIGURE 7–11
Cabling Diagram of Basement Area

to the circuit supplying the general-purpose receptacles. Note that the stairway lighting is switched from two levels, as required.

The cabling diagram for the garage area is shown in Figure 7–12. The lighting fixtures are located between the logical parking spot for each vehicle to provide the required illumination. These lighting outlets are switched from each entry into the garage. The outdoor lighting is switched from the side service door and from inside the residence. The outdoor lighting at the rear service door is switched from this service door only. The receptacle mounted in the ceiling is for the overhead door operator and does not require GFI protection. The other general-purpose receptacles must be GFI protected, as required by the *NEC*.

An example of a cabling diagram for a general office area is shown in Figure 7–13. Note that the lighting and receptacles are placed on separate circuits and supplied from separate panels. This is due to the fact that in most larger commercial and industrial occupancies, the lighting is 277 V, while the receptacles are 120 V. The switching arrangement of the lighting fixtures is also shown. Note that to give two levels of lighting there are two sets of switching for the fixtures. On some three- and four-lamp fluorescent fixtures, it is possible to switch the inner and outer lamps of a single fixture to accomplish the same effect. Note also that there is a key-operated switch controlling one of the fixtures to provide a night light for the area.

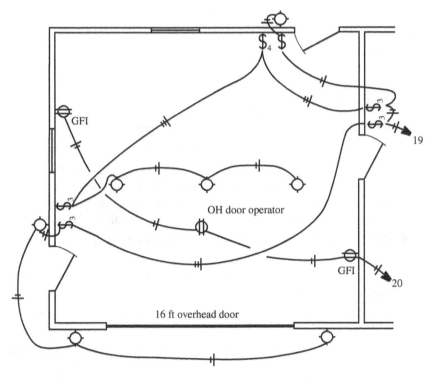

FIGURE 7–12
Cabling Diagram of Garage Area

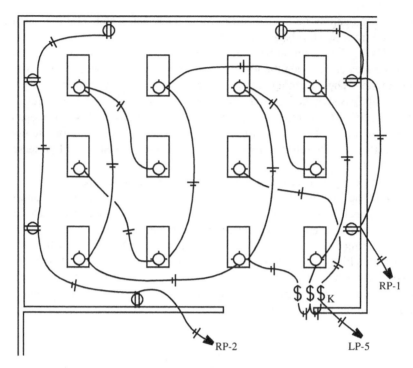

FIGURE 7–13
Cabling Diagram of Office Area

PROBLEMS

1. Is it permissible to connect a 15 A single receptacle to a 20 A individual branch circuit?

2. Is it permissible to connect 15 A duplex receptacles to a 20 A multioutlet branch circuit?

3. What is the maximum load permitted on a 15 A receptacle?

4. What is the maximum rating permitted for a fastened-in-place appliance connected to a 20 A circuit if there are other loads connected to the circuit as well?

5. State in your own words the required locations for receptacles in habitable rooms of dwelling units.

6. State in your own words the required locations for receptacles in kitchen and dining areas of dwelling units.

7. State in your own words the required locations for receptacles in bathrooms of dwelling units.

8. State in your own words the required locations for outdoor receptacles of dwelling units.

9. State in your own words the required locations for laundry area receptacles of dwelling units.

10. State in your own words the required locations for receptacles in hallways of dwelling units.

11. State in your own words the required locations for receptacles near equipment requiring servicing in dwelling units.

12. State in your own words the recommended locations for receptacles in commercial and industrial areas.

13. State in your own words the requirements for switched lighting outlets in habitable rooms of dwelling units.

14. State in your own words the requirements for switched lighting outlets in hallways.

15. State in your own words the requirements for switched lighting outlets to provide illumination of stairways.

16. State in your own words the requirements for switched lighting outlets in attached garages and detached garages.

17. State in your own words the requirements for switched lighting outlets near entrances to a building.

18. State in your own words the requirements for switched lighting outlets near equipment requiring servicing.

19. List the receptacle locations requiring ground fault circuit interruption protection.

20. Is GFCI protection required for basement receptacles supplying the laundry equipment?

21. Is GFCI protection required for basement receptacles supplying dedicated equipment or equipment not readily accessible?

22. Explain the operation of an arc fault circuit interruption device.

23. Determine the minimum number of 20 A circuits required to supply the general lighting load in a residence of 1750 sq ft.

24. How many small appliance branch circuits are required to supply receptacles in the kitchen and dining areas of residences? May lighting outlets be connected to these branch circuits? What is the required rating of these branch circuits?

25. What are the requirements for the laundry circuit in residences? Are lighting outlets permitted on the circuit supplying receptacle outlets in the laundry area?

26. What are the requirements for circuits supplying bathrooms in residences? Are lighting outlets permitted on the circuits supplying bathroom receptacles?

27. What is the maximum number of receptacles permitted on a 15 A 120 V branch circuit? A 20 A 120 V circuit?

28. In terms of good design practice, what is the maximum number of receptacles allowed on a general-purpose 15 A 120 V circuit? A 20 A 120 V circuit?

29. In terms of good design practice, what is the maximum number of receptacles allowed on a dedicated small appliance branch circuit?

30. Define *multiwire branch circuit.*

31. What information is contained in a cabling diagram?

32. List the steps necessary to develop a cabling diagram for a given occupancy.

8

Conduit and Raceway Systems

INTRODUCTION

Previous chapters have discussed the proper sizing of conductors, conductor insulation types, and the development of cabling diagrams. With the exception of nonmetallic sheathed cable, metal-clad, and armored cable, virtually all conductor and cable installations require the use of conduit, wireways, cable tray, or other raceway system to enclose, support, and protect the electrical power conductors. This chapter discusses some of the characteristics of the various types of wiring methods, sizing of the raceway system components, expansion characteristics of conduit, conduit fittings and support, and cable pulling calculations.

OBJECTIVES

Upon completion of this chapter, you will be able to:

- Properly size conduit
- Properly size device boxes
- Properly size pull and junction boxes
- Determine the thermal expansion of conduit
- Understand wiring and installation requirements
- Perform cable pulling calculations

8–1   CONDUIT TYPES

Electrical conduit is commonly used to enclose, support and protect electrical conductors for both power and control circuits. These electrical conduits are either metallic or nonmetallic in construction and have a circular cross section. In addition, the conduit may be rigid or flexible and may have an outer PVC covering for corrosion resistance or weatherproofing.

Rigid Metal Conduit

Rigid metal conduit (RMC) is a conduit having a circular cross section and the heaviest wall thickness of all metal conduit. Article 344 of the *NEC* discusses the requirements for rigid metal conduit installation and use. RMC is commonly available in either steel or aluminum construction, with trade sizes ranging from ½″ to 6″. The standard length of rigid conduit is 10 ft; it is threaded at both ends and supplied with one coupling per 10 ft length. A cutaway view of rigid metal conduit is shown in Figure 8–1(A).

For field installation, the conduit can be cut to length, reamed, and threaded as required. Field bending of the conduit is permitted as necessary, with minimum bending radius according to Table 344.24 of the *NEC,* as shown in Table 8–1. The minimum radius is measured from the centerline of the conduit. Table 344.24 lists the minimum radius for bends done with one-shot and full-shoe benders, as well as other bends. The bends must be made so as not to damage or kink the conduit or reduce the internal diameter of the conduit. Also, Section 344.26 of the *NEC* does not permit more than a total of 360° of bends between pull boxes or other conduit bodies.

For straight conduit runs where threaded couplings are used to connect the conduit, the support distance may be increased to the maximum distances shown in Table 344.30(B)(2) of the *NEC,* which is shown in Table 8–2. Other support requirements for RMC are discussed in Section 344.30 of the *NEC.* Note that in most instances, it is not desirable to connect rigid conduit directly to equipment, since vibration produced by the equipment will be transmitted to the conduit system.

The outer finish of rigid steel conduit is usually hot-dipped, galvanized for corrosion protection. In some instances, an enameled finish may be used for conduit installed indoors in noncorrosive environments only. Rigid steel conduit may be used in all applications and all environments, including direct encasement in concrete, direct burial, or

TABLE 8–1
Table 344.24 Radius of Conduit Bends

Conduit Size		One-Shot and Full-Shoe Benders		Other Bends	
Metric Designator	Trade Size	mm	in.	mm	in.
16	½	101.6	4	101.6	4
21	¾	114.3	4½	127	5
27	1	146.05	5¾	152.4	6
35	1¼	184.15	7¼	203.2	8
41	1½	209.55	8¼	254	10
53	2	241.3	9½	304.8	12
63	2½	266.7	10½	381	15
78	3	330.2	13	457.2	18
91	3½	381	15	533.4	21
103	4	406.4	16	609.6	24
129	5	609.6	24	762	30
155	6	762	30	914.4	36

Source: Reprinted with permission from NFPA 70 *The National Electric Code* © 2002, National Fire Protection Association, Quincy, MA 02269. This reprinted material is not the referenced subject which is represented only by the standard in its entirety.

FIGURE 8–1
Rigid and Intermediate Metal Conduit

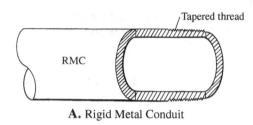

A. Rigid Metal Conduit

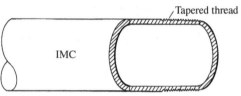

B. Intermediate Metallic Conduit

corrosive areas where suitably protected. Other permitted uses are given in Section 344.10 of the *NEC*. Figure 8–2 shows examples of rigid steel conduit and conduit sweeps.

Intermediate Metal Conduit

Intermediate metal conduit (IMC) is a rigid steel conduit having a circular cross section, available in trade sizes of ½″ to 4″. Article 342 of the *NEC* discusses the requirements for intermediate metal conduit installation and use. The wall thickness of intermediate metal conduit is less than that of rigid metal conduit, resulting in lighter weight. Similar to rigid

TABLE 8–2
Table 344.30(B)(2) Supports for Rigid Metal Conduit

Conduit Size		Maximum Distance Between Rigid Metal Conduit Supports	
Metric Designator	Trade Size	m	ft
16–21	½–¾	3.0	10
27	1	3.7	12
35–41	1¼–1½	4.3	14
53–63	2–2½	4.9	16
78 and larger	3 and larger	6.1	20

Source: Reprinted with permission from NFPA 70 *The National Electric Code* © 2002, National Fire Protection Association, Quincy, MA 02269. This reprinted material is not the referenced subject which is represented by the standard in its entirety.

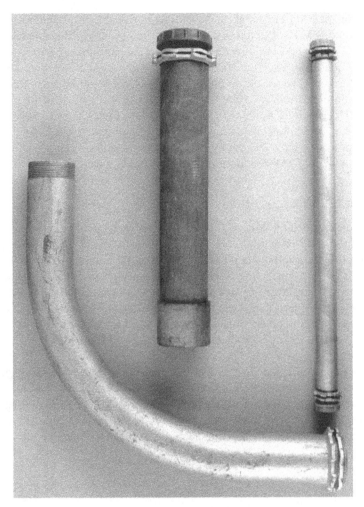

FIGURE 8–2
Rigid Steel Conduit and Conduit Sweeps

metal conduit, IMC may be cut to length, reamed, and threaded, as required in the field. The minimum bending radius, support, and permitted uses of IMC are the same as for rigid metal conduit. In accordance with Section 342.120 of the *NEC*, IMC conduit must be clearly identified at least every 5 ft along its length. A cutaway view of intermediate metal conduit is shown in Figure 8–1(B).

Electrical Metallic Tubing

Electrical metallic tubing, or EMT, is a conduit having a circular cross section, available in steel or aluminum construction in trade sizes ranging from ½″ to 4″. Article 358 of the *NEC* discusses the requirements for electrical metallic tubing installation and use. The outer finish on the EMT must make it clearly distinguishable from rigid metal conduit. The wall thickness of EMT is much less than that of rigid or intermediate metal conduit. EMT conduit is not permitted to be threaded in the field. The minimum bending radius for EMT is shown in Table 344.24 of the *NEC* under the one-shot and full-shoe benders column. Support requirements for EMT are given in Section 358.30 of the *NEC*. Permitted uses of EMT are given in Section 358.10 of the *NEC,* and uses not permitted are given in Section 358.12. EMT is generally used for indoor applications in dry, noncorrosive environments. A cutaway view of electrical metallic tubing is shown in Figure 8–3. Note that both a standard length of tubing and a length of tubing with an integral set-screw coupling are shown. Figure 8–4 shows an EMT conduit installation containing data cabling.

Rigid Nonmetallic Conduit

Rigid nonmetallic conduit, or RNC, is a conduit having a circular cross section that is typically constructed of polyvinyl chloride (PVC). Article 352 of the *NEC* discusses the requirements for its installation and use. The material used in the construction of the conduit must be moisture and chemical resistant. The standard length is 10 ft, including a coupling on one end of the conduit. The conduit may be field cut to the desired length, with the ends deburred and cleaned to prepare for joining. Threading of rigid nonmetallic conduit is not permitted. Conduit and conduit fittings are joined by applying conduit cement to the connecting surfaces. Figure 8–5 shows a cutaway view of rigid nonmetallic conduit with a flared end coupling.

Rigid nonmetallic conduit is available as either Schedule 40—heavy wall, or Schedule 80—extra-heavy wall. Schedule 40 and Schedule 80 have the same outside diameter, with Schedule 80 having a heavier wall thickness and a corresponding reduction in interior cross-sectional area. Since the conduits have the same outside diameter, the same fittings may be used to join the conduit sections. Schedule 40 may be used in exposed or

FIGURE 8–3
Electrical Metallic Tubing

Standard

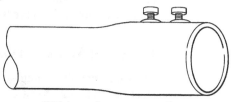

With integral set-screw coupling

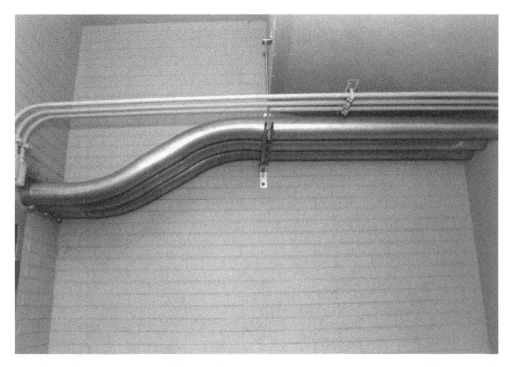

FIGURE 8–4
EMT Conduit Installation *Source:* Courtesy of Youngstown State University.

concealed aboveground applications where not subject to physical damage. For underground applications, Schedule 40 must be encased in concrete if the possibility of exposure to physical damage exists or may be direct buried where not exposed to physical damage. Schedule 80 may be used above- or belowground, either exposed or concealed, in applications that may be subject to physical damage.

Permitted uses of RNC are described in Section 352.10 of the *NEC;* uses not permitted are described in Section 352.12. Support requirements for RNC are given in Section 352.10. Rigid nonmetallic conduit must be securely fastened within 3 feet of any conduit termination, unless listed for support at a greater distance from the termination. Intermediate conduit supports must be in accordance with Table 352.30(B) of the *NEC,* as shown in Table 8–3. It is permitted to increase the support distances above those listed in Table 352.30(B), provided the conduit is listed for such application. Horizontal runs of

FIGURE 8–5
Rigid Nonmetallic Conduit

Flared end coupling

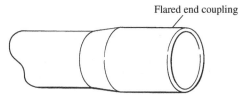

TABLE 8–3
Table 352.30(B) Support of Rigid Nonmetallic
Conduit (RNC)

Conduit Size		Maximum Spacing Between Supports	
Metric Designator	Trade Size	mm or m	ft
16–27	½–1	900 mm	3
35–53	1¼–2	1.5 m	5
63–78	2½–3	1.8 m	6
91–129	3½–5	2.1 m	7
155	6	2.5 m	8

Source: Reprinted with permission from NFPA 70 *The National Electric Code* © 2002, National Fire Protection Association, Quincy, MA 02269. This reprinted material is not the referenced subject which is represented by the standard in its entirety.

rigid nonmetallic conduit may be supported by framing members at spacing distances not exceeding those shown in Table 352.30(B), provided the conduit is securely fastened at each end termination.

Conduit bends can be made in the field by use of suitable bending equipment. Usually, the conduit section to be field bent has its ends capped and is then placed in a "hot box" and heated to soften the PVC material. The conduit is then removed and placed in a suitable jig to obtain the desired curvature. Preformed 30°, 45°, and 90° sweeps are typically available from the conduit manufacturers. The minimum bending radius of the conduit must comply with Table 344.24 under the column labeled "Other Bends." An installation of nonmetallic conduit is shown in Figure 8–6.

Electrical Nonmetallic Tubing

Electrical nonmetallic tubing (ENT) is a corrugated, pliable raceway having a circular cross section. Article 362 of the *NEC* discusses the requirements for installation and use of ENT. This tubing is designed to be easily bent to accommodate field installation. The minimum radius of the bend shall comply with Table 344.24 under the column listed as "Other Bends." ENT is generally available in 10 ft lengths in trade sizes of ½" to 2". Couplings and fittings must be listed for use with this type of conduit. Construction features of electrical nonmetallic tubing are shown in Figure 8–7.

Permitted uses of ENT are discussed in Section 362.10 of the *NEC;* uses not permitted are discussed in Section 362.12. Support requirements are discussed in Section 362.30.

Flexible Metal Conduit

Flexible metal conduit, or FMC, consists of a helical-wound metal strip formed to produce a circular cross section, as shown in Figure 8–8. Article 348 of the *NEC* discusses the

FIGURE 8–6
Nonmetallic Conduit Installation *Source:* Courtesy of Youngstown State University.

requirements for installation and use of FMC. This type of conduit is available in trade sizes from ⅜″ to 4″ and may be used in both exposed and concealed applications. Flexible metal conduit is commonly used for equipment connections, where it is required to minimize the transmission of vibration from the equipment to the conduit system. Section 348.12 of the *NEC* lists uses not permitted for flexible metal conduit.

Due to its physical construction, flexible metal conduit does not seal the conductors from the environment. Therefore, it may not be used where the conductors may be exposed to deteriorating materials. Generally, the smallest trade size of FMC permitted is ½″.

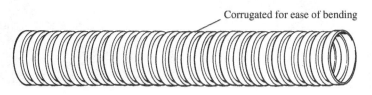

Corrugated for ease of bending

FIGURE 8–7
Electrical Nonmetallic Tubing

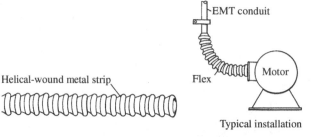

FIGURE 8–8
Flexible Metal Conduit

However, the use of ⅜″ flexible metal conduit is permitted under the requirements of Section 348.20(A) of the *NEC*. Generally, ⅜″ FMC is permitted in lengths not to exceed 6 ft for connection to equipment or fixture whips or for manufactured wiring systems or other listed assemblies. Support requirements for FMC are given in Section 348.30 of the *NEC*. Figure 8–9 shows a typical installation of flexible metal conduit used as a fixture whip for a fluorescent light fixture.

FIGURE 8–9
Flexible Metal Conduit Used as Fixture Whip *Source:* Courtesy Youngstown State University.

Liquidtight Flexible Metal Conduit

Liquidtight flexible metal conduit, or LFMC, is a raceway having a circular cross section that is designed to prevent the infiltration of liquids, vapors, or solid materials into the conduit. Article 350 of the *NEC* discusses the application and installation of LFMC. The conduit is usually constructed of an interlocked metal strip covered by a liquidtight, nonmetallic, sunlight-resistant outer jacket, as shown in Figure 8–10(A). This type of conduit is available in trade sizes from ⅜″ to 4″ and may be used in both exposed and concealed applications. Generally, the smallest trade size of LFMC permitted is ½″. However, the use of ⅜″ LFMC is permitted under the requirements of Section 348.20(A) of the *NEC*. Note that these requirements are the same as those for FMC. Liquidtight flexible metal conduit is commonly used for equipment connections, where it is required to minimize the transmission of vibration from the equipment to the conduit system. Section 350.10 of the *NEC* permits LFMC to be direct buried where listed for the application and in certain hazardous locations. Section 350.12 of the *NEC* does not permit LFMC to be used where subject to physical damage or in temperatures greater than the temperature rating of the jacket material. Support requirements for LFMC are given in Section 350.30 of the *NEC*. Figure 8–11 shows a typical installation of liquidtight flexible metal conduit for connection to an air-conditioning unit.

FIGURE 8–10
Liquidtight Flexible Metal Conduit

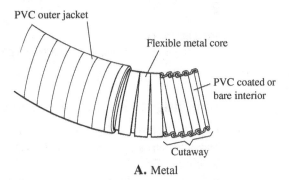

PVC outer jacket

Flexible metal core

PVC coated or bare interior

Cutaway

A. Metal

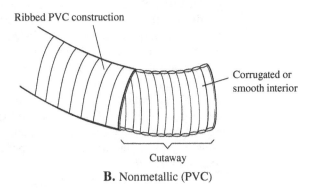

Ribbed PVC construction

Corrugated or smooth interior

Cutaway

B. Nonmetallic (PVC)

FIGURE 8–11
Liquidtight Flexible Metal Conduit Installation *Source:* Courtesy of Youngstown State University.

Liquidtight Flexible Nonmetallic Conduit

Liquidtight flexible nonmetallic conduit, or LFNC, may have smooth or corrugated inner and outer surfaces, either bonded together or manufactured as an integral assembly. Article 356 of the *NEC* discusses the application and installation of LFNC. Figure 8–10(B) shows the construction features of liquidtight flexible nonmetallic conduit. The nonmetallic conduit may be reinforced to increase strength. Section 356.10 of the *NEC* permits LFNC to be used where flexibility of connection to equipment is required and where protection of conductors from vapors, liquids, and solids is desired. Direct burial and outdoor installation are permitted if the conduit is listed for this purpose. Section 356.12 of the *NEC* does not permit LFNC to be installed where subject to physical damage or in temperatures greater than the temperature rating of the jacket material. In addition, this type of conduit is not permitted for systems greater than 600 V nominal. Generally, the smallest trade size of LFNC permitted is ½″. However, the use of ⅜″ LFNC is permitted under the requirements of Section 356.20(A) of the *NEC*. Generally, ⅜″ LFNC is permitted in lengths not to exceed 6 ft for connection to equipment or fixture whips or for manufactured wiring systems or other listed assemblies. Support requirements for LFNC are given in Section 356.30 of the *NEC*.

8–2   CONDUIT SIZING

Proper sizing of conduit is necessary to ensure ease of installation and to prevent damage to the conductors during installation. Among the factors affecting the selection of the appropriate-size conduit are fill and the probability of jamming. Initial selection of conduit size is usually based on the allowable fill factor. The jamming ratio is usually calculated next to determine if jamming of the conductors is likely to occur during installation.

The maximum allowable conduit fill is based on the number of conductors, the cross-sectional area of the conduit, and the total cross-sectional area of the conductors to be installed in a given conduit. The *NEC* requires that the total cross-sectional area of all conductors in a conduit shall not exceed the percentages of conduit cross-sectional area listed in Table 1 of the *NEC,* which is shown in Table 8–4. For most common design applications, the 40% fill factor is used. To determine the correct conduit size, the sum of the cross-sectional area of all conductors is divided by the allowable fill factor, as designated above. The result is the minimum conduit cross-sectional area required. The trade-size conduit is selected based on the minimum required area. Table 8–5 lists the inside diameters of some of the more common trade-size conduits. Table 8–6 lists the outer diameter and cross-sectional area of some of the more common copper conductors. Consult manufacturers' data for other conduit and cable sizes and types.

TABLE 8–4
Table 1 Percent of Cross Section of Conduit and Tubing for Conductors

Number of Conductors	All Conductor Types
1	53
2	31
Over 2	40

FPN No. 1: Table 1 is based on common conditions of proper cabling and alignment of conductors where the length of the pull and the number of bends are within reasonable limits. It should be recognized that, for certain conditions, a larger size conduit or a lesser conduit fill should be considered.

FPN No. 2: When pulling three conductors or cables into a raceway, if the ratio of the raceway (inside diameter) to the conductor or cable (outside diameter) is between 2.8 and 3.2, jamming can occur. While jamming can occur when pulling four or more conductors or cables into a raceway, the probability is very low.

Source: Reprinted with permission from NFPA 70 *The National Electric Code* © 2002, National Fire Protection Association, Quincy, MA 02269. This reprinted material is not the referenced subject which is represented only by the standard in its entirety.

TABLE 8–5
Conduit Dimensions

Trade	Rigid Metal Conduit		Intermediate Metal Conduit		Electrical Metallic Tubing		Flexible Metal Conduit	
Size (in.)	Diam. (in.)	Area (sq. in.)	Diam. (in.)	Area (sq. in.)	Diam. (in.)	Area (sq. in.)	Diam. (in.)	Area (sq. in.)
⅜	N/A	N/A	N/A	N/A	N/A	N/A	0.384	0.116
½	0.632	0.314	0.660	0.342	0.622	0.304	0.635	0.317
¾	0.836	0.549	0.864	0.586	0.824	0.533	0.824	0.533
1	1.063	0.887	1.105	0.959	1.049	0.864	1.020	0.817
1¼	1.394	1.526	1.448	1.647	1.380	1.496	1.275	1.277
1½	1.624	2.071	1.683	2.225	1.610	2.036	1.538	1.858
2	2.083	3.408	2.150	3.630	2.067	3.356	2.040	3.269
2½	2.489	4.866	2.557	5.135	2.731	5.858	2.500	4.909
3	3.090	7.499	3.176	7.922	3.356	8.846	3.000	7.069
3½	3.570	10.010	3.671	10.584	3.834	11.545	3.500	9.621
4	4.050	12.882	4.166	13.631	4.334	14.753	4.000	12.566
5	5.073	20.212	N/A	N/A	N/A	N/A	N/A	N/A
6	6.093	29.158	N/A	N/A	N/A	N/A	N/A	N/A

Source: Reprinted with permission from NFPA 70 *The National Electric Code* © 2002, National Fire Protection Association, Quincy, MA 02269. This reprinted material is not the referenced subject which is represented only by the standard in its entirety.

EXAMPLE 8–1

Determine the required trade-size rigid steel conduit required to accommodate four 500 kcmil XHHW-2 copper conductors.

Solution: From Table 8–6, the diameter and cross-sectional area of the conductor is 0.9430 in. and 0.6984 sq in., respectively. The total cross-sectional area of all four conductors is

$$(4 \text{ conductors})(0.6984 \text{ sq in. per conductor}) = 2.7936 \text{ sq in.}$$

The fill factor is 40% since there are four conductors in the conduit. Therefore, the minimum conduit cross-sectional area is

$$(2.7936 \text{ sq in.}) \div (0.40) = 6.9840 \text{ sq in.}$$

From Table 8–5, the minimum required conduit size based on percentage fill is 3 in.

EXAMPLE 8–2

Determine the required trade-size PVC Schedule 40 conduit to accommodate four #4/0 THHN copper conductors and one #1 bare-stranded-copper equipment grounding conductor.

TABLE 8–5
Continued

Rigid NonMetallic Conduit (SCH 80)		Rigid NonMetallic Conduit (SCH 40)		Electrical NonMetallic Tubing		Liquidtight Flexible Metal Conduit	
Diam. (in.)	Area (sq. in.)	Diam. (in.)	Area (sq. in.)	Diam. (in.)	Area (sq. in.)	Diam. (in.)	Area (sq. in.)
N/A	N/A	N/A	N/A	N/A	N/A	0.494	0.192
0.526	0.217	0.602	0.285	0.560	0.246	0.632	0.314
0.722	0.409	0.804	0.508	0.760	0.454	0.830	0.541
0.936	0.688	1.029	0.832	1.000	0.785	1.054	0.873
1.255	1.237	1.360	1.453	1.340	1.410	1.395	1.528
1.476	1.711	1.590	1.986	1.570	1.936	1.588	1.981
1.913	2.874	2.047	3.291	2.020	3.205	2.033	3.246
2.290	4.119	2.445	4.695	N/A	N/A	2.493	4.881
2.864	6.442	3.042	7.268	N/A	N/A	3.085	7.475
3.326	8.688	3.521	9.737	N/A	N/A	3.520	9.731
3.786	11.258	3.998	12.554	N/A	N/A	4.020	12.692
4.768	17.855	5.016	19.761	N/A	N/A	N/A	N/A
5.709	25.598	6.031	28.567	N/A	N/A	N/A	N/A

Solution: From Table 8–6, the cross-sectional area of the #4/0 THHN conductors is 0.3237 sq in., and the cross-sectional area of the #1 equipment grounding conductor is 0.0845 sq in. The total cross-sectional area of all conductors in the conduit is

Total area = 4 × (0.3237 sq in.) + 1 × (0.0845 sq in.) = 1.3793 sq in.

The minimum required conduit cross-sectional area is based on a 40% fill as follows:

(1.3793 sq in.) ÷ (0.40) = 3.4483 sq in.

Therefore, a 2½" trade-size PVC Schedule 40 conduit having a cross-sectional area of 4.695 sq in. is required for this installation.

EXAMPLE 8–3

Determine the required trade-size electrical metallic tubing to accommodate ten #12 THHN copper conductors.

Solution: From Table 8–6, the cross-sectional area of the #12 THHN conductors is 0.0133 sq in. The total cross-sectional area of all conductors in the conduit is

Total area = 10 × (0.0133 sq in.) = 0.133 sq in.

TABLE 8–6
Conductor Dimensions

Size AWG or kcmil	RHW RHW-2 USE-2		XHHW-2		THHN THWN-2		Bare Copper (Solid)		Bare Copper Stranded	
	Diam. (in.)	Area (sq. in.)	Diam. (in.)	Area (sq. in.)	Diam. (in.)	Area (sq. in.)	Diam. (in.)	Area (sq. in.)	Diam. (in.)	Area (sq. in.)
14	0.1630	0.0209	0.1330	0.0139	0.1110	0.0097	0.0640	0.0032	0.0730	0.0042
12	0.1820	0.0260	0.1520	0.0181	0.1300	0.0133	0.0810	0.0052	0.0920	0.0066
10	0.2060	0.0333	0.1760	0.0243	0.1640	0.0211	0.1020	0.0082	0.1160	0.0106
8	0.2660	0.0556	0.2360	0.0437	0.2160	0.0366	0.1280	0.0129	0.1460	0.0167
6	0.3040	0.0726	0.2740	0.0590	0.2540	0.0507	0.1620	0.0206	0.1840	0.0266
4	0.3520	0.0973	0.3220	0.0814	0.3240	0.0824	0.2043	0.0328	0.2320	0.0423
3	0.3800	0.1134	0.3500	0.0962	0.3520	0.0973	0.2294	0.0413	0.2600	0.0531
2	0.4120	0.1333	0.3820	0.1146	0.3840	0.1158	0.2576	0.0521	0.2920	0.0670
1	0.4920	0.1901	0.4420	0.1534	0.4460	0.1562	0.2893	0.0657	0.3280	0.0845
1/0	0.5320	0.2223	0.4820	0.1825	0.4860	0.1855	N/A	N/A	0.3680	0.1064
2/0	0.5780	0.2624	0.5280	0.2190	0.5320	0.2223	N/A	N/A	0.4190	0.1379
3/0	0.6300	0.3117	0.5800	0.2642	0.5840	0.2679	N/A	N/A	0.4640	0.1691
4/0	0.6880	0.3718	0.6380	0.3197	0.6420	0.3237	N/A	N/A	0.5280	0.2190
250	0.7650	0.4596	0.7050	0.3904	0.7110	0.3970	N/A	N/A	0.5750	0.2597
300	0.8200	0.5281	0.7600	0.4536	0.7660	0.4608	N/A	N/A	0.6290	0.3107
350	0.8710	0.5958	0.8110	0.5166	0.8170	0.5242	N/A	N/A	0.6780	0.3610
400	0.9180	0.6619	0.8580	0.5782	0.8640	0.5863	N/A	N/A	0.7260	0.4140
500	1.0030	0.7901	0.9430	0.6984	0.9490	0.7073	N/A	N/A	0.8130	0.5191
600	1.1130	0.9729	1.0530	0.8709	1.0510	0.8676	N/A	N/A	0.8910	0.6235
750	1.2180	1.1652	1.1580	1.0532	1.1560	1.0496	N/A	N/A	0.9980	0.7823
1000	1.3720	1.4784	1.3120	1.3519	1.3100	1.3478	N/A	N/A	1.1520	1.0423

Source: Reprinted with permission from NFPA 70 *The National Electric Code* © 2002, National Fire Protection Association, Quincy, MA 02269. This reprinted material is not the referenced subject which is represented only by the standard in its entirety.

The minimum required conduit cross-sectional area is based on a 40% fill as follows:

$$(0.133 \text{ sq in.}) \div (0.40) = 0.3325 \text{ sq in.}$$

Therefore, a ¾″ trade-size EMT conduit having a cross-sectional area of 0.533 sq in. is required for this installation.

Jamming of conductors in a conduit can occur as the conductors twist during installation or are pulled around bends. The jamming ratio is defined as the ratio of conduit inside diameter to cable outside diameter:

$$\text{Jamming ratio} = \frac{\text{Conduit inside diameter}}{\text{Cable outside diameter}} \qquad (8–1)$$

If the jamming ratio lies between 2.4 and 3.2, there is a good possibility that cable jamming may occur during installation. The use of a larger conduit is recommended in this case.

EXAMPLE 8–4

Determine the jamming ratio for the conditions of Example 8–1 and determine if this is an acceptable installation.

Solution: The internal diameter of the 3 in. rigid steel conduit is 3.090 in. as determined from Table 8–5. The outer diameter of the 500 kcmil XHHW-2 copper conductor is 0.943 in. as determined from Table 8–6. The jamming ratio is

$$\text{Jamming ratio} = \frac{3.090 \text{ in.}}{0.943 \text{ in.}} = 3.28$$

Since the jamming ratio lies outside the range of probability for jamming, this installation should be acceptable.

EXAMPLE 8–5

Determine the jamming ratio for the conditions of Example 8–2 and determine if this is an acceptable installation.

Solution: The internal diameter of the 2½″ PVC Schedule 40 conduit is 2.445 in. as determined from Table 8–5. The outer diameter of the #4/0 THHN copper conductor is 0.6420 in. as determined from Table 8–6. The jamming ratio is

$$\text{Jamming ratio} = \frac{2.445 \text{ in.}}{0.642 \text{ in.}} = 3.81$$

Since the jamming ratio lies outside the range of probability for jamming, this installation should be acceptable.

8–3   EXPANSION CHARACTERISTICS

When conduit is subjected to wide temperature variations, as would typically occur in an outdoor installation, the conduit will expand and contract as the temperature fluctuates. The expansion and contraction of nonmetallic conduit can be significant if the conduit is of any appreciable length and if the temperature variation is large. Expansion of nonmetallic conduit must be taken into account in the design of the raceway system. If the expected conduit expansion exceeds ¼″, expansion fittings must be installed to allow for the movement of the conduit. Failure to allow for expansion and contraction of conduit may lead to conduit buckling, damage to the conduit, or damage to termination enclosures at each end of the conduit run. Figure 8–12 shows the construction features of an expansion fitting.

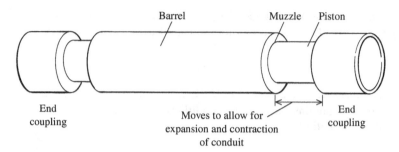

FIGURE 8–12
Conduit Expansion Fitting

To determine the amount of expansion of a conduit run, the overall length of the conduit run and the expected temperature variation must be determined. The following equation is used to determine the expansion of the conduit:

$$\text{Change in length} = \text{Length of run} \times (\Delta L)(\Delta°\text{F}) \qquad \textbf{(8–2)}$$

where:

ΔL = coefficient of thermal expansion
= 4.056×10^{-4} in./ft/°F for PVC conduit
= 1.8×10^{-4} in./ft/°F for fiberglass-reinforced conduit
$\Delta°\text{F}$ = change in temperature in degrees Fahrenheit

In Equation (8–2), the length of the conduit run is expressed in feet and the change in length in inches. If the change in length exceeds ¼″, expansion fittings must be used in the conduit run. The amount of expansion allowed by an expansion fitting is referred to as the *range* of the expansion fitting.

EXAMPLE 8–6

Determine the change in length of a 200 ft run of PVC conduit if the temperature changes from 5°F to 100°F. Also, determine the number of expansion fittings required if the range of each fitting is 3 in.

Solution: The change in temperature is equal to

$$\text{Change in temperature} = 100°\text{F} - 5°\text{F} = 95°\text{F}$$

The total change in length is given by Equation (8–2):

$$\text{Change in length} = (200 \text{ ft})(4.056 \times 10^{-4} \text{ in./ft/°F})(95°\text{F}) = 7.7064 \text{ in.}$$

Therefore, three expansion fittings are required to allow for expansion and contraction of the conduit when subjected to this variation in temperature.

8–4   CABLE TRAY

Cable tray is used in many commercial and industrial applications to provide support for cables and conductors. The cables may be used for power, communication, or control purposes. The minimum conductor size is #1/0 AWG for single-conductor power cables installed in cable tray. Single-conductor power cable must be listed for use in cable tray. Multiconductor power cables smaller than #1/0 AWG are permitted if listed for use in cable tray. Type TC multiconductor control cable is permitted in sizes smaller than #1/0 AWG. Unlike conduit, cable tray is used to run cables and/or conductors in an open manner. Typically, the top of the tray is open or uncovered to allow access to the cables. The tray is commonly available in ladder, trough, and solid-bottom styles. The ladder and trough construction have side rails and an open bottom consisting of "rungs" upon which the cables are placed. If the tray is to contain #1/0 AWG through #4/0 AWG single-conductor power cables, the maximum rung spacing is 9 in. The open bottom allows for the circulation of air over the conductors, thereby minimizing temperature rise. Solid-bottom cable tray consists of a solid metal bottom and therefore does not allow for the free circulation of air over the conductors. Cable tray is commonly available in steel, aluminum, and nonmetallic constructions. Fittings and supports are readily available from the cable tray manufacturer. Specific details regarding cable tray support requirements and environmental application considerations can be obtained from the cable tray manufacturer. Article 392 of the *NEC* discusses the sizing of cable tray, allowable ampacities of cables in cable tray, and the application and installation of cable trays in detail. Figure 8–13 shows an example of a cable tray installation.

8–5   PULL, JUNCTION, DEVICE, AND OUTLET BOXES

Pull and junction boxes are used to provide a means of accessing the cables installed in a conduit or raceway system, primarily for the purposes of installation. Device and outlet boxes are used for mounting various wiring devices such as switches and receptacles. These items constitute a significant part of the raceway system and must be properly sized to accommodate the conductors and devices. Article 314 of the *NEC* discusses the application and installation requirements for various pull, junction, device, and outlet boxes.

Pull and Junction Boxes

Pull and junction boxes are used to provide termination points in a conduit system at various locations to enable pulling of cable and conductors into the conduit system. These boxes are also used where there is a change in the size or number of conduits entering or leaving the raceway system. An example would be a location in the raceway system where several raceways split off from the main run to supply various panelboards, branch circuits, equipment, and so on. The following discussion on pull and junction box sizing applies to boxes containing #4 AWG or larger conductors. Pull and junction boxes are available in both metallic and nonmetallic construction. Bonding jumpers may be required to connect metal conduit sections to maintain continuity of the grounding system if nonmetallic boxes are used.

B-Line Cable Trays-Designed for Your Cable Support Requirements

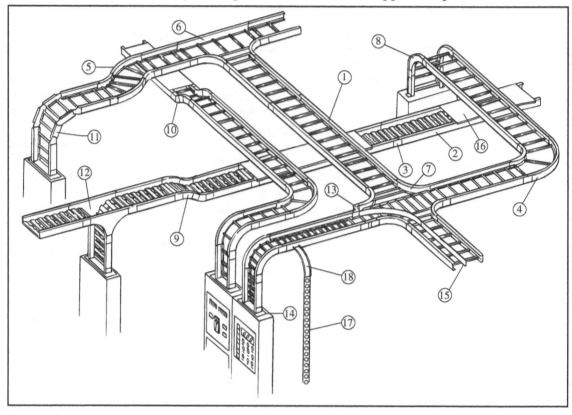

Nomenclature

1. Ladder Type Cable Tray
2. Ventilated Trough Type Cable Tray
3. Straight Splice Plate
4. 90° Horizontal Bend, Ladder Type Cable Tray
5. 45° Horizontal Bend, Ladder Type Cable Tray
6. Horizontal Tee, Ladder Type Cable Tray
7. Horizontal Cross, Ladder Type Cable Tray
8. 90° Vertical Outside Bend, Ladder Type Cable Tray
9. 45° Vertical Outside Bend, Ventilated Type Cable Tray

10. 30° Vertical Inside Bend, Ladder Type Cable Tray
11. Vertical Bend Segment (VBS)
12. Vertical Tee Down, Ventilated Trough Type Cable Tray
13. Left Hand Reducer, Ladder Type Cable Tray
14. Frame Type Box Connector
15. Barrier Strip Straight Section
16. Solid Flanged Tray Cover
17. Ventilated Channel Straight Section
18. Channel Cable Tray, 90° Vertical Outside Bend

FIGURE 8–13
Cable Tray System *Source:* B-Line Systems Inc.

FIGURE 8–14
Pull Box Dimensional Requirements

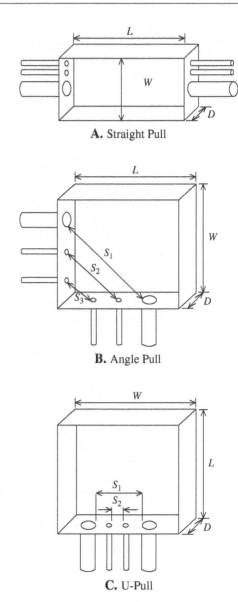

A. Straight Pull

B. Angle Pull

C. U-Pull

For straight pulls, Section 314.28(A)(1) of the *NEC* requires the pull box length, *L*, to be equal to 8 times the diameter of the largest conduit entering the box, as shown in Figure 8–14(A). The conduits are usually placed in a single row along the side of the box. In some instances, a double row may be used. The width of the box, *W*, must allow sufficient space between the conduits and the edge of the box to allow for locknuts, bushings, and other conduit fittings. The width of the box is determined by summing the trade diameter of all conduits along this dimension and adding 2 in. per conduit for spacing between the conduits and the edge of the box. The depth of the box, D, can be determined in the same manner as the width using the trade size of the conduits along this dimension.

An example of a junction box used to allow for an angle pull involving three sets of conduits is shown in Figure 8–14(B). In the discussion that follows, it is assumed that the junction boxes used for angle pulls are square and that the same conduit run is involved in the calculations. The minimum distances between conduit entries containing the same set of conductors are designated S_1, S_2, S_3, and so on. In accordance with Section 314.28(A)(2) of the *NEC*, distances S_1, S_2, S_3, and so on must be at least equal to 6 times the diameter of the respective conduit entering the box. In addition, if there are several different trade-size conduits comprising the angle pull, the minimum distance between the largest conduit entry, S_1, shall be equal to at least 6 times the diameter of the largest raceway plus the sum of the diameters of the other raceways comprising the angle pull. The dimensions L and W shall be at least 6 times the diameter of the largest raceway plus the sum of the diameters of the other raceways entering the opposite sides of the box, as shown in Figure 8–14(B). Finally, the depth of the box, D, shall be determined by summing the trade diameter of all conduits along this dimension and adding 2 in. per conduit. This basic requirement is for a single row of conduits entering a box. For multiple rows of conduits entering a box, the procedure is repeated for each row of conduits. The row giving the largest separation requirement shall be used in the final determination of this dimension. For complicated pulls, sketching the system is recommended to determine minimum dimensional requirements.

The dimensional requirements for a junction box used in a U-pull are shown in Figure 8–14(C). Note that there are two conduit runs involved in this particular case. Section 314.28(A)(2) of the *NEC* requires the distance L to be at least 6 times the trade diameter of the largest raceway plus the sum of the diameters of the other raceways entering the bottom of the box. The distances S_1 and S_2 must be at least 6 times the diameter of the respective conduit. In addition, the distance S_1 must be at least 6 times the diameter of the largest raceway plus the sum of the diameters of the other raceways comprising the U-pull. The width of the box, W, must be the larger of the results of the calculations for S_1 and S_2 or the results of summing the trade diameter of all conduits along this dimension plus 2 in. per conduit. The depth of the box, D, shall be determined by summing the trade diameter of all conduits along this dimension and adding 2 in. per conduit.

EXAMPLE 8–7

Determine the minimum required length of a pull box to be used for a straight pull containing the following: two 4″ EMT conduits, three 2″ EMT conduits, and four 1″ EMT conduits. The conduits are arranged in a single row.

Solution: A sketch of this pull box is shown in Figure 8–15(A). The minimum length, L, is equal to 8 times the diameter of the largest conduit entering the box, 4″ in this case. Therefore, the minimum required length is $8 \times 4″ = 32″$. The width of the box, W, is determined by summing the trade size of all conduits plus 2″ per conduit to allow space between the conduits to accommodate locknuts and bushings. The width is $(2 \times 4″) + (3 \times 2″) + (4 \times 1″) + (9 \times 2″) = 36″$. Since the conduits are arranged in a

FIGURE 8–15
Pull Box Sizing Examples

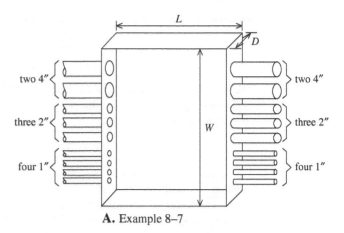

A. Example 8–7

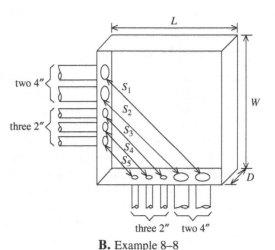

three 2″   two 4″

B. Example 8–8

single row, the depth of the box is based on the largest trade-diameter conduit plus 2″. Therefore, the required depth is $4'' + 2'' = 6''$. The minimum box size is $32'' L \times 36'' W \times 6'' D$.

EXAMPLE 8–8

Determine the required box size for an angle pull consisting of the following: two 4″ EMT conduits and three 2″ EMT conduits.

Solution: A sketch of this system is shown in Figure 8–15(B). The distance S_1 is equal to 6 times the largest trade diameter plus the sum of the trade diameter of the other conduits:

$$S_1 = (6 \times 4'') + 4'' + (3 \times 2'') = 34''$$

The distances S_2, S_3, S_4, and S_5, are calculated:

$$S_2 = 6 \times 4'' = 24''$$
$$S_3 = S_4 = S_5 = 6 \times 2'' = 12''$$

The minimum dimensions for the length L, and the width W of the box are the same since the same-size conduits enter the box on each side to comprise the angle pull. Therefore, L and W are calculated as

$$L = W = (6 \times 4'') + 4'' + (3 \times 2'') = 34''$$

The minimum dimensions L and W must also be compared to the result obtained by summing the trade diameter of all conduits entering the box side plus 2 in. per conduit. This results in a minimum dimension equal to 24''. Therefore, the minimum required L and W is 34''. The minimum required box depth, D, is 6''. A 36'' L × 36'' W × 6'' D box would be required for this application.

Outlet and Device Boxes

Outlet and device boxes are used primarily for the mounting of devices such as switches and receptacles. In some instances, these boxes will be used with a blank cover to serve as junction boxes. Generally, the conductor size is limited to #14 AWG through #6 AWG on circuits rated up to 50 A.

The required size of the device and outlet boxes is governed by the cubic inch capacity of the box and the *NEC* requirements for the volume allowance required for conductors, devices, grounding conductors, fixture support fittings, and so on. The cubic inch capacity of the device box must be equal to or greater than the total required allowance for all conductors, devices, and so on in the box. The cubic inch capacity of some of the more common-size metal boxes is given in Table 314.16(A) of the *NEC*. The volume allowance required per conductor is given in Table 314.16(B) of the *NEC*. These tables are shown in Table 8–7.

The rules for counting conductors are given in Sections 314.16(B)(1) through 314.16(B)(5) of the *NEC*. These rules are summarized here.

- A conductor that originates outside the box and terminates inside the box shall be counted as one conductor, with the applicable cubic inch allowance applied.
- A conductor that passes through the box without a splice or termination shall be counted as one conductor, with the applicable cubic inch allowance applied.
- A conductor contained completely inside the box does not need to be counted as a conductor. However, it is good practice to count this conductor, with the applicable cubic inch allowance applied.
- If there are one or more cable clamps with the clamping mechanism inside the box, an allowance equal to the cubic inch requirement for the largest-size conductor entering the box shall be made. Note that a single allowance is required regardless of the number of clamps. If the cable clamping mechanism is outside the box, no allowance is required.

TABLE 8–7
Table 314.16(A) Metal Boxes

			Minimum Volume		Maximum Number of Conductors*						
mm	in.		cm³	in³	18	16	14	12	10	8	6
100 × 32	(4 × 1¼)	round/octagonal	205	12.5	8	7	6	5	5	5	2
100 × 38	(4 × 1½)	round/octagonal	254	15.5	10	8	7	6	6	5	3
100 × 54	(4 × 2⅛)	round/octagonal	353	21.5	14	12	10	9	8	7	4
100 × 32	(4 × 1¼)	square	295	18.0	12	10	9	8	7	6	3
100 × 38	(4 × 1½)	square	344	21.0	14	12	10	9	8	7	4
100 × 54	(4 × 2⅛)	square	497	30.3	20	17	15	13	12	10	6
120 × 32	(4¹¹⁄₁₆ × 1¼)	square	418	25.5	17	14	12	11	10	8	5
120 × 38	(4¹¹⁄₁₆ × 1½)	square	484	29.5	19	16	14	13	11	9	5
120 × 54	(4¹¹⁄₁₆ × 2⅛)	square	689	42.0	28	24	21	18	16	14	8
75 × 50 × 38	(3 × 2 × 1½)	device	123	7.5	5	4	3	3	3	2	1
75 × 50 × 50	(3 × 2 × 2)	device	164	10.0	6	5	5	4	4	3	2
75 × 50 × 57	(3 × 2 × 2¼)	device	172	10.5	7	6	5	4	4	3	2
75 × 50 × 65	(3 × 2 × 2½)	device	205	12.5	8	7	6	5	5	4	2
75 × 50 × 70	(3 × 2 × 2¾)	device	230	14.0	9	8	7	6	5	4	2
75 × 50 × 90	(3 × 2 × 3½)	device	295	18.0	12	10	9	8	7	6	3
100 × 54 × 38	(4 × 2⅛ × 1½)	device	169	10.3	6	5	5	4	4	3	2
100 × 54 × 48	(4 × 2⅛ × 1⅞)	device	213	13.0	8	7	6	5	5	4	2
100 × 54 × 54	(4 × 2⅛ × 2⅛)	device	238	14.5	9	8	7	6	5	4	2
95 × 50 × 65	(3¾ × 2 × 2½)	masonry box/gang	230	14.0	9	8	7	6	5	4	2
95 × 50 × 90	(3¾ × 2 × 3½)	masonry box/gang	344	21.0	14	12	10	9	8	7	2
min. 44.5 depth	FS—single cover/gang (1¾)		221	13.5	9	7	6	6	5	4	2
min. 60.3 depth	FD—single cover/gang (2⅜)		295	18.0	12	10	9	8	7	6	3
min. 44.5 depth	FS—multiple cover/gang (1¾)		295	18.0	12	10	9	8	7	6	3
min. 60.3 depth	FD—multiple cover/gang (2⅜)		395	24.0	16	13	12	10	9	8	4

*Where no volume allowances are required by 314.16(B)(2) through 314.16(B)(5).

Table 314.16(B) Volume Allowance Required per Conductor

Size of Conductor (AWG)	Free Space Within Box for Each Conductor	
	cm³	in³
18	24.6	1.50
16	28.7	1.75
14	32.8	2.00
12	36.9	2.25
10	41.0	2.50
8	49.2	3.00
6	81.9	5.00

- If a fixture stud or other support fitting is present in the box, an allowance equal to the cubic inch capacity required for the largest conductor entering the box must be made.
- For each device strap, an allowance equal to 2 times the cubic inch capacity required for the largest conductor entering the box must be made. This requirement commonly applies to duplex receptacles mounted on a single strap and switches.
- An allowance equal to the largest equipment grounding conductor shall be made where one or more equipment grounding conductors of a single system are present. Note that only a single allowance is required regardless of the actual number of equipment grounding conductors present. If the grounding conductors of another system are present in the same box, an additional single allowance equal to the largest equipment grounding conductor of the other system must be made.

EXAMPLE 8–9

Determine the minimum required cubic inch capacity for a device box to accommodate the following: four #12 AWG circuit conductors, two #14 AWG equipment grounding conductors of the same system, two cable clamps inside the box, and one duplex receptacle.

Solution: The required cubic inch allowance for the #12 AWG circuit conductors is 2.25 in^3 per conductor. Each circuit conductor must be counted. An allowance equal to 2.00 in^3 is applied for the #14 AWG equipment grounding conductors. Since the equipment grounding conductors are from the same system, an allowance equal to that required for one conductor is applied. The allowance for the cable clamps is that required for the largest conductor entering the box, or 2.25 in^3. For the duplex receptacle, an allowance equal to two of the largest conductors entering the box is required. The minimum required cubic inch capacity is calculated as

$$
\begin{array}{lll}
4 \ \#12 \text{ AWG @ 2.25 in}^3 & = & 9.00 \text{ in}^3 \\
1 \ \#14 \text{ AWG @ 2.00 in}^3 & = & 2.00 \text{ in}^3 \\
\text{Cable clamps: 1 @ 2.25 in}^3 & = & 2.25 \text{ in}^3 \\
\text{Device strap: } 2 \times 2.25 \text{ in}^3 & = & \underline{4.50 \text{ in}^3} \\
& \text{Total} & 17.75 \text{ in}^3
\end{array}
$$

Therefore, a box capacity of at least 17.75 in^3 is required. Referring to Table 8–7, a 3″ × 2″ × 3½″ device box having a capacity of 18 in^3 is the smallest permitted.

8–6   WIREWAYS AND AUXILIARY GUTTERS

Wireways and auxiliary gutters are short sections of metallic or nonmetallic troughs having a rectangular or square cross section. Wireways are generally used to connect electrical equipment such as meter sockets, panels, and disconnect enclosures located in the same general area. Metal and nonmetallic wireways are discussed, respectively, in Articles 376 and 378 of the *NEC*. Auxiliary gutters are usually connected directly to panels, disconnect enclosures, and so on to allow for a larger wire space for banding and termination purposes. Article 366 of the *NEC* discusses the application and installation requirements for auxiliary gutters. Splices and taps are permitted to be made in wireways and auxiliary gutters. Wireways are generally available in the following trade sizes:

$2\frac{1}{2}'' \times 2\frac{1}{2}''$
$4'' \times 4''$
$6'' \times 6''$
$8'' \times 8''$
$10'' \times 10''$
$12'' \times 12''$

Standard lengths are 12", 24", 36", 48", 60", and 120". Figure 8–16 shows examples of wireways and auxiliary gutters.

The following *NEC* rules apply to wireways and auxiliary gutters:

- In metallic wireways, up to 30 current-carrying conductors are permitted to be installed without applying the derating factors for raceway fill. More than 30 current-carrying conductors are permitted if the applicable derating factors are applied. Good design practice will usually limit the number of conductors to less than 30.
- In nonmetallic wireways, conductor ampacities are subject to the derating factors for raceway fill.
- The total cross-sectional area of the conductors shall not exceed 20% of the cross-sectional area of the wireway or auxiliary gutter.

FIGURE 8–16
Wireway and Auxiliary
Gutters

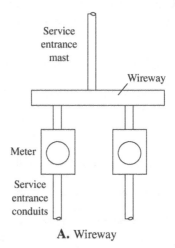

A. Wireway

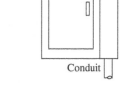

B. Auxiliary Gutter

- The total cross-sectional area of splices and taps shall not exceed 75% of the cross-sectional area of the wireway or gutter at the point of splice or tap.
- When installed in metal gutter, the ampacity of a bare copper bus bar shall not exceed 1000 A per square inch. Likewise, the ampacity of aluminum bus bar shall not exceed 700 A per square inch.

The support requirements for metal and nonmetallic gutters are discussed in Sections 366.4(A) and 366.4(B) of the *NEC,* and support requirements for metal and nonmetallic wireways are discussed in Sections 376.30 and 378.30 of the *NEC.* The reader is referred to Articles 366, 376, and 378 for uses permitted and uses not permitted for the various wireways and auxiliary gutters. Expansion and contraction of nonmetallic wireways and auxiliary gutters must be taken into account when designing the raceway system. The procedure is similar to that for nonmetallic rigid conduit previously discussed.

Although the 20% fill factor will allow for the determination of the required cross-sectional area of the wireway, the deflection of the conductors entering the raceway also needs to be addressed. When the conductor enters the wireway, it will usually be deflected to travel along the length of the wireway to a point of splice, tap, or exiting. If the deflection of the conductor is more than 30°, the dimension of the wireway across from the point of entry must be equal to or greater than the dimensions shown in Table 312.6(A) of the *NEC.* This table is shown in Table 8–8. The number of wires per terminal will be equal to 1 if the conductors enter and exit the wireway without being spliced or tapped. If the wires are spliced or tapped, the number of conductors per terminal is equal to the number of conductors spliced or tapped at a certain point and leaving the wireway in the same general direction.

EXAMPLE 8–10

Determine the required dimensions for a wireway containing eight 400 kcmil XHHW-2 copper conductors and two #1/0 AWG bare copper grounding conductors. The conductors will enter the wireway on top, bend 90°, travel along the wireway, and bend another 90° to exit the wireway. Assume one conductor per terminal.

Solution: The cross-sectional area of the conductors is

$$8\ 400\ \text{kcmil XHHW-2} = 8 \times (0.5782\ \text{in}^2) = 4.6256\ \text{in}^2$$
$$1\ \#1/0\ \text{bare ground}\quad = 1 \times (0.1064\ \text{in}^2) = \underline{0.1064\ \text{in}^2}$$
$$\text{Total}\quad 4.7320\ \text{in}^2$$

The minimum total cross-sectional area of the wireway is based on the 20% fill factor:

$$\text{Minimum wireway cross-sectional area} = (4.7320\ \text{in}^2) \div (0.20) = 23.66\ \text{in}^2$$

Therefore, a 6″ × 6″ wireway is required having a cross-sectional area of 36 in². (Note that a 4″ × 4″ wireway having a cross-sectional area of 16 in² would be too small for this

TABLE 8–8
Table 312.6(A) Minimum Wire-Bending Space at Terminals and Minimum Width of Wiring Gutters

Wire Size (AWG or kcmil)	Wires per Terminal									
	1		2		3		4		5	
	mm	in.	mm	in.	mm	in.	mm	in.	mm	in.
14–10	Not specified		—	—	—	—	—	—	—	—
8–6	38.1	1½	—	—	—	—	—	—	—	—
4–3	50.8	2	—	—	—	—	—	—	—	—
2	63.5	2½	—	—	—	—	—	—	—	—
1	76.2	3	—	—	—	—	—	—	—	—
1/0–2/0	88.9	3½	—	—	—	—	—	—	—	—
3/0–4/0	102	4	127	5	—	—	—	—	—	—
250	114	4½	152	6	203	8	—	—	—	—
300–350	127	5	152	6	203	8	254	10	—	—
400–500	152	6	203	8	254	10	305	12	—	—
600–700	203	8	203	8	254	10	305	12	456	14
750–900	203	8	254	10	305	12	356	14	406	16
1000–1250	254	10	305	12	356	14	406	16	457	18
1500–2000	305	12	—	—	—	—	—	—	—	—

Note: Bending space at terminals shall be measured in a straight line from the end of the lug or wire connector (in the direction that the wire leaves the terminal) to the wall, barrier, or obstruction. Source: Reprinted with permission from NFPA 70 *The National Electric Code* © 2002, National Fire Protection Association, Quincy, MA 02269. This reprinted material is not the referenced subject which is represented only by the standard in its entirety.

application.) The minimum wire-bending space for the purposes of conductor deflection is equal to 6″, as determined from Table 8–8. The 6″ × 6″ wireway meets this requirement.

8–7 WIRING METHODS

A knowledge of some of the fundamental *NEC* requirements for electrical installations is important in the design of electrical systems. Specifically, Article 300 of the *NEC* discusses wiring methods and deals primarily with installation methods. Some of the more common requirements are discussed next.

Generally, conductors of circuits rated 600 V and below must be kept physically separated from conductors of circuits above 600 V, as required by Section 300.3(C)(2) of the *NEC*. In addition, Section 300.3(C)(1) of the *NEC* requires conductors of different circuits occupying the same raceway to have an insulation rating equal to the maximum circuit voltage in the raceway.

Nonmetallic sheathed cable installed in bored holes in wood framing members must be protected from penetration by nails or other objects as required by Section 300.4(B)(2)

TABLE 8–9

Table 300.5 Minimum Cover Requirements, 0 to 600 Volts, Nominal, Burial in Millimeters (Inches)

	Type of Wiring Method or Circuit			
Location of Wiring Method or Circuit	Column 1 Direct Burial Cables or Conductors		Column 2 Rigid Metal Conduit or Intermediate Metal Conduit	
	mm	in.	mm	in.
All locations not specified below	600	24	150	6
In trench below 50-mm (2-in.) thick concrete or equivalent	450	18	150	6
Under a building	0 (in raceway only)	0	0	0
Under minimum of 102-mm (4-in.) thick concrete exterior slab with no vehicular traffic and the slab extending not less than 152 mm (6 in.) beyond the underground installation	450	18	100	4
Under streets, highways, roads, alleys, driveways, and parking lots	600	24	600	24
One- and two-family dwelling driveways and outdoor parking areas, and used only for dwelling-related purposes	450	18	450	18
In or under airport runways, including adjacent areas where trespassing prohibited	450	18	450	18

Notes:

1. Cover is defined as the shortest distance in millimeters (inches) measured between a point on the top surface of any direct-buried conductor, cable, conduit, or other raceway and the top surface of finished grade, concrete, or similar cover.
2. Raceways approved for burial only where concrete encased shall require concrete envelope not less than 50 mm (2 in.) thick.
3. Lesser depths shall be permitted where cables and conductors rise for terminations or splices or where access is otherwise required.

of the *NEC*. This is accomplished by maintaining the bored holes a minimum distance of 1¼″ from the edge of the wood framing member. If this separation cannot be achieved, a steel plate or bushing at least ¹⁄₁₆″ thick must be placed over the wiring to provide the required protection. Steel plates are not required to protect rigid metal conduit, intermediate metallic conduit, electrical metallic tubing, or rigid nonmetallic conduit.

Underground installations shall be made with the minimum cover requirements listed in Table 300.5 of the *NEC,* which is shown in Table 8–9. These minimum cover

TABLE 8–9
Continued

Type of Wiring Method or Circuit					
Column 3 Nonmetallic Raceways Listed for Direct Burial Without Concrete Encasement or Other Approved Raceways		Column 4 Residential Branch Circuits Rated 120 Volts or Less with GFCI Protection and Maximum Overcurrent Protection of 20 Amperes		Column 5 Circuits for Control of Irrigation and Landscape Lighting Limited to Not More Than 30 Volts and Installed with Type UF or in Other Identified Cable or Raceway	
mm	in.	mm	in.	mm	in.
450	18	300	12	150	6
300	12	50	6	50	6
0	0	0	0	0	0
		(in raceway only)		(in raceway only)	
100	4	150	6	150	6
		(direct burial)			
		100	4		
		(in raceway)			
600	24	600	24	600	24
450	18	300	12	450	18
450	18	450	18	450	18

4. Where one of the wiring method types listed in Columns 1-3 is used for one of the circuit types in Columns 4 and 5, the shallower depth of burial shall be permitted.
5. Where solid rock prevents compliance with the cover depths specified in this table, the wiring shall be installed in metal or nonmetallic raceway permitted for direct burial. The raceways shall be covered by a minimum of 50 mm (2 in.) of concrete extending down to rock.

Source: Reprinted with permission from NFPA 70 *The National Electric Code* © 2002, National Fire Protection Association, Quincy, MA 02269. This reprinted material is not the referenced subject which is represented only by the standard in its entirety.

requirements must be maintained and cannot be reduced as a result of excavation after the cables or raceway has been installed. It is recommended that the final grade be established prior to trenching for underground installations. Backfill of underground raceway and cable systems shall be free of any material that may cause damage to the raceway or cable. Where underground raceways enter buildings, moisture must be prevented from entering the building and electrical equipment by use of suitable raceway seals or plugs. Underground cables and raceway systems must be protected from damage that may occur due to settling of the earth, heaving due to frost, additional excavation, and so on. It is generally good practice to install underground cables and raceway systems in undisturbed soil or soil that has been suitably compacted.

Section 300.5(D)(3) of the *NEC* requires cables that are direct buried to be marked by a warning tape placed at least 12″ above the cable. In addition, Section 300.5(D)(1) of the *NEC* requires direct-buried cables to be protected from physical damage by a suitable raceway at the point where they leave the earth at places such as riser poles and service entrances, as shown in Figure 8–17.

The circulation of air between sections of a raceway system subjected to widely varying temperatures must be prevented as required by Section 300.7(A) of the *NEC.* This requirement is necessary to prevent condensation from building up in the raceway. The circulation of air may be prevented by sealing the raceway with putty or other suitable material at the point where the raceway enters the cooler environment.

8–8   CABLE PULLING CALCULATIONS

Cable pulling calculations are necessary to ensure that maximum tension on the cable is not exceeded during installation. If the actual pulling tension exceeds the maximum permitted, damage to the cable insulation may result. The maximum allowable tension on a conductor is a function of the maximum allowable conductor stress. This is generally expressed in terms of lb/cmil. For soft-drawn copper, the maximum allowable conductor

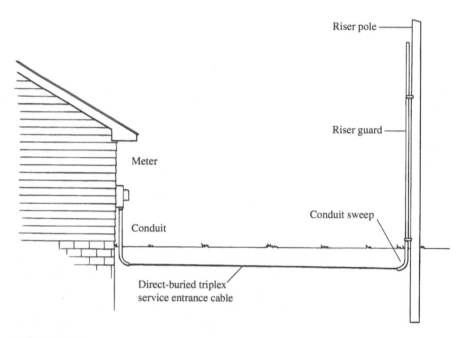

FIGURE 8–17
Underground Service Entrance Cable Protection Requirements

stress is 0.008 lb/cmil.* For aluminum AA-8000 alloy, the maximum allowable conductor stress is 0.006 lb/cmil.* Therefore, the allowable tension per conductor is equal to

$$T_c = 0.008 \times \text{Area in circular mils} \quad \text{(copper)} \tag{8–3a}$$

$$T_c = 0.006 \times \text{Area in circular mils} \quad \text{(aluminumAA-8000)} \tag{8–3b}$$

For multiconductor cable containing three or fewer conductors, the maximum allowable tension is equal to

$$T_m = \text{Number of conductors} \times T_c \tag{8–4}$$

For multiconductor cable containing more than four conductors, the maximum allowable tension is equal to*

$$T_m = 0.8 \times \text{Number of conductors} \times T_c \tag{8–5}$$

In addition to maximum cable tension, the maximum tension of the pulling device must be taken into account. Unless otherwise known, a maximum value of 10,000 lb for a pulling eye may be assumed. For basket grips, a maximum value of 1,000 lb is recommended. Also, it is generally not recommended to pull conductors of different sizes at the same time, nor is it advisable to pull conductors into a raceway already containing conductors.

EXAMPLE 8–11

Determine the maximum allowable pulling tension on (a) single 300 kcmil copper conductor and (b) four-conductor (4/C), 250 kcmil copper, multiconductor cable.

Solution:

a) Application of Equation (8–3a) results in

$$T_c = 0.008 \text{ lb/cmil} \times 300,000 \text{ cmil} = 2,400 \text{ lb}$$

b) Application of Equation (8–3a) results in

$$T_c = 0.008 \text{ lb/cmil} \times 250,000 \text{ cmil} = 2,000 \text{ lb per conductor}$$

Equation (8–5) is applied to determine the maximum allowable tension for the entire cable:

$$T_m = 0.8 \times 4 \times 2,000 \text{ lb} = 6,400 \text{ lb}$$

The tension required to install cable into a conduit is equal to the tension in the cable entering the conduit section plus the frictional force of the cable against the conduit wall. This frictional force depends on the weight of the cable and the coefficient of dynamic friction. The coefficient of dynamic friction depends on the type of insulation on the cable and

---

*From *Southwire Power Cable Manual*. Southwire Company, Carrolton, GA. Data and equations used by permission.

TABLE 8–10
Coefficients of Dynamic Friction

	Type of Conduit			
Cable Insulation	Metallic, Steel, or Aluminum	PVC	Fiber Conduit	Asbestos Cement
PVC—Polyvinyl Chloride	0.4	0.35	0.5	0.5
PE—Low-Density HMW Polyethylene	0.35	0.35	0.5	0.5
CSPE—Hypalon	0.5	0.5	0.7	0.6
XLPE—Cross-Linked Polyethylene	0.35	0.35	0.5	0.5
Nylon	0.4	0.35	0.5	0.5

Source: Southwire Power Cable Manual and Product Catalog, © Southwire Company.

the type of conduit. Table 8–10 lists representative coefficients of dynamic friction for several of the more common types of insulation and conduit.

The equations for tension are given in reference to Figure 8–18. In reference to Figure 8–18(A), the tension in the cable for a horizontal straight pull is*

$$T_{out} = w\mu WL + T_{in} \tag{8–6}$$

where:

w = weight correction factor
μ = coefficient of dynamic friction
W = conductor weight (lb/ft)
L = length of straight horizontal section of pull (ft)
T_{in} = tension of cable entering section (lb)

Weights of several common conductors are shown in Table 8–11. The weight correction factor is a dimensionless quantity that depends primarily on the way in which the cables are configured inside the conduit. For applications in which three cables are pulled, the weight correction factor will typically lie in the range of 1.15 to 1.35.* A value of 1.4 is recommended for applications involving four or more cables.

For pulling upwards in an inclined straight section of conduit, as shown in Figure 8–18(B), the tension is given by*

$$T_{out} = WL (\sin \theta + w\mu \cos \theta) + T_{in} \tag{8–7}$$

For pulling downward in an inclined straight section of conduit, as shown in Figure 8–18(C), the tension is given by*

$$T_{out} = -WL (\sin \theta - w\mu \cos \theta) + T_{in} \tag{8–8}$$

---

*From *Southwire Power Cable Manual*. Southwire Company, Carrolton, GA. Data and equations used by permission.

FIGURE 8–18
Cable Pulling Definitions

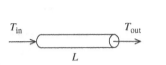

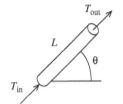

A. Horizontal Straight Pull   **B.** Incline Pulling Up

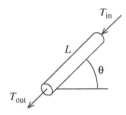

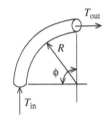

C. Incline Pulling Down   **D.** Bend or "Sweep"

In Equations (8–7) and (8–8), the angle θ is measured with respect to the horizontal, as shown in Figures 8–18(B) and (C).

For pulls around a bend or sweep, as shown in Figure 8–18(D), the tension is given by*

$$T_{out} = T_{in}\, e^{w\mu\varphi} \tag{8–9}$$

The angle ϕ is the angle of the sweep expressed in radians. Recall that to convert from degrees to radians, multiply degrees by $\pi/180$, or 0.0174533.

In addition to the tension in the cable at the outlet of the raceway system, the sidewall pressure of the cable must be calculated. Sidewall pressure is the amount of force in lb/ft that is exerted against the wall of the conduit when cables are pulled around sweeps. Excessive sidewall pressure can lead to damage of the cable. Generally, the maximum permitted sidewall pressure for control cables is 300 lb/ft, and for power cables, 500 lb/ft.* Sidewall pressure is a function of the tension at the outlet of the bend, the radius of the bend, and the weight correction factor. The sidewall pressure for a single cable installed in a conduit is given by*

$$SP = \frac{T_{out}}{R} \tag{8–10}$$

where:

T_{out} = tension at the outlet of the sweep (lb)
R = radius of the sweep (ft)

---

*From *Southwire Power Cable Manual*. Southwire Company, Carrolton, GA. Data and equations used by permission.

TABLE 8–11
Conductor Weights (lb/ft)

Conductor Size	Copper			Aluminum		
	THHN THWN-2	XHHW-2	RHH RHW-2 USE-2	THHN THWN-2	XHHW-2	RHH RHW-2 USE-2
14	0.016	0.018	0.022	N/A	N/A	N/A
12	0.024	0.027	0.029	N/A	N/A	N/A
10	0.038	0.040	0.045	N/A	N/A	N/A
8	0.063	0.064	0.073	N/A	0.028	0.036
6	0.095	0.098	0.107	0.038	0.040	0.049
4	0.153	0.150	0.157	0.062	0.058	0.065
2	0.234	0.231	0.239	0.091	0.085	0.094
1	0.300	0.291	0.308	0.116	0.109	0.125
1/0	0.372	0.362	0.380	0.142	0.133	0.151
2/0	0.463	0.451	0.471	0.172	0.163	0.182
3/0	0.576	0.563	0.585	0.210	0.200	0.221
4/0	0.719	0.704	0.728	0.258	0.247	0.269
250	0.849	0.835	0.866	0.310	0.296	0.326
300	1.010	0.995	1.029	0.364	0.349	0.381
350	1.172	1.115	1.191	0.417	0.401	0.435
400	1.332	1.314	1.352	0.470	0.453	0.489
500	1.652	1.632	1.674	0.575	0.556	0.595
600	1.990	1.966	2.012	0.698	0.679	N/A
750	2.468	2.441	2.492	0.855	0.834	0.882
1000	3.263	3.231	3.288	1.116	1.091	1.146

Source: Southwire Power Cable Manual and Product Catalog, © Southwire Company.

As previously stated, a weight correction factor of 1.4 may be used if four or more cables are installed in a conduit. Under these conditions, the sidewall pressure may be estimated as*

$$SP \approx 0.75 \left[\frac{T_{out}}{R} \right] \tag{8–11}$$

EXAMPLE 8–12

Determine the tension in the cable, and sidewall pressure where applicable, for four 500 kcmil XHHW-2 copper conductors in 4″ PVC conduit under the following conditions. Assume a tension equal to 100 lb at the input to the conduit section. Use a weight correction factor of 1.4 for all calculations.

---

*From *Southwire Power Cable Manual.* Southwire Company, Carrolton, GA. Data and equations used by permission.

a) 200 ft straight horizontal pull
b) 50 ft pull up 30° incline
c) 50 ft pull down 30° incline
d) pull around 90° sweep, 24″ radius

Solution: For all cases, the coefficient of dynamic friction is 0.35. Referring to Table 8–11, the weight of the cable is 1.632 lb/ft.

a) The tension is given by Equation (8–6) as

$$T_{out} = (1.4)(0.35)(1.632 \text{ lb/ft})(200 \text{ ft}) + 100 = 260 \text{ lb}$$

b) The tension is given by Equation (8–7) as

$$T_{out} = WL (\sin \theta + w\mu \cos \theta) + T_{in}$$
$$= (1.632 \text{ lb/ft})(50 \text{ ft})[\sin 30° + (1.4)(0.35)\cos 30°] + 100$$
$$= (81.6)[0.5 + 0.4244] + 100$$
$$= 175.4 \text{ lb}$$

c) The tension is given by Equation (8–8) as

$$T_{out} = -WL (\sin \theta - w\mu \cos \theta) + T_{in}$$
$$= -(1.632 \text{ lb/ft})(50 \text{ ft})[\sin 30° - (1.4)(0.35)\cos 30°] + 100$$
$$= -(81.6)[0.5 - 0.4244] + 100$$
$$= 93.8 \text{ lb}$$

Note that the tension at the outlet is less than the tension at the inlet to the conduit section. This is due to the fact that the weight of the cable exceeds the frictional force in the conduit and subtracts from the tension at the inlet.

d) The angle of the sweep is converted from degrees to radians by multiplying 90° by $\pi/180$. Therefore, 90° = 1.5707 rad. The tension is given by Equation (8–9) as

$$T_{out} = T_{in} e^{w\mu\varphi}$$
$$= (100 \text{ lb})e^{(1.4)(0.35)(1.5707)}$$
$$= (100 \text{ lb})(2.159)$$
$$= 216 \text{ lb}$$

The sidewall pressure is calculated from Equation (8–11) as

$$SP \approx 0.75 \left[\frac{216 \text{ lb}}{2 \text{ ft}} \right] = 81 \text{ lb/ft}$$

This value of sidewall pressure is acceptable for this application.

In many practical installations, the conduit system will consist of various sections of horizontal and vertical runs, as well as sweeps between pull and junction boxes. The pull and junction boxes must be located to minimize the pulling tension during installation. The method used to determine the tension in the cable is to start with the end of the conduit system where the cable is inserted. Then, for each section, calculate the tension on the outlet side of that particular section. This tension then becomes the tension at the inlet of the next section. The process is repeated until the end of this particular run of the conduit system. If the resulting tension exceeds the allowable maximum, additional pull boxes must be located to split up the conduit run into smaller sections. The method is illustrated in the following example.

EXAMPLE 8–13

Determine (a) the maximum allowable tension and (b) the actual pulling tension at the end of the conduit run and sidewall pressure where applicable. The raceway system is shown in Figure 8–19. There are four 500 kcmil XHHW-2 copper conductors in 4″ PVC conduit. Use a weight correction factor of 1.4 for all calculations. Assume a basket grip having a maximum allowable tension of 1000 lb is used.

Solution:

a) The maximum allowable tension is equal to: 4×0.008 lb/cmil $\times 500,000 = 16,000$ lb. The maximum allowable tension due to the limitation of the basket grip is 1000 lb. Therefore, the maximum permitted tension for this installation is 1000 lb.

b) The coefficient of dynamic friction is 0.35. In reference to Figure 8–19, the conduit sections are designated 1, 2, 3, 4, and 5. The tension will be determined starting with section 1 and in each section in progression from sections 1 through 5.

Section 1: $T_{out} = (1.4)(0.35)(1.632 \text{ lb/ft})(100 \text{ ft}) = 80$ lb

Section 2: $T_{out} = (80 \text{ lb}) \, e^{(1.4)(0.35)(1.5707)} = 172.7$ lb. Note that the 80 lb tension at the outlet of section 1 became the tension at the input to section 2. The sidewall pressure is

$$SP \approx 0.75\left[\frac{172.7 \text{ lb}}{2 \text{ ft}}\right] = 65 \text{ lb}$$

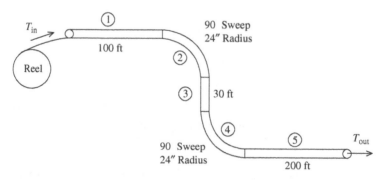

FIGURE 8–19
Example of Cable Pulling Calculations

TABLE 8–12
Cable and Conduit Schedule

No.	From	To	Conduit Size & Type	Conductors Number & Type	Length	Notes
1	UT-Utility Transf	MDP-Main Distr Panel	4" Rigid Steel	4-500 kcmil XHHW-2	30 ft	Service Entrance
2	UT-Utility Transf	MDP-Main Distr Panel	4" Rigid Steel	4-500 kcmil XHHW-2	30 ft	Run Through
3	UT-Utility Transf	MDP-Main Distr Panel	4" Rigid Steel	4-500 kcmil XHHW-2	30 ft	Metering CT's
4	MDP-Main Distr Panel	LP-2	2" EMT	4-#1 AWG THHN 1-#8 AWG ground	30 ft	
5	MDP-Main Distr Panel	LP-3	2" EMT	4-#1 AWG THHN 1-#8 AWG ground	50 ft	
6	MDP-Main Distr Panel	Transfer Switch	2" EMT	4-#3 AWG THHN 1-#8 AWG ground	25 ft	
7	MDP-Main Distr Panel	Chiller	2" EMT	3-#3/0 AWG THHN 1-#6 AWG ground	50 ft	

Section 3: $T_{out} = (1.4)(0.35)(1.632 \text{ lb/ft})(30 \text{ ft}) + 172.7 = 196.7 \text{ lb.}$

Section 4: $T_{out} = (196.7 \text{ lb}) \, e^{(1.4)(0.35)(1.5707)} = 424.7 \text{ lb.}$ The sidewall pressure in conduit section 4 is equal to

$$ SP \approx 0.75 \left[\frac{424.7 \text{ lb}}{2 \text{ ft}} \right] = 159.3 \text{ lb} $$

Section 5: $T_{out} = (1.4)(0.35)(1.632 \text{ lb/ft})(200 \text{ ft}) + 424.7 = 584.6 \text{ lb.}$

8–9   CABLE AND CONDUIT SCHEDULE

To convey the design information regarding conduit and raceway systems to the electrical contractor, a cable and conduit schedule is typically developed by the designer. This schedule contains pertinent information regarding the conduit size and type; conduit originating point (FROM); conduit terminating point (TO); the number, size, and type of cables in the raceway; the length of the raceway; and other special notes regarding the installation. As a general rule, only main feeders supplying panelboards, motors, HVAC equipment, and other major electrical equipment are listed in the cable and conduit schedule. Branch circuits supplying lighting and general-purpose receptacle loads are not usually described in the cable/conduit schedule. The schedule typically includes conduit numbers (or other designation) keyed to the electrical drawings. An example of a cable and conduit schedule is shown in Table 8–12.

PROBLEMS

1. For what reasons are electrical conductors routed in conduit and raceway systems?
2. Are running threads permitted on rigid metal conduit?
3. List the standard trade sizes of rigid metal conduit.
4. What is the minimum bending radius permitted for 2-inch rigid conduit?
5. List the support requirements for rigid metal conduit.
6. How does intermediate metal conduit differ from rigid metal conduit? How is it similar to rigid metal conduit?
7. In what ways does electrical metallic tubing differ from rigid metal conduit?
8. Is electrical metallic tubing permitted to be threaded?
9. List the support requirements for EMT.
10. In what types of areas is EMT permitted to be installed? In what areas is it prohibited?
11. Describe the construction features of rigid nonmetallic conduit.
12. In what types of areas is rigid nonmetallic conduit permitted to be installed? In what areas is it prohibited?
13. Is rigid nonmetallic conduit permitted to be threaded?
14. What are the support requirements for rigid nonmetallic conduit?

15. What is the maximum number of bends (degrees) permitted in any single conduit run?

16. List the construction features, trade sizes, support requirements, permitted uses, and prohibited uses of electrical nonmetallic tubing.

17. List the construction features, trade sizes, support requirements, permitted uses, and prohibited uses of flexible metal conduit.

18. List the construction features, trade sizes, support requirements, permitted uses, and prohibited uses of liquidtight flexible metal conduit.

19. List the construction features, trade sizes, support requirements, permitted uses, and prohibited uses of liquidtight flexible nonmetallic conduit.

20. Determine the minimum trade-size rigid steel conduit required to accommodate four 300 kcmil THW copper conductors and one #2/0 AWG bare copper ground conductor.

21. Determine the minimum trade-size SCH 80 PVC conduit required to accommodate four 600 kcmil THW copper conductors and one 350 kcmil bare copper ground conductor.

22. Determine the minimum trade-size EMT required to accommodate six #4 AWG THW copper conductors.

23. Determine the jamming ratio for the conduit systems described in Problems 20 and 21.

24. Determine the change in length and number of expansion fittings required for a 300 ft run of PVC SCH 80 conduit if the temperature ranges from −10°F to +100°F. Each expansion fitting has a range of 4 in.

25. Determine the minimum pull box length and width required for a straight run consisting of four 4″ EMT and six 2″ EMT conduits. The conduits are arranged in a single row.

26. Determine the minimum pull box length and width required for an angle pull consisting of four 4″ EMT and six 2″ EMT conduits. The conduits are arranged in a single row.

27. Determine the minimum cubic inch capacity of a device box containing the following: six #14 AWG circuit conductors, three #14 AWG equipment grounding conductors, two 15 A SPST toggle switches.

28. How many conductors are permitted in a wireway before application of the derating factors on ampacity are required?

29. What is the maximum percentage fill permitted in a wireway?

30. What are the support requirements for wireways?

31. What size wireway is required for six #4/0 XHHW and three #2/0 XHHW aluminum conductors? The conductors will enter the wireway on top, bend 90°, travel along the wireway, and bend another 90° downward to exit the wireway.

32. What are the protection requirements for nonmetallic sheathed cable run in holes through wood framing members?

33. What is the minimum burial depth of direct-buried cable located under a residential driveway?

34. Why must a seal be placed in a conduit run where adjacent sections of the conduit are subjected to different temperatures?

35. Determine the maximum pulling tension on (a) a single 500 kcmil copper conductor and (b) four-conductor 350 kcmil copper cable.

36. Determine the tension in the cable, and sidewall pressure where applicable, for four 300 kcmil XHHW-2 single-conductor copper cables installed in 3″ rigid steel conduit under the following conditions. Assume a tension equal to 100 lb at the input to the conduit section and a weight correction factor of 1.4 for all calculations.
   a. 300 ft straight pull
   b. 25 ft pull up 45° incline
   c. 40 ft pull down 20° incline
   d. pull around 90° sweep, 24″ radius

37. A raceway system consists of a straight run of 100 ft; a 90°, 36 in. radius sweep; a 50 ft straight run; a 45°, 36 in. radius sweep; a 30 ft straight run; a 90°, 36 in. radius sweep; and a 75 ft straight run. The conduit is 4″ rigid steel containing four 350 kcmil XHHW-2 copper conductors. Sketch the system and determine the actual pulling tension at the end of the conduit run. Assume a basket grip having a maximum tension of 1000 lb is used and a weight correction factor of 1.4.

38. What type of information is typically contained in a cable/conduit schedule?

9

Grounding

INTRODUCTION

Grounding of electrical systems, services, and equipment is done primarily for reasons of safety. In the event of an electrical short circuit between an energized supply conductor and any of the metallic raceway components, the hazards of electrocution must be minimized. In addition, short circuits to ground may produce an excessive amount of arcing at the point of fault, resulting in fires with subsequent damage to property and possibly loss of life. Lightning-induced surges must also be discharged to earth ground to prevent dangerous overvoltages from occurring in various equipment and on equipment enclosures.

System grounding refers to the intentional connection of one of the supply circuit conductors to earth at a particular location. *Service grounding* refers to the connection of the supply conductors and service entrance equipment, such as meters, panels, and disconnects, to earth ground. *Equipment grounding* refers to the intentional connection of equipment enclosures and raceways as well as to earth ground. This chapter discusses the reasons for grounding electrical systems, the types of systems that are required to be grounded, methods of grounding, the grounding electrode system, and methods of equipment and raceway grounding.

OBJECTIVES

Upon completion of this chapter, you will:

- Understand the need to properly ground systems and circuits
- Understand the types of systems required to be grounded and the ways in which these systems are grounded
- Understand the requirements for grounding of service conductors
- Understand the difference between the grounded conductor and the equipment grounding conductor
- Understand the installation and bonding requirements for the grounding electrode system
- Understand service entrance grounding requirements
- Understand requirements for grounding of separately derived systems
- Understand the requirements for grounding and bonding of subpanels
- Be able to properly size equipment bonding jumpers
- Be able to properly size equipment grounding conductors

9–1   REASONS FOR GROUNDING

Minimize Overvoltages

As previously stated, grounding is done primarily for reasons of safety. Figure 9–1 illustrates the need for grounding to prevent overvoltages from occurring on the power system. Note that a lightning arrester is located on the top of the pole-mounted transformer, next to the transformer bushing. The utility phase conductor is connected to the arrester, as shown in the schematic. The other side of the arrester is connected to ground, as shown. For normal power system voltages and operation, the lightning arrester assumes an open circuit condition. If the voltage across the arrester exceeds the voltage rating of the arrester, it

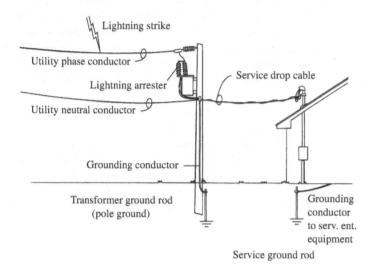

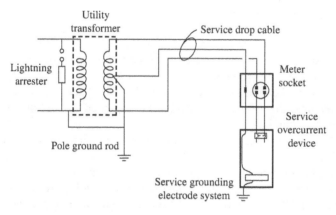

FIGURE 9–1
Reasons for Grounding

goes into operation, resulting in a low-impedance path to ground through the arrester. The utility neutral conductor is also connected to the earth ground, as shown.

On the low-voltage side of the transformer, one of the secondary terminals is connected to earth ground. The grounded service conductor is routed, along with the ungrounded service conductors, to the meter socket, then to the service entrance panel of the building. Note that the grounded service conductor is also connected to earth ground at the service entrance through the grounding electrode system.

In reference to Figure 9–1, assume a lightning strike occurs on the utility phase conductor. This lightning strike will induce a surge voltage in the phase conductor as the surge current travels along the phase conductor toward earth ground. A surge voltage will also be induced in the utility neutral conductor due to electromagnetic induction. When the lightning-induced surge voltage reaches the pole-top transformer, the large magnitude of the surge voltage causes the lightning arrester to operate. Operation of the lightning arrester allows the surge to discharge to ground, traveling down the grounding conductor alongside the pole, and then to the ground rod located next to the pole. Essentially, a closed path to ground for the flow of surge current electrons has been established. Once the flow of electrons ceases, the lightning arrester once again assumes an open circuit condition to the normal system voltage.

In addition to providing a path to ground for the flow of electrons, the connection of one of the service supply conductors to earth ground stabilizes service voltage. Without the earth ground, the service voltage may float and could become dangerously high under certain conditions. Likewise, the connection of the utility neutral to earth ground ensures that the voltage on the utility system neutral with respect to the surrounding earth remains at an acceptable level.

Limit Voltage Potential on Equipment Enclosures

Grounding as a means of limiting the voltage potential on equipment enclosures is illustrated in Figure 9–2. Note that conditions are shown for both an ungrounded motor frame and a grounded motor frame. The ungrounded motor will operate satisfactorily with no obvious indication that the motor frame is not grounded. But consider what happens if an insulation failure occurs in one of the motor leads or the windings themselves, resulting in one of the phase (ungrounded) conductors coming in contact with the motor frame. Since the motor frame is not grounded, there is no path for the flow of current to return to the system, with the result that there is no increase in current through the motor feeder overcurrent devices and the system remains energized. However, the connection of the energized conductor to the motor frame now places a voltage equal to the line-to-ground voltage of the system onto the motor frame. On a 480 V, three-phase system, the result is a voltage of 277 V applied to the motor frame. If someone were to place one hand on the motor frame and the other hand on a grounded surface, such as the building structural steel, the path of current flow would be directly through the heart, resulting in electrocution.

Connecting the motor frame to ground by use of an equipment grounding conductor provides a low-impedance path between the motor frame and ground. Since the equipment grounding conductor is connected to the grounding electrode system at the supply, the motor frame is essentially tied to ground potential. If an ungrounded phase conductor were

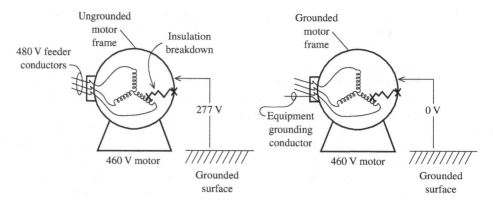

FIGURE 9–2
Limiting of Voltage Potential on Equipment

to come in contact with the motor frame, there would be no appreciable voltage difference present between the frame and ground. Thus, a person in contact with the motor frame and a grounded surface will not experience any appreciable voltage difference. In effect, the connection of the equipment grounding conductor to the motor frame has ensured that the voltage on the motor frame will be kept to a minimum in the event of a phase-to-ground short circuit in the motor windings.

Provide a Low-Impedance Path for Fault Current

Grounding as a means of providing a low-impedance path for the flow of fault current is illustrated in Figure 9–3. As in Figure 9–2, conditions are shown for both an ungrounded motor frame and a grounded motor frame. As before, for the ungrounded situation, the motor will operate satisfactorily in the event of a fault between the ungrounded conductor and the motor frame with no obvious indication that the motor frame is not grounded.

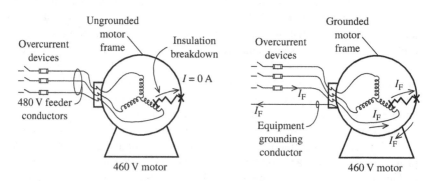

FIGURE 9–3
Providing Path for Flow of Short Circuit Current

There is no path for the flow of current to return to the system, since the motor frame is not grounded. The result is that there is no appreciable increase in current through the motor feeder overcurrent devices. The overcurrent device contacts remain closed, and the system remains energized.

Connecting the motor frame to ground by use of an equipment grounding conductor provides a low-impedance path between the motor frame and ground. An ungrounded energized conductor coming in contact with the motor frame will result in an appreciable amount of short circuit current flowing through the overcurrent devices. The overcurrent devices will operate to clear the short circuit, thereby removing the dangerous condition and causing the motor to shut down. In this case, the equipment ground serves as a means to allow a sufficient magnitude of short circuit current to flow, permitting operation of the protective devices.

9–2   SYSTEM GROUNDING

The *NEC* requires grounding of certain systems for safety purposes. Specifically, Section 250.20(B)(1) of the *NEC* requires grounding of a system that can be grounded such that the maximum voltage between the ungrounded (phase) conductors and the grounded conductor does not exceed 150 V. This requirement would apply to the 120 V, single-phase, two-wire system shown in Figure 9–4(A) and the 120/240 V, single-phase, three-wire system shown in Figure 9–4(B). Section 250.20(B)(2) of the *NEC* also states that any three-phase, four-wire, wye-connected system that uses the neutral conductor as a return for unbalanced load current must be grounded. Examples of three-phase, four-wire, wye-connected systems that must be grounded are the 208Y/120 V and 480Y/277 V systems shown in Figure 9–4(C). Three-phase, four-wire systems supplied from a delta connection with one of the transformers tapped midphase are required to be grounded in accordance with Section 250-20(B)(3) of the *NEC*. The 240/120 V, three-phase, four-wire delta system shown in Figure 9–4(E) is an example of this requirement. Three-phase, three-wire systems supplied from a delta connection, as shown in Figure 9–4(D), are not required to be grounded by the *NEC*. While it is not required, the three-phase, three-wire delta system is permitted to be grounded. Certain industrial applications require an ungrounded three-phase, three-wire system. Typical system voltages for three-phase, three-wire delta systems are 240 V, 480 V, and 600 V.

The secondary supply of each system in Figure 9–4 is shown as being derived from the secondary of a utility transformer. The primary winding configuration will vary depending on the practices of the local service utility. The service entrance conductors are shown between the utility transformer and the service entrance. These conductors may be installed by either the utility company or the electrical contractor, depending on the local requirements and regulations. The service entrance is shown to the far right in each schematic.

Note that in each system shown in Figure 9–4, an earth ground is provided on the secondary of each transformer. To provide this earth ground, a driven ground rod or other made electrode is placed either near the pole, for overhead service, or near the pad-mount transformer, for underground services. For reasons previously discussed, the earth ground at the transformer provides a means of grounding the secondary winding of the transformer.

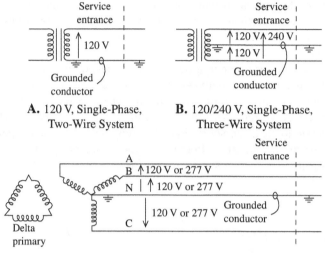

A. 120 V, Single-Phase,
Two-Wire System

B. 120/240 V, Single-Phase,
Three-Wire System

C. 208Y/120 V, or 480Y/277 V, Three-Phase, Four-Wire Wye System

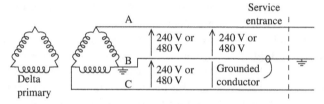

D. 240 V or 480 V, Three-Phase, Three-Wire Delta System

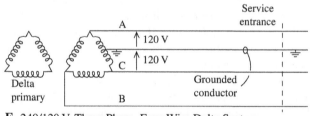

E. 240/120 V, Three-Phase, Four-Wire Delta System

FIGURE 9–4
Grounding of Common Systems

The grounded service conductor is connected to the grounded transformer secondary terminal as shown. This grounded conductor is routed with the ungrounded conductors to the service entrance. At the service entrance, an additional earth ground is provided by the grounding electrode system. The actual components comprising the grounding electrode system are discussed in the next section. On the load side of the service entrance, separate grounded conductor and equipment grounding conductors are required.

9–3   GROUNDING ELECTRODE SYSTEM

The grounded conductor of the supply system is connected to the grounding electrode system at the service entrance. The grounding electrode system effectively ties the system to earth ground at this point. The purpose of connecting the system to earth ground is to provide a means for overvoltages and induced surges to dissipate to ground. The grounding electrode system also forms a zero-voltage-potential plane in the vicinity of the electrical service. Thus, the bonding of all metal components of the raceway system and equipment enclosures to the grounding electrode system will ensure that there is no appreciable voltage difference between these components and earth ground.

The components of the grounding electrode system are shown in Figure 9–5. To form a true zero-potential grounding plane for all components of the system, Section 250.50 of the *NEC* requires that where present in the building, the metal framework of the building, metal underground water pipe, concrete-encased electrode, ground ring, and any other made or supplemental electrodes must be bonded together. *Bonding* refers to the intentional electrical connection between two or more metallic components. This bonding will ensure that all components so connected will assume the same electrical potential, with no potential difference between them.

The grounding electrode conductor is typically bare copper and must be protected where subject to physical damage. Protection is usually afforded by installing the grounding electrode conductor in rigid metal conduit, intermediate metal conduit, electrical metallic tubing, or rigid nonmetallic conduit (SCH 80). If protected by metallic conduit, both ends of the conduit must be bonded to the grounding electrode conductor to prevent the chocking effect of inductance, which will increase the effective impedance of the grounding electrode conductor during fault conditions. Section 250.64(C) of the *NEC* prohibits splicing of grounding electrode conductors unless connectors listed for such an application are used. Splicing may be done with irreversible compression-type connectors or exothermic weld.

Metal Underground Water Pipe

The metal underground water pipe is a required part of the grounding electrode system, subject to several *NEC* rules, which are covered in Section 250.52(A)(1). Essentially, any metal underground water pipe in contact with the earth for at least 10 feet of its length must be part of the grounding electrode system. This 10 foot section of underground pipe must be continuous and cannot be made discontinuous by removal of any joints or by the installation of nonmetallic sections. Continuity must be maintained by installing suitable bonding jumpers around devices likely to be disconnected and around nonmetallic sections.

It is common practice in many installations to use the interior metal water pipe as a bus for the connection of other grounding electrode conductors. In other words, a single grounding electrode conductor may be run from the service entrance equipment to the interior metal water pipe. Other grounding electrodes are then connected to the interior metal water pipe and run to their respective grounding electrodes. Section 250.52(A)(1) of the *NEC* restricts this practice to interior metal water pipe within 5 feet of the service entrance equipment. The interior metal water piping that is more than 5 feet from the service entrance cannot be used as a bus for the connection of other grounding electrode conductors.

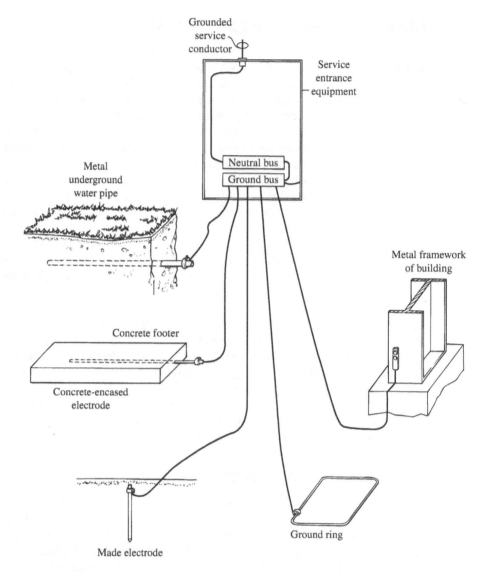

FIGURE 9–5
Grounding Electrode System Requirements

The exception to this rule is commercial and industrial occupancies where qualified maintenance personnel are permitted to maintain the system. Also, the entire length of the interior metal water piping used for the purpose of connecting other grounding electrode conductors must be exposed.

Sizing of the grounding electrode conductor connecting the metal underground water pipe to the ground bus of the service entrance equipment is based on the size of the ungrounded service entrance conductors. Table 250.66 of the *NEC,* shown in Table 9–1,

TABLE 9–1

Table 250.66 Grounding Electrode Conductor for Alternating-Current Systems

Size of Largest Ungrounded Service-Entrance Conductor or Equivalent Area for Parallel Conductors[a] (AWG/kcmil)		Size of Grounding Electrode Conductor (AWG/kcmil)	
Copper	Aluminum or Copper-Clad Aluminum	Copper	Aluminum or Copper-Clad Aluminum[b]
2 or smaller	1/0 or smaller	8	6
1 or 1/0	2/0 or 3/0	6	4
2/0 or 3/0	4/0 or 250	4	2
Over 3/0 through 350	Over 250 through 500	2	1/0
Over 350 through 600	Over 500 through 900	1/0	3/0
Over 600 through 1100	Over 900 through 1750	2/0	4/0
Over 1100	Over 1750	3/0	250

Notes:
1. Where multiple sets of service-entrance conductors are used as permitted in 230.40, Exception No. 2, the equivalent size of the largest service-entrance conductor shall be determined by the largest sum of the areas of the corresponding conductors of each set.
2. Where there are no service-entrance conductors, the grounding electrode conductor size shall be determined by the equivalent size of the largest service-entrance conductor required for the load to be served.

[a]This table also applies to the derived conductors of separately derived ac systems.
[b]See installation restrictions in 250.64(A).
Source: Reprinted with permission from NFPA 70 *The National Electric Code* © 2002, National Fire Protection Association, Quincy, MA 02269. This reprinted material is not the referenced subject which is represented only by the standard in its entirety.

lists the minimum required size of the grounding electrode conductor for connection to the metal water pipe. Note that although the required grounding electrode conductor may be copper, aluminum, or copper-clad aluminum, copper is usually used. Also note that for service entrance conductors larger than 1100 kcmil copper, or 1750 kcmil aluminum, the minimum-size grounding electrode conductor required for connection to the metal water pipe is #3/0 copper or 250 kcmil aluminum.

EXAMPLE 9–1

Determine the minimum-size copper grounding electrode conductor for connection of the system to the metal underground water pipe for services consisting of the following ungrounded service entrance conductors:

a) #4/0 XHHW aluminum
b) 500 kcmil XHHW copper
c) four 500 kcmil XHHW copper parallel per phase

Solution:

a) From Table 250.66, the required minimum size is #4 copper.
b) From Table 250.66, the required minimum size is #1/0 copper.
c) The total equivalent cross-sectional area is 4×500 kcmil $= 2000$ kcmil. Thus, from Table 250.66, the required minimum size is #3/0 copper.

The metal underground water pipe must be supplemented with an additional electrode as required by Section 250.53(D)(2) of the *NEC*. This additional electrode can be the metal framework of the building, a concrete-encased electrode, a grounding ring, or a made electrode, as appropriate.

Metal Framework of Building

The connection of the metal framework of the building to the grounding electrode system ensures that any accidental contact between an ungrounded conductor of the supply to the building structural steel will result in no excessive voltage on the structural steel members. This connection will also ensure that sufficient fault current will flow to operate any overcurrent protective devices on the source side of the fault. The minimum size for the grounding electrode conductor connected to the building structural steel is also based on Table 250.66 of the *NEC*.

Concrete-Encased Electrode

An electrode embedded in the concrete foundation or footer in direct contact with the earth can serve as part of the grounding electrode system according to Section 250.52(A)(3) of the *NEC*. To serve this purpose, the *NEC* requires the embedded conductor to be bare or galvanized steel reinforcing bar not less than ½ inch in diameter or a minimum of 20 feet of #4 AWG or larger bare copper conductor. The *NEC* also requires these electrodes to be encased in at least 2 inches of concrete and to be placed near the bottom of the footing. The grounding electrode conductor that serves as the connection to this concrete-encased electrode is not required to be larger than #4 AWG copper. Consultation with the local electrical inspector to determine if bonding of the reinforcing steel is required is strongly advised if reinforcing bar is to be used as part of the foundation or footing in any building.

Ground Ring

A ground ring is defined by Section 250.52(A)(4) of the *NEC* as consisting of at least 20 feet of #2 AWG or larger bare copper conductor directly buried at least 30 inches below the top of finished grade. This ground ring typically encircles the entire building. The grounding electrode conductor that serves as the connection to the ground ring is not required to be larger than the conductor used for the ground ring.

Made Electrode

As previously mentioned, a grounding electrode system consisting solely of a metal under-ground water pipe must be supplemented with an additional grounding electrode. The supplemental electrode may be the building structural steel, a ground ring, or a concrete-encased electrode. Section 250.52(B) of the *NEC* prohibits metal underground gas pipe or aluminum electrodes to be used as a grounding electrode. The most common practice is to use a rod and pipe electrode or plate electrodes as the supplemental made electrode. The grounding electrode conductor that serves as the connection to the made electrode is not required to be larger than the #6 AWG copper or #4 AWG aluminum.

Section 250.52(A)(5) of the *NEC* allows a pipe electrode to consist of pipe or conduit no smaller than ¾ inch trade size and at least 8 feet in length. In addition, the *NEC* requires a rod electrode to be at least ⅝ inch in diameter and 8 feet in length. Where not inherently corrosion resistant, the outer surface of any rod or pipe electrode must be galvanized or coated to prevent corrosion. Aluminum ground rods are not permitted by the *NEC*. The most common rod electrode is the ⅝ inch diameter, 8 foot long, copper-clad steel ground rod. In accordance with Section 250.53(G) of the *NEC*, rod and pipe electrodes are typically driven vertically to a depth of 8 feet below finished grade. If rock prevents the rod from being driven vertically to a depth of 8 feet, the rod may be driven at an angle not to exceed 45 degrees from the vertical. The rod may also be buried horizontally in the trench at least 30 inches below finished grade. In all cases, the rod must be in direct contact with the earth for at least 8 feet of its length. Requirements for plate-type electrodes are covered in Section 250.52(A)(6) of the *NEC*.

The resistance to ground of any made electrode must not exceed 25 ohms, as required by Section 250.56 of the *NEC*. If the resistance exceeds 25 ohms, the made electrode must be supplemented by at least one additional electrode. This additional electrode may be the metal underground water pipe, a concrete-encased electrode, a ground ring, the metal frame of the building, or other made electrode. Typically, an additional made rod or plate electrode is installed to meet this requirement. Additional made electrodes must be spaced at least 6 feet apart to obtain maximum benefit.

9–4   SERVICE GROUNDING REQUIREMENTS

Single Service Disconnect

The requirements for grounding services differ somewhat depending on the arrangement of the service entrance equipment. The requirements for grounding at the service entrance comprised of a single panelboard containing the main service disconnect are shown in Figure 9–6(A). Note that in Figure 9–6(A), the grounded service conductor is connected to the neutral bus in the service entrance equipment. A separate ground bus for connection of the equipment grounding conductors and grounding electrode conductors is also shown. The neutral bus is bonded to the ground bus by means of a main bonding jumper. The main bonding jumper also connects the ground bus to the service entrance equipment enclosure.

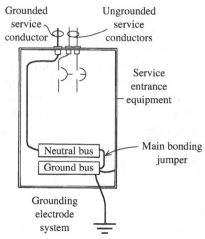

A. Service Disconnect Located in Panel

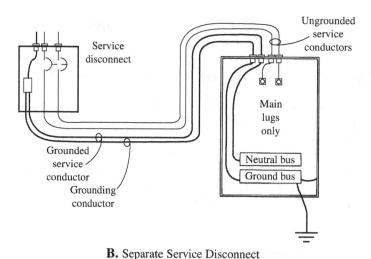

B. Separate Service Disconnect

FIGURE 9–6
Service Grounding Requirements—Single Service Disconnect

Most panelboards marked as suitable for use as service entrance equipment have a combined neutral bus and ground bus. This combined bus consists of a terminal strip with terminals for connection of the grounded conductor and the grounding conductors of the system. The combined bus is typically insulated from the equipment enclosure itself. In these types of panelboards, the main bonding jumper consists of a screw terminal in the neutral bus. Bonding of the enclosure is accomplished by turning the screw, thereby connecting the combined neutral and ground bus to the equipment enclosure. The grounding electrode conductors connect each of the components of the grounding electrode system to the ground bus, as shown.

In many installations, the main service disconnect is separated from the main service panel, as shown in Figure 9–6(B). An installation where the main service disconnect is located near the service drop and meter, with the panel located inside the building, is an example of such a separation. To meet the requirements of Section 250.6(A) of the *NEC*, bonding of the grounded service conductor and the grounding electrode system can occur only at the service entrance equipment. No other connection between the grounded conductor and grounding conductors is permitted. In the system shown in Figure 9–6(B), a separate, insulated grounded conductor is required to run from the service disconnect to the panel. An equipment grounding conductor is also run from the service disconnect to the panel. In the panel, there is no connection between the neutral bus and the ground bus. If a panelboard having a single neutral/ground bus is installed, the main bonding jumper screw must not be installed. In addition, a separate equipment ground bus must be installed to allow for connection of the equipment grounding conductors.

The main bonding jumper connects the service equipment enclosure to the grounded service conductor of the system. In the event of a short circuit to ground on the supply side of the main service overcurrent device, ground fault current will flow through the service raceway to the service equipment enclosure, then through the main bonding jumper to the grounded conductor of the system. Thus, the main bonding jumper must be sized to carry the ground fault current until the upstream protective devices operate to clear the fault.

The main bonding jumper is sized according to Table 250.66, as shown in Table 9–1, for service entrance conductors having a cross-sectional area up to 1100 kcmil for copper or 1750 kcmil for aluminum. Above these maximum-size service entrance conductors, Section 250.102(C) of the *NEC* requires the cross-sectional area of the main bonding jumper to be at least equal to 12.5% of the cross-sectional area of the service entrance conductors. Where different conductor material is used for the service conductor and main bonding jumper, the size of the main bonding jumper is determined by assuming a phase conductor of the same material as the bonding jumper. The ampacity of the assumed phase conductor must be at least equal to the ampacity of the installed phase conductors.

EXAMPLE 9–2

Determine the required copper main bonding jumper for the following service entrance conductors:

a) #4/0 XHHW copper
b) 500 kcmil XHHW copper
c) four 500 kcmil XHHW copper per phase
d) 600 kcmil XHHW aluminum
e) four 500 kcmil XHHW aluminum per phase

Solution:

a) The required copper main bonding jumper is read directly from Table 250.66 as #2 AWG.
b) The required copper main bonding jumper is read directly from Table 250.66 as #1/0 AWG.

c) The total equivalent cross-sectional area of all phase conductors is 2000 kcmil. The minimum required cross-sectional area for the main bonding jumper is

$$(12.5\%)(2000 \text{ kcmil}) = 250 \text{ kcmil}$$

Therefore, a 250 kcmil copper conductor at minimum is required for the main bonding jumper.

d) The minimum required main bonding jumper size is based on the copper equivalent of the 600 kcmil aluminum service-phase conductors. From Table 310.16 of the *NEC*, the ampacity of the 600 kcmil XHHW aluminum conductors is 340 A @ 75°C. The equivalent copper conductor is 500 kcmil, having a table-listed ampacity of 380 A @ 75°C. The required copper main bonding jumper size is based on 500 kcmil copper. From Table 250.66, the required main bonding jumper is #1/0 copper.

e) The minimum required main bonding jumper size is based on the copper equivalent of the four 500 kcmil XHHW aluminum conductors per phase. These conductors have an ampacity of 310 A each @ 75°C, or 1240 A for all four in parallel. The equivalent copper conductor is 350 kcmil, having a table-listed ampacity of 310 A @ 75°, or 1240 A for four conductors parallel per phase. The total cross-sectional area of four 350 kcmil conductors per phase is 1400 kcmil. The minimum required cross-sectional area for the main bonding jumper is

$$(12.5\%)(1400 \text{ kcmil}) = 175 \text{ kcmil}$$

Therefore, a minimum #4/0 copper conductor having a cross-sectional area of 211.6 kcmil is required for the main bonding jumper.

The grounded service conductor originates from the utility supply and terminates in the service entrance equipment. Section 250.24(B) of the *NEC* requires the grounded conductor to be run to each service disconnect and to be routed with the ungrounded phase conductors. The minimum required size of the grounded service conductor is based on the size of the ungrounded phase conductors in accordance with Table 250.66. For ungrounded phase conductors larger than 1100 kcmil copper or 1750 kcmil aluminum, Section 250.24(B)(1) of the *NEC* requires the grounded conductor to be sized no smaller than 12.5% of the cross-sectional area of the phase conductors. The grounded service conductor is not required to be larger than the ungrounded phase conductors.

For cases where the service conductors are installed in parallel in two or more raceways, the grounded conductor shall also be routed in parallel in each raceway. Section 250.24(B)(2) of the *NEC* requires the size of the parallel grounded conductor in each raceway to be based on the cross-sectional area of the ungrounded phase conductor in each raceway. The grounded service conductor cannot be smaller than #1/0 for parallel installations.

Note that sizing of the grounded conductor for the purposes of this section does not take into account the requirements for sizing based on the unbalanced load current expected. Sizing of the grounded conductor to carry the maximum unbalanced load current is determined in Chapter 10, on services. The actual size of the grounded conductor is based on the larger of that required for grounding and that required to carry the maximum unbalanced load current.

EXAMPLE 9–3

Determine the size of copper grounded conductor required for the following based solely on grounding requirements:

a) 500 kcmil XHHW copper
b) four 500 kcmil XHHW copper parallel per phase run in four raceways.

Solution:

a) The minimum required grounded conductor is read directly from Table 250.66 as #1/0 AWG copper.
b) Since each raceway contains one 500 kcmil conductor per phase, the minimum required grounded service conductor in each raceway is also #1/0 AWG copper. Therefore, each conduit will contain three 500 kcmil XHHW copper ungrounded phase conductors and one #1/0 AWG grounded conductor.

Multiple Service Disconnect

In multiple occupancy units, or in other, similar installations, the service may consist of several service disconnects, as shown in Figure 9–7. Under this condition, the grounded service conductor must be run to each service disconnect as required by Section 250.24(B) of the *NEC*. The exception to this rule is that a single grounded conductor may be run to a group of service disconnects located in the same equipment enclosure. The size of the grounded service conductor entering the wireway from the service would be based on the cross-sectional area of the service conductors. The size of the grounded service conductor taps from the wireway to the individual service disconnects would be based on the cross-sectional area of the ungrounded tap conductors.

EXAMPLE 9–4

A service consisting of three disconnects is supplied by one 500 kcmil XHHW copper conductor per phase. The service disconnects are rated 100 A, 100 A, and 200 A. The tap conductors to the 200 A disconnect are #3/0 AWG XHHW copper, and the tap conductors to the 100 A disconnect is #3 AWG XHHW copper. Determine the size of the copper conductor that will meet the requirements for grounding for (a) the grounded service conductor, (b) the grounded service conductor tap to the 100 A disconnect, and (c) the grounded service conductor tap to the 200 A disconnect.

Solution:

a) The size of the grounded service conductor is based on the 500 kcmil service conductors and is read directly from Table 250.66. The required size is #1/0 AWG copper.
b) The size of the grounded service conductor is based on the #3 AWG copper tap conductors and is read directly from Table 250.66. The required size is #8 AWG copper.
c) The size of the grounded service conductor is based on the #3/0 AWG copper tap conductors and is read directly from Table 250.66. The required size is #4 AWG copper.

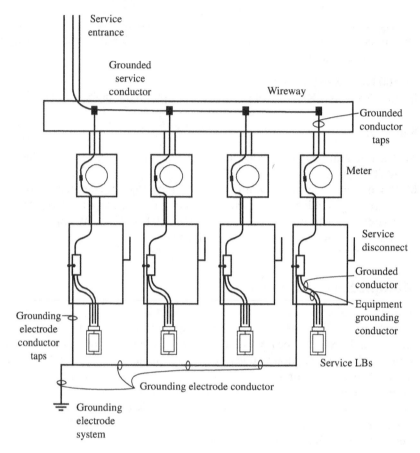

FIGURE 9–7
Service Grounding Requirements—Multiple Service Disconnect

Section 250.64(D) of the *NEC* permits the grounding electrode conductor to be tapped, as shown in Figure 9–7. The grounding electrode conductor must remain intact without any splices or joints that will compromise the continuity of the grounding electrode conductor. The size of the grounding electrode conductor is determined as previously discussed for the individual service disconnect and grounding electrode system. The grounding electrode taps to each service disconnect are sized based on the size of the ungrounded phase conductors supplied by the respective service disconnect enclosure.

EXAMPLE 9–5

Determine the required grounding electrode conductor for the service configuration of Example 9–4.

Solution: The main grounding electrode conductor is based on the 500 kcmil copper service conductors. The grounding electrode conductor taps are sized based on the size of the conductor taps entering the individual service disconnects. Therefore, the required grounding electrode conductors are #1/0 AWG copper for the main grounding electrode conductor, #8 AWG copper for the grounding electrode conductor tap to the 100 A disconnect, and #4 AWG copper for the grounding electrode conductor tap to the 200 A disconnect.

Service Supplied from Another Building

The method of grounding a service supplied from another building is shown in Figure 9–8. Note that the grounded service conductor is connected to the grounding electrode system at the main service panel. Separate equipment-grounding conductors and grounded conductors are run from the main panel to the subpanel. This situation is similar to the grounding requirements of the system shown in Figure 9–6(B). A grounding electrode system satisfying the requirements as previously stated is required in the separate building.

EXAMPLE 9–6

A separate building is supplied with a 200 A service from the main service entrance. A 200 A overcurrent device located in the main service panel protects the #3/0 XHHW copper feeder conductors to the separate building service. Determine the size of the copper conductor required for (a) the grounded service conductor and (b) the equipment grounding conductor for this installation.

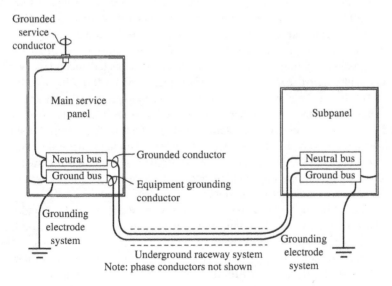

FIGURE 9–8
Grounding of Service Supplied from a Separate Building

Solution:

a) The minimum-size grounded service conductor required between the main panel and subpanel is based on the size of the feeder conductors and is read from Table 250.66. Therefore, the minimum required grounded service conductor is #4 AWG copper. This conductor must be insulated to ensure that there is no connection between the grounded conductor and the grounding system on the load side of the service disconnect. Keep in mind that this is the minimum required for grounding purposes only. The actual size will be determined only after unbalanced current is taken into account.

b) The minimum-size equipment grounding conductor required is based on the 200 A overcurrent device protecting the feeder conductors. The required equipment grounding conductor is read directly from Table 250.122, as shown in Table 9–2 on page 227. The required size is #6 AWG copper as read from the table.

9–5   GROUNDING OF SEPARATELY DERIVED SYSTEMS

A separately derived system is a system in which there is no direct electrical connection between the ungrounded phase conductors of the service and the ungrounded phase conductors of the separately derived system. In addition, there is no direct electrical connection between the grounded (neutral) conductor of the service and the grounded (neutral) conductor of the separately derived system. The need for a separately derived system occurs in many commercial and industrial power distribution systems where a supply voltage different from that of the service voltage is required for certain loads. A common example is a commercial establishment supplied at a service voltage of 480Y/277 V that requires 120 V for general-use receptacles and other 120 V loads. A single-phase or three-phase dry-type transformer is commonly used to step down the voltage to the appropriate level. In the example just described, a three-phase transformer having a 480 V, delta-connected high-side winding and a 208Y/120 V wye-connected secondary winding could be used. As an alternative, a single-phase transformer having a 480 V high-voltage winding and a 120/240 V low-voltage winding could also be used to provide the required low voltage.

Another example of a separately derived system is an emergency generator connected to the building electrical system by means of a transfer switch. If the transfer switch switches all ungrounded and grounded conductors, then the generator system is considered a separately derived system. If, however, the transfer switch does not switch the grounded conductor along with the ungrounded phase conductors, then the generator system is not considered a separately derived system.

Section 250.30(A)(1) of the *NEC* requires that the grounded conductor of a separately derived system must be connected to the equipment grounding conductors either at the source of the separately derived system or at the first disconnect. The grounding requirements for separately derived systems supplied from transformers are shown in Figure 9–9. With reference to Figure 9–9(A), the bonding jumper is shown connected between the secondary neutral terminal of the transformer and the transformer enclosure. The secondary neutral terminal is also connected to the grounding electrode system.

FIGURE 9–9
Grounding of Separately
Derived System

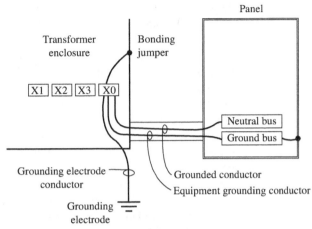

A. Bonding at Transformer Enclosure

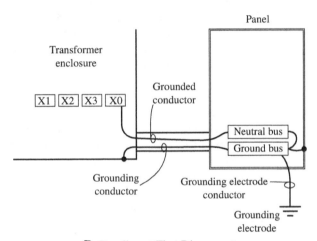

B. Bonding at First Disconnect

Separate equipment grounding and grounded conductors are run from the grounded trans-former secondary terminal to the panel.

Figure 9–9(B) shows the requirements for grounding if the bonding jumper is placed in the panel. In this situation, there can be no connection between the grounded trans-former secondary terminal and the transformer enclosure in the transformer enclosure itself if a metal raceway is used between the transformer enclosure and the panel. Bonding the transformer grounded secondary terminal to the transformer enclosure and bonding the grounded conductor to the equipment ground in the panel would create a parallel path for the flow of unbalanced neutral current between the panel and the transformer enclosure. The unbalanced neutral current would flow from the panel back to the transformer through the parallel path created by the grounded conductor and the metal raceway system. This would be a violation of Section 250.6(A) of the *NEC* and could result in unsafe neutral-to-earth voltages in the system.

The transformer enclosure can be grounded by running a separate equipment-grounding conductor from the panel back to the transformer enclosure, as shown in Figure 9–9(B). It is also possible to use a metallic raceway as the grounding conductor between the panel and the transformer enclosure. If the metal raceway is used as the equipment grounding conductor between the panel and transformer enclosure, the raceway and fittings must be listed for the application. This will ensure that a solid connection exists for proper grounding continuity. Note that in the arrangement shown in Figure 9–9(B), there is no possibility for unbalanced neutral current to find a parallel path from the panel back to the transformer secondary.

The size of the bonding jumper is based on the size of the phase conductors of the separately derived system in accordance with Sections 250.30(A)(1) and 250.28(D) of the *NEC*. Table 250.66 applies if the ungrounded phase conductors of the derived system are smaller than 1100 kcmil copper or 1750 kcmil aluminum. If the ungrounded phase conductors are larger than 1100 kcmil copper or 1750 kcmil aluminum, the bonding jumper must be sized no smaller than 12.5% of the cross-sectional area of the ungrounded phase conductor. The equipment grounding conductor between the transformer enclosure and the panel should be sized in the same manner as the bonding jumper, since it is on the line side of the first disconnect of the separately derived system.

EXAMPLE 9–7

A separately derived system is supplied by a three-phase step-down transformer. The ungrounded secondary conductors of the derived system are 300 kcmil THW copper. Determine the required copper bonding jumper and copper equipment-grounding conductor for this installation.

Solution: The size is read directly from Table 250.66 as #2 AWG copper.

The grounding electrode conductor must be connected to the grounding electrode system either at the transformer enclosure, as shown in Figure 9–9(A), or at the first disconnect, as shown in Figure 9–9(B). Section 250.30(A)(2) of the *NEC* requires connection of the grounding electrode conductor to the system in the same location as the bonding jumper. Section 250.30(A)(4) of the *NEC* requires that the connection to the grounding electrode system be as near as practicable to the grounding electrode conductor connection to the system. Also, Section 250.30(A)(4) of the *NEC* requires that, if available, the grounding electrode system of the separately derived system must be comprised of the effectively grounded building structural steel or effectively grounded metal water pipe within 5 feet of the entrance to the building. If structural steel or a metal water pipe is not available, a concrete-encased electrode, ground ring, or made electrode can be used. If the separately derived system originates in service entrance equipment, the grounding electrode system of the service may also be used as the grounding electrode system for the separately derived system. Sizing of the grounding electrode conductor is based on Table 250-66 for the derived phase conductors.

EXAMPLE 9–8

Determine the required copper grounding-electrode conductor for the separately derived system of Example 9–7.

Solution: In this case, the grounding electrode conductor is based on the 300 kcmil copper ungrounded phase conductors of the separately derived system. The required size is read from Table 250.66 as #2 AWG copper.

The grounding requirements for a separately derived system supplied from an emergency generator are illustrated in Figure 9–10. Recall that a separately grounded system is

FIGURE 9–10
Grounding of Separately Derived
Emergency Generator Supply

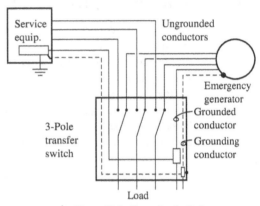

A. Three-Pole Transfer Switch

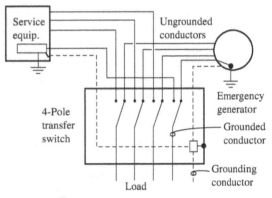

B. Four-Pole Transfer Switch

one in which there is no direct electrical connection between the ungrounded and grounded conductors of the main supply and the derived system. Figure 9–10(A) shows a generator connected to a transfer switch in which only the ungrounded conductors are switched. The grounded conductor is not switched by the transfer switch. Since this is not considered a separately derived system, connection of the grounded conductor to the grounding electrode system or other grounding conductor is not permitted. In this instance, the grounded conductor is connected to the grounding electrode system only at the service disconnect, as shown. The grounding conductor is run to the generator only to provide for equipment grounding.

In the system shown in Figure 9–10(B), the transfer switch switches both the ungrounded and grounded conductors. By definition, this is considered a separately derived system. As such, bonding of the grounded conductor to the grounding electrode system is required at the generator. Failure to do so will result in the loss of system ground when the transfer switch switches to the generator source.

9–6   EQUIPMENT GROUNDING

Grounding of electrical equipment will ensure that dangerous voltages will not be present on equipment enclosures should a ground fault occur. The grounding of equipment enclosures is accomplished by connecting an equipment grounding conductor to the equipment enclosure. This equipment grounding conductor is then connected to the grounding electrode system at the point of supply. In addition, equipment enclosures are often connected to grounding electrodes placed in the vicinity of the equipment. However, it must be understood that a metallic path is required to complete the return path for the flow of fault current back to the source. A grounding connection that relies solely on an earth return path is a violation of the *NEC*.

In the event of a ground fault between the ungrounded conductor and ground, fault current will flow from the ungrounded conductor through the equipment grounding conductor and back to the source. Since the grounding conductor is expected to carry fault current, it must be sized large enough to carry the fault current without damage. Figure 9–11 shows the method used to ground the metal service raceways entering the service equipment enclosure. Since these raceways contain the service entrance conductors, they are considered electrical equipment on the line side of the service overcurrent device. As a result, the equipment bonding jumpers are sized based on Table 250.66 of the *Code.* As in the case of the sizing of the main bonding jumper, Section 250.102(C) of the *NEC* requires sizing the equipment bonding jumper at 12.5% of the cross-sectional area of the service entrance conductor for service entrance conductors larger than 1100 kcmil copper or 1750 kcmil aluminum. Also, Section 250.102(C) requires that if aluminum service entrance conductors are used, the copper equipment-bonding jumper is sized based on the equivalent-size copper service entrance conductors. If the equipment bonding jumpers are run in parallel with the service entrance conductors, as shown in Figure 9–11(A), Section 250.102(C) requires each equipment bonding jumper to be sized based on the cross-sectional area of the service conductors in each conduit. A single, unspliced equipment bonding jumper run through the grounding bushings, as shown in Figure 9–11(B), is also

FIGURE 9–11
Grounding of Service Entrance Conduits

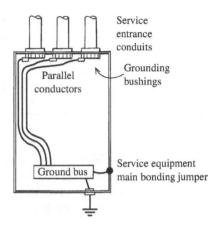

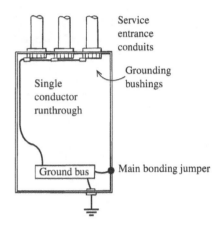

permitted to bond the raceways on the supply side of the service overcurrent device. The size of this single equipment-bonding jumper must be based on the total cross-sectional area of all ungrounded phase conductors.

EXAMPLE 9–9

A service consists of four 350 kcmil XHHW copper conductors per phase routed in rigid steel conduit. Determine the required equipment bonding jumpers to bond the raceway to the ground bus in the service equipment enclosure.

Solution: For parallel installation of the equipment bonding jumpers, the size is based on the cross-sectional area of the conductors in each conduit. Since the conductors in each conduit are 350 kcmil, the required bonding jumper size is read directly from Table 250.66

as #2 AWG copper. If a single bonding jumper is used, the size is based on the cross-sectional area of all phase conductors, or 1400 kcmil in this case. The 12.5% rule applies since the equivalent cross-sectional area exceeds 1100 kcmil for copper service-entrance conductors. The required cross-sectional area of the bonding jumper is (12.5%) × (1400 kcmil) = 175 kcmil. Therefore, a #4/0 AWG copper conductor having a cross-sectional area of 211.6 kcmil is required for this installation.

The arrangement of the equipment bonding jumpers located on the load side of the service overcurrent device is shown in Figure 9–12. If the equipment bonding jumpers are run in parallel with the feeder conductors, as shown in Figure 9–12(A), the size of each equipment bonding jumper is based on the rating of the overcurrent

FIGURE 9–12
Grounding of Feeder and Branch Circuit Conduits

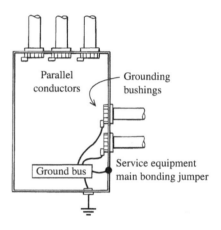

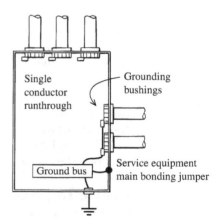

device protecting the feeder conductors. Likewise, a single, unspliced equipment bonding jumper may be used, as shown in Figure 9–12(B). The size of this single equipment-bonding jumper is also based on the rating of the overcurrent device protecting the feeder conductors. The required size is selected from Table 250.122 as required by Section 250.102(D) of the *NEC*. This table is shown in Table 9–2. Note that the table lists both copper and aluminum or copper-clad aluminum equipment grounding conductors.

TABLE 9–2
Table 250.122 Minimum Size Equipment Grounding Conductors for Grounding Raceway and Equipment

Rating or Setting of Automatic Overcurrent Device in Circuit Ahead of Equipment, Conduit, etc., Not Exceeding (Amperes)	Size (AWG or kcmil)	
	Copper	Aluminum or Copper-Clad Aluminum*
15	14	12
20	12	10
30	10	8
40	10	8
60	10	8
100	8	6
200	6	4
300	4	2
400	3	1
500	2	1/0
600	1	2/0
800	1/0	3/0
1000	2/0	4/0
1200	3/0	250
1600	4/0	350
2000	250	400
2500	350	600
3000	400	600
4000	500	800
5000	700	1200
6000	800	1200

Note: Where necessary to comply with 250.4(A)(5) or 250.4(B)(4), the equipment grounding conductor shall be sized larger than given in this table.
*See installation restrictions in 250.120.
Source: Reprinted with permission from NFPA 70 *The National Electric Code* © 2002, National Fire Protection Association, Quincy, MA 02269. This reprinted material is not the referenced subject which is represented only by the standard in its entirety.

EXAMPLE 9-10

A 600 A feeder consists of two 350 kcmil THW copper conductors per phase. The feeder is protected by a 600 A breaker in the main service panel. The feeder conductors are arranged in parallel in two raceways. Determine the required copper equipment-bonding jumper.

Solution: The size of the bonding jumpers is the same regardless of whether the jumpers are run in parallel or as a single, unspliced conductor. The required size is read from Table 250.122 as #1 AWG copper.

The routing of equipment grounding conductors from the panel to the equipment is shown in Figure 9–13. Note that Figure 9–13(A) pertains to the case where there is a single ungrounded conductor per phase. In this instance, the size of the equipment grounding conductor is determined by the rating or setting of the overcurrent device supplying the ungrounded conductors. For feeders involving parallel conductors, the equipment grounding conductor must be run in each conduit from the panel to the equipment, as shown in Figure 9–13(B). The size of the equipment grounding conductor in each conduit is based on the rating or setting of the overcurrent device protecting the ungrounded feeder conductors.

Although equipment grounding conductors are usually copper, Section 250.118 of the *NEC* permits the use of several other raceway systems as equipment grounding conductors.

FIGURE 9–13
Equipment Grounding
Conductor

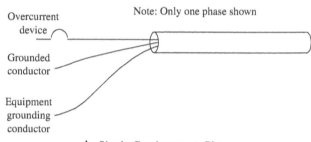

A. Single Conductor per Phase

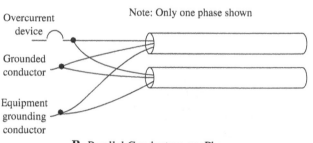

B. Parallel Conductors per Phase

The reader is referred to this *NEC* section for a list of suitable raceway systems and application requirements.

Where flexible conduit is used to prevent the transmission of vibration from electrical equipment to the raceway system, or where employed to allow for flexibility of connections, a separate equipment grounding conductor must be used. This equipment grounding conductor is generally a copper conductor and must be routed with the circuit conductors. The equipment grounding conductor must be bonded to the equipment enclosures at both ends to ensure continuity of the ground path. Section 250.102(E) of the *NEC* allows the equipment grounding conductor to be routed on the outside of the flexible conduit provided the grounding conductor is securely fastened to the conduit and does not exceed 6 feet in length. There is no restriction on length if the equipment grounding conductor is run inside the flexible conduit.

In most instances, the equipment grounding conductor size is based on the rating of the overcurrent device protecting the ungrounded circuit conductors. In instances where the size of the ungrounded circuit conductors is increased to compensate for voltage drop, or for other reasons, Section 250.122(B) of the *NEC* requires the size of the equipment grounding conductor to be increased in proportion to the increase in the cross-sectional area of the ungrounded conductors as well. This requirement is due to the fact that the lower resistance of the larger conductor will result in an increase in the magnitude of the ground fault current. The equipment grounding conductor will be expected to carry this increased fault current. The following example illustrates the calculation.

EXAMPLE 9–11

A 200 A feeder would normally consist of one #3/0 AWG THW copper conductor per phase. The feeder would be protected by a 200 A breaker in the originating panel. However, due to voltage drop considerations, the feeder conductor size was increased to 250 kcmil THW copper. The lower resistance of the larger conductor would result in less voltage drop for this feeder. Determine the required copper equipment-bonding jumper.

Solution: From Table 250.122, a #6 AWG copper equipment-grounding conductor would be required if the equipment grounding conductor were sized based on the use of a #3/0 AWG copper phase-conductor and a 200 A overcurrent device. This #6 AWG copper conductor has an area of 26,240 cmil. To determine the size of the equipment grounding conductor required for use with the 250 kcmil phase conductors, the cross-sectional area must be increased by the same percent as the phase conductors. The cross-sectional area of the #3/0 AWG copper conductor is 167,800 cmil. The percent increase in circular mil area between the #3/0 AWG and 350 kcmil conductor is

$$\% \text{ increase} = \frac{250,000 - 167,800}{167,800} \times 100 = 49\%$$

This increase is now applied to the cross-sectional area of the original #6 AWG copper equipment-grounding conductor to determine the minimum required area of the new grounding conductor:

Required cross-sectional area $= 26,240 \text{ cmil} + (0.49)(26,240 \text{ cmil}) = 39,098 \text{ cmil}$

Therefore, a copper conductor having a cross-sectional area of at least 39,098 cmil is required. The required equipment grounding conductor is #4 AWG copper having a cross-sectional area of 41,740 cmil.

The use of instantaneous trip circuit breakers or motor circuit protectors to provide overcurrent protection of motor circuits requires special consideration when determining the size of the equipment grounding conductor. As discussed in Chapter 13, the *NEC* allows the setting of these overcurrent devices to exceed the ampacity of the motor feeder conductors. In essence, the instantaneous trip breaker or motor circuit protector protects the motor feeder conductors against short circuit fault current levels only. The use of a motor overload element provides the necessary overload protection for the motor. These overload elements are generally sized at 115% to 125% of the full-load current of the motor. When instantaneous trip breakers or motor circuit protectors are used, Section 250.122(D) permits the required equipment grounding conductor to be determined using the rating of the overload element, then referring to Table 250.122. The rating of the motor branch circuit overcurrent device is used as the basis for sizing the equipment grounding conductor if inverse time breakers or time delay fuses are used to protect the motor branch circuit conductors.

Section 250.97 of the *NEC* specifies requirements for bonding metal raceways and cables containing circuits operating above 250 volts to ground. These methods of bonding will ensure continuity around any concentric or eccentric knockouts encountered. These requirements would apply to branch circuit raceway systems operating at 277 volts to ground supplied from a 480Y/277 V system. The reader is referred to the appropriate *NEC* code section for specific details and application information.

Sections 250.92(B) and 250.94 of the *NEC* specify the requirements for bonding service raceways, meter troughs, wireways, and other enclosures located on the supply side of the service overcurrent device. These methods of bonding are required to guarantee the integrity of the ground path in the event of a line-to-ground fault involving the service conductors located on the supply side of the main service overcurrent device. The reader is referred to the appropriate *NEC* code section for specific details and application information.

9–7   GROUND FAULT CIRCUIT INTERRUPTION

The basic principle of operation and location requirements for ground fault protection of receptacles were discussed in Chapter 5. In addition to the requirements for receptacles, the *NEC* requires the use of ground fault protection on services and feeders under certain conditions. Specifically, Sections 230.95 and 215.10 of the *NEC* require ground fault protection on disconnecting devices rated at 1000 A or more on solidly grounded wye systems of greater than 150 V to ground but not exceeding 600 V phase to phase. Bear in mind that GFCI detectors are not required on all feeders if GFCI protection is provided by an upstream device. For example, a 1000 A feeder disconnect is not required to have a GFCI detection scheme if the upstream service disconnect is provided with GFCI detection. Section 230.95 of the *NEC* specifies that the rating of the disconnect is the maximum fuse rating capable of being installed in the disconnecting switch. For circuit breakers, the rating is considered to be the maximum possible setting of the adjustable trip circuit breaker.

Two configurations for the detection of ground faults are possible, as shown in Figure 9–14. Figure 9–14(A) shows the window-type detector in which all ungrounded conductors (phase) and the grounded conductor (neutral) pass through the detector window. Under normal operating conditions, the load current will flow toward the load in the phase conductors, with the unbalanced neutral current returning through the ungrounded conductor. The vector sum of the phase and neutral currents will equal zero under normal conditions. If a ground fault occurs between an ungrounded conductor and the grounded metal raceway, as shown in Figure 9–14(A), the ground fault current, I_G, will flow as shown. This ground fault current will return to the source by means of the raceway and

FIGURE 9–14
Ground Fault Circuit
Interrupting Devices

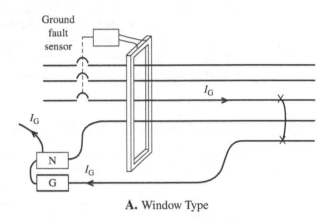

A. Window Type

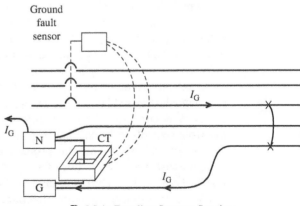

B. Main Bonding Jumper Sensing

equipment bonding jumper without passing through the window detector. This creates an unbalance of current through the window, causing the ground fault detector to operate and trip the breaker. This type of window sensor is used on either service or feeder disconnects.

The configuration shown in Figure 9–14(B) utilizes a current transformer that detects the current passing between the grounding terminal and the neutral terminal in the panelboard. Note again that under normal operating conditions, there is no current flowing in this connection. If, however, a phase-to-ground fault occurs, as shown, current will return to the grounding terminal by means of the equipment grounding conductor. The fault current flows from the grounding terminal to the neutral terminal and back to the source by means of the grounded circuit conductor. The ground fault sensor detects the ground fault and causes the disconnecting device to open. This type of detector can only be used where it is permitted to connect the grounded conductor to the grounding conductor.

Section 230.95(A) of the *NEC* specifies that the trip setting of the ground fault sensor cannot exceed 1200 A. In addition, the time delay cannot exceed 1 second for ground fault currents of 3000 A or more. Operation of the ground fault detector must result in the opening of all ungrounded conductors in the system on the load side of the disconnecting device. It is also important to note that the ground fault detection schemes just described will detect ground faults only on the load side of the GFCI sensing device. Also, the GFCI detector will not detect overloads or phase-to-phase faults not involving ground.

9–8   GROUNDING OF INSTRUMENT TRANSFORMERS

In many commercial and industrial applications, instrument transformers are used to transform the high load currents and voltages to smaller levels that can be applied to various metering and protective devices. The most common use of instrument transformers is as current transformers applied to large ampacity services. In addition, voltage transformers are commonly used to step down the voltage of services rated above 600 V. All medium voltage installations use voltage and current transformers to provide the appropriate levels to the metering elements and protective relays.

Instrument transformer secondaries must be grounded to prevent dangerous overvoltages from occurring on the secondary system. Section 250.170 of the *NEC* requires that the secondary circuits of instrument transformers operating on systems where the primary voltage is 300 V or more to ground must be grounded. Also, Sections 250.174(A) and 250.174(B) require the cases of instrument transformers not mounted on switchboards, or mounted on switchboards not having any live parts exposed, must be grounded in most locations. Section 250.174(C) specifies that cases of instrument transformers mounted on live front switchboards must not be grounded.

Figure 9–15(A) shows the proper location of the secondary ground connection for a current transformer. Grounding of a voltage or potential transformer secondary is shown in Figure 9–15(B). In each figure, only one instrument transformer is shown for the purpose of clarity. Instrument transformers connected to other ungrounded conductors must be similarly grounded. Section 250.178 of the *NEC* also requires that the minimum-size grounding conductor shall be #12 copper or #10 aluminum.

FIGURE 9–15
Grounding of Instrument Transformers

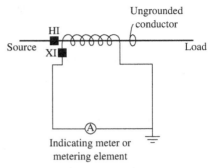

A. Current Transformer

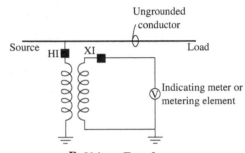

B. Voltage Transformer

PROBLEMS

1. State in your own words the reasons for grounding electrical distribution systems.

2. Which common low-voltage distribution systems are required to be grounded? Provide a sketch of these systems showing the location of the required ground.

3. List the major components of the grounding electrode system

4. Under what conditions is the interior metal water pipe permitted to be used as a ground bus?

5. Determine the minimum-size copper conductor required for connection of the system to the metal underground water pipe for a service consisting of #2/0 XHHW aluminum conductor.

6. Determine the minimum-size copper conductor required for connection of the system to the metal underground water pipe for a service consisting of two 500 kcmil XHHW copper conductors parallel per phase.

7. What are the requirements for use of a concrete-encased electrode as part of the grounding electrode system?

8. What are the requirements for use of a made electrode as part of the grounding electrode system? Include minimum dimensions of the electrode, electrode material, installation requirements, and resistance measurements for both rod and plate electrodes.

9. What is the purpose of the main bonding jumper? How is the main bonding jumper sized?

10. Determine the required main bonding jumper for a service consisting of a single 350 kcmil XHHW copper conductor per phase.

11. Determine the required main bonding jumper for a service consisting of three 400 kcmil XHHW copper conductors per phase.

12. Discuss the grounding requirements, and routing of the grounded conductor and equipment grounding conductors, for an installation in which the main service disconnect is separate from the main service panel.

13. What two conditions must be taken into consideration when determining the size of the grounded service conductor?

14. Determine the minimum-size copper conductor required for the grounded conductor for a service consisting of a single 350 kcmil XHHW copper conductor per phase.

15. Determine the minimum-size copper conductor required for the grounded conductor for a service consisting of three 400 kcmil XHHW copper conductors per phase.

16. A service consists of three 500 kcmil XHHW copper conductors per phase routed in rigid steel conduit. Determine the required parallel equipment bonding jumpers to bond the service raceways to the ground bus in the service equipment enclosure.

17. A 400 A feeder consists of one 500 kcmil THW copper conductor per phase. Determine the required copper equipment bonding jumper.

18. List at least three types of raceway systems permitted for use as equipment grounding conductors.

19. Under what conditions is liquidtight flexible metal conduit permitted for equipment grounding?

20. A 100 A feeder would normally consist of a #1/0 AWG THW copper conductor. Due to voltage drop considerations, the size has been increased to #3/0 AWG THW. Determine the required equipment grounding conductor.

21. Describe how the equipment grounding conductor is sized for motor circuits protected by instantaneous trip breakers or motor circuit protectors.

22. What methods are permitted to bond the equipment on the supply side of the service overcurrent device?

23. What methods are permitted to bond equipment operating above 250 V to ground?

24. Is GFCI required for a 1200 A, 480Y/277 V, three-phase, four-wire service having a single service disconnect?

25. Is GFCI required for a 1200 A, 480Y/277 V, three-phase, four-wire service having two 600 A service disconnects?

26. Is GFCI required for a 800 A, 480Y/277 V, three-phase, four-wire service having a single service disconnect?

27. Is GFCI required for a 1200 A, 208Y/120 V, three-phase, four-wire service having a single service disconnect?

28. Is GFCI required for a 1200 A, 208Y/120 V, three-phase, four-wire service having two 600 A service disconnects?

29. Describe the operation of the "window-type" ground fault detector and the detector connected between the ground and neutral bus.

30. What is the maximum trip setting of a ground fault sensor? What is the maximum time delay?

10

Services

INTRODUCTION

The building electrical service consists of the conductors connecting the building electrical system to the local utility power source, the raceway system containing the service entrance conductors, metering, the main service disconnect, and the main overcurrent protection devices. Since the service is the point of connection to the local utility, coordination with the utility is of extreme importance. The local utility will provide the location for the electrical service, metering requirements, and other pertinent information regarding the electrical service. In many instances, the local utility may have special service requirements that the electrical designer must be aware of when designing the electrical system for a building. From the point of connection to the utility toward the inside of the building, the service equipment must meet all requirements of the *NEC*.

This chapter will introduce you to the design elements and *NEC* requirements for service entrances. The subject of metering is included to provide the reader with an insight into utility metering practices. Also, the subject of rates and the calculation of power bills is included.

OBJECTIVES

Upon completion of this chapter, you will:

- Be able to size service entrance conductors
- Be aware of the clearance requirements for overhead conductors
- Be aware of burial depth requirements for underground conductors
- Be able to determine the required rating of the service overcurrent protection device
- Understand the disconnect requirements for electrical service conductors
- Understand metering principles
- Have an understanding of rates and billing for electrical power

10–1   SERVICE DROP AND SERVICE LATERAL GENERAL REQUIREMENTS

The electrical service to a building must meet the requirements of both the *NEC* and the local electrical utility. Several utility companies have requirements that differ from the requirements of the *NEC*, so it is important for the designer to coordinate the service requirements of the building with the local utility providing the service.

In general, a single building may be supplied by only one service as specified in Section 230.2 of the *NEC*. This typically means that only one set of service conductors is permitted between the utility and the building itself. Under certain conditions, additional services may be supplied to a building. Section 230.2(A) of the *NEC* allows dedicated services to supply fire pumps, emergency systems, standby systems, and parallel power production systems in addition to the normal supply. Section 230.2(B)(2) of the *NEC* permits multiple services where the physical size of the building makes multiple services practical. In multiple occupancy buildings, Section 230.2(B)(1) of the *NEC* permits additional services if there is insufficient space for service equipment when this service equipment is required to be accessible to all occupants. If a building is supplied by more than one service, Section 230.2(E) of the *NEC* requires a plaque to be installed at each service disconnect designating all other services, circuits, feeders, and so on supplying the building.

Additional services are permitted where capacity requirements dictate. Specifically, Section 230.2(C)(1) of the *NEC* permits additional services where capacity requirements exceed 2000 A for low-voltage (600 V or less) services. Some utilities may limit the maximum ampacity rating of services in a given class. For example, 120/240 V, single-phase services may be limited to a certain ampacity. If load conditions dictate a higher ampacity service, multiple services may be required as permitted by Section 230.2(C)(2) of the *NEC*.

Section 230.2(D) of the *NEC* permits additional services when different service characteristics are required. An example would be a building supplied by a 120/240 V, single-phase, three-wire service and a 240 V, three-phase, three-wire service. Several supplying utilities permit combining this service into a single 240/120 V, three-phase, four-wire service. It is unlikely that a supplying utility would provide both a 480Y/277 V, three-phase, four-wire service and a 120/240 V, single-phase service to a single building. Typically, the 120/240 V, single-phase system would be created inside the building through a step-down transformer.

Basic Elements

The basic elements of low-voltage electrical services are shown in Figure 10–1. Figure 10–1(A) shows the major elements of an overhead service supplying a residence. The service drop conductors supply the connection between the service entrance conductors and the utility. These overhead service-drop conductors may consist of either single, open conductors or multiplexed cable assembly. For a single-phase, three-wire service, the service drop conductors would typically be a triplexed cable comprised of two insulated phase conductors and a bare grounded conductor. Three-phase, four-wire services are usually supplied with quadruplex cable comprised of three insulated phase conductors and a bare grounded conductor. Multiplex cable is utilized on lower-ampacity services, up to 200 A. Higher-ampacity services are supplied by single-conductor insulated cable. The overhead service-drop cable is typically supplied and installed by the local utility.

The service drop conductors typically terminate on either a service mast or rack assembly mounted on the building wall. The service entrance raceway contains the service

FIGURE 10–1
Basic Elements of Low-Voltage
Service

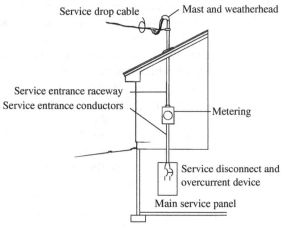

A. Overhead Service Drop

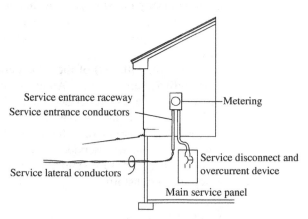

B. Underground Service Lateral

entrance conductors from the point of attachment to the service drop conductors to the meter and then to the service disconnect and service entrance panel, as shown. The service entrance raceway, conductors, disconnect, and panel are typically furnished and installed by the electrical contractor. The meter socket is furnished by the local utility and installed by the electrical contractor. The meter itself is furnished and installed by the local utility.

The basic elements of an underground service lateral are shown in Figure 10–1(B). As with the overhead service shown in Figure 10–1(A), the service lateral conductors connect the service entrance conductors to the utility, usually at a transformer or handhole. Underground service conductors must be listed as suitable for installation underground and are commonly available in both multiplex and single-conductor configurations. The underground service lateral conductors may be installed by either the electrical contractor or the utility company. The designer or electrical contractor must consult with the local utility to determine who is responsible for installation. The termination point of the underground service lateral conductors is usually in the meter socket. The electrical contractor is responsible for installation of the service entrance raceway, service entrance conductor, and service disconnect.

The main components of a medium-voltage electrical service are shown in Figure 10–2. Medium-voltage services generally range from 4.16 kV to 35 kV. Figure 10–2(A) shows a medium-voltage service supplied from the utility underground distribution system. The medium-voltage cables terminate in a set of medium-voltage switchgear in the building. Outdoor medium-voltage switchgear is also available. The cables terminate in a switchgear section containing the medium-voltage service disconnect and metering equipment. The metering current transformers and potential transformers may be located in this section. The power meter is typically located near the switchgear itself. All compartments containing metering equipment are typically required by the local utility to be sealed.

Figure 10–2(B) shows an example of a medium-voltage service supplied from the utility overhead distribution feeder. In this example, the metering equipment is shown mounted on a primary metering pole. The required metering current and potential transformers are mounted in a cluster on top of the pole, as shown. The power meter itself is typically mounted on the pole approximately 5 feet above finished grade. The medium-voltage service conductors connect to the overhead distribution circuit on the load side of the metering pole. These service conductors terminate in the incoming cable compartment section of the medium-voltage switchgear.

Clearances

Section 230.24 of the *NEC* requires that service drop conductors not be readily accessible. This means that the service drop conductors cannot be accessed without the use of a ladder, scaffolding, and such. The *NEC* requires certain clearances to meet the conditions of non-accessibility, which can be grouped into three different categories: clearances above roofs, vertical clearance above ground, and clearances from building openings. Clearance above swimming pools is covered in Section 680.8 of the *NEC*. It is generally not advisable to locate a service drop or other overhead conductors above swimming pools. Clearances above railroad rights-of-way are covered in the *National Electrical Safety Code* and are not covered in this text.

Section 230.24(A) of the *NEC* lists the general clearance requirements for overhead service drops above rooftops. These requirements are illustrated in Figure 10–3. Figure 10–3(A) shows the general requirement of 8 feet clearance above roofs not subject to pedestrian or vehicular traffic. Clearances above roofs subject to pedestrian or vehicular traffic are the same as clearances required above ground. Note that these clearance requirements apply regardless of the circuit voltage or roof slope.

Figure 10–3(B) illustrates Exception No. 2 to Section 230.24(A) of the *NEC* for circuits having a voltage not over 300 V and roofs having a slope of at least 4 inches rise per 12 inches of run (4/12 pitch). Under these conditions, the clearance may be reduced to 3 feet, as shown.

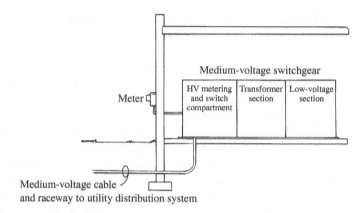

A. Underground Feed with Metering in Medium-Voltage Switchgear

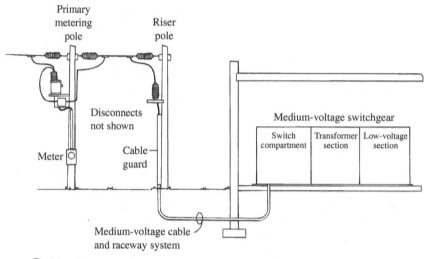

B. Riser Pole Installation with Metering on Utility Primary Metering Pole

FIGURE 10–2
Basic Elements of Medium-Voltage Service

Figure 10–3(C) illustrates a further reduction in clearance, as permitted by Exception No. 3 to Section 230.24(A) of the *NEC*, to 18 inches, provided the circuit voltage does not exceed 300 V, the roof pitch is 4/12 or more, and the service drop cable does not pass over more than 4 feet of rooftop measured horizontally.

The clearance requirement of open-wire or multiplexed service entrance cable assemblies not contained in a service raceway from building openings is shown in Figure 10–4. Section 230.9 of the *NEC* specifies the requirement that service conductors must

FIGURE 10–3
Clearance Requirements Above Roofs

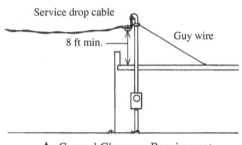

A. General Clearance Requirement

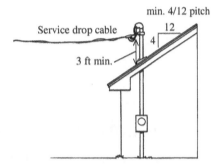

B. Exception for Pitched Roof (<300 V)

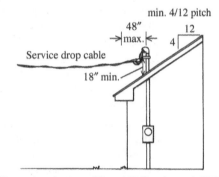

C. Exception for Less Than 48″ Overhang (<300 V)

have a clearance of at least 3 feet from any window, porch, balcony, and so on. Also, service drop conductors are not permitted to be installed beneath openings through which material may be passed.

Section 230.24(B) of the *NEC* lists the requirements for final vertical clearance of service drop conductors above finished grade. The reader is referred to this section of the *NEC* for detailed information on clearance requirements.

FIGURE 10–4
Clearance Requirements Near Openings

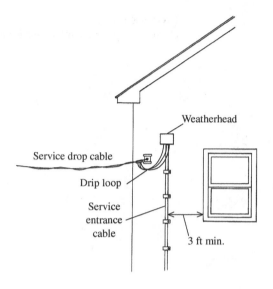

Weatherhead

Service drop cable

Drip loop

Service
entrance
cable

3 ft min.

Protection of Underground Conductors

Underground service laterals must be protected from physical damage by appropriate burial depth and raceways. The required burial depth is listed in Table 300.5 of the *NEC* and is
a function of the raceway method employed and the location of the conductors. Trenching
for underground cable installations should only be done in undisturbed earth, earth that has
been compacted, or where the probability of settlement is low. Backfill of these conductors
shall be free of any rock, debris, or other sharp objects that may damage the cable. Also,
the backfill must be free of any corrosive materials or substances. Section 300.5(D) of the
NEC requires placement of a warning ribbon at least 12 inches above any direct-buried
conductors located 18 inches or more below finished grade.

Section 230.32 of the *NEC* requires underground conductors to be installed in a raceway where the conductors enter the building. Section 230.8 of the *NEC* requires a bushing,
or seal that provides the same protection as a bushing, where the underground conductors
enter the building. In addition, Section 300.5(D)(1) of the *NEC* requires physical protection where the underground service conductors extend from the ground, as in the case of a
riser pole. This protection must be installed to a point at least 8 feet above finished grade
and to a point at least equal to the minimum cover depth. Section 300.5(D)(4) of the *NEC*
requires the use of rigid metal conduit, intermediate metal conduit, or Schedule 80 rigid
nonmetallic conduit where the service raceway may be subjected to physical damage.

Conductors Considered Outside of Building

In general, the service conductors supplying a building are not permitted to pass through
the interior of another building, as specified in Section 230.3 of the *NEC*. It is good design
practice to locate service conductors in an appropriate manner to avoid passing through or

under other buildings. Section 230.6 of the *NEC* defines an outside conductor as including conductors installed under at least 2 inches of concrete beneath a building, conductors installed in raceway and covered by at least 2 inches of concrete or brick, conductors installed in a transformer vault having an appropriate fire rating, and conductors installed in conduit directly buried under at least 18 inches of earth under a building. Figure 10–5 illustrates several conditions under which the service entrance conductors are considered outside the building. In accordance with Section 230.70(A)(1) of the *NEC*, the service

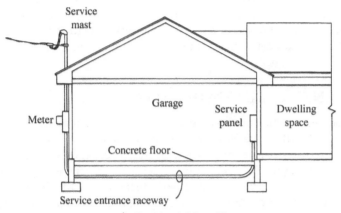

A. Residential Dwelling

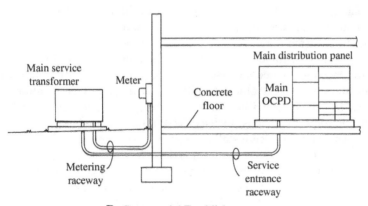

B. Commercial Establishment

FIGURE 10–5
Conductors Considered Outside the Building

disconnecting means must be located as near as possible to the entrance of the service conductors into the building.

Raceway Seals

To prevent the penetration of moisture and water, Section 230.8 of the *NEC* requires raceway seals to be installed at locations where the underground service raceways enter the building. All raceways must be sealed, including spare raceways not containing service conductors, telephone raceways, and so on. Section 230.54(A) of the *NEC* requires a raintight service weatherhead on overhead services to prevent the penetration of water into the service equipment. In addition, Section 230.54(C) of the *NEC* requires the point of attachment of the service drop conductors to the service entrance conductors to be at a point below the service weatherhead. This is illustrated in Figure 10–4.

10–2   SERVICE ENTRANCE CONDUCTORS

The service entrance cable connects the service entrance equipment to the service drop location. Section 230.40 of the *NEC* permits one set of service entrance conductors to be supplied from a given service drop or lateral. However, several exceptions to Section 230.40 of the *NEC* permit the installation of several different arrangements for service entrance conductors, as shown in Figure 10–6. Exception No. 1 to Section 230.40 permits separate service entrance cable sets for multiple-occupancy buildings where different classes of services are supplied, as shown in Figure 10–6(A). A multifamily dwelling unit such as an apartment may have a separate service supplying common lighting loads, laundry area, and other "house" service loads. Exception No. 2 to Section 230.40 permits multiple service entrance cable sets if the service consists of multiple disconnects supplying separate loads. Exception No. 3 to Section 230.40 permits one set of service entrance conductors to supply a dwelling unit and another set to supply a separate building, such as a detached garage. This type of installation is illustrated in Figure 10–6(B).

In an overhead service, service entrance cable runs from the service drop to the meter socket and from the meter socket to the service entrance panel. Since the service entrance cable may be subjected to wet conditions, the conductor insulation must be suitable for wet locations. Three- or four-conductor, type SE (Service Entrance) cable having copper or aluminum conductors is typically used for this application. If the service entrance cables are contained in a suitable raceway, single insulated conductors having a rating suitable for wet locations, such as XHHW, may be used.

In underground service installations, the service entrance cable typically provides the connection between the meter socket and the service entrance panel. Single, insulated conductors contained in a suitable raceway are generally used for this purpose. As with the overhead service entrance cables, the insulation must be suitable for wet locations. Single-conductor cable with a USE (Underground Service Entrance) rating installed in rigid metal, intermediate metal, or rigid nonmetallic (PVC) conduit is typically used for underground services.

FIGURE 10–6
Service Entrance Conductors

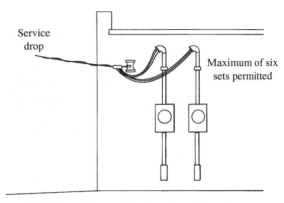

A. Different Class of Service, House Service, or
Individual Services for Multiple Occupancy

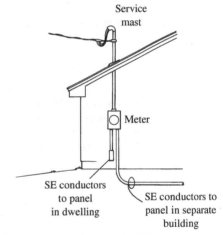

B. Services to Separate Building
and Dwelling Unit

Sizing of Ungrounded Service Entrance Conductors

The ampacity rating of the ungrounded service entrance conductors must be sufficient to supply the demand load of the building or occupancy. The demand load is determined using the procedures in Chapter 3. Section 230.42 of the *NEC* also requires the ampacity of the service entrance cable to equal or exceed the sum of the noncontinuous loads plus 125% of the continuous loads. If the service overcurrent device is capable of being operated at 100% of its rating on a continuous basis, the required ampacity of the service entrance cable may be based on the sum of the noncontinuous loads plus 100% of the continuous loads. The cable ampacity is determined before the application of ambient temperature correction or raceway fill adjustment factors. Separate calculations are required for the phase and neutral conductors to determine the required sizing. For services supplying single-phase, three-wire services in dwelling units, the service entrance cable, service lateral conductors, and feeder conductors are permitted to be sized in accordance with Table 310.15(B)(6), which is shown in Table 10–1. The procedure for sizing parallel service entrance conductors follows that outlined for the sizing of feeder conductors.

Sizing of Grounded Service Entrance Conductor

The loading on the grounded (neutral) service entrance conductor must be determined to properly size the grounded conductor. The maximum loading on the grounded conductor is a result of unbalanced single-phase loading on the system. For the purposes of computation, it is assumed that all single-phase loads connected between phase and neutral are balanced between the phases. Single-phase loads connected phase-to-phase are not included in this calculation, since these loads do not produce any current flow in the grounded service conductor. The maximum possible unbalanced loading occurs when only the loads

TABLE 10–1
Table 310.15(B)(6) Conductor Types and Sizes for 120/240-Volt, 3-Wire, Single-Phase Dwelling Services and Feeders.

Conductor (AWG or kcmil)		
Copper	Aluminum or Copper-Clad Aluminum	Service or Feeder Rating (Amperes)
4	2	100
3	1	110
2	1/0	125
1	2/0	150
1/0	3/0	175
2/0	4/0	200
3/0	250	225
4/0	300	250
250	350	300
350	500	350
400	600	400

Source: Reprinted with permission from NFPA 70 *The National Electric Code* © 2002, National Fire Protection Association, Quincy, MA 02269. This reprinted material is not the referenced subject which is represented only by the standard in its entirety.

connected between one of the phase conductors and neutral are energized, with all other phase-to-neutral loads deenergized.

To determine the unbalanced neutral current, the volt-ampere demand load of all single-phase loads connected between phase and neutral are added together. In addition, the demand load of electric ranges, wall-mounted ovens, counter-mounted cooktops, and electric dryers is considered to be 70% of the load on the ungrounded conductors for these appliances. The volt-ampere demand load is then divided by the number of ungrounded conductors in the system to determine the phase-to-neutral loading. The neutral current is then calculated by dividing the volt-ampere demand load by the line-to-neutral voltage of the system. Section 220.22 of the *NEC* also permits a demand factor of 70% to be applied to the portion of the neutral current exceeding 200 A for single-phase, three-wire and three-phase, four-wire systems. The minimum size of the neutral conductor based on the loading considerations can be determined from the ampacity tables.

The grounded conductor size as determined by loading conditions must be compared to the size required for grounding purposes. For that portion of the service cable located on the supply side of the main service disconnect/overcurrent device, there is no separation between the grounded conductor and the grounding conductor. A single conductor serves as both the grounded conductor and the grounding conductor on the supply side of the main service OCPD and disconnect. The minimum size of this grounding conductor is taken from Table 250.66 of the *NEC* for phase conductors up to 1100 kcmil copper or 1750 kcmil aluminum. For phase conductors larger than 1100 kcmil copper or 1750 kcmil aluminum, Section 250.24(B)(1) of the *NEC* requires the neutral to be sized at least equal to 12.5% of the cross-sectional area of the phase conductor. The actual size of the grounded conductor (neutral) in this portion of the service will be the larger of the two based on loading and grounding requirements.

Recall that on the load side of the service disconnect/overcurrent device, the grounded conductor of the supply (neutral) and the equipment grounding conductor are separate. The grounded conductor of that portion of the service entrance cable located between the main service disconnect/overcurrent device and any subpanel is not permitted to be used as the equipment grounding conductor. Therefore, the size of the grounded conductor located on the load side of the main service disconnect/overcurrent device is based on the maximum neutral current demand load. The equipment grounding conductor on the load side of the service disconnect/overcurrent device is sized based on the rating of the overcurrent device as determined from Table 250.122 of the *NEC*.

Special consideration must be given to three-phase, four-wire, wye-connected systems that supply nonlinear loads. These nonlinear loads produce harmonic currents that add rather than cancel in the neutral conductor. In some instances, the current in the neutral may exceed the current in the phase conductors. As such, the sizing of the neutral conductor may require special consideration if harmonic currents are anticipated.

EXAMPLE 10–1

Determine the neutral loading on a wye-connected service in which the current in each phase conductor consists of 50% third harmonic current. The 60 Hz component of the phase current in each phase conductor is 100 A.

Solution: While the fundamental (60 Hz) components of the phase currents add up to zero in a balanced system, the third harmonic component of current adds in the neutral of the wye-connected system. Therefore, the current in the neutral conductor is

$$I_N = 3(50\%)\,(100\text{ A}) = 150\text{ A}$$

Note that in this instance the neutral current exceeds the phase current even though the system is balanced!

10–3   SERVICE DISCONNECT REQUIREMENTS

As previously mentioned, each service is required to have a means of disconnecting located as close as possible to the point of entrance to the building. The service disconnect may be located outdoors or indoors but as close as possible to the point of entry of the service entrance conductors. Recall the definitions for conductors considered outside the building. As previously mentioned, service conductors passing under a minimum of 2 inches of concrete slab are not considered to be located inside the building. As such, a service disconnect is not required at the point where the service conductors begin passing under the slab. An example of this is where the service entrance conductors pass under the garage floor of a residential dwelling and terminate in a panel located in the basement. The conductors passing under the garage floor are not considered to be inside the building. The service conductors enter the building in the basement. Thus, the service disconnect is permitted to be located in the panel, provided the panel is located as close as possible to the point of entrance of the service conductors.

Section 230.70 of the *NEC* requires the use of a disconnect to open all service entrance conductors, including both the ungrounded and grounded conductors. Typically, the service disconnect is arranged to simultaneously disconnect all ungrounded conductors. Multiple-pole, fused disconnect switches or circuit breakers are generally used as the means of disconnecting. Section 230.75 of the *NEC* permits the disconnect for the grounded conductor to be the connection of the grounded conductor to the neutral terminal in the service panel, switchboard, or disconnect enclosure. Section 230.70(B) of the *NEC* requires the service disconnect to be marked as suitable for service entrance equipment and also to indicate the open and closed positions. Section 230.76 of the *NEC* specifies that the disconnect may be either manually or power operated. If power operated, backup power provisions must be made to allow operation of the disconnect during power outages.

Section 230.71(A) of the *NEC* permits the disconnect of a service to consist of up to six separate disconnecting devices. A building supplied by a single electrical service may have up to six disconnects. These disconnects may be arranged in separate enclosures, as shown in Figure 10–7(A), or in a panelboard, as shown in Figure 10–7(B). Likewise, a building supplied by two services may have twelve disconnects, six for each service. Generally, all disconnects associated with a particular service are grouped in the same location, as required by Section 230.72(A) of the *NEC*. However, Section 230.72(B) of the *NEC* requires the disconnect used to supply fire pumps or standby power systems to be located away from the general service disconnects to prevent inadvertent disconnection of

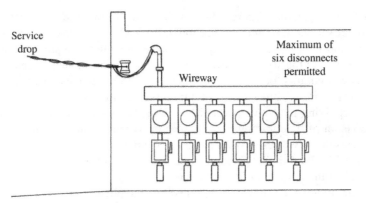

A. Multiple Gang Metering

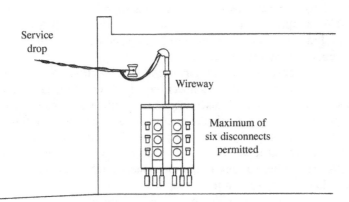

B. Multimeter Service Equipment

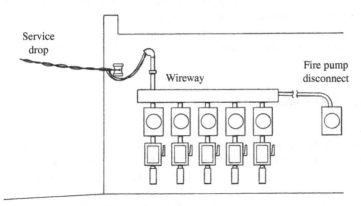

C. Separate Disconnect for Fire Pump

FIGURE 10–7
Grouping of Service Disconnects

these emergency systems. Figure 10–7(C) shows a fire pump disconnect located away from the other service disconnects. Section 230.71(A) of the *NEC* specifies that disconnects for ground fault protection equipment, power monitoring equipment, and so on not be counted as one of the six disconnects permitted. Only disconnects connected to circuits supplying power circuits for lighting, receptacles, motors, and so on need to be counted. In addition, it is required that occupants of a multiple-occupancy building have access to the disconnect supplying their own particular area. If the electrical system is under the constant supervision of the building maintenance or management personnel, the disconnect may be accessible only to these maintenance personnel.

Section 230.79 of the *NEC* requires the ampere rating of the disconnect to be greater than or equal to the computed load of the occupancy to be supplied. The minimum-size disconnect permitted for a single-family dwelling supplied by a 120/240 V single-phase, three-wire system is 100 A, as specified by Section 230.79(C) of the *NEC*. For services supplying smaller, nondwelling occupancies, Section 230.79(A) of the *NEC* specifies the minimum-size disconnect rating of 15 A for loads supplied by a single branch circuit, and Section 230.79(B) specifies a minimum disconnect rating of 30 A for loads supplied by two two-wire branch circuits. Section 230.79(D) specifies the minimum-size disconnect for all other nondwelling occupancies at 60 A.

For services consisting of multiple disconnects, Section 230.80 of the *NEC* requires that the sum of the ratings of all disconnects equal or exceed the rating required for a single disconnect. In addition, each disconnect of a multiple-disconnect installation must be rated to supply the load on its particular circuit. For example, three 400 A disconnects may be used as to disconnect service that would normally require a single 1200 A disconnect. However, the computed load supplied by each of the disconnects individually cannot exceed 400 A. The voltage rating of the disconnect must be greater than or equal to the line-to-line voltage of the system to be supplied.

In general, equipment is not permitted to be connected to the supply side of the service disconnect. However, Section 230.82 of the *NEC* does permit connection of certain types of equipment to the supply side, including cable limiters, metering equipment including current and potential transformers, surge protectors, control circuits required for the operation of power-operated disconnects, and ground fault protection systems. Suitable disconnect and overcurrent protection must be provided for control circuits and ground fault equipment circuits.

Ground Fault Protection

Section 230.95 of the *NEC* requires ground fault protection on each service disconnect rated 1000 A or more on solidly grounded, wye-connected services of more than 150 V to ground but not exceeding 600 V phase-to-phase. This requirement commonly applies to 480Y/277 V, three-phase, four-wire services where the disconnecting means is rated 1000 A or more. Note that these requirements apply to each service disconnect rated 1000 A or more. A 480Y/277 V three-phase, four-wire service consisting of a single 2000 A disconnecting device is required to have ground fault protection. However, if this service were split up into five 400 A disconnects, ground fault protection would not be required on each of the service disconnects.

EXAMPLE 10–2

Determine which of the following service disconnects requires ground fault protection.

a) 800 A, 480Y/277 V
b) 1200 A, 208Y/120 V
c) 2000 A, 480Y/277 V
d) 2000 A, 208Y/120 V

Solution:

a) GFCI not required since less than 1000 A
b) GFCI not required since less than 150 V phase-to-ground
c) GFCI required since greater than 1000 A and greater than 150 V to ground
d) GFCI not required since less than 150 V phase-to-ground

10–4   SERVICE OVERCURRENT PROTECTION DEVICE

Section 230.91 of the *NEC* requires an overcurrent protection device for each service disconnect. Section 230.90 requires this overcurrent protection device for each ungrounded conductor of the system. An overcurrent device may be inserted in the grounded conductor only if the operation of the device causes both the grounded and all ungrounded conductors to open as well. The overcurrent device may be a circuit breaker or a set of fuses. A circuit breaker may be used to provide both the required disconnect and overcurrent protection.

The overcurrent protection device must be located adjacent to the service disconnecting device. In a single-family dwelling, the overcurrent protection device is typically a circuit breaker located in the main panel, as shown in Figure 10–8(A). An enclosed circuit breaker may be used if the service disconnect and the overcurrent protection device are separate from the main panel, as shown in Figure 10–8(B). For multioccupancy buildings, the service overcurrent devices and service disconnect are typically located near the service drop, as shown in Figure 10–8(C).

In general, the rating or setting of the overcurrent protection device must be less than or equal to the ampacity of the service entrance conductors as required by Section 230.90(A) of the *NEC*. (As in the case of feeders, rounding up to the next-higher standard rated device is permitted if the device is rated equal to or less than 800 A.) The sizing of overcurrent protection devices for services supplying motor starting currents is covered in a subsequent chapter. Overcurrent protection for fire pump services must be sized to carry the locked rotor current of the fire pump motor and all other auxiliary motors and necessary control equipment on a continuous basis.

If a service consists of two to six disconnects as previously discussed, the rating of each overcurrent device must be less than or equal to the ampacity of the service entrance conductors they protect. (Again, rounding up to the next-higher standard rating is permitted if the device is rated equal to or less than 800 A.) Each service overcurrent device must also be rated sufficient to carry the computed load of the service it protects. Exception No. 3 to Section 230.90(A) of the *NEC* permits the sum of the ratings of all overcurrent devices in a multiple installation to exceed the ampacity of the service conductors that

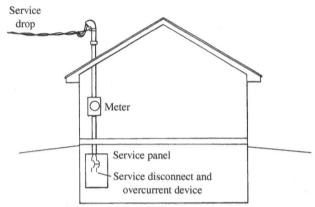

A. Service Overcurrent Device Located in Main Service Panel

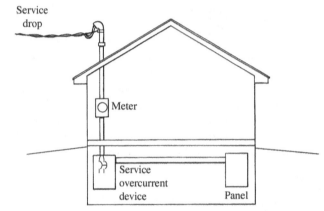

B. Service Overcurrent Device Separate from Main Service Panel

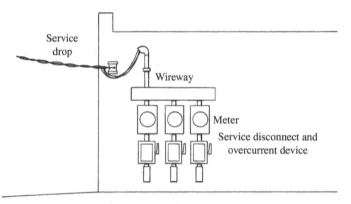

C. Service Overcurrent Devices for Multioccupancy Building

FIGURE 10–8
Service Overcurrent Protection Devices

supply the multiple installation as a whole. However, the ampacity of the service conductors supplying the entire installation must be equal to or greater than the computed load of the entire installation.

In general, the requirements for equipment permitted on the supply side of the service overcurrent protection device are the same as those for the service disconnect. These items are listed in Section 230.94 of the *NEC*.

10–5   EXAMPLES OF SERVICE ENTRANCE CALCULATIONS

EXAMPLE 10–3

Determine the estimated demand, overcurrent protection, and the required size for the service entrance phase and neutral conductors for the residence in Example 3–13. Specify the required size for both copper and aluminum phase conductors, XHHW insulation, 75°C rating. Allow 25% for load growth and use a 75°C terminal temperature rating for all terminations.

Solution: The estimated demand load on the ungrounded service conductors as determined from Example 3–13 is 33,125 VA. This corresponds to a load current of 138 A @ 240 V. Allowing for 25% load growth, the demand load current is

$$\text{Demand load current} = (125\%) \times (138 \text{ A}) = 173 \text{ A}$$

Based on the demand load current of 173 A, a 175 A overcurrent device would be appropriate. However, it is common practice to specify a 200 A overcurrent device for this installation.

Based on the use of a 200 A overcurrent device, the minimum-size XHHW copper conductor is #2/0 AWG, as determined from Table 310.15(B)(6). For aluminum conductor, the minimum size is #4/0 AWG. Note that it is permissible to use Table 310.15(B)(6) since this application is for a 120/240 V, single-phase, three-wire residential service.

To determine the loading on the neutral conductors, the sum of the 120 V loads must be determined. The 120 V loads consisted of the loads for general illumination and the fastened-in-place appliances. It is necessary to add 25% of the largest motor load connected between phase and neutral (120 V) to the neutral load computation. The neutral load for an electric range is computed at 70% of the demand load for the range. The total 120 V load is

General illumination (refer to Ex. 3–10):	= 7,935 VA
Fastened in place appliances (refer to Ex. 3–12):	= 5,290 VA
25% of largest 115 V motor (refer to Ex. 3–12): (1127 VA) × (25%)	= 282 VA
Range (refer to Ex. 3–6): (8,000 VA) × (70%)	= 5,600 VA
Total neutral load	= 19,107 VA

Assuming the total 120 V load is evenly connected between the two ungrounded conductors and neutral, the load on any given phase is one-half the total, or 9,554 VA. This corresponds to 79.6 A @ 120 V, which is the estimated load on the neutral conductor.

The estimated demand load on the neutral conductor must now be increased to account for the actual rating of the service OCPD. In this example, the estimated demand load on the ungrounded conductors was 173 A and the OCPD rating selected was 200 A. This allows for additional loading on the ungrounded conductors of 27 A. If it is assumed that the additional load will be distributed proportionally between the 120 V and 240 V loads the same as the initial load, the additional demand load on the neutral conductor will increase at the same proportion as on the phase conductors. Thus, the proportional increase in neutral conductor loading is the rating of the service OCPD divided by the computed load on the phase conductors. A multiplying factor to be applied to the computed neutral load can therefore be calculated as follows:

$$\text{Multiplier} = \frac{\text{Service OCPD rating}}{\text{Computed load on ungrounded conductors}}$$

$$= \frac{200\ \text{A}}{173\ \text{A}} = 1.1561$$

The adjusted demand load on the neutral is $1.1561 \times 79.6\ \text{A} = 92.0\ \text{A}$. From Table 310.16, a #3 AWG copper or #1 AWG aluminum conductor is required for the grounded service conductor.

A further check must be made to determine the required size of the grounded conductor based on grounding requirements. For both the #2/0 AWG copper and the #4/0 AWG aluminum phase conductors, a minimum-size #4 AWG copper or #2 AWG aluminum conductor is required per Table 250.66. Therefore, the minimum required grounded conductor is #3 AWG copper, or #1 AWG aluminum, the larger of the two.

EXAMPLE 10–4

A commercial establishment is supplied by a 208Y/120 V, three-phase, four-wire service. The total estimated demand load is 65 kVA, of which 45 kVA is three phase. All loads are continuous. Determine the rating of the service overcurrent device and the required size of the service entrance phase and neutral conductors. Assume type XHHW insulation and copper conductors. Also, apply a growth factor of 25%.

Solution: The required size of the ungrounded phase conductors is determined by using the total estimated demand load on the system and applying the 25% growth factor. Since the loads are considered continuous, the demand load is 125% of the continuous load as required by the *NEC*. The estimated demand load current is

$$\text{Estimated demand load current} = (125\%) \times (125\%) \times \left[\frac{65{,}000\ \text{VA}}{\sqrt{3}\ 208\ \text{V}} \right] = 282\ \text{A}$$

Based on a demand load current of 282 A, a 300 A overcurrent device would be required. The required conductor size would be 350 kcmil copper having a table-rated ampacity of 310 A.

The total demand of all single-phase loads connected between phase and neutral is determined by subtracting the three-phase demand load from the total demand load. The result is

$$\text{Total phase-to-neutral demand load} = 65 \text{ kVA} - 45 \text{ kVA} = 20 \text{ kVA}$$

Note that in this example, the 20 kVA of single phase is assumed to be equally distributed among all three phases. The single-phase demand load connected between each phase and neutral is

$$\text{Maximum load per phase} = 20,000 \text{ VA} \div 3 \text{ phases} = 6,667 \text{ kVA/phase}$$

The neutral current corresponding to this demand load with the application of the 25% growth factor and consideration of continuous loading is

$$\text{Neutral current} = (125\%) \times (125\%) \times \left[\frac{6,667 \text{ VA}}{120 \text{ V}} \right] = 86.8 \text{ A}$$

The multiplying factor applied to the neutral current to allow for an increase in neutral loading due to the OCPD rating is

$$\text{Multiplying factor} = (300 \text{ A}) \div (282 \text{ A}) = 1.064$$

The adjusted neutral current is $1.064 \times 86.8 \text{ A} = 92.4 \text{ A}$. The required conductor size based on this neutral current is #3 AWG copper having a table-listed ampacity of 100 A.

The minimum required equipment grounding conductor is based on the 350 kcmil copper phase conductors. From Table 250.66, the required size is #2 AWG copper. Therefore, the neutral conductor must be #2 AWG—as required for grounding purposes—not the #3 AWG based on loading considerations.

EXAMPLE 10–5

A commercial establishment is supplied by a 480Y/277 V, three-phase, four-wire service. The total estimated demand load is 550 kVA, of which 400 kVA is three phase. Determine the rating of the service overcurrent device and the required size of the service entrance phase and neutral conductors. Assume type XHHW insulation and copper conductors. Also assume all loads are continuous and apply a growth factor of 25%.

Solution: The required size of the ungrounded phase conductors is determined by using the total estimated demand load on the system, by considering continuous load, and by applying the 25% growth factor:

$$\text{Estimated demand load current} = (125\%)(125\%) \frac{550,000 \text{ VA}}{\sqrt{3} \, 480 \text{ V}} = 1037 \text{ A}$$

Based on a load current of 1037 A, a 1200 A overcurrent device would be required. Note also that ground fault circuit interruption would be required for this service disconnect.

The use of parallel conductors is necessary for this large service. The required conductor size is selected to be three 600 kcmil conductors having a table-rated ampacity of 420 A each, for a total rating of 1260 A.

The total demand of all single-phase loads connected between phase and neutral is determined by subtracting the three-phase demand load from the total demand load. The result is

$$\text{Total phase-to-neutral demand load} = 550\,\text{kVA} - 400\,\text{kVA} = 150\,\text{kVA}$$

As in the previous example, the 150 kVA of single phase is assumed to be equally distributed among all three phases. The single-phase load connected between each phase and neutral is

$$\text{Maximum load per phase} = 150{,}000\,\text{VA} \div 3\,\text{phases} = 50{,}000\,\text{kVA/phase}$$

The neutral current corresponding to this demand load with the application of the 25% growth factor and consideration of continuous load is

$$\text{Neutral current} = (125\%)(125\%)\frac{50{,}000\,\text{VA}}{277\,\text{V}} = 282\,\text{A}$$

Section 220.22 of the *NEC* permits an additional demand factor of 70% to be applied to the neutral current in excess of 200 A. Application of this factor results in a neutral current of

$$\text{Neutral current} = 200\,\text{A} + (70\%)(282\,\text{A} - 200\,\text{A}) = 257.4\,\text{A}$$

Since the phase conductors are connected in parallel, the neutral conductors must be connected in parallel as well. For three conductors in parallel, the neutral current is assumed to divide equally between the three conductors, resulting in a current of 257.4 A ÷ 3 = 86 A per conductor. The multiplying factor applied to the neutral current to allow for the increase in neutral loading due to the OCPD rating is

$$\text{Multiplying factor} = (1200\,\text{A}) \div (1037\,\text{A}) = 1.1572$$

The adjusted neutral current is 1.1572 × 86 A = 100 A. The required conductor size based on a neutral current of 100 A is #3 AWG having a table-listed ampacity of 100 A.

The minimum required equipment grounding conductor is based on three 600 kcmil conductors per phase. Since the equipment grounding conductor is run in parallel with the phase conductors, the size is required to be based on the size of the phase conductors in each raceway. From Table 250.66, a #1/0 AWG copper conductor must be used to meet grounding requirements. Therefore, the neutral conductor must be #1/0 AWG, as required for grounding purposes, not the #3 AWG based on loading considerations.

The previous examples have illustrated the procedure necessary to determine the overcurrent device rating and the required size of ungrounded (phase) and grounded (neutral) conductors for service entrance applications. In particular, the grounded conductor size was based on the actual demand loading on the neutral conductor and the minimum size required for grounding purposes. In most commercial and industrial applications, the grounded conductor is often sized the same as the ungrounded conductors. Note that sizing the grounded conductor in this manner exceeds the *NEC* minimum requirements.

10–6   METERING

Measurement of electrical quantities in electrical power systems is done for several reasons. The metering of electrical power is used for revenue billing, energy management, and transaction purposes. The quantities measured include active power, reactive power, apparent power, power factor, watthours, varhours, current, voltage, and so on. Metering may be done directly at low voltage or through voltage and current transformers for higher-voltage and higher-current systems. Either single-phase or total three-phase quantities may be metered.

Two types of electric meters are available: self-contained and transformer rated. The self-contained meter is directly connected to the service entrance conductors. The current rating of the meter must be sufficient to carry the maximum current drawn by the load. The meter class designation indicates the maximum continuous current rating of the meter. Self-contained meters are typically available in classes 100 and 200. Some manufacturers offer meters in classes 320 and 400 as well. Likewise, the voltage rating of the meter must be equal to the service voltage. Typical self-contained voltage ratings are 120, 240, 277, and 480 volts.

Transformer-rated meters are typically used for services of 400 A and above. These meters require the use of current transformers (CTs) to step the current down to a level that is suitable for metering. Since current transformers are used, the class designation for these meters is typically 10 or 20. In addition to current transformers, voltage or potential transformers (PTs) are required for high-current, high-voltage services. The purpose of the voltage transformers is to step the high voltage down to a lower voltage suitable for metering.

Induction Disk Watthour Meter

The induction disk watthour meter uses the principle of induction to produce a torque on a small rotating disk. This torque is produced by the interaction of the magnetic flux produced by the stator(s) in the meter. Each stator of the meter has a voltage coil and one or more current coils. The torque produced by the stator causes rotation of the disk at a speed proportional to the amount of energy consumed by the load. For polyphase watthour meters, there may be as many as three stators acting independently to produce torque on the rotating disk. Therefore, the amount of energy used in all three phases will be measured and recorded.

In the conventional dial-type register, the mechanical rotation of the disk causes several dials to rotate, thereby recording the amount of energy being used. These dial registers are read from right to left, with the dial on the far right having units of 1s. The next dial to the left has units of 10s, and so on. Typically, units of 1s, 10s, 100s, 1000s, and 10,000s are indicated. In order to read the meter, start at the left dial. If the dial pointer is between two numbers, read the lower number. If a certain dial pointer appears to be exactly on a

FIGURE 10–9
Dial Register Meter Readings

number, it is necessary to check the next dial to the right. If the next dial pointer has not yet reached 0, then read the lower number. If the reading of the next dial has gone past 0, then read the number as indicated. For example, consider the dial register shown in Figure 10–9. The left dial appears to be directly on 4. However, the dial to the right has not yet rotated past 0, so the number is recorded as 3. The remaining dials are read as 9, 4, and 7, respectively. Therefore, the meter reading is 3947. The previous reading is subtracted from the present reading to determine the amount of kWh consumed.

In the cyclometer type of meter register, the mechanical rotation of the induction disk causes the indicating register to advance. The cyclometer display is similar to the odometer found in an automobile. The readings are taken directly from the indicating wheels, in a manner similar to the dial-type register.

In addition to measuring energy usage, it is also possible to obtain an estimate of the demand of the load from a watthour meter. As previously discussed, the rotational speed of the disk is proportional to the amount of energy used. The number of watthours per revolution is referred to as the *meter constant* and is usually designated K_h. Therefore, the demand in kilowatts can be calculated from:

$$\text{Demand} = \frac{3.6 \times \text{\#Disk revolutions} \times K_h}{\text{Time in seconds}} \text{ (kW)} \qquad \textbf{(10–1)}$$

For example, assume that the disk rotates 20 revolutions in 130 seconds and that the meter constant is 7.2. The average demand is

$$\text{Demand} = \frac{3.6 \times (20) \times (7.2)}{130} = 4.0 \text{ kW}$$

Equation (10–1) applies to self-contained meters that are connected directly to the service entrance conductors without the use of instrument transformers. If the meter is connected to a high-voltage or high-current service through instrument transformers, the demand as well as kWh usage must be modified to include the instrument transformer turns ratios as follows:

$$\text{Demand} = \frac{3.6 \times (\text{Disk revolutions}) \times K_h \times (\text{CT ratio}) \times (\text{PT ratio})}{\text{Time in seconds}} \text{ (kW)} \qquad \textbf{(10–2)}$$

where:

  CT ratio = current transformer ratio
  PT ratio = voltage or potential transformer ratio

EXAMPLE 10–6

A three-phase induction disk watthour meter is connected to a 12.47 kV three-phase, four-wire system through instrument transformers. The PTs are connected in a wye–wye configuration, with a voltage rating of 7200–120 V. The CTs are wye connected and have a turns ratio of 400:5 A. The polyphase meter has a meter constant K_h of 1.8. Determine the estimated demand if the disk rotates 5 revolutions in 120 seconds.

Solution:

$$\text{Demand} = \frac{3.6 \times 5 \times 1.8 \times (400/5) \times (7200/120)}{120} = 1{,}296 \text{ kW}$$

In addition to measuring energy usage, many induction disk watthour meters are equipped with a demand register to measure peak energy consumption. This register will record the peak average demand for a specified demand interval. Typically, demand intervals of 15 or 30 minutes are used. Certain utility rate structures are designed to include the peak demand in the rate calculations because the utility must design and construct power generation, transmission, and distribution facilities to meet peak demands on the system. A user with a high peak demand and low kWh (energy) consumption is generally penalized for having a poor load factor.

The instantaneous demand of a load may be measured directly by use of an indicating wattmeter. A permanent record of the instantaneous demand may be obtained by use of a strip chart, circular disk, magnetic tape, or other type of recording medium. The maximum demand may then be determined by referring to the recorded data and reading the appropriate value. In metering installations using magnetic tape, the tape is removed from the recorder and taken to a magnetic tape reader, where the billing information is obtained.

The integrating demand register operates by counting the number of disk revolutions for a specified demand time interval. Since the demand interval is a fixed value, the maximum demand occurs in the time interval with the greatest number of disk revolutions. At the end of each time interval, the register is reset to zero and the process repeated. A separate register will store the maximum demand until manually reset to zero.

The thermal or lagged type of demand meter is the most common for small services. In the thermal type of demand meter, the thermal element produces heat that is proportional to the amount of energy being used at a given time. The heat energy is used to drive a pointer that indicates the instantaneous demand. A friction pointer is also advanced by the indicating pointer, thereby indicating the maximum demand. As the indicating pointer advances, the friction pointer advances along with it. If the demand decreases, however, the friction pointer will remain at the maximum value until manually reset. In most meters, the indicating pointer is black and the friction pointer is red. The friction pointer is reset after each meter reading.

Solid-State Metering

The use of solid-state microprocessor-based metering is becoming more and more widespread in the utility industry. Multifunction meters are able to replace several induction

FIGURE 10–10
Self-Contained Metering
Schematics

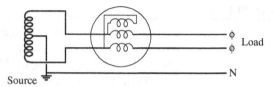

A. Single-Phase, Three-Wire, 120/240 V

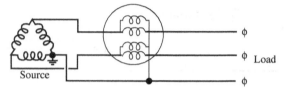

B. Three-Phase, Three-Wire, 120 V, 240 V, and 480 V

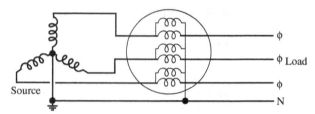

C. Three-Phase, Four-Wire, 208Y/120 V, and 480Y/277 V

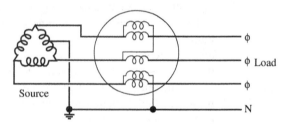

D. Three-Phase, Four-Wire, Delta, 240/120 V

disk-type meters for various metering schemes. For example many solid-state meters can be programmed to measure and display quantities such as polyphase and single-phase watthours (Wh), varhours (Vh), and voltamperehours (VAh); watts, vars, and voltamperes delivered and received; peak demand, time of peak, and minimum demand; power factor, and so on. In addition to measuring and displaying electrical quantities, solid-state meters have the capability of storing the information in memory. The stored information can then be downloaded to a computer for billing calculations or load analysis. The downloading can be done either on site by direct connection to the meter or by remote communication by use of a built-in modem. Fiber-optic, power line carrier, radio, or telephone channels may be used as the communication link between the meter and the computer.

FIGURE 10–11
Single-Phase, Three-Wire Meter
Installation *Source:* Courtesy of
Ohio Edison Company.

Metering Connections

This section will show some of the more common connections for metering of electric power. The diagrams are simplified to show only one meter connection. In some instances, it is desirable to meter other electrical quantities as well. The instrument transformers and meters are usually furnished by the utility and installed by the customer's electrician.

The metering schematics shown in Figure 10–10 are for self-contained meters that do not require instrument transformers. Figure 10–10(A) shows the connection for a typical 120/240 volt, single-phase, three-wire system. This is the common service voltage for residential and small commercial establishments. The stator consists of one voltage coil and two current coils. Since the voltage coil is connected between the two "hot" conductors, the voltage rating of the meter is 240 V. The current or class rating of the meter must be sufficient to carry the maximum load current. Figure 10–11 shows a typical single-phase meter installed in a residential dwelling.

The circuit shown in Figure 10–10(B) shows the metering connections for three-phase, three-wire services. Typical service voltages are 120 V, 240 V, and 480 V. The metering in this situation is similar to the two-wattmeter method used for three-phase, three-wire loads. Note that the meter has two stators, with voltage coils connected from phase-to-phase. Therefore, the voltage rating of the meter must be equal to the phase-to-phase voltage of the service.

Three-phase, four-wire services are typically metered using the configuration shown in Figure 10–10(C). Service voltages are either 480Y/277 V or 208Y/120 V. The meter shown has three stators, with each stator having one potential coil and one current coil. Since the voltage coils are connected from phase-to-neutral, the voltage rating of the meter coils is either 277 V, for 480Y/277 V services or 120 V, for 208Y/120 V services.

Three-phase, four-wire, delta-connected services are metered by the configuration shown in Figure 10–10(D). Two stators are used, with one of the stators having two current coils and one voltage coil and the other stator having one current coil and one voltage coil. The meter will have a voltage rating of 240 V for this type of service.

The metering connections shown in Figure 10–12 are for transformer-rated meters. The meter connections shown are for high-current, low-voltage services. For example, on a 480Y/277 V, 2000 A, three-phase, four-wire service, current transformers are required to

FIGURE 10–12
Low-Voltage Transformer-Rated
Schematics

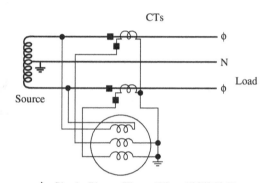

A. Single-Phase, Three-Wire, 120/240 V

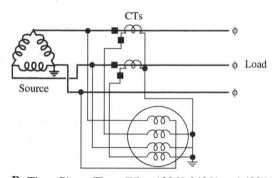

B. Three-Phase, Three-Wire, 120 V, 240 V, and 480 V

FIGURE 10–12
(Continued)

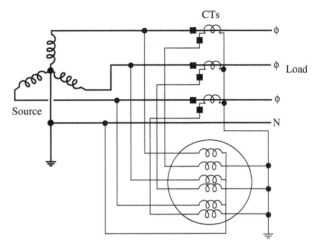

C. Three-Phase, Four-Wire, 208Y/120 V, and 480Y/277 V

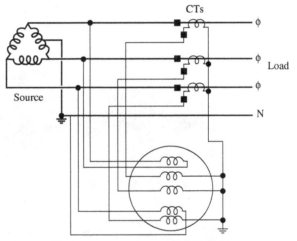

D. Three-Phase, Four-Wire, 240/120 V

step down the current from 2000 A to 5 A. Generally, the primary rating of the CT is selected to match the ampacity of the service. The secondary rating of the CTs is typically 5 A. As a result, it is common to use Class 10 or 20 meters for these configurations. The meter voltage rating is selected to match the voltage ratings of the services, as was done for the metering configurations in Figure 10–10.

The current transformers are typically of the window type, with the service conductor passing through the CT window. Essentially, the primary of the CT has one turn, that of the service conductor itself. For overhead services, the CTs are typically mounted on the exterior building wall near the service drop location. In underground services, the CTs may be mounted in a cabinet near the service entrance or over the secondary terminals of the pad-mount distribution transformer supplying the service. Figure 10–13 shows a CT-metered, low-voltage metering installation for a small commercial establishment.

For high-voltage, high-current services, voltage transformers as well as current transformers are required. Figure 10–14(A) shows the metering connections for three-phase, four-wire services. Figure 10–14(B) shows the connections for the three-phase, three-wire service. These services are common among larger commercial and industrial

FIGURE 10–13
Low-Voltage, CT-Metered Service *Source:* Courtesy of Ohio Edison Company.

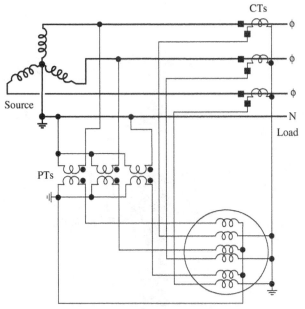

CTs

φ

φ

φ

N

Load

Source

PTs

A. Three-Phase, Four-Wire Wye Service

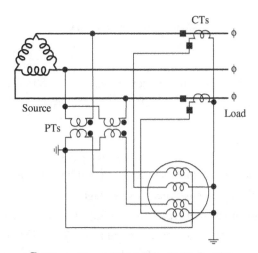

CTs

φ

φ

φ

Source

Load

PTs

B. Three-Phase, Three-Wire Delta Service

FIGURE 10–14
Primary Metering Schematics

FIGURE 10–15
Primary Metering Installation *Source:* Courtesy of Ohio Edison Company.

establishments and would be typical for service voltages above 600 V. Figure 10–15 shows a primary metering installation on a 12.47 kV medium-voltage service.

PROBLEMS

1. Under what conditions are multiple services to a building permitted?
2. Describe the basic elements of a typical low-voltage overhead service.
3. Describe the basic elements of a typical low-voltage underground service.
4. Describe the basic elements of a typical medium-voltage overhead service.
5. Describe the basic elements of a typical medium-voltage underground service.
6. What are the basic clearance requirements for supply conductors above rooftops?
7. What is the minimum clearance requirement from building openings for service conductors? Are service conductors permitted under openings through which material may be passed?
8. What is the clearance requirement for a 120/240 V, single-phase, three-wire service at the point of attachment to the building? Over the driveway? Over the main roadway?

9. What is the clearance requirement for a 480Y/277 V, three-phase, four-wire service at the point of attachment to the building? Over the driveway? Over the main roadway?

10. What are the protection requirements for underground service conductors at the point from which they extend from the ground?

11. What types of conduit are permitted in areas where the service conductors may be subject to physical damage?

12. Give an example where multiple service entrance sets are permitted.

13. What types of cable are permitted to be used for service entrances?

14. A residence supplied by a 120/240 V, single-phase, three-wire service has a total estimated demand load of 25,000 VA. The total estimated neutral loading is 17,000 VA. Determine the service overcurrent protection device rating and ungrounded and grounded service conductor size. Use XHHW aluminum conductor and 75°C device terminal ratings and allow for 25% load growth.

15. A commercial establishment supplied by a 208Y/120 V, three-phase, four-wire service has a total estimated demand load of 250,000 VA. The total estimated single-phase loading is 35,000 VA. Determine the service overcurrent protection device rating and ungrounded and grounded service conductor size. Use XHHW copper conductor and 75°C device terminal ratings and allow for 25% load growth. Do not use larger than 600 kcmil conductor size.

16. An industrial facility supplied by a 480Y/277 V, three-phase, four-wire service has a total estimated demand load of 950,000 VA. The total estimated single-phase loading is 135,000 VA. Determine the service overcurrent protection device rating and ungrounded and grounded service conductor size. Use XHHW copper conductor and 75°C device terminal ratings and allow for 25% load growth. Do not use larger than a 600 kcmil conductor size.

17. What is meant by "self-contained" meter?

18. Why are current transformers used in some metering applications? Why are voltage transformers used?

19. What is meant by the "class" designation of a meter?

11

Panelboards and Switchboards

INTRODUCTION

The distribution of power for lighting, receptacle, and other loads within a building is accomplished by use of panelboards and switchboards. Panelboards are used as the point of supply for the branch circuits in a certain area of the building. The panelboard will often contain the last overcurrent protective device for the circuits it supplies. The supply for the panelboard is typically the service entrance or a feeder from a main distribution panel or switchboard. A main overcurrent device is commonly installed in the panelboard to protect it. The rating of the panelboard and overcurrent device must be sufficient to supply the load to be served.

This chapter will introduce you to some of the more common design elements associated with the application of panelboards and switchboards, specifically, the busbar arrangements, phase arrangement, overcurrent protection, and application of panelboard and switchboards. In addition, the development of panel schedules, panel layout, and panel load balancing will be discussed.

OBJECTIVES

Upon completion of this chapter, you will:

- Understand the phase arrangement in panelboards and switchboards
- Be able to determine overcurrent protection for panelboards
- Be able to define lighting and appliance branch circuit panelboards
- Be able to define power panelboards
- Be able to develop panel schedules
- Be able to properly balance a panelboard
- Understand main distribution panel applications
- Understand medium-voltage switchgear applications

11–1   PANELBOARD BUSBAR ARRANGEMENTS

The function of a panelboard is to distribute the power to the branch circuits and feeders through suitable overcurrent protection. The internal bus structure of the panelboard must allow for the application of the proper voltage to these branch circuits and feeders. For example, a single-phase panelboard applied to a 120/240 V, single-phase, three-wire system must properly distribute power to individual branch circuits such that the voltage is either 120 V phase-to-neutral or 240 V phase-to-phase. A single-pole breaker would be installed in the panelboard to protect the ungrounded conductor of a 120 V branch circuit. Likewise, a two-pole breaker would be installed to protect both ungrounded conductors of a 240 V branch circuit. Thus, the voltage between any two adjacent poles in the 120/240 V, single-phase, three-wire panelboard must be 240 V to accommodate the two-pole breaker.

To understand how the panelboard accomplishes the distribution of voltage, consider the busbar arrangement of the panelboard shown in Figure 11–1. The incoming supply for the panelboard is shown connected to the main lugs at the top of the panel. It is also possible for a main circuit breaker to be used instead of main lugs. Each of the ungrounded supply conductors of the source are connected to the main busbars, labeled "A" and "B" in the figure. The neutral or grounded conductor of the supply connects to the neutral bus, as shown. The main and neutral busbars are typically of rectangular cross section and are made of copper or aluminum. Note that the main busbars run the entire vertical length of the panel. Also, note that the neutral bus is present on each side of the panel, in close proximity to the main busbars. This arrangement facilitates the connection of the ungrounded and grounded conductors of the branch circuit.

As shown in Figure 11–1, the main busbars have fingers or projections that tend to interleave with each other toward the center of the panel. Each of these fingers has either a stab or other type of projection to allow connection of the branch circuit breakers to the main busbars. Panelboards accommodating plug-on or bolt-on circuit breakers are available, depending on the application. Typically, the breakers are arranged in two columns in the panelboard. Several rows of breakers complete the arrangement. These breakers may

FIGURE 11–1
Single-Phase Panelboard
Busbar Arrangement

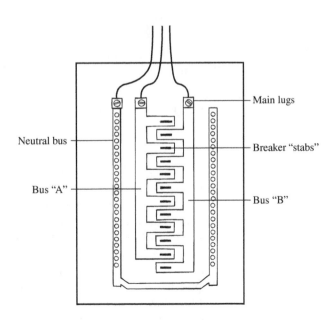

FIGURE 11–2
Single-Phase Panel Installation

be either single pole or double pole, depending on the required branch circuit voltage. Figure 11–2 shows a single-phase panel rated 150 A serving as the main service panel in a residence. The panel is shown with the cover removed.

To understand the phase arrangement of the single-phase panelboard, consider the schematic shown in Figure 11–3. Note that the breaker poles in any given row are connected to the same busbar ("A" or "B") of the panelboard. Adjacent rows of breaker poles alternate connection between busbar "A" and busbar "B" of the panelboard. Thus, a double-pole breaker mounted in the panelboard will have one pole connected to busbar "A" and the other pole connected to busbar "B", resulting in a voltage between poles of 240 V. A branch circuit requiring 240 V (220 V) for a large electrical load, such as a hot

FIGURE 11–3
Single-Phase Panel Schematic

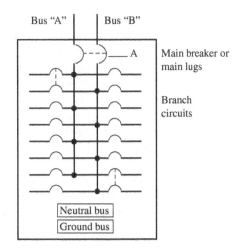

water heater, clothes dryer, range, well pump, or HVAC unit would originate from a two-pole breaker in the panelboard. Two-pole breakers are designated with a dashed line connecting the two poles to indicate common tripping of both poles in the event of a fault.

Two possible arrangements of the busbars in three phase panelboards are shown in Figure 11–4. Figure 11–4(A) illustrates an interleaved busbar arrangement similar to that shown in Figure 11–1. Phases A and C are shown as the left and right buses, respectively. Phase B extends down the center of the panel between phases A and C. As in the

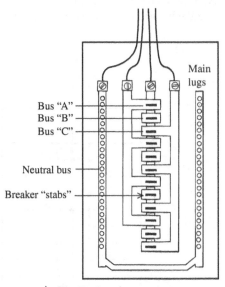

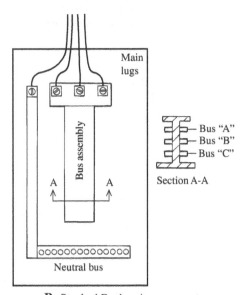

A. Flat Busbar Arrangement   **B.** Stacked Busbar Arrangement

FIGURE 11–4
Three-Phase Panelboard Busbar Arrangement

single-phase panel, the breakers are arranged in two columns, with the breakers in any given row connected to the same phase. Thus, the phase arrangement of the breakers from top to bottom on each side of the panel is A-B-C. The voltage between any two of the main busbars is equal to the line-to-line voltage of the system.

The arrangement shown in Figure 11–4(B) has the main busbars arranged in a vertical fashion. However, in this arrangement, the busbars are stacked on top of each other with an insulating medium in between, as shown in the cross-sectional view. The phases are arranged A-B-C from the front toward the back of the panel. The circuit breakers plug onto the bus, thereby making the required electrical connection.

Single-pole, double-pole, and three-pole breakers are available for installation in either of the panelboard arrangements shown in Figure 11–4. The phase connection for breakers installed in a panel with the busbar arrangement shown in Figure 11–4(A) is explained by use of the three-phase panel schematic shown in Figure 11–5. For single-pole breakers, the phase connection will depend on the row in which the breaker is located. The phase connections for double-pole breakers can be A-B, B-C, or C-A, depending on the specific placement of the breaker in the panel. Three-pole breakers will have a phase connection of A-B-C, B-C-A, or C-A-B. All phase connection designations are from top to bottom in the panel.

Single-pole breakers placed in a panel having the busbar arrangement shown in Figure 11–4(B) will have a phase connection that is independent of the location of the breaker in the panel. The phase connections for single-pole and double-pole breakers are determined by the construction of the breaker itself. The phase connections for the breaker are usually specified in the catalog number for the breaker. For example, the designer must specify to which phase (A, B, or C) a single-pole breaker is to be connected. A similar phase designation (A-B, B-C, or C-A) applies to double-pole breakers as well. Three-pole breakers usually have an A-B-C phase designation. However, three-pole breakers with a

FIGURE 11–5
Three-Phase Panel Schematic

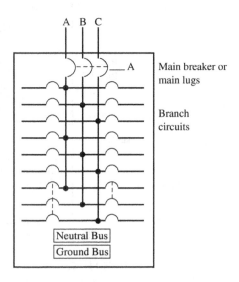

FIGURE 11–6
Three-Phase Panel Installation *Source:* Courtesy Youngstown State University.

C-B-A designation are also available. A typical three-phase panel installation is shown in Figure 11–6.

11–2 CLASSIFICATION AND RATINGS OF PANELBOARDS

Panelboards are classified as either power panelboards or lighting and appliance branch circuit panelboards. Section 408.14(A) of the *NEC* defines a lighting and appliance branch circuit panelboard as a panelboard having more than 10% of its overcurrent devices supplying lighting and appliance branch circuits. For the purposes of this definition, an overcurrent device consists of each pole of a single or multipole circuit breaker. For example, a two-pole circuit breaker counts as two overcurrent devices and a three-pole breaker counts as three overcurrent devices. In addition, any unused spaces in the panelboard should be considered as likely to supply lighting and appliance branch circuits. Section 408.14 of the *NEC* defines a lighting and appliance branch circuit as a circuit rated 30 A or less, with one of the branch circuit conductors connected to the neutral of the panel. An example of a lighting and appliance branch circuit would be a 20 A, 277 V branch circuit supplying the lighting in a commercial building. The majority of panelboards encountered in practice are considered lighting and appliance branch circuit panelboards.

Section 408.14(B) of the *NEC* defines a power panelboard as a panelboard having 10% or fewer of its overcurrent devices protecting lighting and appliance branch circuits. An example of a power panelboard is a panelboard supplying only three-phase, three-wire branch circuits consisting only of the ungrounded conductors of the system, with no connection to the system neutral. Typically, the feeder supplying a power panelboard will not have the system neutral conductor present as part of the supply feeder. As a result, the power panel will not have provisions for connection of branch circuits requiring connection to the system neutral. Connection of branch circuit loads between any ungrounded conductor and the equipment grounding conductors is not permitted.

The rating of a panelboard typically refers to the ampacity rating. Single-phase, three-wire panelboards for residential applications are commonly available with ratings of 100 A, 150 A, and 200 A. Ratings of 300 A and 400 A are also available from some manufacturers. For commercial applications, panelboards having ratings of 100 A, 225A, 400 A, and 600 A are typically available. The rating of the panelboard selected must be equal to or greater than the computed load to be served.

The ability of a panelboard to withstand short circuit currents in the event of a fault either in the panelboard or on one of the branch circuits is also of interest. In the event of a short circuit condition, the high-magnitude short circuit current will flow from the source through the panelboard busbars to the location of the fault. The magnitude of the short circuit current is a function of the system voltage, the impedance of the circuit between the source and the fault, and the amount of fault resistance. The short circuit current is generally expressed in terms of rms symmetrical amperes and may be 25 times rated current or higher in many situations. The high-level fault current flowing through the panelboard busbars produces high levels of mechanical force acting on the busbars themselves. These mechanical forces are proportional to the square of the current. Panelboard busbars must be braced to withstand the high mechanical forces produced as a result of short circuit currents. As a result of these short circuit considerations, panelboards must have a short circuit rating equal to or greater than the maximum short circuit current expected on the system. Panelboards with short circuit ratings of 10,000 A, 22,000 A, 65,000 A, and 100,000 A are commonly available. In addition, some panelboards may have a short circuit rating of 200,000 A if protected by a current-limiting fuse or circuit breaker.

The voltage rating of panelboards is also of prime consideration. Generally, voltage ratings of 240 V and 600 V are available. This voltage rating refers to the maximum phase-to-phase voltage permitted. For example, a voltage rating of 240 V would be required for panels supplied by a 120/240 V, 1ϕ, 3W; 208Y/120 V, 3ϕ, 4W; 240 V, 3ϕ, 3W, and 240/120, 3ϕ, 4W systems. The 600 V voltage rating generally applies to panelboards supplied from a 480Y/277 V, 3ϕ, 4W system. Manufacturers' data must be referred to for appropriate voltage and current ratings.

The number of spaces in a panel refers to the number of single-pole overcurrent devices that can be installed in the panel. A two-pole breaker would occupy two spaces on one side of the panel. Likewise, a three-pole breaker would occupy three spaces on one side of the panel. Panels with 16, 24, 30, and 42 spaces are commonly available from most manufacturers. The number of spaces on each side of the panel is one-half of the total number of spaces in the panel. Section 408.15 of the *NEC* specifies that a lighting and appliance branch circuit panelboard is not permitted to have more than 42 spaces. The actual number of spaces required will depend on the particular design. It is good design practice to allow for at least 10% spare or unused spaces in any given panel application.

Larger single-phase and three-phase panels designed for commercial and industrial applications may specify the breaker space in terms of total breaker mounting height rather than spaces. The individual branch circuit breakers used in the panel will have a certain required mounting height. For example, a three-phase panel may specify a total of 63" of total mounting space. The individual branch circuit breakers may require $1\frac{1}{2}$" of mounting height per pole. Thus, a single-pole breaker would require $1\frac{1}{2}$", a double-pole breaker 3", and a three-pole breaker $4\frac{1}{2}$" of mounting height. Higher-ampacity breakers for large feeders may require a larger amount of mounting space in the panel. The designer must refer to manufacturers' data to determine the required mounting heights and space available.

EXAMPLE 11–1

A three-phase panel having a bus arrangement as shown in Figure 11–4(B) is to accommodate the following breakers:

Quantity of two: 3-pole, 200 A
Quantity of four: 2-pole, 20 A
Quantity of ten: 1-pole, 20 A

Each breaker pole occupies $1\frac{1}{2}$" of mounting space in the panel. In addition, the main breaker is 600 A, requiring 9.0" of mounting space. Determine the total mounting space in inches required.

Solution: The total space required is calculated as

Two, 3-pole, 200 A breakers: 2×3 poles $\times 1.5" = 9.0"$

Four, 2-pole, 20 A breakers: 4×2 poles $\times 1.5" = 12.0"$

Ten, 1-pole, 20 A breakers: 10×1 poles $\times 1.5" = 15.0"$

Main breaker: 9.0"

Total = 45.0"

Thus, the panel must provide at least 45" of mounting space for the required breakers. Space should also be provided for future mounting of breakers.

11–3 OVERCURRENT PROTECTION OF PANELBOARDS

Generally, panelboards must be protected by an overcurrent device having a rating equal to or less than the rating of the panelboard main busbars. Section 408.16(A) of the *NEC* specifically requires overcurrent protection for all lighting and appliance branch circuit panelboards. In addition, Section 408.16(B) requires overcurrent protection for power panelboards that have the system neutral brought to the panelboard and have more than 10% of the branch circuit overcurrent devices rated 30 A or less. Power panelboards that do not have the system neutral supplied to the panel and that supply branch circuit loads involving only the ungrounded circuit conductors are not required to have overcurrent protection. But even though overcurrent protection is not required, it is desirable to provide this protection to protect the panelboard.

Panelboards may be provided with the necessary overcurrent protection by use of a main circuit breaker, as shown in Figure 11–7(A). This is the common arrangement for panelboards used as service entrance equipment. The main circuit breaker is mounted inside the panelboard enclosure and has one set of terminal lugs for connection of the supply conductors. The terminal lugs on the main breaker must be suitable for the connection of the supply conductors in terms of material type (CU/AL) and conductor size. The load side of the main circuit breaker is connected directly to the panel main busbars. The main circuit breaker will open all ungrounded conductors in the event of a short circuit involving any of the ungrounded conductors. The rating of the main circuit breaker must not exceed the rating of the panelboard busbars.

A panelboard may be provided with overcurrent protection by the feeder overcurrent device, as shown in Figure 11–7(B). In this instance, the overcurrent device provides overcurrent protection for both the panelboard and the feeder conductors. When applied in this manner, the panelboard will be equipped with main lugs only (MLO) for connection of the supply conductors. As with the main breaker panelboard, the terminal lugs on the MLO panelboard must be suitable for the connection of the supply conductors. The required overcurrent protection can be a fused switch or enclosed circuit breaker.

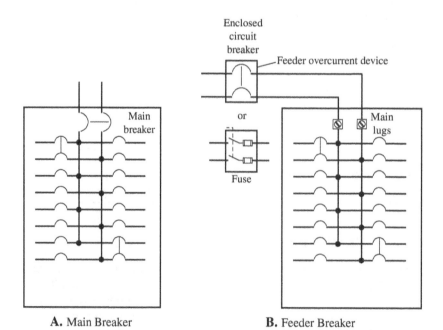

A. Main Breaker   **B.** Feeder Breaker

FIGURE 11–7
Overcurrent Protection of Panelboards

Where a panel is supplied from a 240/120 V, three-phase, four-wire system, Section 408.3(E) of the *NEC* requires the phase conductor having the high voltage-to-ground to be designated as phase B and connected to the center busbar in the panel. The voltage between this high leg and the grounded conductor is 208 V. Connection of single-phase loads between this high leg and the grounded conductor is not permitted. Good design practice is to install two separate panels for systems supplied by the 240/120 V, three-phase, four-wire system. One panel supplies 120/240 V, single-phase, three-wire loads, and the other supplies 240 V, three-phase, three-wire loads. This arrangement is shown in Figure 11–8.

Panels supplied by three-phase, three-wire systems such as 240 V and 480 V generally supply only three-phase loads. These loads typically consist of motors, step-down and isolation transformers, and electric heating elements. For corner-grounded systems, the grounded conductor is designated as B-phase. This phase must be connected to the center busbar in the panel. Panels supplied by these systems typically contain three-pole branch circuit breakers only.

EXAMPLE 11–2

A 24-space panel is supplied from a 208Y/120 V, 3φ, 4W supply. All phase and neutral conductors are brought to the panelboard. The overcurrent devices in the panel, excluding the main, consist of four three-pole, 30 A breakers protecting branch circuits supplying three-phase motor loads. Each branch circuit consists of three ungrounded conductors and an equipment-grounding conductor. Is this panel classified as a power panelboard or an appliance and branch circuit panelboard?

FIGURE 11–8
Panelboard Arrangement to Supply
120/240 V, Single-Phase, Three-Wire
and 240 V, Three-Phase, Three-Wire
Service

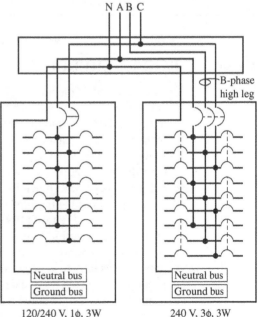

Solution: Although the overcurrent devices in this panel supply branch circuits that do not involve the system neutral, there are 12 spaces available that could supply lighting and appliance branch circuits in the future. In addition, the problem statement mentions that the system neutral is brought to the panelboard. Therefore, this panel should be considered a lighting and appliance branch circuit panelboard. As such, main overcurrent protection of the panel is required.

EXAMPLE 11-3

A 42-space panel is supplied from a 480Y/277 V, 3ϕ, 4W system. All phase and neutral conductors are brought to the panel. The overcurrent devices in the panel, excluding the main, consist of six three-pole, 40 A breakers supplying branch circuits consisting of three ungrounded conductors and an equipment-grounding conductor. In addition, there are ten 20 A, single-pole breakers protecting branch circuits supplying 277 V lighting circuits. Is this panel classified as a power panelboard or an appliance and branch circuit panelboard?

Solution: The 20 A, 277 V lighting circuits involve connection between the phase and neutral conductor of the system. As a result, there are ten lighting and appliance branch circuit overcurrent devices. Each of the six three-pole breakers count as three overcurrent devices, for a total of 18. Therefore, there are a total of 28 overcurrent devices in this panel, of which 10 are considered lighting and appliance branch circuit overcurrent devices. Since the number of lighting and appliance branch circuit overcurrent devices exceeds 10% of the total, this panel is classified as a lighting and appliance branch circuit panelboard and requires overcurrent protection.

11-4   PANEL SCHEDULES

To keep a record of the branch circuits in a panelboard, a panel schedule is developed. The panel schedule is essentially a bookkeeping tool that lists items such as circuit number, circuit load description, number of poles, circuit loading, and any special notes regarding the branch circuits. The panel schedule is designed to allow easy tabulation of the loads on the individual branch circuits. This load data is then used to determine the balance in load among the ungrounded conductors. Sample panel schedules for single-phase and three-phase panelboards are shown in Figures 11-9 and 11-10. The panel schedules will aid in the development of the required circuit directory of the panel.

Referring to Figures 11-9 and 11-10, note that the poles or spaces are numbered from left to right, top to bottom, starting with space number 1 at the top left-hand side. Similar to the convention developed for numbering the spaces or poles in the panel, circuit numbers are usually assigned to the individual branch circuits from left to right, top to bottom, starting at the top left-hand side of the panel with circuit number 1. Thus, a branch circuit supplied by a single-pole breaker will have a single circuit number and a single pole or space number. Branch circuits supplied by a two-pole or three-pole breaker may have a single circuit number corresponding to the first pole number to which the breaker is

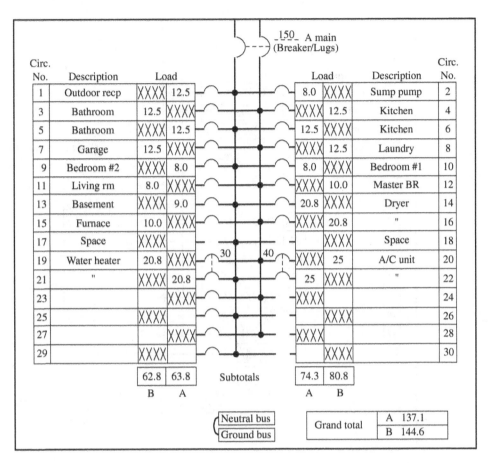

FIGURE 11–9
Single-Phase Panel Schedule

connected. Referring to Figure 11–10, the branch circuit labeled as circuit number 4 is supplied from a two-pole breaker connected to spaces 4 and 6 of the panel. Likewise, branch circuit number 7 is supplied by a three-pole breaker occupying spaces 7, 9, and 11 of the panel.

Although the loading on the individual branch circuits may be expressed in either amperes or volt-amperes, this text will express the branch circuit loading in amperes. The loading on the branch circuits is determined using the methods discussed in Chapter 3. The branch circuit loading is recorded on the panel schedule as shown in Figures 11–9 and 11–10. Note that the arrangement of the busbars in the panel allows for the distribution of the branch circuit loads to the various phases.

Single-phase loads involving a phase-to-neutral connection will result in the load being placed on one of the panel main busbars. The actual phase will be determined by the location of the breaker in the panel. Single-phase loads involving a phase-to-phase connection will result in the load being placed on two of the panel main busbars. The actual

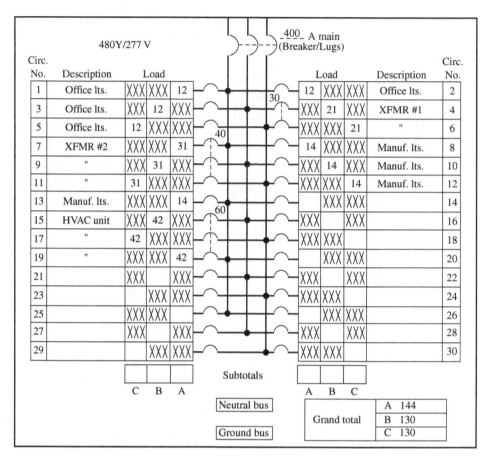

FIGURE 11–10
Three-Phase Panel Schedule

phases affected will be determined by the location of the breaker in the panel. Lastly, a three-phase load involving all three phases will result in the load being placed on all three phases of the panel.

The panel schedule also contains the voltage and current rating of the main overcurrent device. The current rating of the individual branch circuit breakers is also recorded on the panel schedule. In some instances, the legend to the panel schedule may indicate that all breakers are 20 A unless otherwise indicated. In addition, any special breaker features such as GFCI, key operated, shunt trip, and so on will be specified on the panel schedule.

The panel schedule also contains information regarding the neutral and ground bus. Recall that in certain applications, the neutral bus must be insulated and separated from the equipment-grounding or ground bus. In such cases, the panel schedule will specify an insulated neutral bus and a separate ground bus. Virtually all manufactured panels are supplied with an insulated neutral. If the neutral bus and ground bus are to be common, as in service entrance equipment, a grounding screw in the neutral bus is provided to connect the grounded conductor (neutral) to the panel enclosure. This grounding screw also serves as the main bonding jumper in service entrance equipment. For installations requiring an insulated neutral, a separate ground bus must be specified. The grounded conductors of the branch circuits are connected to the neutral bus, and the equipment-grounding conductors are connected to the ground bus.

The neutral bus is typically rated to carry 100% of the panel rated current under normal conditions. This is referred to as a "100% rated neutral." In applications involving high levels of harmonic load currents, the neutral may be expected to carry current that exceeds the panel rated current. Panels are available with neutrals rated to carry 200% of the rated phase current. These panels are listed as having a "200% rated neutral." (The subject of harmonics is treated in a later chapter.)

EXAMPLE 11–4

Determine the loading, expressed in amperes, on each ungrounded conductor (phase conductor) for the following load specifications:

a) 120 V, single-phase, phase-to-neutral connection, 1250 VA
b) 240 V, single-phase, phase-to-phase connection, 3000 VA
c) 208 V, single-phase, phase-to-phase connection, 2500 VA
d) 277 V, single-phase, phase-to-neutral connection, 2000 VA
e) 480 V, single-phase, phase-to-phase connection, 15,000 VA
f) 240 V, three-phase, 5000 VA
g) 208 V, three-phase, 4000 VA
h) 480 V, three-phase, 25,000 VA

Solution:

a) $I = \dfrac{1250 \text{ VA}}{120 \text{ V}} = 10.4 \text{ A}$

b) $I = \dfrac{3000 \text{ VA}}{240 \text{ V}} = 12.5 \text{ A}$

c) $I = \dfrac{2500 \text{ VA}}{208 \text{ V}} = 12.0 \text{ A}$

d) $I = \dfrac{2000 \text{ VA}}{277 \text{ V}} = 7.2 \text{ A}$

e) $I = \dfrac{15{,}000 \text{ VA}}{480 \text{ V}} = 31.3 \text{ A}$

f) $I = \dfrac{5000 \text{ VA}}{\sqrt{3} \times 240 \text{ V}} = 12.0 \text{ A}$

g) $I = \dfrac{4000 \text{ VA}}{\sqrt{3} \times 208 \text{ V}} = 11.1 \text{ A}$

h) $I = \dfrac{25{,}000 \text{ VA}}{\sqrt{3} \times 480 \text{ V}} = 30.1 \text{ A}$

EXAMPLE 11–5

Given the panel schedule shown in Figure 11–9, answer the following questions:

a) What is the loading on circuit #12?
b) What is the total loading on the main bus labeled "A"?
c) What area does circuit number #8 supply?
d) What is the loading on circuit #4 expressed in volt-amperes?
e) What is the rating of the circuit breaker protecting circuit #20?
f) What is the voltage rating of the load supplied by circuit #20?
g) What is the loading on circuit #20 expressed in volt-amperes?

Solution:

a) 10.0 A or 1200 VA
b) 137.1 A
c) Laundry circuit for laundry equipment
d) 1500 VA
e) 40 A
f) A two-pole breaker protects this circuit. Voltage rating = 240 V
g) The circuit voltage rating is 240 V. The loading in VA is thus:

$$\text{Loading} = (240 \text{ V}) \times (25 \text{ A}) = 6000 \text{ VA}$$

11–5   PANEL BALANCING

Proper electrical design requires an even loading of the service and feeder conductors. To accomplish this, the branch circuit loads must be evenly distributed among the phase conductors of a panelboard. Even distribution of the branch circuit loads on a panelboard is determined by calculating the percentage unbalance of the loads in a panel. For proper design, the total percentage unbalance must not exceed 10%.

To determine the percentage unbalance, the total loading on each phase of the panel must be determined. This can be accomplished by referring to the panel schedule and summing all branch circuit loads connected to each phase of the panel. The average loading on the panel is determined by calculating the average value among the phases. The deviation from average is calculated for each phase by subtracting the average loading from the total loading on that particular phase. The maximum deviation from average is the absolute value of the largest deviation from average. The percentage unbalance is given by

$$\% \text{ Unbalance} = \frac{\text{Maximum deviation from average}}{\text{Average phase loading}} \times 100\% \qquad \textbf{(11.1)}$$

EXAMPLE 11–6

Determine the % unbalance for the following panels:

a) Single-phase panel with tabulated loads of 120 A and 75 A on each of the panel busbars.
b) Three-phase panel with tabulated loads of 120 A, 80 A, and 135 A on each of the panel busbars.

Solution:

a) The average load is

$$\text{Average loading} = \frac{120\ A + 75\ A}{2} = 97.5\ A$$

The deviations from average are calculated for each phase:

$$\text{Deviation } \varphi A = 120\ A - 97.5\ A = 22.5\ A$$
$$\text{Deviation } \varphi B = 75\ A - 97.5\ A = -22.5\ A$$

Note that for the single-phase panel, the deviations from average are equal and opposite. The absolute value of the deviation from average for each phase is 22.5 A. Thus, the maximum deviation from average is 22.5 A in this case. The % unbalance is given by

$$\% \text{ Unbalance} = \frac{22.5\ A}{97.5\ A} \times 100\% = 23.1\%$$

Note that since the calculated percent unbalance exceeds 10%, rearrangement of some of the branch circuits in the panel is required. In this case, shifting approximately 15 A to 20 A of load from ϕA to ϕB would be required to achieve proper balance.

b) The average load is

$$\text{Average loading} = \frac{120\ A + 80\ A + 135\ A}{3} = 111.7\ A$$

The deviations from average are calculated for each phase:

$$\text{Deviation } \varphi A = 120\ A - 111.7\ A = 8.3\ A$$
$$\text{Deviation } \varphi B = 80\ A - 111.7\ A = -31.7\ A$$
$$\text{Deviation } \varphi C = 135\ A - 111.7\ A = 23.3\ A$$

Note that for the three-phase panel, the deviations from average are generally not equal. The absolute value of the maximum deviation from average is 31.7 A, occurring on B-phase. The % unbalance is given by

$$\% \text{ Unbalance} = \frac{31.7\ A}{111.7\ A} \times 100\% = 28.4\%$$

Note that since the calculated percent unbalance exceeds 10%, rearrangement of some of the branch circuits in the panel are required. In this case, shifting some of the load from phases A and C to phase B would be required.

11–6   MAIN DISTRIBUTION PANEL SCHEDULES

Installations requiring the distribution of power to several panelboards located throughout the building typically use main distribution panelboards, or MDPs. The main distribution panel typically serves as service entrance equipment for larger services and supplies feeders to other panels. Main distribution panels with main bus ratings ranging from 800 A to 5000 A are commonly available.

The schedule for the main distribution panel usually consists of a pictorial view of the front of the panel, as shown in Figure 11–11(A). The pictorial view shows the physical layout and location of the individual units mounted in the MDP. The MDP consists of several vertical sections bolted together to form the complete switchboard assembly. Full-height vertical sections are usually required for auxiliary sections to allow for top feed of cables, main switch, or main circuit breaker. Each full-height vertical section is designated A, B, C, and so on, as shown in Figure 11–11(A). Other designations are possible as well.

Distribution sections allow for the installation of individual distribution units, such as breaker or fused switch units for feeders, step-down transformer units, motor starter units, lighting and appliance branch circuit panelboard units, and power panelboard units. Blanking units are available to cover any unused portions of the distribution section. The type of units available differs based on the manufacturer. The designer must refer to manufacturers' data to determine the proper application for the individual units. Specifically, the physical dimensions of the individual units must be determined in order to accomplish the layout of the MDP. As shown in Figure 11–11(A), the individual units in each vertical section are numbered 1, 2, 3, and so on, starting at the top. Thus, any individual unit will be designated by a letter indicating the vertical section and a number indicating the location in the vertical section. These unit identification numbers are cross-referenced to the listing shown in Figure 11–11(C).

The schedule shown in Figure 11–11(C) provides specific details of the individual units installed in the MDP and is included as part of the MDP schedule. The information contained on the MDP schedule is similar to that of the panelboards previously discussed and includes the type of unit installed, rating of fuses, breakers, and switches, and so forth.

In addition to the front view of the panel, a plan view or footprint of the panel is also included to show the physical dimensions of the panel and the amount of floor space required. Also, the footprint will show the required location of conduit entry into the bottom of the panel. This information is necessary to ensure that proper clearances are maintained around the equipment. An example footprint showing physical dimensions and conduit entry area is shown in Figure 11–11(B).

11–7   MEDIUM-VOLTAGE SWITCHGEAR AND UNIT SUBSTATIONS

Medium-voltage switchgear is typically used where the service to a commercial or industrial facility is supplied from the medium-voltage distribution system of the supplying utility. Voltage levels for medium-voltage services in this category range from 5 kV to 35 kV. Medium-voltage switchgear assemblies have grounded metal barriers separating the compartments and structures within the assembly. This type of construction is commonly referred to as *metal-clad switchgear.* Low-voltage panelboards and switchboards typically do not have this type of protection. Figure 11–12(A) shows a front view of a typical medium-voltage switchgear assembly.

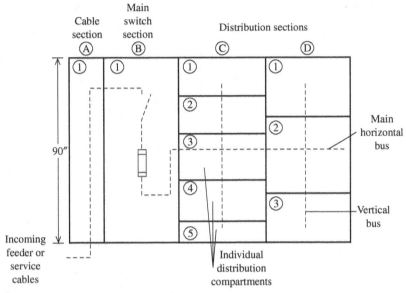

A. Front View

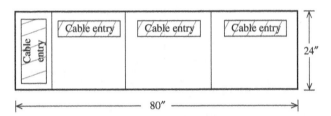

B. Plan View (Footprint)

MDP Schedule		
Comp. No.	Description	Mtg. Ht.
A1	Incoming cable compartment	Full Ht.
B1	1200 A fused sw unit, 1000 A fuse, GFCI	Full Ht.
C1	100 A fused disconnect, 80 A fuse	15 in.
C2	100 A fused disconnect, 80 A fuse	15 in.
C3	200 A fused disconnect, 175 A fuse	20 in.

C. Partial Schedule Listing

FIGURE 11–11
Main Distribution Panel Layout and Schedule

FIGURE 11–12
Medium-Voltage
Switchgear Assembly

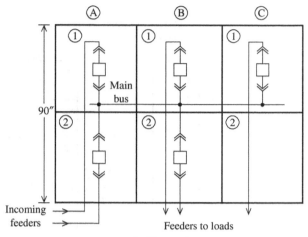

A. Front View

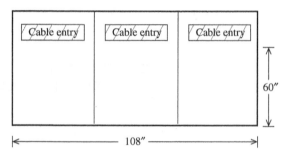

B. Plan View (Footprint)

MDP Schedule		
Comp. No.	Description	Mtg. Ht.
A1	Main circuit breaker 1200 A, 15 kV	1/2 Ht.
A2	Main circuit breaker 1200 A, 15 kV	1/2 Ht.
B1	Feeder circuit breaker 800 A, 15 kV	1/2 Ht.
B2	Feeder circuit breaker 800 A, 15 kV	1/2 Ht.
C1	Feeder circuit breaker 800 A, 15 kV	1/2 Ht.

C. Partial Schedule Listing

The vertical sections and individual units making up the switchgear are identified in the same manner as with the MDP. The individual units or compartments may contain medium-voltage circuit breakers, fuses, and switches for feeders, surge arresters, or instrument transformers for metering and protection. These compartments are commonly assembled as draw-out units, mounted on guide rails to allow for easy installation or removal. When inserted into the switchgear, the draw-out rack makes contact with the main bus running the length of the section. The rack is then fastened into position to allow normal operation. A detailed schedule listing the specific equipment installed in each compartment and plan view are provided, as shown in Figure 11–12(C).

Medium-voltage switchgear is commonly available in ratings ranging from 5 kV to 38 kV, with current ratings ranging from 600 A to 2000 A. The ampacity ratings apply to the main bus, which usually runs the horizontal length of the switchgear. The switchgear must also be rated to withstand the expected short circuit current of the system. Short circuit ratings ranging from 16 kA to 40 kA are also available.

Various high-voltage feeder and switching arrangements are available, as shown in Figure 11–13. The radial feed is the most common form of feeder, having a single main circuit breaker or switch supplying the switchgear. A loop feed configuration is possible where it is desirable to supply the switchgear from a main source and an alternate or standby sources.

A unit substation consists of a high-voltage incoming line section, transformer section, and low-voltage distribution section, as shown in Figure 11–14. The high-voltage incoming line compartment is generally of metal-clad construction. Incoming medium-

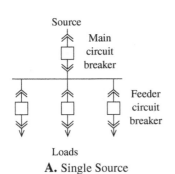

A. Single Source

B. Normal and Alternate Source

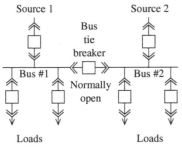

C. Normal and Alternate Source
with Bus Tie Breaker

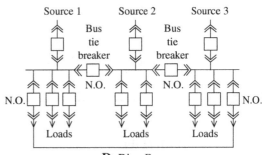

D. Ring Bus

FIGURE 11–13
Medium-Voltage Bus Arrangements

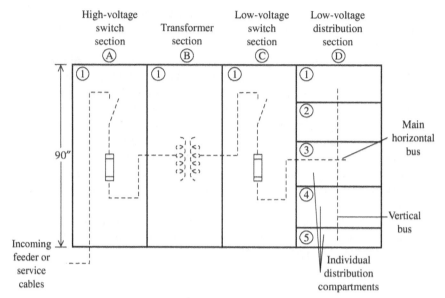

A. Front View

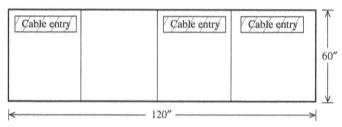

B. Plan View (Footprint)

MDP Schedule		
Comp. No.	Description	Mtg. Ht.
A1	HV switch 5 kV, 200 A switch 100E fuse	Full Ht.
B1	XFMR: 500 kVA, 4.16 kV—480Y/277 V	Full Ht.
C1	600 V, 1200 A switch, 800 A fuse	Full Ht.
D1	600 V, 200 A switch, 175 A fuse	15 in.
D2	600 V, 100 A switch, 80 A fuse	20 in.

C. Partial Schedule Listing

FIGURE 11–14
Unit Substation Layout and Schedule

FIGURE 11–15
Unit Substation Installation *Source:* Courtesy Youngstown State University.

voltage distribution cables enter the incoming cable compartment and are terminated on the line side terminals of a medium-voltage switch or circuit breaker. Radial and loop feed configurations are available for the incoming line configuration. The transformer compartment contains a dry-type transformer that steps down the medium voltage (5 kV to 35 kV) to low voltage (less than 600 V). The low-voltage distribution section may contain fused switches, circuit breakers, motor starter units, distribution panels, and so on. The physical layout, plan view, and detailed equipment list are generally provided as part of the schedule for the unit substation. Figure 11–15 shows a unit substation switchgear assembly serving an institutional building. The incoming voltage is 4160 V and the low voltage is 480Y/277 V.

11–8   CLEARANCES AROUND PANELBOARDS AND SWITCHGEAR

To ensure a safe electrical installation, proper clearances must be maintained around electrical panels and switchgear. These clearances are necessary to provide for adequate working space around electrical equipment and to ensure a safe means of egress away from electrical equipment in the event of an equipment failure.

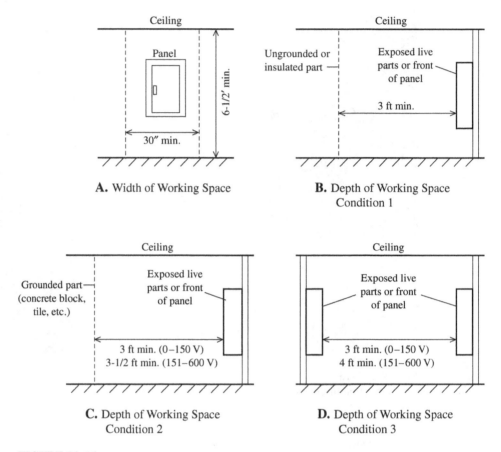

FIGURE 11–16
Clearance and Workspace Requirements of Low-Voltage Equipment

Figure 11–16(A) illustrates the basic requirement for working space in front of electrical equipment such as panelboards. Section 110.26(A)(2) of the *NEC* specifies a clear working space of at least 30″, unless the equipment itself is wider than 30″, in which case the required width of the working space in front of the equipment must not be less than the width of the equipment. Also, the width of the working space must be sufficient to allow for hinged doors or panels to open at least 90° without obstruction. Section 110.26(A)(3) of the *NEC* requires that the height of the working space must be at least 6½′ or the height of the equipment, whichever is larger.

The required depth of working space around electrical equipment of 600 V and less is given in Table 110–26(A)(1) of the *NEC*, which is shown in Table 11–1. Note that the required depth is a function of the nominal voltage to ground and the condition in which the equipment is installed. These depths are measured either from the exposed live parts themselves or from the front of the enclosure if the live parts are enclosed.

TABLE 11–1
Table 110.26(A)(1) Working Spaces

Nominal Voltage to Ground	Minimum Clear Distance		
	Condition 1	Condition 2	Condition 3
0–150	900 mm (3 ft)	900 mm (3 ft)	900 mm (3 ft)
151–600	900 mm (3 ft)	1 m (3½ ft)	1.2 m (4 ft)

Note: Where the conditions are as follows:
Condition 1—Exposed live parts on one side and no live or grounded parts on the other side of the working space, or exposed live parts on both sides effectively guarded by suitable wood or other insulating materials. Insulated wire or insulated busbars operating at not over 300 volts to ground shall not be considered live parts.
Condition 2—Exposed live parts on one side and grounded parts on the other side. Concrete, brick, or tile walls shall be considered as grounded.
Condition 3—Exposed live parts on both sides of the work space (not guarded as provided in Condition 1) with the operator between.

Table 110.334(A) Minimum Depth of Clear Working Space at Electrical Equipment

Nominal Voltage to Ground	Minimum Clear Distance		
	Condition 1	Condition 2	Condition 3
601–2500 V	900 mm (3 ft)	1.2 m (4 ft)	1.5 m (5 ft)
2501–9000 V	1.2 m (4 ft)	1.5 m (5 ft)	1.8 m (6 ft)
9001–25,000 V	1.5 m (5 ft)	1.8 m (6 ft)	2.8 m (9 ft)
25,001 V–75 kV	1.8 m (6 ft)	2.5 m (8 ft)	3.0 m (10 ft)
Above 75 kV	2.5 m (8 ft)	3.0 m (10 ft)	3.7 m (12 ft)

Note: Where the conditions are as follows:
Condition 1—Exposed live parts on one side and no live or grounded parts on the other side of the working space, or exposed live parts on both sides effectively guarded by suitable wood or other insulating materials. Insulated wire or insulated busbars operating at not over 300 volts shall not be considered live parts.
Condition 2—Exposed live parts on one side and grounded parts on the other side. Concrete, brick, or tile walls shall be considered as grounded surfaces.
Condition 3—Exposed live parts on both sides of the work space (not guarded as provided in Condition 1) with the operator between.
Source: Reprinted with permission from NFPA 70 *The National Electric Code* © 2002, National Fire Protection Association, Quincy, MA 02269. This reprinted material is not the referenced subject which is represented only by the standard in its entirety.

Condition 1 applies if there are live parts on one side of the work space and no live or grounded parts on the other, as shown in Figure 11–16(B). Condition 2 applies if there are live parts on one side and grounded parts on the other side, as shown in Figure 11–16(C). Concrete, brick, tile, and other masonry construction is considered to be grounded for the purposes of this discussion. Condition 3 applies if there are live parts on both sides of the working space, as shown in Figure 11–16(D). If there is doubt concerning which condition should apply, application of Condition 3 would yield the most conservative design.

In addition to the required working space around electrical equipment, Section 110.26(C) of the *NEC* specifies clearance requirements for access to these working spaces. Generally, the means of egress must be sufficient to allow a person to step back out of the work space away from the equipment and proceed to a suitable exit. Section 110.26(C)(1) states that at least one entrance of sufficient area is required to provide access to the working space. Typically, this means an entrance at least 24″ wide and 6½′ high. Of course, the actual dimensions must be sufficient to allow for placement of the equipment in the room as well. This general requirement is shown in Figure 11–17(A).

For panelboards and switchgear rated 1200 A or more and over 6′ wide, Section 110.26(C)(2) of the *NEC* requires one entrance at each end of the working space, as shown in Figure 11–17(B). Note that in this situation it is necessary to travel through the work space in order to reach an exit. Thus, if an equipment failure occurred at some point in the switchgear, it is possible to safely exit the area.

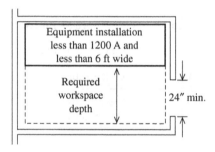

A. General Requirement

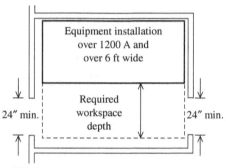

B. General Requirement for Equipment Over 1200 A and Over 6 ft Wide

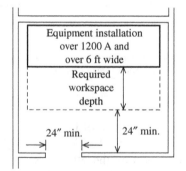

C. Exception #1: Clear and Unobstructed Means of Egress.

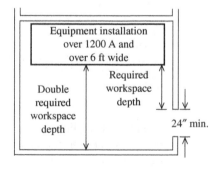

D. Exception #2: Doubling of Required Workspace

FIGURE 11–17
Access Requirements Around Electrical Equipment

The two entrance requirement for panelboards and switchgear rated 1200 A or more and more than 6′ wide may be reduced to one entrance as permitted by Section 110.26(C)(2)(a) of the *NEC* if it is possible to safely step back out of the defined work space and proceed to an exit. An individual would not have to travel through the work space to exit the room. This exception is illustrated in Figure 11–17(C).

Lastly, if the work space as required in Table 110.26(A)(1) is doubled, Section 110.26(C)(2)(b) allows for one entrance to the work space. However, the distance from the equipment to the edge of the entrance must be at least equal to the required work space depth. This is illustrated in Figure 11–17(D).

The required depth of working space around electrical equipment over 600 V is given in Table 110.34(A) of the *NEC* shown in Table 11–1. As with system voltages of 600 V and below, the required depth is a function of the nominal voltage-to-ground and the condition in which the equipment is installed. Again, the required depths of the working space are measured either from the exposed live parts themselves or from the front of the enclosure if the live parts are enclosed. Definitions for Conditions 1, 2, and 3 are the same as in the low-voltage case.

The requirements for access to working space differ slightly for equipment over 600 V. Section 110.33(A) of the *NEC* states that at least one entrance at least 24″ wide and 6½′ high is required to provide access to the working space. For switchgear over 6′ wide, Section 110.33(A)(1) requires one entrance at each end of the working space. One entrance to the work space is permitted if it is possible to safely step back out of the defined work space and proceed to an exit or if the work space as required in Table 110.34(A) is doubled. As in the low-voltage case, the distance from the equipment to the edge of the entrance must be at least equal to the required work space.

PROBLEMS

1. A 30-space panel is supplied from a 208Y/120 V, 3φ, 4W system. Three-phase conductors, the neutral, and the equipment-grounding conductor are brought to the panel. The overcurrent devices in the panel, excluding the main, consist of ten three-pole, 30 A breakers protecting branch circuits supplying three-phase motor loads. Each branch circuit consists of three ungrounded conductors and an equipment grounding conductor. Is this panel classified as a power panelboard or an appliance and branch circuit panelboard?

2. A 42-space panel is supplied from a 480Y/277 V, 3φ, 4W system. Three-phase conductors, the neutral, and the equipment-grounding conductor are brought to the panel. The overcurrent devices in the panel, excluding the main, consist of nine three-pole, 30 A breakers supplying branch circuits consisting of three ungrounded conductors and an equipment-grounding conductor. In addition, there are two 20 A, single-pole breakers protecting branch circuits supplying 277 V lighting circuits. Is this panel classified as a power panelboard or an appliance and branch circuit panelboard?

3. What is the maximum percentage unbalance permitted in a panelboard?

4. Define *lighting and appliance branch circuit panelboard*.

5. Define *power panelboard*.

6. Why is the short circuit withstand capability of a panelboard important?

7. How many spaces are commonly available in most panelboards?

8. Under what conditions are power panelboards not required to have overcurrent protection?

9. Is the panelboard overcurrent protection device required to be located in the panelboard itself?

10. How is the conductor having the high voltage-to-ground on a three-phase, four-wire delta system required to be designated?

11. What information is typically included in a panel schedule?

12. Determine the percent unbalance for a 120/240 V, single-phase, three-wire panel having 135 A on one leg and 70 A on the other. Is this acceptable?

13. Determine the percent unbalance for a 480Y/277 V, three-phase, four-wire panel having 75 A on phase A, 90 A on phase B, and 110 A on phase C. Is this acceptable?

14. What is a main distribution panel? What information is typically contained in an MDP schedule? Why is the plan view of the MDP important?

15. What significant construction feature distinguishes metal-clad, medium-voltage switchgear from low-voltage panelboards and switchboards?

16. Identify and describe the major components of a unit substation.

17. What is the common range of voltage and current ratings for medium-voltage switchgear?

18. What advantage does a loop feed medium-voltage switchgear configuration have compared to a radial feed configuration?

19. What is the required working space width in front of a panel 24″ wide? 36″ wide? What is the required height of the working space?

20. List three reasons for maintaining adequate work space and means of egress from electrical equipment.

21. In your own words, describe Conditions 1, 2, and 3 as applied to the determination of minimum clearances around electrical equipment.

12

Lighting Fundamentals

INTRODUCTION

One of the most important aspects of electrical system design for buildings is the design of the lighting system. The lighting system must not only provide adequate lighting levels but must also produce visual comfort, proper color rendition, and ambiance. The designer of the lighting system must have knowledge of the lighting sources and lighting fixtures available. Information regarding the electrical characteristics and installation requirements of the fixtures is commonly available from the manufacturers' data.

OBJECTIVES

Upon completion of this chapter, you will:

- Understand the operation of various light sources
- Understand fundamental lighting terms and definitions
- Understand the operation of lighting ballasts
- Be able to apply manufacturers' photometric lighting data
- Be able to design interior and exterior lighting systems to provide adequate general-area illumination levels
- Be able to determine the coefficient of utilization for a particular lighting fixture
- Be able to determine the various light-loss factors associated with lighting design
- Be able to apply data contained in isofootcandle curves in the design of outdoor lighting systems
- Understand the basic operation of a lighting control circuit
- Understand the basic information contained in a lighting fixture schedule

12–1 LIGHT SOURCES

Incandescent

The incandescent lamp developed by Thomas Edison in the 1870s is one of the earliest types of electric lamp. Typical incandescent lamp construction is shown in Figure 12–1. The lamp consists of a tungsten filament contained in a glass envelope or bulb. The bulb is filled with argon gas to improve performance and increase lamp life. The inside of the bulb may be frosted or clear. A screw shell base allows for insertion into the socket. In normal operation, full voltage is applied to the filament. As a result, the filament is heated to a very

FIGURE 12–1
Basic Construction of Incandescent Lamp

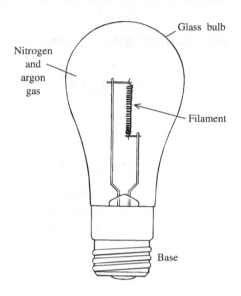

Glass bulb

Nitrogen
and
argon
gas

Filament

Base

high temperature by the electric current passing through it. At this high temperature the filament starts to glow and gives off light.

Many different sizes of lamps are available, depending on the application. The letter designation specifies the shape of the bulb. The A designation is the most common shape for general use and has a pearlike appearance, as shown in Figure 12–1. The overall diameter of the bulb is specified in eighths of an inch. Thus, an A-19 lamp will be the common pear-shaped lamp, having an outer diameter of $^{19}/_{8}''$, or $2\frac{3}{8}''$. Other shapes are available. The screw shell, medium base is typically used for lamps having a voltage of 120 V. Lamps rated at higher wattages generally have a mogul base. Bayonet- and candle-type bases are used for smaller-rated lamps.

Fluorescent

The fluorescent lamp was developed in the late 1930s and is common in offices and other commercial and industrial applications. Typical fluorescent lamp construction is shown in Figure 12–2(A). These lamps typically have a long, tubular shape with electrode connections at each end. The tube typically contains argon gas and a small amount of mercury.

Unlike the incandescent lamp, which produces light by passing current through a filament, the fluorescent lamp operates by application of a voltage potential difference across the tube, which is produced by applying a suitable voltage to the electrodes located at each end of the lamp. The electrodes emit electrons, which travel through the gas vapor, resulting in the vaporization of the mercury in the tube. Due to the vaporization of the mercury, radiation in the ultraviolet region is emitted. This radiation causes excitation of the phosphor coating on the inside of the tube, producing visible light. The composition of the phosphor determines the color of the lamp.

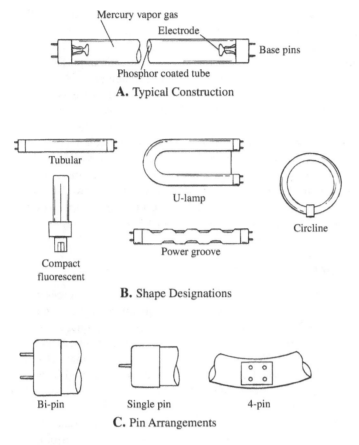

A. Typical Construction

B. Shape Designations

C. Pin Arrangements

FIGURE 12–2
Fluorescent Lamp Construction, Shapes, and Pin Designations

Fluorescent lamps are commonly available in either cool white or warm white. The cool white lamp produces light that is more toward the blue end of the spectrum; warm white lamps have more of a yellow/orange appearance and less of a blue appearance.

The lamp code for fluorescent lamps always begins with the letter F, representing fluorescent. The next number may indicate the lamp wattage or the length of the lamp in inches. The next letter identifies the lamp shape. Typical shape designations are shown in Figure 12–2(B). The most common lamp is the T lamp, indicating a tubular construction. The identifier in the code is a number indicating the diameter in eighths of an inch. Thus, an F40T12 lamp is a tubular lamp, 40 W, having a tubular shape, $1\frac{2}{8}$″, or $1\frac{1}{2}$″, in diameter. Other identifiers may be appended to the code to indicate lamp color, type of starting, and so on. Manufacturers' literature must be consulted for the particular lamp of interest.

Figure 12–2(B) also shows the circline lamp, designated C, which is basically a tubular-shaped lamp bent to form a circle. The U-type lamp is essentially a 4 ft lamp bent into the shape of a U to allow for installation in a 2 ft by 2 ft fixture. The PG lamp is a high-output lamp with grooved sides. The compact fluorescent lamp is available for use in recessed or other small fixtures.

The fluorescent lamp is connected electrically and supported by pin-type connections at each end of the lamp. The pin connections match up to slots in the fixture socket. Figure 12–2(C) shows some of the more common pin arrangements. The base pin arrangements are mechanically designed so that only the proper type of lamp can be installed in a given fixture. The bi-pin arrangement consists of two pins located at each end of the tube and is the most common pin arrangement for most fluorescent lamps. The single-pin base has one pin at each end of the tube and is commonly used on instant-start lamps. The single-ended bi-pin has two bi-pin assemblies on one end of the lamp and is commonly used for PL-type lamps. The four-pin assembly is essentially two bi-pin assemblies at one end of the lamp and is commonly used for circline-type lamps. The recessed double-contact pin arrangement is used for high-output and very high output lamps.

Mercury Vapor

The mercury vapor (MV) lamp falls into a category of light sources referred to as high-intensity-discharge, or HID, lamps. Construction features of the mercury vapor lamp are shown in Figure 12–3(A). This type of lamp incorporates a quartz arc tube that contains gases such as argon, neon, and mercury. Main electrodes are placed at each end of the arc tube. In addition, a starting electrode is placed near one of the main electrodes, typically at the top of the lamp as shown. The arc tube is supported inside a glass bulb by metal wires. A phosphor coating is commonly applied to the inside of the glass bulb to improve the color rendition of the lamp.

The mercury vapor lamp produces light by passing electrical current through mercury vapor. Ionization of the mercury in the arc tube must occur prior to successful operation of the lamp. This is accomplished by the presence of an electrical arc between the main electrodes. Initially, an arc is established between the main and starting electrodes in the arc tube. As the resistance of the mercury vapor in the tube decreases, an arc will be established between the two main electrodes, resulting in current flow between the two electrodes. The entire process takes between five and ten minutes from initial energization of the lamp to full light output. Restriking or restarting a previously energized lamp requires approximately the same amount of time. Mercury vapor lamps typically produce a blue-gray light and do not produce a very favorable color rendition.

The most common lamp shape for mercury vapor lamps is the bulged tubular type, BT, as shown in Figure 12–3(A). Mercury vapor lamps typically have a mogul base in wattages above 100 W and a medium base for lamps of 100 W or less.

Metal Halide

Metal halide (MH) lamps are also classified as high-intensity-discharge lamps. Construction features of the metal lamp are similar to the mercury vapor lamp shown in Figure 12–3(A). The metal halide lamp incorporates a quartz arc tube that contains gases

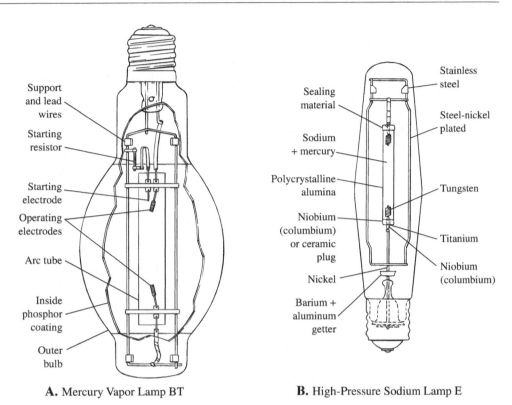

A. Mercury Vapor Lamp BT   **B.** High-Pressure Sodium Lamp E

FIGURE 12–3
Mercury Vapor and High-Pressure Sodium Lamp Construction *Source:* IES Lighting Handbook Reference Volume, © 1981, Illuminating Engineering Society of North America.

such as argon, neon, and mercury. In addition, halide salts are added to the arc tube. Main electrodes and starting electrodes are also used to initiate and maintain the electric arc necessary for light production. The arc tube is supported inside a clear glass bulb by metal wires. The metal halides added to the arc tube produce a more balanced spectrum of light output than the mercury vapor lamp. Specifically, more red, orange, and yellow visible light is present in the spectrum, resulting in a whiter light output. Due to the quality of light output, phosphor coatings are not required on the inside of the glass bulb to improve the color rendition of the lamp.

The theory of operation of the metal halide lamp is similar to that of the mercury vapor lamp. The entire start-up process takes approximately five minutes from initial energization of the lamp to full light output. Restriking or restarting a previously energized lamp requires a much longer period of time. This is due to the fact that the lamp must cool prior to restrike, a process that will take approximately five to ten minutes. Metal halide lamps are also sensitive to burning position. Lamps typically designed for vertical or straight-up burning position must not be used in the horizontal position and vice versa.

Failure to operate lamps in the position they were designed for can lead to overheating and subsequent failure. Lamps are typically designated for horizontal or vertical use.

The most common lamp shape for metal halide lamps is the bulged tubular type, BT. Metal halide lamps typically have a mogul base in wattages above 70 W and a medium base for lamps of 70 W or less.

High-Pressure Sodium

The high-pressure sodium (HPS) lamp is also classified as a high-intensity-discharge lamp. Construction features of the high-pressure sodium lamp are shown in Figure 12–3(B). Due to the corrosive nature of sodium, the HPS lamp incorporates a translucent ceramic arc tube that contains xenon, mercury, and sodium. Main electrodes are placed at each end of the arc tube. A starting electrode is typically not used in this type of lamp due to the small size of the arc tube. The arc tube is supported inside a clear glass bulb by metal wires.

The high-pressure sodium lamp produces light by passing electrical current through sodium vapor. Since the arc tube does not incorporate a starting electrode, a high-voltage pulse is momentarily applied to the main electrodes. The resulting arc will ionize the sodium vapor in the tube, resulting in current flow through the tube between the electrodes. Normal operating voltage can now be applied to the arc tube to sustain the arc. The entire start-up process takes approximately three minutes from initial energization of the lamp to full light output. Restriking or restarting a previously energized lamp requires a shorter amount of time than the initial starting, usually about one minute. High-pressure sodium lamps typically produce a yellow-orange appearance and do not produce a very favorable color rendition.

The most common lamp shape for high-pressure sodium lamps is the elliptical type, E, as shown in Figure 12–3(B). High-pressure sodium lamps typically have a mogul base in wattages above 150 W. A medium or mogul base is available for lamps rated between 50 W to 150 W. The medium base is commonly used for 35 W HPS lamps.

Auxiliary Lighting

As mentioned in the previous sections, many of the HID lamps require several minutes to restrike after being deenergized. If these types of light sources are used for indoor lighting or any other area where emergency exit may be required, auxiliary lighting must be used. The auxiliary lighting is required to provide illumination during the time it takes for the lamps to restrike and return to normal operating conditions. Some manufacturers of lighting fixtures have available as an option auxiliary lighting sources built into the fixture itself. With this option, typically referred to as *quartz restrike*, the quartz lamp will provide the required illumination in the event of a power failure, until the main lamp restrikes.

12–2   BALLASTS

In order for a lamp to start and operate satisfactorily, the proper voltage and current must be supplied. With the exception of incandescent lamps, which are designed to operate with line voltage applied, an auxiliary means of starting and operating the lamp is required. This auxiliary means is referred to as a *ballast* and is commonly found in lighting fixtures equipped with fluorescent and HID lamps. The lighting ballast is either an electromagnetic or electronic device that is specifically designed to provide the necessary current and voltage required to start the lamp. In addition, the ballast provides the required voltage and current to the lamp for normal sustained operation. Ballasts are designed specifically for fluorescent and high-intensity-discharge lamps and are generally not interchangeable from one lamp type to another.

Multitapped ballasts are available for installation in systems having different voltages. The commonly available multitap ballast allows for application to 120 V, 208 V, 240 V, or 277 V branch circuits. Thus, it is possible to use the same ballast on different voltage systems by connecting to the proper voltage tap on the ballast.

Class P ballasts have an integral thermal protector that opens the circuit in the event the ballast overheats. The thermal protector will reset after the ballast cools. In addition, it is common practice to install external in-line fuses to provide additional protection to the ballast and to isolate a faulty ballast from the rest of the system in the event of a failure or overheating.

The use of an iron core in electromagnetic-type ballasts produces noise due to the magnetically induced vibrations of the core material. This noise may be a nuisance in various office settings but may be acceptable in an industrial setting. Sound ratings of A through F are typically assigned to ballasts, with the A rating producing the least amount of noise.

Fluorescent Preheat Ballast

The schematic diagram of the fluorescent preheat ballast is shown in Figure 12–4(A). In this type of ballast, voltage is applied to the lamp with the contacts in the starter closed. With the starter contacts closed, a small current will flow through the electrodes, causing the electrodes to heat. Heating the electrodes results in the emission of electrons, and the presence of the additional electrons results in a decrease in the internal resistance of the gas in the tube. Therefore, a lower voltage is required to initiate an arc in the tube. When the starter contacts open, an inductive voltage kick is produced between the electrodes at each end of the tube due to the interruption of current flow through the ballast inductance. This inductive voltage kick establishes an arc between the electrodes, resulting in normal lamp operation. The starting process takes approximately one to two seconds.

Fluorescent Rapid-Start Ballast

The schematic diagram of the fluorescent rapid-start ballast is shown in Figure 12–4(B). In this type of ballast, a tapped coil on the ballast is used to produce a small voltage that is applied across each of the electrodes. In addition, a larger voltage is applied to the electrodes at each end of the tube, as shown. The voltage applied across each of the electrodes causes them to heat, with subsequent emission of electrons and lowering of the internal resistance of the gas in the tube, as with the preheat ballast. As the electrodes are heated, the internal resistance drops to a value low enough to allow arcing to occur between the electrodes at each end of the tube. Once arcing between the electrodes occurs, continuous

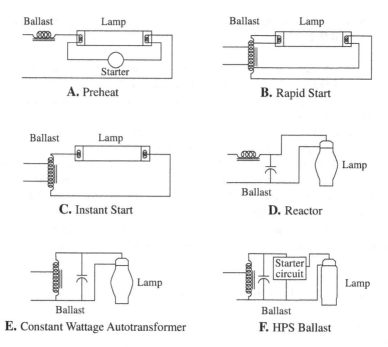

FIGURE 12–4
Ballast Circuits

operation of the lamp will result. Note that with this type of starter, the electrodes are heated continuously, resulting in improved lamp performance. The entire starting process takes a fraction of a second. The rapid-start method is the most common for fluorescent lamps.

Fluorescent Instant-Start Ballast

The schematic diagram for the fluorescent instant-start ballast is shown in Figure 12–4(C). In this type of ballast, the arc is initiated by applying a very high voltage (up to 1000 V) to the lamp. After the arc is established, the arc current produces the necessary heating of the electrodes. The ballast circuit is designed to apply a lower voltage to the lamp after starting, thereby limiting the current through the lamp. Instant-start fluorescent lamps generally have a single pin at each end and are commonly referred to as "Slimline lamps" by several manufacturers.

Fluorescent Electronic Ballasts

In recent years, electronic ballasts have been developed for use in fluorescent lighting systems. Electronic ballasts may contain electromagnetic cores in conjunction with electronic devices or electronic devices alone. Essentially, the electronic ballast converts the 60 Hz input frequency to a higher frequency, up to approximately 50 kHZ. The application of high frequency to the fluorescent lamp results in less flicker, longer life, reduced noise, reduced heat, improved efficiency, and increased light output. However, electronic ballasts are generally more expensive than electromagnetic ballasts.

Reactor HID Ballast

The reactor-type ballast suitable for HID lamps is shown in Figure 12–4(D). In this type of ballast, the primary function of the reactor is to limit the current flow to the lamp. The starting current for this type of ballast is approximately 150% of the normal operating current. The normal power factor (NPF) reactor ballast operates at a power factor of around 50%. The high power factor (HPF) reactor ballast incorporates a capacitor across the input lines, thereby improving the power factor to over 90%. The presence of the capacitor has little effect on lamp performance. This type of ballast does not regulate the power supplied to the lamp and is not recommended if voltage fluctuations are expected to exceed ±5%.

Constant Wattage Autotransformer HID Ballast

The constant wattage autotransformer (CWA) ballast is shown in Figure 12–4(E); it is the most common type of ballast in HID lamps. This ballast incorporates a high-reactance autotransformer to limit the current through the lamp. In addition, a capacitor is placed in parallel with the lamp to improve the voltage regulation to the lamp and to improve the power factor. The CWA ballast regulates the power supplied to the lamp and is recommended where line voltage variations exceeding ±5% are expected.

HID Lamp Starting Considerations

Mercury lamps may generally be used directly with the reactor-type or constant-wattage-type ballast. The reactor- and constant-wattage-type ballasts used with metal halide lamps must incorporate circuitry to apply the proper voltage to the lamp during starting. Ballasts used with high-pressure sodium lamps must incorporate a pulse-generating circuit to apply a high-voltage (approximately 2500 V) pulse to the lamp to initiate the arc in the tube. An example of a constant-wattage, autotransformer-type ballast incorporating the pulse-generating starter circuit for HPS lamps is shown in Figure 12–4(F).

12–3   LIGHTING FIXTURES

The lamp and ballast assemblies previously discussed are housed in a lighting fixture or luminaire. In addition to providing the necessary support for the lamp and ballast, the luminaire is designed to optimize the transmittal of light from the fixture to the surface of interest. Luminaires are also designed to direct the light from the source to the work space in a defined, predictable manner. Proper design of the reflector system of a given luminaire will produce the desired lighting results.

For interior lighting, there are six classifications of luminaire lighting distribution patterns. Four of the more common distributions are shown in Figures 12–5(A) through

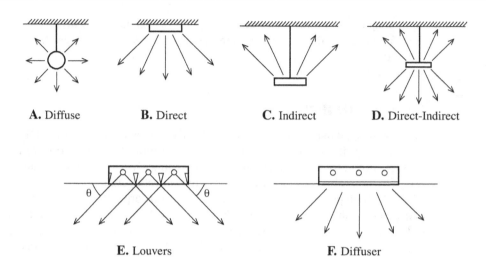

A. Diffuse   **B.** Direct   **C.** Indirect   **D.** Direct-Indirect

E. Louvers   **F.** Diffuser

FIGURE 12–5
Light Distribution Patterns

(D). The general diffuse distribution shown in Figure 12–5(A) is characteristic of a luminaire in which the light is dispersed evenly in all directions away from the source. The direct distribution pattern shown in Figure 12–5(B) is characteristic of a luminaire that directs 90% to 100% of the light produced in a downward fashion to the surface. Direct distribution is the most common for interior lighting systems using lay-in or surface-mount fixtures. Recessed fixtures also produce a direct lighting pattern. The indirect distribution shown in Figure 12–5(C) directs 90% to 100% of the light produced upward, away from the surface to be illuminated. With indirect lighting systems, the luminaire is typically pendant mounted, as shown, with the majority of light output reflected off the ceiling back down to the work surface. The direct-indirect distribution shown in Figure 12–5(D) directs approximately 50% of the light upward and 50% of the light downward. The direct-indirect distribution is thus a combination of the indirect and direct lighting distribution. Semidirect and semi-indirect distributions are also available.

The area where the light leaves the luminaire may be open, as in the case of a strip fluorescent fixture covered with a louvered panel, or closed with a diffuser. The louvered panel is shown in Figure 12–5(E). The design of the louver is such that it aids in the direction of the light from the source to the surface to be illuminated. Several individual cells are employed to direct the light as desired. In addition to directing the light, the louver serves as a shield to minimize glare. The angle θ as shown in Figure 12–5(E) is referred to as the *shielding angle*. The light intensity drops off dramatically in the area beyond the shielding angle of the luminaire. Louvers with various numbers of cells and cell configurations are commonly available.

A luminaire with a diffuser is shown in Figure 12–5(F). The diffuser generally does not serve to direct the light, but rather aids in scattering the light in a more diffuse pattern than would be obtained by use of a louver, but the diffuser does not provide for glare

FIGURE 12–6
Lay-In Fluorescent Fixture Installation *Source:* Courtesy Youngstown State University.

reduction as well as the louvered panel does. One of the advantages of using a diffuser is to aid in keeping the interior reflecting surfaces of the light fixture clean. Figure 12–6 shows a typical lay-in fluorescent fixture installation; Figure 12–7 shows an indirect lighting fixture in a commercial establishment.

12–4   PHOTOMETRICS

The study of light properties and the determination of light levels produced by various sources is generally referred to as *photometrics.* The lighting designer must have a basic understanding of the properties of light and light levels to properly design a lighting system. The concepts presented in this section form the basis of lighting design.

Lighting Terms and Definitions

To understand the terminology associated with photometric data, consider a single point source of light, as shown in Figure 12–8(A). The intensity of light at the point source is termed *candlepower* and is expressed in units of candela (cd). Luminous flux will leave the

FIGURE 12–7
Indirect Lighting Installation *Source:* Courtesy Youngstown State University.

point source and travel in all directions away from the source in a uniform manner. The total amount of luminous flux produced by a source is measured in lumens (lm). Lamps are commonly rated in terms of the total number of lumens produced. For example, a 100 W frosted incandescent lamp produces approximately 1700 lumens.

As the luminous flux travels further away from the source, the flux density will decrease. Note that the total number of lumens produced by the source is the same but that the luminous flux is spread out over a larger area, resulting in lower flux density. The electrical analogy would be a conductor having a cross-sectional area of 0.2 sq in. carrying 100 A of current. The resulting current density is 100 A ÷ 0.2 sq in. = 500 A per sq in. The same 100 A current flowing in a conductor having a cross-sectional area of 0.4 sq in.

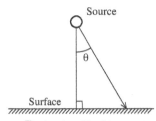

A. Point Source

B. Angle of Incidence

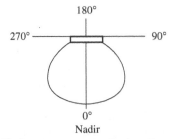

C. Candlepower Distribution Curve

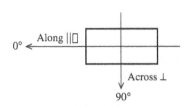

D. Plan View of Fixture

FIGURE 12–8
Photometric Definitions

would be 250 A per sq in. Note that the total current is the same, but the current density is lower in the larger conductor.

The quantity of light at a given point is referred to as the *illuminance* at that point. The quantity of light is expressed in terms of the average number of lumens per unit of area. In the English system, this quantity of light is measured in footcandles (fc), with one footcandle being equal to one lumen per square foot. In the SI system, the quantity of light is measured in lux (lx), with 1 lux being equal to 1 lumen per square meter. Note that 1 footcandle = 10.764 lux.

EXAMPLE 12–1

Determine the illuminance of a 10 ft by 12 ft office area if a total of 6000 lumens are directed from the light source to the work area.

Solution:

$$\text{Illuminance} = \frac{6000 \text{ lumens}}{120 \text{ ft}^2} = 50 \text{ footcandles}$$

In addition to the quantity of light produced by a source, the quality of light is also of prime concern. Two quantities, the color rendering index (CRI) and the color temperature,

TABLE 12–1

Lamp Type	Color Temperature	Color Rendering Index
Cool white fluorescent	4200°K	62
Warm white fluorescent	3000°K	52
Daylight fluorescent	6250°K	75
Incandescent	2800°K	100
Mercury vapor (deluxe white)	3900°K	50
Metal halide (clear)	3200°K	70
High-pressure sodium	1900°K	22

quantify the ability of a light source to produce a light as close as possible to natural daylight. The color rendering index quantifies the amount of color shift an object will experience when placed under a given light source. The CRI is generally measured on a scale from 0 to 100, with 100 being the color rendering of natural daylight and incandescent lamp sources. The CRI of a given lamp is readily available from the manufacturer's data sheets. The color temperature is a measurement in degrees Kelvin of the wavelengths making up the light source. Higher color temperatures generally mean a bluer light source. Typical values for color temperature and the color rendering index for some of the more common lamps are shown in Table 12–1.

Inverse-Square Law

As mentioned in the previous section, the luminous flux radiating from a point source will disperse in a uniform fashion away from the source. Assuming a uniform dispersion of flux from the source, the decrease in flux density varies as a function of the distance squared. The decrease in flux density reaching a given surface area results in a decrease in the average illuminance at that particular surface. Specifically, the illuminance at a given distance from the source varies according to the inverse-square law:

$$E = \frac{I}{D^2} \qquad\qquad (12\text{--}1)$$

where:

I = candlepower of source in units of candela (cd)
D = distance from source to surface

If D is expressed in feet, then the illuminance E, would have units of footcandles or fc. Likewise, if D is expressed in meters, then the illuminance E has units of lux. Equation (12–1) can be applied in instances where the distance D is at least 5 times greater than the diameter of the point source.

EXAMPLE 12–2

A point source has a value of 1500 cd in the direction of interest. Determine the illuminance a distance of (a) 10 ft and (b) 5 m from the source.

Solution:

a) $E = \dfrac{1500 \text{ cd}}{(10 \text{ ft})^2} = 15 \text{ fc}$

b) $E = \dfrac{1500 \text{ cd}}{(5 \text{ m})^2} = 60 \text{ lx}$

Angle of Incidence

When light reaches a surface at an angle other than 90°, as shown in Figure 12–8(B), the illuminance produced is that due to the perpendicular component of the light ray reaching the surface. For light rays reaching a surface at an angle θ, the illuminance is given by

$$E = \frac{I}{D^2} \times \cos \theta \tag{12–2}$$

Note that Equation (12–2) is simply Equation (12–1) modified to account for the angle of incidence.

EXAMPLE 12–3

A point source produces 2500 cd in the direction of interest. The angle of incidence with respect to the vertical is 30°. Determine the illuminance at a point 12.5 ft from the source.

Solution: The illuminance is given by

$$E = \frac{2500 \text{ cd}}{(12.5 \text{ ft})^2} \times \cos 30° = 13.9 \text{ fc}$$

Candlepower Distribution Curves

For a given fixture, a candlepower distribution curve may be obtained from the manufacturer. This curve provides the designer with the candlepower intensity of the fixture at various points away from the fixture. The candlepower distribution curve and data are specified for a given fixture type, number of lamps, ballast, and lamp lumen output rating.

The typical distribution curve shown in Figure 12–8(C) is essentially a profile view of the light distribution of the fixture in a given vertical plane. The point directly below the fixture is the 0° axis, or nadir. The 90° and 270° axes are in the horizontal direction away from the fixture. The 180° axis is behind the fixture. The candlepower distribution data is commonly tabulated from 0° up to 180° in steps of 5°. This data thus shows the candlepower of the fixture at various angles. One set of data would be displayed if the candlepower distribution is the same in all vertical planes through the fixture.

For lighting distributions that are not symmetrical, the candlepower data is presented in tables representing various vertical planes through the fixture. Two of the vertical planes through the fixture are defined in the plan view shown in Figure 12–8(D) as along and across. Looking down from the top of the fixture, the plane intersecting the long dimension of the fixture is commonly designated 0°, or ‖; the direction across the fixture is designated

90°, or ⊥. For fixtures with widely varying distribution patterns, data for several interme-diate planes, such as angles of 22.5°, 45°, and 67.5° may be available. When required, data must be interpolated for intermediate angles.

EXAMPLE 12–4

Referring to Table 12–2 and given the following photometric data, determine:

a) Candlepower along the fixture, at an incidence angle of 20°
b) Candlepower along the fixture, at an incidence angle of 43°
c) Candlepower in a vertical plane of 22.5°, directly below the fixture, at an incidence angle of 0°
d) Candlepower in a vertical plane of 22.5°, at an incidence angle of 32°

Solution:

a) From the tabulated data, $I = 3408$ cd.
b) Since the angle of incidence is between 40° and 45°, linear interpolation between the candlepower values at 40° and 45° is required. The result is

$$I = 2475 - \frac{43° - 40°}{45° - 40°} [2475 - 2102] = 2251.2 \text{ cd}$$

c) The results are the same for all vertical planes directly below the fixture. Thus the can-dlepower is 3670 cd.

TABLE 12–2
Candlepower Data

Angle	Along ‖	45°	Across ⊥
0	3670	3670	3670
5	3644	3667	3687
10	3604	3634	3681
15	3532	3582	3639
20	3408	3516	3596
25	3264	3417	3528
30	3080	3269	3410
35	2837	3081	3169
40	2475	2754	2797
45	2102	2220	2358
50	1673	1700	1853
55	1301	1219	1394
60	1014	802	1000
65	718	497	674
70	499	367	484
75	359	329	350
80	229	293	239
85	138	143	131
90	0	0	0

d) Double interpolation is required since the correct value lies between the given data for both the vertical plane and the angle of incidence. The resultant candlepower at the vertical plane of 22.5° is arrived at first, followed by the value at the incidence angle of 32°.

The values at a vertical plane of 22.5° from the "along" direction of the fixture lies halfway between the values listed for 0° and 45°. Two sets of values are determined, one at 30° and the other at 35°, since the incidence angle is 32°. The results are

$$\text{At } 30°: \quad I = 3269 - \frac{45° - 22.5°}{45° - 0°} [3269 - 3080] = 3174.5 \text{ cd}$$

$$\text{At } 35°: \quad I = 3081 - \frac{45° - 22.5°}{45° - 0°} [3081 - 2837] = 2959 \text{ cd}$$

Next, the candlepower at 32° is determined by interpolation between 30° and 35°:

$$I = 3147.5 - \frac{32° - 30°}{35° - 30°} [3174.5 - 2959] = 3088.3 \text{ cd}$$

EXAMPLE 12–5

Using the candlepower data from Example 12–4, determine the following:

a) Illuminance at a distance of 10 ft directly beneath the fixture
b) Illuminance at a distance of 12 ft from the fixture, in the direction along the fixture, and an angle of incidence of 20°
c) Illuminance at a distance of 12 ft from the fixture, in the direction across from the fixture, and an angle of incidence of 20°
d) Illuminance at a distance of 9 ft, in the vertical plane at 22.5°, and an angle of incidence of 30°

Solution:

a) The illuminance is given by Equation (12–2):

$$E = \frac{3670 \text{ cd}}{(10 \text{ ft})^2} \times \cos(0°) = 36.7 \text{ fc}$$

b) $E = \dfrac{3408 \text{ cd}}{(12 \text{ ft})^2} \times \cos(20°) = 22.2 \text{ fc}$

c) $E = \dfrac{3596 \text{ cd}}{(12 \text{ ft})^2} \times \cos(20°) = 23.5 \text{ fc}$

d) Interpolating between the 0° and 45° vertical plane at an incidence angle of 30° results in a candlepower of 3174.5 cd. The illuminance is

$$E = \frac{3174.5 \text{ cd}}{(9 \text{ ft})^2} \times \cos(30°) = 33.9 \text{ fc}$$

In many applications, the physical dimensions of the space to be illuminated are given. The designer must calculate all distances and angles in order to determine the illumination at a given point. The following example illustrates the procedure.

EXAMPLE 12–6

For the space shown in Figure 12–9(A), determine the illuminance at points O, A, B, and C. Use the candlepower distribution data from Table 12–2.

Solution: Figures 12–9(B), (C), and (D) are sketches of various plan and profile views of the space. It is highly recommended that the student draw similar sketches of the space to be illuminated to assist in the determination of all angles and distances.

a) Point O. This point lies directly beneath the fixture a distance of 8 ft. The angle of incidence is 0°. The illuminance is therefore

$$E = \frac{3670 \text{ cd}}{(8 \text{ ft})^2} \times \cos(0°) = 57.34 \text{ fc}$$

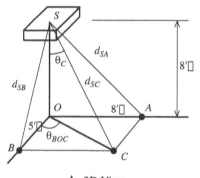

A. 3D View

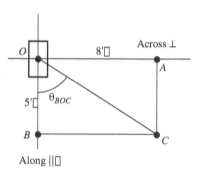

B. Plan View

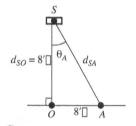

C. Profile Looking Along

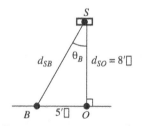

D. Profile Looking Across

FIGURE 12–9
Example of Lighting Calculations Using Point Method

b) Point A. The distance from the fixture (point S) to point A is

$$d_{SA} = \sqrt{(8 \text{ ft})^2 + (8 \text{ ft})^2} = 11.31 \text{ ft}$$

The angle of incidence is

$$\theta_A = \tan^{-1}\left(\frac{8 \text{ ft}}{8 \text{ ft}}\right) = 45°$$

The candlepower at 45° in the plane across from the fixture is 2358 cd. The illuminance is

$$E = \frac{2358}{(11.31 \text{ ft})^2} \times \cos(45°) = 13.04 \text{ fc}$$

c) Point B. The distance from the fixture (point S) to point B is

$$d_{SB} = \sqrt{(8 \text{ ft})^2 + (5 \text{ ft})^2} = 9.43 \text{ ft}$$

The angle of incidence is

$$\theta_B = \tan^{-1}\left(\frac{5 \text{ ft}}{8 \text{ ft}}\right) = 32°$$

The candlepower at 32° in the plane along the fixture is found by linear interpolation:

$$I = 3080 - \frac{32° - 30°}{35° - 30°}[3080 - 2837] = 2982.8 \text{ cd}$$

The illuminance is

$$E = \frac{2982 \text{ cd}}{(9.43 \text{ ft})^2} \times \cos(32°) = 28.44 \text{ fc}$$

d) Point C. The distance from point O to point C is

$$d_{OC} = \sqrt{(8 \text{ ft})^2 + (5 \text{ ft})^2} = 9.43 \text{ ft}$$

The distance from the fixture (point S) to point C is

$$d_{SC} = \sqrt{(8 \text{ ft})^2 + (9.43 \text{ ft})^2} = 12.37 \text{ ft}$$

The angle of incidence is

$$\theta_C = \tan^{-1}\left(\frac{9.43 \text{ ft}}{8 \text{ ft}}\right) = 49.7°$$

The angle of the vertical plane incorporating point C is

$$\theta_{BOC} = \tan^{-1}\left(\frac{8 \text{ ft}}{5 \text{ ft}}\right) = 58°$$

The candlepower at point C is found by double interpolation as follows:

Angle	45°	58°	90°
45°	2200		2358
49.7°	X1	X3	X2
50.0°	1700		1853

Interpolate for the candlepower at X1:

$$X1 = 2220 - \frac{49.7° - 45°}{50° - 45°}[2220 - 1700] = 1731.2 \text{ cd}$$

Similarly, the candlepower at X2 is

$$X2 = 2358 - \frac{49.7° - 45°}{50° - 45°}[2358 - 1853] = 1883.3 \text{ cd}$$

Lastly, the candlepower at X3 is:

$$X3 = 1731.2 - \frac{58° - 45°}{90° - 45°}[1731.2 - 1883.3] = 1775.3 \text{ cd}$$

The illuminance is

$$E = \frac{1775.3 \text{ cd}}{(12.37 \text{ ft})^2} \times \cos(49.7°) = 12.91 \text{ fc}$$

12–5   INDOOR LIGHTING DESIGN

The design of lighting for interior spaces begins with a determination of the coefficient of utilization for a given fixture. The coefficient of utilization is a measure of how effective a given fixture is in directing the light produced by the lamps to a given work plane. This method of determining light levels using the coefficient of utilization is referred to as the *lumen method.* Unlike the point method discussed in the previous section, the lumen method determines the average lighting level produced on a given surface area. Several factors affect the coefficient of utilization of a given fixture, among them are the physical dimensions of the room; the reflectance of the ceiling, wall, and floor surfaces; the physical environment of the space; and other factors to be described.

Zonal Cavity Method

To determine the coefficient of utilization, the zonal cavity method is often employed. The zonal cavity method is one form of the lumen method commonly used by lighting

FIGURE 12–10
Zonal Cavity Method Definitions

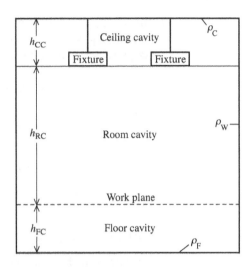

designers. It involves the separation of the area to be illuminated into three separate cavities, as shown in Figure 12–10. The ceiling cavity extends from the bottom of the light fixture to the ceiling. The height of the ceiling cavity is designated h_{CC}. For lay-in fixtures, the height of the ceiling cavity is zero. The room cavity extends from the bottom of the fixture to the work plane. The height of the room cavity is designated h_{RC}. The floor cavity extends from the work plane to the surface of the floor. The height of the work plane is designated h_{FC}.

The work plane is defined as the surface area to be illuminated. In office areas, the work plane is typically the top of desks, tables, and so on and is generally taken as 30 in. or 2.5 ft. In other areas, such as manufacturing and industrial, the height of the work plane is typically 3 ft.

Cavity Ratio

The first step in determining the coefficient of utilization is the calculation of the ceiling cavity ratio (CCR), room cavity ratio (RCR), and floor cavity ratio (FCR) as given by the following:

$$\text{Cavity ratio} = \frac{5 \times h \times (\text{Room length} + \text{Room width})}{(\text{Room length} \times \text{Room width})} \qquad \textbf{(12–3)}$$

where h is the ceiling cavity, room cavity, or floor cavity height.

EXAMPLE 12–7

Determine the CCR, RCR, and FCR for an office area 20 ft × 25 ft, with a ceiling height of 9 ft and a work plane height of 36 in. Assume lay-in fluorescent fixtures are used.

Solution: Since lay-in fixtures are used, the ceiling cavity height h_{CC} is 0. The room cavity height h_{RC} is equal to 9 ft − 36 in = 6 ft. The floor cavity height h_{FC} is equal to the work plane height of 36 in. or 3 ft. The cavity ratios are calculated as

$$\text{CCR} = \frac{5 \times (0 \text{ ft}) \times (20 \text{ ft} + 25 \text{ ft})}{(20 \text{ ft} \times 25 \text{ ft})} = 0.0$$

$$\text{RCR} = \frac{5 \times (6 \text{ ft}) \times (20 \text{ ft} + 25 \text{ ft})}{(20 \text{ ft} \times 25 \text{ ft})} = 2.7$$

$$\text{FCR} = \frac{5 \times (3 \text{ ft}) \times (20 \text{ ft} + 25 \text{ ft})}{(20 \text{ ft} \times 25 \text{ ft})} = 1.35$$

Light Loss Factors

The Illuminating Engineering Society defines several light loss factors (LLFs) to provide a means of quantifying the change in light output due to environmental factors in the space to be illuminated. The individual LLFs are numbers ranging from 0.0 to 1.0. These factors are broadly classified into recoverable factors and nonrecoverable factors. The recoverable factors can be affected by maintenance of the lamps and cleaning of the room. Recoverable factors include room surface dirt depreciation (RSDD), luminaire dirt depreciation (LDD), lamp burnout (LBO), and lamp lumen depreciation (LLD). The unrecoverable factors are not easily modified and are considered a characteristic of the light source. Unrecoverable factors include luminaire ambient temperature (LAT), ballast factor (BF), voltage factor (VF), and luminaire surface depreciation (LSD).

The room surface dirt depreciation factor, RSDD, is a function of the type of environment the luminaire is to be placed in and the frequency of cleaning of the room surfaces. The first step in determining the RSDD factor is to assign a dirt condition to the space. Table 12–3(A) lists the five degrees of dirt conditions as defined by the Illuminating Engineering Society. Next, the percent expected dirt depreciation is determined from the chart shown in Table 12–3(B). Last, the RSDD factor is determined from the table shown in Table 12–3(B). Note that the RSDD factor is a function of the room cavity ratio as well. The RSDD is a recoverable factor since the room can be cleaned to restore the reflectance values of the surfaces to their original values.

EXAMPLE 12–8

Determine the RSDD for the office space of Example 12–7. Assume a clean environment that is cleaned every 36 months. Also, assume direct light distribution from the lay-in fixtures.

Solution: From Table 12–3, the % expected dirt depreciation is approximately 21%. The actual RSDD is determined by interpolation of the factors shown in Table 12–3. Interpolation of values for the actual RCR of 2.7 is performed first, followed by interpolation at the expected dirt depreciation of 21%. The results are shown here.

RCR	% Expected Dirt Depreciation		
	20%	21%	30%
2.0	0.96		0.94
2.7	X1	X3	X2
3.0	0.95		0.93

$$X1 = 0.96 - \frac{2.7 - 2.0}{3.0 - 2.0}[0.96 - 0.95] = 0.953$$

$$X2 = 0.94 - \frac{2.7 - 2.0}{3.0 - 2.0}[0.94 - 0.93] = 0.933$$

$$X3 = 0.953 - \frac{21 - 20}{30 - 20}[0.953 - 0.933] = 0.951$$

Therefore, the RSDD is 0.951. Note that the RCR entered into the calculations.

The luminaire dirt depreciation factor, LDD, is a function of the maintenance category of the luminaire, the degree of dirt condition, and the frequency of cleaning. The maintenance category is a function of the construction of the luminaire and is readily available from the fixture manufacturer. Once the maintenance category has been determined, the LDD factor can be found from the graphs shown in Figure 12–11. The LDD is recoverable by cleaning the fixture and restoring the reflectances of the fixture surfaces to their original values.

EXAMPLE 12–9

Determine the LDD factor for a luminaire having a maintenance category IV located in a clean environment that is cleaned every 24 months.

Solution: From Figure 12–11, the LDD is read as 0.8.

The lamp burnout factor, LBO, is a number that depends on the number of lamps permitted to burn out before replacement. For example, if 10% of the lamps are allowed to burn out prior to replacement, the LBO would be equal to 0.9. Likewise, if 5% of the lamps were allowed to burn out prior to replacement, the LBO factor would be 0.95. In essence, the LBO represents the per unit value of lamps remaining in service. The LBO is recoverable by lamp replacement.

The lamp lumen depreciation factor, LLD, provides a measure of how the light output of a lamp changes as the lamp ages. This value is typically available from the manufacturer. The LLD factor is recoverable in the sense that the lamp may be replaced if light output decreased to a low value with time.

TABLE 12–3
Room Surface Dirt Depreciation Factors

A. Degrees of Dirt Conditions

	Very Clean	Clean	Medium	Dirty	Very Dirty
Generated Dirt	None	Very little	Noticeable but not heavy	Accumulates rapidly	Constant accumulation
Ambient Dirt	None (or none enters area)	Some (almost none enters)	Some enters area	Large amount enters area	Almost none excluded
Removal or Filtration	Excellent	Better than average	Poorer than average	Only fans or blowers if any	None
Adhesion	None	Slight	Enough to be visible after some months	High—probably due to oil, humidity or static	High
Examples	High grade offices, not near production; laboratories; clean rooms	Office in older buildings or near production; light assembly; inspection	Mill offices; paper processing; light machining	Heat treating; high speed printing; rubber processing	Similar to Dirty but luminaires within immediate area of contamination

B. RSDD Factors

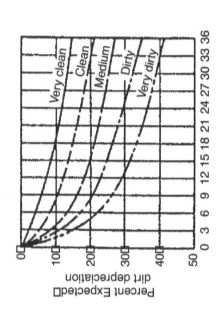

Luminaire Distribution Type

Months	Direct				Semi-Direct				Direct-Indirect				Semi-Indirect				Indirect			
Percent Expected Dirt Depreciation	10	20	30	40	10	20	30	40	10	20	30	40	10	20	30	40	10	20	30	40
Room Cavity Ratio																				
1	.98	.96	.94	.92	.97	.92	.89	.84	.94	.87	.80	.76	.94	.87	.80	.73	.90	.80	.70	.60
2	.98	.96	.94	.92	.96	.92	.88	.83	.94	.87	.80	.75	.94	.87	.79	.72	.90	.80	.69	.59
3	.98	.95	.93	.90	.96	.91	.87	.82	.94	.86	.79	.74	.94	.86	.78	.71	.90	.79	.68	.58
4	.97	.95	.92	.90	.95	.90	.85	.80	.94	.86	.79	.73	.94	.86	.78	.70	.89	.78	.67	.56
5	.97	.94	.91	.89	.94	.90	.84	.79	.93	.86	.78	.72	.93	.86	.77	.69	.89	.78	.66	.55
6	.97	.94	.91	.88	.94	.89	.83	.78	.93	.85	.78	.71	.93	.85	.76	.68	.89	.77	.66	.54
7	.97	.94	.90	.87	.93	.88	.82	.77	.93	.84	.77	.70	.93	.84	.76	.68	.89	.76	.65	.53
8	.96	.93	.89	.86	.93	.87	.81	.75	.93	.84	.76	.69	.93	.84	.76	.68	.88	.76	.64	.52
9	.96	.92	.88	.85	.93	.87	.80	.74	.93	.84	.76	.68	.93	.84	.75	.67	.88	.75	.63	.51
10	.96	.92	.87	.83	.93	.86	.79	.72	.93	.84	.75	.67	.92	.83	.75	.67	.88	.75	.62	.50

Source: IES Lighting Handbook Reference Volume, © 1981, Illuminating Engineering Society of North America.

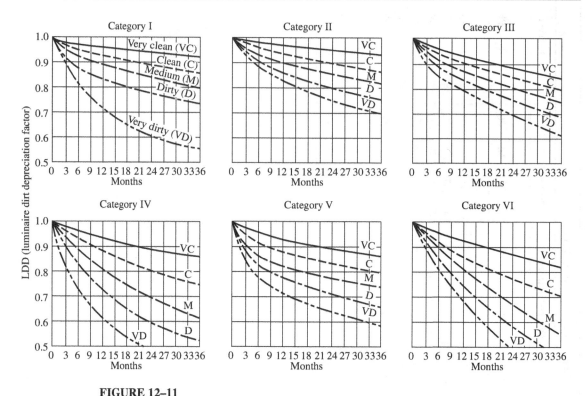

FIGURE 12–11
Luminaire Dirt Depreciation Factors *Source:* IES Lighting Handbook Reference Volume, © 1981, Illuminating Engineering Society of North America.

The luminaire ambient temperature factor, LAT, provides a means of quantifying the change in light output of a given fixture as a function of ambient temperature. This factor is generally not recoverable since the ambient temperature is typically not adjustable for the purposes of optimizing light output.

The voltage factor, VF, quantifies the effect the voltage applied to the luminaire will affect the light output. Representative voltage factors for several different lamp types are shown in Figure 12–12. Note that the lumen output varies as a function of the voltage applied to the lamp or ballast. This factor is also generally not recoverable since the voltage applied to the luminaire depends on the voltage drop in the feeders and branch circuits supplying the luminaires.

The ballast factor, BF, is a measure of how well the ballast is matched to the lamp. It is generally in the range of 0.9 to 1.0 for most ballast/lamp configurations. It is not recoverable once the ballast/lamp combination is installed in the fixture.

The luminaire surface depreciation factor, LSD, quantifies the effect that aging has on the surface of the luminaire. This factor essentially measures the decrease in reflectance value of the reflective surfaces of the luminaire. It is not recoverable since the depreciation is due to normal aging of the fixture surfaces.

FIGURE 12–12
Lamp Voltage Factor *Source:*
IES Lighting Handbook
Reference Volume, © 1981,
Illuminating Engineering
Society of North America.

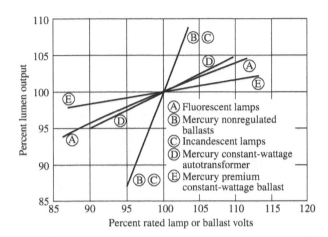

The total light loss factor, LLF, is the product of the individual factors:

$$LLF = RSDD \times LDD \times LBO \times LLD \times LAT \times VF \times BF \times LSD \quad \textbf{(12–4)}$$

Effective Reflectances

The effective floor and ceiling cavity reflectances must be calculated in order to determine the coefficient of utilization from the manufacturer's data. The effective reflectances take into account the effect the dimensions of the ceiling and floor cavities have on the base reflectance values. In effect, the base reflectances must be modified to account for the dimensions of the given cavity. Table 12–4 can be used to determine the appropriate effective reflectances. The following example illustrates the procedure.

EXAMPLE 12–10

Determine the effective ceiling cavity reflectance and effective floor cavity reflectance for a room 28 ft × 36 ft, with a ceiling height of 9 ft and a work plane height of 3 ft. Base reflectances for the ceiling, wall, and floor are 80%, 50%, and 20%, respectively. Lay-in type fluorescent fixtures are to be used.

Solution: First, the required cavity ratios must be determined. Since lay-in fixtures are used, the ceiling cavity height and consequently the CCR is zero. Therefore, the effective ceiling cavity reflectance is equal to the base reflectance of 80%. The FCR is calculated based on a work plane height of 3 ft:

$$FCR = \frac{5 \times (3 \text{ ft}) \times (28 \text{ ft} + 36 \text{ ft})}{(28 \text{ ft} \times 36 \text{ ft})} = 0.95$$

TABLE 12–4
Effective Floor and Ceiling Cavity Reflectances

Percent Base* Reflectance	90										80										70										60										50									
Percent Wall Reflectance	90	80	70	60	50	40	30	20	10	0	90	80	70	60	50	40	30	20	10	0	90	80	70	60	50	40	30	20	10	0	90	80	70	60	50	40	30	20	10	0	90	80	70	60	50	40	30	20	10	0
Cavity Ratio																																																		
0.2	89	88	88	87	86	85	85	84	84	82	79	78	78	77	77	76	76	75	74	72	70	69	68	68	67	66	66	66	65	64	60	59	59	58	57	56	56	56	55	53	50	49	49	48	48	48	47	46	46	44
0.4	88	87	86	85	84	83	81	80	79	76	79	77	76	75	74	73	72	71	70	68	69	68	67	66	65	64	63	62	61	58	60	59	58	57	55	54	53	52	52	50	50	49	48	47	46	45	45	44	44	42
0.6	87	86	84	82	80	79	77	76	74	73	78	76	75	73	71	70	68	66	65	63	69	67	65	64	62	60	59	58	57	54	60	58	56	55	53	51	51	50	48	46	50	48	47	46	45	44	43	42	41	38
0.8	87	85	82	80	77	75	73	71	69	67	78	75	73	71	69	67	65	63	61	57	68	66	64	62	60	58	56	55	53	50	59	57	56	54	51	49	48	47	46	43	50	48	47	45	44	42	40	39	38	36
1.0	86	83	80	77	75	72	69	66	64	62	77	74	72	69	67	65	62	60	57	55	68	65	62	60	58	55	53	52	50	47	59	57	55	53	51	49	46	44	43	41	50	48	46	44	43	41	38	37	36	34
1.2	86	82	78	75	72	69	66	63	60	57	77	73	70	67	64	61	58	55	53	51	67	64	61	59	57	53	50	48	46	44	59	56	54	51	49	46	44	42	40	38	50	47	45	43	41	39	36	35	34	29
1.4	85	80	77	73	69	65	62	59	57	52	76	72	68	65	62	59	55	53	50	48	67	63	60	58	54	51	50	45	44	41	59	54	51	49	47	44	41	39	38	36	50	47	45	42	40	38	35	34	32	27
1.6	84	79	75	71	67	63	59	56	53	50	75	71	67	63	60	57	53	50	47	44	67	62	59	56	53	49	47	45	43	38	59	55	51	47	44	42	39	37	35	33	50	47	44	41	39	36	33	32	30	26
1.8	83	78	73	69	64	60	56	53	50	48	75	70	66	62	58	54	50	47	44	41	66	61	58	54	51	46	45	42	40	35	58	55	51	47	44	40	37	35	33	31	50	46	43	40	38	35	31	30	28	25
2.0	83	77	72	67	62	56	53	50	47	43	74	69	64	60	56	52	48	45	41	38	66	60	56	52	49	45	42	40	38	33	58	54	50	46	43	39	35	33	31	29	50	46	43	40	37	34	30	28	26	24
2.2	82	76	70	65	59	54	50	47	44	40	74	68	63	58	54	49	45	42	38	35	66	60	55	51	48	43	40	38	36	31	58	53	49	45	42	37	34	31	29	28	50	46	42	38	36	33	29	27	24	22
2.4	82	75	69	64	58	53	48	45	41	37	73	67	61	56	52	47	43	40	36	33	65	60	54	50	46	41	38	36	34	28	58	53	48	44	41	36	32	30	28	26	50	46	42	37	35	31	27	25	23	21
2.6	81	74	67	62	56	51	46	42	38	35	73	66	60	55	50	45	41	38	34	31	65	59	54	49	45	40	37	35	33	26	58	53	48	43	39	35	31	28	26	24	50	46	41	37	34	30	26	23	21	20
2.8	81	73	66	60	54	49	44	40	36	34	73	65	59	53	48	43	39	36	32	29	65	59	53	48	43	38	35	33	30	24	57	52	47	43	38	34	30	27	24	22	50	46	41	36	33	29	25	22	20	19
3.0	80	72	64	58	52	47	42	38	34	30	72	65	58	52	47	42	37	34	30	27	64	58	52	47	42	37	34	32	29	22	57	52	46	42	37	32	28	25	23	20	50	45	40	36	32	28	24	21	19	17
3.2	79	71	63	56	50	45	40	36	32	28	72	65	57	51	45	40	35	33	28	25	64	58	51	46	41	36	33	31	28	20	57	51	45	41	36	31	27	23	22	18	50	44	39	35	31	27	23	20	18	16
3.4	79	70	62	54	48	43	38	34	30	27	71	64	56	49	44	39	34	32	27	24	64	57	50	45	40	35	33	29	27	19	57	51	45	40	35	30	26	23	20	17	50	44	39	35	30	26	22	19	17	15
3.6	78	69	61	53	47	42	36	32	28	25	71	63	54	48	42	36	32	25	25	22	63	56	49	44	38	34	31	28	25	17	57	50	44	39	34	29	25	22	19	16	50	44	38	34	29	25	21	18	16	14
3.8	78	69	60	51	45	40	35	31	27	23	70	62	53	47	41	36	31	28	24	20	63	56	48	43	37	33	30	26	24	15	57	50	43	38	33	29	24	21	19	14	50	44	38	33	28	25	21	17	15	13
4.0	77	69	58	51	44	39	33	29	25	22	70	61	53	46	40	35	30	26	22	20	63	55	48	42	36	31	26	23	21	14	56	49	42	37	32	27	22	19	17	14	50	44	37	33	28	24	20	17	15	12
4.2	77	62	57	50	43	37	32	28	24	21	69	60	52	45	39	34	29	25	21	18	62	55	47	41	35	30	25	22	19	16	56	49	42	37	32	27	22	19	16	13	50	43	37	32	28	24	20	17	14	12
4.4	76	61	56	49	42	36	31	27	23	20	69	60	51	44	38	33	28	24	20	17	62	54	46	40	34	29	24	21	18	15	56	49	42	36	31	27	22	18	16	13	50	43	37	32	27	23	19	16	13	11
4.6	76	60	55	47	40	35	30	26	22	19	69	59	50	43	37	33	28	23	19	15	62	54	46	39	33	28	24	20	16	13	56	48	41	36	30	26	21	18	15	11	50	43	36	31	26	21	18	15	13	11
4.8	75	59	54	46	39	34	28	25	21	18	68	58	49	42	36	31	26	22	18	14	62	53	45	38	32	28	23	20	16	12	56	48	41	34	29	25	21	18	15	12	50	43	36	31	26	22	18	15	12	09
5.0	75	59	53	45	38	33	28	24	20	16	68	58	48	41	35	30	25	21	18	14	61	52	44	37	31	26	22	18	15	12	56	48	40	34	29	25	20	17	14	11	50	42	35	30	25	21	17	14	12	09
6.0	73	61	49	41	34	29	24	20	16	11	66	55	44	38	31	27	22	19	15	10	60	50	41	35	28	24	18	15	12	09	55	45	37	31	26	21	17	14	11	07	50	42	34	29	23	19	15	13	10	06
7.0	70	58	45	38	30	27	21	18	14	08	64	53	41	35	28	24	19	16	12	07	58	48	38	32	25	21	16	13	10	07	54	43	35	30	24	21	16	13	11	06	49	41	32	27	21	18	14	11	08	05
8.0	68	55	42	35	27	23	18	15	12	06	62	50	38	32	25	21	17	14	11	05	57	46	35	29	23	19	14	11	08	04	53	42	33	28	22	18	14	11	08	05	49	40	30	25	19	16	12	10	07	03
9.0	66	52	38	31	25	21	16	14	11	05	61	49	36	30	23	19	16	13	10	04	56	45	33	27	21	18	13	10	07	03	52	40	31	26	20	16	12	10	07	03	48	39	29	24	18	15	11	09	07	03
10.0	65	51	36	29	22	19	15	11	09	04	59	46	33	27	21	18	14	11	08	03	55	43	31	25	19	16	12	09	07	02	51	39	29	24	18	15	11	09	07	02	47	37	27	22	17	14	10	08	06	02

Percent Base* Reflectance →	40										30										20										10										0									
Percent Wall Reflectance → / Cavity Ratio ↓	90	80	70	60	50	40	30	20	10	0	90	80	70	60	50	40	30	20	10	0	90	80	70	60	50	40	30	20	10	0	90	80	70	60	50	40	30	20	10	0	90	80	70	60	50	40	30	20	10	0
0.2	40	40	39	39	39	38	38	37	36	36	31	31	30	30	29	29	28	28	28	27	21	20	20	20	20	19	19	19	19	17	11	11	11	10	10	10	10	09	09	09	02	02	01	01	01	01	01	00	00	00
0.4	41	40	39	39	38	37	36	35	34	34	31	31	31	30	29	28	28	27	26	25	22	21	20	19	19	19	19	18	18	16	12	11	11	11	11	10	10	09	09	08	04	03	03	02	02	02	02	01	01	00
0.6	41	40	39	38	37	36	35	33	32	31	32	31	30	29	28	27	26	25	25	23	23	21	21	20	19	18	18	17	17	15	13	13	12	11	11	10	10	09	08	08	05	05	04	03	03	03	02	01	01	01
0.8	41	40	38	37	36	35	33	32	31	29	32	31	30	29	28	26	25	23	22	20	23	22	21	19	18	17	16	15	14	13	14	13	12	12	11	11	10	09	08	07	07	06	05	04	04	03	02	02	01	01
1.0	42	40	38	37	35	33	32	31	29	27	33	32	30	29	27	25	24	22	21	19	24	23	21	19	18	17	16	14	13	12	15	14	13	12	11	11	10	09	08	07	08	07	06	05	04	04	03	02	02	01
1.2	42	40	38	36	34	32	30	29	27	25	33	32	30	28	26	24	22	21	19	18	25	23	22	19	18	16	15	13	12	11	16	14	13	12	12	11	09	08	07	06	10	08	07	06	05	04	03	02	02	01
1.4	42	39	37	35	33	31	29	27	25	23	34	32	30	28	26	24	22	20	18	17	25	23	22	20	17	16	14	13	11	10	17	15	14	13	12	11	09	08	07	06	11	09	08	07	06	05	04	03	02	01
1.6	42	39	37	35	32	30	27	25	23	22	34	32	29	27	25	23	20	18	17	15	26	24	22	19	17	15	13	12	10	09	18	16	14	13	12	11	09	08	07	06	12	10	09	07	06	05	04	03	02	01
1.8	42	39	36	34	31	29	26	24	22	21	35	33	29	27	25	22	20	17	16	14	26	24	22	20	17	15	13	11	10	08	18	16	15	13	12	11	09	08	06	05	13	11	09	08	07	05	04	03	03	01
2.0	42	39	36	34	31	28	25	23	21	19	35	33	29	26	24	22	19	17	15	13	27	25	23	20	17	15	13	11	09	08	19	17	15	14	13	11	09	08	06	05	14	12	10	09	07	05	04	03	03	01
2.2	42	39	36	33	30	27	24	23	19	18	36	32	29	26	24	21	18	16	14	12	28	25	23	20	18	16	13	11	09	07	20	18	16	14	13	11	09	07	06	05	15	13	11	09	08	06	04	03	03	01
2.4	43	39	35	33	29	27	23	21	18	16	36	33	29	26	23	20	18	16	14	12	28	26	23	20	16	14	12	10	08	06	21	19	16	14	13	11	09	07	06	04	16	13	11	09	08	06	04	03	03	02
2.6	43	39	35	32	29	26	23	20	17	15	36	33	29	25	23	20	17	15	13	11	29	26	23	20	18	15	12	10	08	06	22	19	16	15	13	11	09	07	06	04	17	14	12	10	08	06	05	03	02	02
2.8	43	39	35	32	28	25	22	19	16	14	37	33	29	25	23	20	17	15	13	11	29	26	23	20	18	15	12	10	08	05	23	20	17	15	14	11	09	07	05	03	17	15	13	10	08	07	05	03	02	02
3.0	43	39	35	31	27	24	21	18	16	13	37	33	29	25	22	19	16	14	12	10	30	27	23	20	15	13	11	09	07	05	23	20	18	16	13	11	09	07	05	03	18	16	13	11	09	07	05	03	02	02
3.2	43	39	35	31	27	23	20	17	15	12	37	33	29	25	21	19	16	14	12	10	30	27	23	20	17	14	11	09	07	04	24	21	18	16	14	11	09	07	05	03	19	16	14	11	09	07	05	03	02	02
3.4	43	39	34	30	26	22	19	16	14	11	37	33	29	24	21	18	15	13	11	09	31	27	23	20	17	14	11	09	07	04	25	21	18	16	14	11	09	07	05	03	20	17	14	12	09	07	05	03	02	02
3.6	44	39	34	30	26	22	18	16	13	11	38	33	28	24	21	18	15	13	10	09	32	27	24	20	17	14	11	08	06	03	26	22	18	16	14	11	09	06	04	03	20	17	15	12	10	08	05	04	02	02
3.8	44	38	33	29	25	21	18	15	12	10	38	33	28	24	21	18	14	13	10	08	32	28	23	19	16	13	10	08	06	03	26	22	19	16	14	11	09	06	04	02	21	18	15	12	10	08	05	04	02	02
4.0	44	38	33	29	25	21	18	15	12	10	38	33	28	24	20	17	14	12	09	07	33	28	23	19	16	13	10	08	05	02	27	23	19	17	14	11	09	06	04	02	22	18	15	13	10	08	05	04	02	02
4.2	44	38	33	28	24	20	17	13	11	09	38	33	28	24	20	17	14	12	09	07	33	28	22	19	16	13	10	07	05	02	27	23	19	17	14	11	09	06	04	02	22	19	16	13	10	08	06	04	02	02
4.4	44	38	33	28	24	20	17	14	11	09	39	33	28	24	20	17	14	11	09	06	34	28	23	19	16	13	10	07	04	02	28	24	19	16	14	11	08	06	04	02	23	19	16	13	10	08	06	04	02	02
4.6	44	38	32	28	23	19	16	14	11	08	39	33	28	24	20	17	13	11	08	06	34	29	23	19	14	11	08	06	04	02	29	24	20	17	14	11	08	06	04	02	23	20	17	13	11	08	06	04	02	02
4.8	44	38	32	27	22	19	16	13	10	08	39	33	28	24	19	16	13	10	08	05	35	29	23	19	15	12	08	06	04	02	29	25	20	17	14	11	08	06	04	02	24	20	17	14	11	08	06	04	02	02
5.0	45	38	31	27	22	19	15	13	10	08	39	33	27	23	19	16	13	10	08	05	35	29	23	18	15	12	08	06	04	02	30	25	20	17	14	11	08	06	04	02	24	20	17	14	11	09	06	04	03	02
6.0	44	37	31	25	21	17	13	11	08	05	39	33	27	23	18	15	11	09	06	04	36	30	24	19	14	11	08	05	03	01	31	26	21	18	14	11	08	06	03	01	27	23	18	15	12	09	06	04	03	02
7.0	44	37	30	24	19	16	12	10	07	04	40	33	26	22	17	14	10	08	05	03	37	30	23	18	14	10	07	05	03	01	32	27	21	17	13	10	07	05	03	01	28	24	19	15	12	09	06	04	03	02
8.0	44	35	29	23	18	15	11	09	06	03	40	33	26	21	16	13	09	07	04	02	37	30	23	18	13	09	06	03	01	01	33	27	21	17	13	10	07	05	03	01	30	25	20	16	12	09	06	04	03	02
9.0	44	35	26	21	16	13	10	08	05	02	40	33	25	20	15	12	08	06	03	01	37	29	22	16	12	08	06	03	01	01	34	28	21	17	13	10	07	04	02	01	31	25	20	15	12	09	06	04	03	02
10.0	43	34	25	20	15	12	08	07	05	02	40	32	24	19	14	11	08	06	03	01	37	29	22	18	13	10	07	05	03	01	34	28	21	17	12	10	07	05	02	01	31	25	20	15	12	09	06	04	02	02

*Ceiling, floor or floor of cavity.

Source: IES Lighting Handbook Reference Volume, © 1981, Illuminating Engineering Society of North America.

From Table 12–4, the following data are obtained:

FCR	Base Floor Reflectance $\rho_F = 20\%$
0.8	0.19
0.95	X1
1.0	0.19

By interpolation, the effective floor cavity reflectance, X1, is 0.19.

Coefficient of Utilization

As previously mentioned, the coefficient of utilization is a number between 0.0 and 1.0 that quantifies the effectiveness of the fixture in distributing light to the surface to be illuminated. The CU tables are readily available from the manufacturer. These tables typically list CU values for an effective floor cavity reflectance of 20% and various ceiling and wall reflectance values. In addition, the CU data is a function of the room cavity ratio. Once the effective ceiling reflectance and room cavity ratio have been determined, the CU can be determined from the tables directly. Table 12–5 shows typical CU data available from the manufacturer. The following example illustrates the procedure used to determine the CU of a given fixture.

EXAMPLE 12–11

Using the CU data shown in Table 12–5, determine the CU for the condition specified in Example 12–10.

Solution: The following data is obtained:

RCR	Effective Ceiling Reflectance $\rho_{CC} = 80\%$
1.0	0.70
1.9	X1
2.0	0.64

$$X1 = 0.70 - 0.9 \times [0.70 - 0.64] = 0.646$$

Therefore, the CU is 0.646.

TABLE 12-5
Photometric Data for Lay-In Fluorescent Fixture

Photometrics

Coefficients of Utilization

Effective floor cavity reflectance 20%

rc	80%				70%				50%			30%			10%			0%
rw	70	50	30	10	70	50	30	10	50	30	10	50	30	10	50	30	10	0
RCR																		
0	77	77	77	77	75	75	75	75	72	72	72	69	69	69	66	66	66	65
1	72	70	68	66	71	69	67	65	66	65	63	64	62	61	61	60	60	58
2	68	64	61	58	66	63	60	57	61	58	56	59	57	55	57	55	54	52
3	63	58	54	51	62	57	53	50	55	52	50	54	51	49	52	50	48	47
4	59	52	48	45	57	52	47	44	50	47	44	49	46	43	47	45	43	41
5	54	47	43	39	53	47	42	39	45	41	38	44	41	38	43	40	38	36
6	50	43	38	34	49	42	38	34	41	37	34	40	36	34	39	36	33	32
7	46	39	34	30	45	38	33	30	37	33	30	36	32	29	35	32	29	28
8	43	35	30	26	42	34	29	26	33	29	26	33	29	26	32	28	26	25
9	39	31	26	23	38	31	26	23	30	26	23	29	25	22	29	25	22	21
10	36	28	23	20	35	28	23	20	27	23	20	27	23	20	26	22	20	19

Zonal Lumen Summary

Zone	Lumens	%Lamp	%Fixture
0-30	2666	23.00	35.60
0-40	4397	37.90	58.70
0-60	7275	62.70	97.10
0-90	7494	64.60	100.0
0-180	7494	64.60	100.0

Typical VCP Percentages

Room Size (Ft.)	Height Along		Height (Across)	
	8.5'	10.0'	8.5'	10.0'
20 × 20	85	78	88	81
30 × 30	89	84	91	87
30 × 60	91	87	91	88
60 × 30	89	84	91	87

Candlepower

60 × 60   91   91   87

Angle	Along II	45°	Across ⊥
0	3461	3461	3461
5	3449	3447	3450
10	3386	3398	3407
15	3282	3309	3333
20	3148	3186	3207
25	2988	3011	3145
30	2801	2852	3091
35	2580	2716	3043
40	2332	2542	3031
45	2040	2322	2635
50	1402	1970	1901
55	1287	1343	1054
60	672	678	355
65	136	212	45
70	48	44	25
75	24	23	14
80	12	11	7
85	4	3	2
90	0	0	0

2P2GAX-432S511I
Energy Saving Ballast
F32T8/35K lamps
3150 lumens
Spacing criterion:
(II) 1.2 × mounting height, (⊥) 1.4 × mounting height
Efficiency = 62.1 %
Test Report #104P180
LER = FP-59
Yearly Cost of 1000 lumens, 3000 hrs at .08 kWh = $4.07

Source: Cooper Lighting, Division of Cooper Industries.

Floor Cavity Correction Factor

The coefficient of utilization data is generally presented by the manufacturer for an effective floor cavity reflectance of 20%. In situations where the effective floor cavity reflectance is other than 20%, a correction factor must be applied to the CU. This correction factor is a multiplier that accounts for the variation in effective floor cavity reflectance. Table 12–6 lists the multiplying factors for other than 20% effective floor cavity reflectance. The following example illustrates the procedure for determining the appropriate multiplying factor.

EXAMPLE 12–12

Determine the multiplying factor to be applied to the CU for the conditions specified in Examples 12–10 and 12–11.

Solution: The appropriate multiplying factors are obtained from Table 12–6. First, the data are interpolated based on an effective floor cavity reflectance of 30%, an RCR of 1.9, and an effective ceiling cavity reflectance of 80%. Next, the interpolation is repeated for an effective floor cavity reflectance of 10%, an RCR of 1.9, and 80% ρ_{CC}. Last, the interpolation for an effective floor cavity reflectance of 19% and RCR of 1.9 is performed to arrive at the final result.

The results for an effective floor cavity reflectance of 30% are shown below:

RCR	Effective Ceiling Reflectance $\rho_{CC} = 80\%$
1.0	1.082
1.9	$X1$
2.0	1.066

$$X1 = 1.082 - \left(\frac{1.9 - 1.0}{2.0 - 1.0}\right) \times [1.082 - 1.066] = 1.068$$

The results for an effective floor cavity reflectance of 10% are

RCR	Effective Ceiling Reflectance $\rho_{CC} = 80\%$
1.0	0.929
1.9	$X1$
2.0	0.942

$$X1 = 0.942 - \left(\frac{2.0 - 1.9}{2.0 - 1.0}\right) \times [0.942 - 0.929] = 0.941$$

Interpolating between the results for effective floor cavity reflectances of 30% and 10%:

ρ_{FC}	Multiplier
30%	1.068
19%	X1
10%	0.942

$$X1 = 1.068 - \left(\frac{30 - 19}{30 - 10}\right) \times [1.068 - 0.942] = 0.9987$$

Therefore, the appropriate multiplier to be applied to the CU is 0.9987. Note that in most instances this multiplier is very close to 1.0. Thus, in typical designs, it is possible to assume a multiplier of 1.0. This assumption will not significantly affect the results in most cases.

Recommended Lighting Levels

Recommended lighting levels for various indoor and outdoor applications have been established by the Illuminating Engineering Society. Table 12–7 shows representative lighting levels expressed in footcandles for various indoor and outdoor applications. These tables can be used to determine the level of lighting required for a given space.

Determination of Required Number of Fixtures

The number of lighting fixtures required to provide a given amount of illumination can be calculated as follows:

$$\# \text{ Fixtures} = \frac{(\text{fc level}) \times (\text{Room length} \times \text{Room width})}{(\text{CU}) \times (\text{Mult. fac.}) \times (\text{LLF}) \times (\# \text{ Lamps per fix.}) \times (\text{Lumens per lamp})} \quad \textbf{(12–5)}$$

Note that Equation (12–5) takes into account the footcandle level desired, area to be illuminated, coefficient of utilization, floor cavity correction factor, total light loss factor, number of lamps per fixture, and lumen output per lamp.

EXAMPLE 12–13

Determine the required number of fixtures to illuminate the office area of Examples 12–10, 12–11, and 12–12 to 80 footcandles maintained. Assume that the total light loss factor is 0.75. The fixture data is presented in Table 12–5. The lamp lumen output is 3150 lumens per lamp, and the fixture may contain either three or four lamps, depending on the specification. Determine the maximum separation both along and across the fixture given the specified mounting height. Sketch the resulting layout.

TABLE 12-6
Floor Cavity Correction Factor

For 30 Percent Effective Floor Cavity Reflectance (20 Percent = 1.00)

% Effective Ceiling Cavity Reflectance, ρcc	80				70				50			30			10		
% Wall Reflectance, ρw	70	50	30	10	70	50	30	10	50	30	10	50	30	10	50	30	10
Room Cavity Ratio																	
1	1.092	1.082	1.075	1.068	1.077	1.070	1.064	1.059	1.049	1.044	1.040	1.028	1.026	1.023	1.012	1.010	1.008
2	1.079	1.066	1.055	1.047	1.068	1.057	1.048	1.039	1.041	1.033	1.027	1.026	1.021	1.017	1.013	1.010	1.006
3	1.070	1.054	1.042	1.033	1.061	1.048	1.037	1.028	1.034	1.027	1.020	1.024	1.017	1.012	1.014	1.009	1.005
4	1.062	1.045	1.033	1.024	1.055	1.040	1.029	1.021	1.030	1.022	1.015	1.022	1.015	1.010	1.014	1.009	1.004
5	1.056	1.038	1.026	1.018	1.050	1.034	1.024	1.015	1.027	1.018	1.012	1.020	1.013	1.008	1.014	1.009	1.004
6	1.052	1.033	1.021	1.014	1.047	1.030	1.020	1.012	1.024	1.015	1.009	1.019	1.012	1.006	1.014	1.008	1.003
7	1.047	1.029	1.018	1.011	1.043	1.026	1.017	1.009	1.022	1.013	1.007	1.018	1.010	1.005	1.014	1.008	1.003
8	1.044	1.026	1.015	1.009	1.040	1.024	1.015	1.007	1.020	1.012	1.006	1.017	1.009	1.004	1.013	1.007	1.003
9	1.040	1.024	1.014	1.007	1.037	1.022	1.014	1.006	1.019	1.011	1.005	1.016	1.009	1.004	1.013	1.007	1.002
10	1.037	1.022	1.012	1.006	1.034	1.020	1.012	1.005	1.017	1.010	1.004	1.015	1.009	1.003	1.013	1.007	1.002

For 10 Percent Effective Floor Cavity Reflectance (20 Percent = 1.00)

Room Cavity Ratio																	
1	.923	.929	.935	.940	.933	.939	.943	.948	.956	.960	.963	.973	.976	.979	.989	.991	.993
2	.931	.942	.950	.958	.940	.949	.957	.963	.962	.968	.974	.976	.980	.985	.988	.991	.995
3	.939	.951	.961	.969	.945	.957	.966	.973	.967	.975	.981	.978	.983	.988	.988	.992	.996
4	.944	.958	.969	.978	.950	.963	.973	.980	.972	.980	.986	.980	.986	.991	.987	.992	.996
5	.949	.964	.976	.983	.954	.968	.978	.985	.975	.983	.989	.981	.988	.993	.987	.992	.997
6	.953	.969	.980	.986	.958	.972	.982	.989	.977	.985	.992	.982	.989	.995	.987	.993	.997
7	.957	.973	.983	.991	.961	.975	.985	.991	.979	.987	.994	.983	.990	.996	.987	.993	.998
8	.960	.976	.986	.993	.963	.977	.987	.993	.981	.988	.995	.984	.991	.997	.987	.994	.998
9	.963	.978	.987	.994	.965	.979	.989	.994	.983	.990	.996	.985	.992	.998	.988	.994	.999
10	.965	.980	.989	.995	.967	.981	.990	.995	.984	.991	.997	.986	.993	.998	.988	.994	.999

For 0 Percent Effective Floor Cavity Reflectance (20 Percent = 1.00)

Room Cavity Ratio																	
1	.859	.870	.879	.886	.873	.884	.893	.901	.916	.923	.929	.948	.954	.960	.979	.983	.987
2	.871	.887	.903	.919	.886	.902	.916	.928	.926	.938	.949	.954	.963	.971	.978	.983	.991
3	.882	.904	.915	.942	.898	.918	.934	.947	.936	.950	.964	.958	.969	.979	.976	.984	.993
4	.893	.919	.941	.958	.908	.930	.948	.961	.945	.961	.974	.961	.974	.984	.975	.985	.994
5	.903	.931	.953	.969	.914	.939	.958	.970	.951	.967	.980	.964	.977	.988	.975	.985	.995
6	.911	.940	.961	.976	.920	.945	.965	.977	.955	.972	.985	.966	.979	.991	.975	.986	.996
7	.917	.947	.967	.981	.924	.950	.970	.982	.959	.975	.988	.968	.981	.993	.975	.987	.997
8	.922	.953	.971	.985	.929	.955	.975	.986	.963	.978	.991	.970	.983	.995	.976	.988	.998
9	.928	.958	.975	.988	.933	.959	.980	.989	.966	.980	.993	.971	.985	.996	.976	.988	.998
10	.933	.962	.979	.991	.937	.963	.983	.992	.969	.982	.995	.973	.987	.997	.977	.989	.999

Source: IES Lighting Handbook Reference Volume, © 1981, Illuminating Engineering Society of North America.

TABLE 12–7
Recommended Lighting Levels

Indoor			
Banks		Assembly	
General Lobby	10–20	Simple	20–50
Writing Area	20–50	Moderately Difficult	50–100
Tellers Station	50–100	Difficult	100–200
Conference Room	20–50	Very Difficult	200–500
Court Rooms		Exacting	500–1000
Seating Area	10–20	Breweries	20–50
Court Activity Area	50–100	Foundries	
Educational Facilities		Annealing	20–50
General Classroom	50–100	Cleaning	20–50
Drafting	50–100	Core Making–Fine	100–200
Lecture Room	20–50	Core Making–Med.	50–100
Study Hall	20–50	Grinding/Chipping	100–200
Residences		Inspection–Fine	200–500
General Lighting	5–10	Inspection–Med.	100–200
Dining	10–20	Molding–Med.	100–200
Grooming	20–50	Molding–Large	50–100
Kitchen	50–100	Pouring	50–100
Laundry	20–50	Sorting	50–100
Reading	20–50	Cupola	10–20
Sewing	50–100	Shakeout	20–50
Service Spaces		Garages	
Stairways	10–20	Repairs	50–100
Elevators	10–20	Traffic Areas	10–20
Restrooms	10–20	Write Up	20–50
Offices		Machine Shop	
Lobbies	10–20	Rough Bench	20–50
General	50–100	Medium	50–100
		Fine	200–500
		Extra Fine	500–1000

Outdoor			
Building Exterior		Freeway	0.6
Entrances–Active	5	Local Roadway	0.4–0.9
Entrances–Inactive	1	Alley	0.4–0.6
Vital Locations	5	Parking Lots	1
Building Surrounds	1	Sidewalks	0.2–0.9

Solution: From Example 12–11, the CU was 0.646. The multiplying factor to be applied to the CU was 0.9987. Start by assuming a four-lamp fixture. The number of fixtures is determined by applying Equation (12–5):

$$\# \text{Fixtures} = \frac{(80 \text{ fc})(28 \text{ ft} \times 36 \text{ ft})}{(0.646) \times (0.9987) \times (0.75) \times (4 \text{ lamps} \times 3150 \text{ lumens per lamp})} = 13.2$$

Therefore, at least 14 fixtures are required.

The maximum spacing between fixtures is obtained by multiplying the spacing criteria by the mounting height of the fixture above the work plane. The following maximum spacings result:

Along: Maximum Spacing = 1.2 × 6 ft = 7.2 ft

Across: Maximum Spacing = 1.4 × 6 ft = 8.4 ft

It is now necessary to examine the actual floor plan to determine the actual fixture placement. The actual fixture layout and electrical circuiting are shown on the reflected ceiling plan of Figure 12–13. In this plan, the ceiling grid is shown assuming the standard

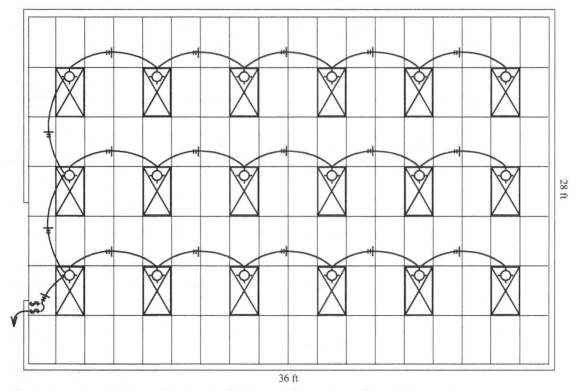

36 ft

Note: Lamps switched separately   one inner and two outer

FIGURE 12–13
Lighting Layout of General Office Area

2 ft × 4 ft lay-in ceiling tile. Based on this arrangement, it can be seen that a uniform arrangement of 14 fixtures is not possible without exceeding the spacing criteria for the fixture. The solution to this problem is to use a greater number of fixtures, each having a lower lumen output. Using a greater number of fixtures means that the light distribution will be more uniform.

The number of fixtures required will be recalculated using a three-lamp fixture:

$$\# \text{ Fixtures } = \frac{(80 \text{ fc})(28 \text{ ft} \times 36 \text{ ft})}{(0.646) \times (0.9987) \times (0.75) \times (3 \text{ lamps} \times 3150 \text{ lumens per lamp})} = 17.6$$

Therefore, approximately 18 fixtures are required. This can be accomplished by arranging the fixtures in three rows of six, as shown in Figure 12–13.

Circuiting

To determine the number of circuits required for a lighting installation, the electrical data for the lamp/ballast must be obtained from the manufacturer. Typical data is shown in Table 12–8 for various lamp types. Since lighting is considered a continuous load, the loading on a circuit must be limited to 80% of the circuit rating. Thus, the maximum loading on a 20 A circuit is 16 A. The maximum number of fixtures permitted on a given circuit is equal to the maximum loading permitted on the circuit divided by the load of each individual fixture. The following example illustrates the procedure.

EXAMPLE 12–14

Determine the maximum number of fixtures permitted on a 20 A, 277 V, 20 branch circuit for the final design of Example 12–13.

Solution: From the data of Table 12–8, each fixture will draw a current of 0.51 A at 277 V. The maximum load on the circuit is limited to 16 A (80% of 20 A). The maximum number of fixtures is

$$\text{Maximum number of fixtures } = \frac{16 \text{ A per circuit}}{0.51 \text{ A per fixture}} = 31 \text{ fixtures per circuit}$$

Based on the results of Example 12–14, all 18 fixtures can be placed on a single 20 A circuit. The switching and circuiting arrangement is shown in Figure 12–13. Other switching schemes are possible based on the individual requirements.

12–6   OUTDOOR LIGHTING DESIGN

The design of outdoor lighting systems begins with an understanding of the light distribution patterns produced by the various fixtures. The basic distribution pattern shown in Figure 12–14(A) is referred to as an *isofootcandle curve*. This curve is essentially a plan view looking down at the light pattern a given fixture will produce on the surface being

TABLE 12–8
Ballast Data

				Mercury Vapor	
		Rated		**Ballast Input**	
Watts	**Lumens**	**Life**	**Watts**	**Voltage**	**Current**
75	2800	24,000	99	120/208/240/277/480	0.9/0.5/0.45/0.4/0.2
100	4300	24,000	120	120/208/240/277/480	1.0/0.6/0.5/0.45/0.28
175	7900	24,000	205	120/208/240/277/480	1.9/1.1/0.95/0.8/0.48
250	12,100	24,000	290	120/208/240/277/480	2.8/1.6/1.4/1.2/0.7
400	21,000	24,000	450	120/208/240/277/480	4.0/2.4/2.0/1.8/1.0
1000	60,000	24,000	1050	120/208/240/277/480	8.9/5.0/4.5/3.8/2.2

				High Pressure Sodium	
		Rated		**Ballast Input**	
Watts	**Lumens**	**Life**	**Watts**	**Voltage**	**Current**
35	2250	16,000	45	120	0.83
50	3800	24,000	63	120	1.18
70	6300	24,000	95	120/208/240/277	0.8/0.5/0.4/0.37
100	9500	24,000	135	120/208/240/277/480	1.2/0.7/0.6/0.55/0.3
150	16,000	24,000	200	120/208/240/277/480	1.8/1.0/0.9/0.8/0.45
250	27,500	24,000	305	120/208/240/277/480	2.7/1.5/1.3/1.2/0.67
400	50,000	24,000	465	120/208/240/277/480	3.8/2.3/1.9/1.6/1.0
1000	140,000	24,000	1100	120/208/240/277/480	9.1/5.1/4.6/4.0/2.3

				Metal Halide	
		Rated		**Ballast Input**	
Watts	**Lumens**	**Life**	**Watts**	**Voltage**	**Current**
175	14,000	10,000	210	120/208/240/277/480	1.8/1.1/0.9/0.8/0.47
250	20,500	10,000	300	120/208/240/277/480	2.5/1.5/1.3/1.1/0.65
400	36,000	20,000	460	120/208/240/277/480	4.0/2.4/2.0/1.8/1.0
1000	110,000	12,000	1050	120/208/240/277/480	8.8/4.9/4.4/3.8/2.3
1500	155,000	3,000	1625	120/208/240/277/480	14.0/8.0/7.0/6.0/3.5

				Fluorescent (Rapid Start) F40T12/CW	
		Rated		**Ballast Input**	
Watts	**Lumens**	**Life**	**Watts**	**Voltage**	**Current**
1–40 W	3,150	20,000	47	120/208/240/277	0.43/0.24/0.23/0.19
2–40 W	6,300	20,000	82	120/208/240/277	0.73/0.45/0.42/0.32
3–40 W	9,450	20,000	123	120/208/240/277	1.16/0.69/0.65/0.51
4–40 W	12,600	20,000	164	120/208/240/277	1.46/0.9/0.84/0.64

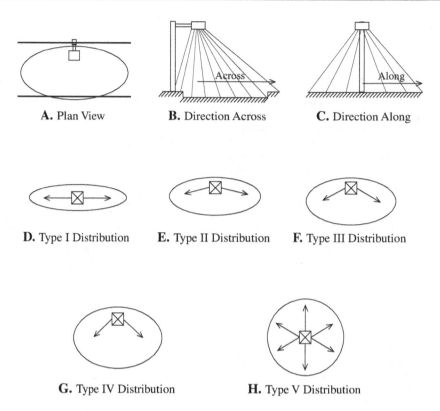

A. Plan View   **B.** Direction Across   **C.** Direction Along

D. Type I Distribution   **E.** Type II Distribution   **F.** Type III Distribution

G. Type IV Distribution   **H.** Type V Distribution

FIGURE 12–14
Outdoor Lighting Fixture Distribution Patterns

illuminated. The lines in the figure represent the constant footcandle levels of the light distribution pattern. Figure 12–14(B) shows the light distribution pattern in the direction across the roadway from the fixture. Figure 12–14(C) shows the distribution pattern in the direction along the roadway. Several distribution patterns are available from the various lighting manufacturers. Several of the more common Illuminating Engineering Society (IES) distribution patterns are shown in Figure 12–14(D) through (H). Figure 12–15 shows an installation using a high cutoff fixture for walkway lighting.

As previously mentioned, the isofootcandle curve for a given fixture/lamp combination is readily available from the manufacturer. Figure 12–16 shows a representative isofootcandle curve and tabulated footcandle data for a commercially available fixture. Note that the data are for a specific fixture containing a certain type of lamp having a given lumen output. Note also that the footcandle data are presented for a given fixture mounting height. The footcandle data thus represent lines of constant footcandle levels for a given reference mounting height and a given reference lamp lumen output. For other lamp lumen output and mounting heights, the footcandle levels are adjusted according to

FIGURE 12–15
Outdoor Lighting Fixture Installation *Source:* Courtesy Youngstown State University.

$$E_{ACT} = E_{REF} \left(\frac{L_{ACT}}{L_{REF}} \right) \times \left(\frac{MH_{REF}}{MH_{ACT}} \right)^2 \qquad (12\text{–}6)$$

where:

E_{ACT} = actual footcandle level
E_{REF} = reference footcandle level (manufacturer s data)
MH_{ACT} = actual fixture mounting height
MH_{REF} = reference fixture mounting height (manufacturer s data)
L_{ACT} = actual lumen output
L_{REF} = reference lumen output (manufacturer s data)

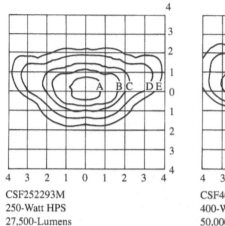

CSF252293M
250-Watt HPS
27,500-Lumens
Type III

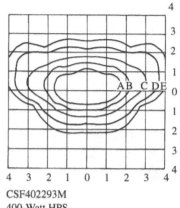

CSF402293M
400-Watt HPS
50,000-Lumens
Type III

Footcandle Table

Select mounting height and read across for footcandle values of each isofootcandle line.

Mounting Height	Footcandle Values for Isofootcandle Lines				
	A	B	C	D	E
35'	2.00	1.00	0.50	0.25	0.10
30'	2.72	1.36	0.68	0.34	0.14
20'	6.12	3.06	1.58	0.77	0.31

FIGURE 12–16

Photometric Data for Outdoor Fixture *Source:* Cooper Lighting, Division of Cooper Industries.

EXAMPLE 12–15

Determine the footcandle level applicable to curve B for the fixture data given in Figure 12–16 for the following:

a) 35 ft mounting height, 400 W HPS lamp
b) 40 ft mounting height, 400 W HPS lamp
c) 40 ft mounting height, 250 W HPS lamp

Solution:

a) $E_{ACT} = 1.0$ fc as read directly from the table
b) Application of Equation (12–6) results in

$$E_{ACT} = 1.0 \times \left(\frac{50,000L}{50,000L}\right) \times \left(\frac{35 \text{ ft}}{40 \text{ ft}}\right)^2 = 0.77 \text{ fc}$$

c) $E_{ACT} = 1.0 \times \left(\frac{27,500L}{50,000L}\right) \times \left(\frac{35 \text{ ft}}{40 \text{ ft}}\right)^2 = 0.42 \text{ fc}$

The design of a lighting system for outdoor applications follows a procedure similar to that of indoor lighting. The first step in the process is to determine the required lighting level for the given application. These lighting levels are tabulated in Table 12–7. Next, the type of light distribution pattern is selected based on the characteristics of the area to be illuminated. For example, a type I or type II distribution pattern would be selected for roadway lighting, whereas a type IV or type V pattern might be selected for parking area lighting. Last, the required fixture spacing is calculated by referring to the isofootcandle data of the selected fixtures. The process is repeated until the desired footcandle level of illumination is obtained for the area of interest.

EXAMPLE 12–16

Determine the required spacing between fixtures to produce a minimum of 1 footcandle illumination between fixtures when used for roadway lighting as shown in Figure 12–17(A). Use 400 W HPS lamps, 35 ft mounting height, and the isofootcandle data in Figure 12–16. Also, determine the lighting level 30 ft directly across the roadway from the fixture.

Solution: Curve C has a 0.5 fc level with a 400 W, HPS lamp and a 35 ft mounting height. In the direction along the roadway, the 0.5 fc level occurs at approximately 2.9 × mounting height, or approximately 100 ft from the pole. The maximum spacing will be twice this value or 200 ft maximum. Therefore, a pole separation not to exceed 200 ft is specified. The actual spacing may be reduced to allow for light loss factors that may occur.

    To determine the illumination a distance of 30 ft directly across the roadway, the distance must be converted to a multiple of the fixture mounting height. Therefore, the

FIGURE 12–17
Outdoor Fixture Spacing
Example

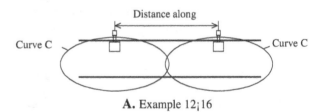

A. Example 12¡16

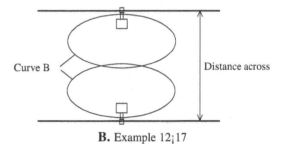

B. Example 12¡17

distance of 30 ft corresponds to 30/35 = 0.857 times the mounting height. From the iso-footcandle characteristic, the corresponding footcandle level is close to curve A and is read as approximately 2.0 fc.

EXAMPLE 12–17

The fixture having the isofootcandle data as shown in Figure 12–16 is employed in a parking area, as shown in Figure 12–17(B). The fixture has a 35 ft mounting height and utilizes a 400 W HPS lamp, producing 50,000 lumens. Determine the maximum separation across to achieve a lighting level of 2.0 fc.

Solution: From Figure 12–16, curve B corresponds to a level of 1.0 fc. This 1 fc level occurs at approximately 1.4 times the fixture mounting height, or approximately 50 ft. Therefore, a maximum separation of approximately 100 ft across will provide a minimum illumination level of 2.0 fc.

The control of outdoor lighting fixtures is commonly performed by photocell, timers, or manual switching. These methods may control a single fixture or a group of fixtures, depending on the specific requirements. It is common in installations involving a large number of outdoor lighting fixtures to employ a lighting contactor to perform the necessary switching operations. The lighting contactor typically contains a set of contacts controlled by an electromagnetic coil. When the coil is energized, the main contacts close to energize the lighting equipment. When the coil is deenergized, the main contacts open. The lighting contactor may control the lighting branch circuits directly or through a separate lighting panel supplying the lighting branch circuits.

The control circuit shown in Figure 12–18 provides for manual or automatic control of the lighting system through use of the Hand-Off-Auto, or HOA, selector switch. With

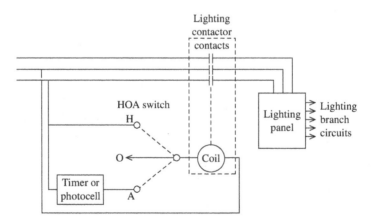

FIGURE 12–18
Lighting Control Circuit

TABLE 12–9
Light Fixture Schedule

			Light Fixture Schedule			
Desig.	Description	Manufacturer	Catalog No.	Lamp Type	Voltage	Notes
A	Lay-In Troffer	Metalux	2P2GAX440	3-F40T12CW	277 V	Electronic Ballast
B	Low Bay	GE Lighting	U4M40MOA519EA	400 W Metal Halide	277 V	CWA Ballast
C	Exterior Parking	McGraw-Edison	CS7252	250 W HPS	277 V	30 ft Pole Ht.
D	Exterior Wall-Pak	Cooper Lighting	WL215229BZ	150 W HPS	277 V	
*						
*						

the selector switch in the OFF position, the coil of the lighting contactor is deenergized, resulting in the lighting circuits being deenergized. Placing the selector switch in the HAND position energizes the lighting contactor coil, thereby energizing the lighting circuits. In the AUTO position, control of the lighting circuits is accomplished automatically by the photocell or timer.

12–7 LIGHT FIXTURE SCHEDULE

In order to provide the electrician with information regarding the lighting installation, a light fixture schedule is often prepared. The fixture schedule contains a description of the fixture, manufacturer, catalog number, number and type of lamp, ballast input voltage, and other notes. In some instances, the circuit number may be included as well. An example of a fixture schedule is shown in Table 12–9.

PROBLEMS

1. Describe the basic operation of incandescent, fluorescent, mercury vapor, metal halide, and high pressure sodium lamps.
2. What is the most common lamp shape for incandescent lamps?
3. Describe lamp shape designations T, PG, C, and U for fluorescent lamps.
4. What is the quartz restrike feature of light fixtures?
5. What purpose does a lighting ballast serve?
6. What is a class P ballast?
7. Describe the operation of fluorescent rapid-start, instant-start, preheat, and electronic ballasts.
8. At what power factor does a normal power factor ballast operate? A high power factor ballast?
9. List the six classifications of luminaire lighting distribution patterns.
10. Of what significance is the shielding angle of a light fixture?

11. Determine the illuminance of a 20 ft by 30 ft office area if a total of 30,000 lumens are directed to the work surface.

12. What is the color rendering index of a lamp?

13. A point source of light has a value of 3000 cd in the direction of interest. Determine the illuminance at a distance of (a) 8 ft and (b) 5 m from the source.

14. A point source of light has a value of 3500 cd in the direction of interest. The angle of incidence of this light ray with respect to the vertical axis is 40°. Determine the illuminance at a distance of 12 ft from the source.

15. Given the photometric data of Example 12–4, determine the following:
    a. candle power along the fixture, angle of incidence of 40°
    b. candle power in a 15° vertical plane, directly below the fixture, incidence angle of 0°
    c. candle power in a 15° vertical plane, at an incidence angle of 35°

16. Given the photometric data of Example 12–4, determine the illuminance at the following points:
    a. 8 ft directly beneath the fixture
    b. 15 ft from the fixture, in the direction along the fixture, at an incidence angle of 25°
    c. 15 ft from the fixture, in the direction across the fixture, at an incidence angle of 25°
    d. 12 ft from the fixture, in the vertical plane at 35°, at an incidence angle of 25°

17. Determine the CCR, RCR, and FCR for an office area 50 ft by 40 ft, with a ceiling height of 10 ft and a work plane height of 30 in. Assume lay-in fluorescent fixtures.

18. Determine the RSDD for a space having an RCR of 3.2, using indirect lighting, medium environment, cleaned every 24 months.

19. Determine the LDD for a category V fixture located in a dirty environment, cleaned every 18 months.

20. What is the LBO factor for an office space containing 20 four-lamp fluorescent fixtures if 4 lamps are permitted to burn out before replacement?

21. What is the voltage factor applicable to an incandescent lamp operating at 95% rated voltage?

22. Determine the effective ceiling cavity reflectance and effective floor cavity reflectance of an office space having a CCR of 0 and an FCR of 1.2. The base ceiling, wall, and floor reflectances are 80%, 50%, and 20%, respectively.

23. Using the CU data shown in Table 12–5, determine the CU for an office space having an RCR of 2.3. The base ceiling, wall, and floor reflectances are 80%, 50%, and 20%, respectively.

24. Determine the multiplying factor to be applied to the CU for a space having an RCR of 2.4, an effective ceiling reflectance of 80%, and an effective floor reflectance of 15%.

25. Determine the number of lighting fixtures required to illuminate a 2000 sq ft area to a level of 50 fc. The CU, LLF, and multiplying factor are 0.6, 0.85, and 0.97, respectively. Each fixture contains three lamps, producing 3000 lumens per lamp.

26. An office area of 75 ft by 75 ft is to be illuminated to a level of 80 fc using lay-in fluorescent fixtures. The ceiling height is 10 ft and the base ceiling, wall, and floor reflectances are 80%, 50%, and 20%, respectively. Determine a suitable fixture layout for this area using the fixture data presented in Table 12–5. Assume a total LLF of 0.8. Use base reflectances directly from the manufacturer's fixture data. Do not calculate effective reflectances.

27. Determine the maximum number of 277 V, 400 W, metal halide fixtures permitted on a 20 A circuit.

28. Determine the lighting level applicable to curve C for the fixture data shown in Figure 12–16 for a mounting height of 25 ft using a 250 W HPS lamp.

29. Determine the maximum spacing permitted to produce 1.5 fc illumination along a roadway using a 35 ft mounting height and a 400 W HPS lamp. The fixture data of Figure 12–16 applies.

30. What type of information is typically contained in a light fixture schedule?

13

Motor Circuits

INTRODUCTION

Electric motors are electromechanical devices that convert electrical energy to mechanical energy. The electrical system must be designed to properly supply motor installations in the facility. Article 430 of the *NEC* specifies the requirements for motor installation. In particular, the sizing of motor circuit conductors, motor disconnecting devices, motor circuit short circuit protection, overload sizing, motor controllers, and motor locked rotor currents are discussed in the *NEC*.

This chapter will provide information regarding the installation of electric motors and motor circuits. It is assumed that motor characteristics and theory have been covered in a course on electrical machinery. A brief discussion of basic motor characteristics has been included to assist students not familiar with motors with some of the terminology found in the *NEC*.

OBJECTIVES

Upon completion of this chapter, you will:

- Understand the basic operation of three-phase and single-phase electric motors
- Understand the manner in which motors are connected to the line voltage supply
- Be able to calculate the blocked rotor current of a motor
- Be able to properly size motor feeder and branch circuit conductors
- Be able to determine the proper rating for motor circuit short circuit protective devices
- Be able to determine the appropriate rating of motor overload protective devices
- Understand the *NEC* requirements for motor and motor controller disconnect devices
- Understand the basic differences between NEMA- and IEC-rated motor controllers and contactors

13–1   BASIC INDUCTION MOTOR OPERATION

Three-Phase Induction Motor

The three-phase induction motor is the most common type of motor found in commercial and industrial applications. Due to simplicity of construction, three-phase induction motors are economical, reliable, require little maintenance, and have standardized

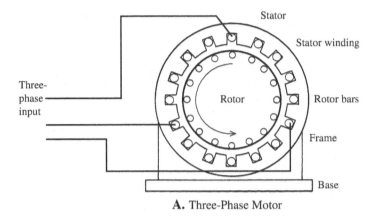

A. Three-Phase Motor

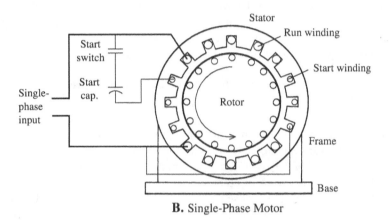

B. Single-Phase Motor

FIGURE 13–1
Basic Motor Operation

construction features and dimensions among different manufacturers. A cross-sectional view of a three-phase induction motor is shown in Figure 13–1(A).

The stator, or stationary part of the motor, has slots into which a distributed three-phase stator winding is placed. By virtue of the stator winding construction, a distinct number of magnetic poles (N and S) will be produced. Application of a balanced set of three-phase voltages to the stator winding results in a balanced set of three-phase current flowing in the stator winding. Due to the 120° phase displacement between these currents, the stator currents interact with each other to produce a uniform rotating magnetic field in the stator. The speed of the rotating magnetic field is a function of the number of poles in the machine and the frequency of the applied voltage. This speed is referred to as the *synchronous speed* of the motor and is given by

$$\text{Synchronous speed} = 120 \times \frac{\text{Frequency in hertz}}{\text{Number of stator poles}} \qquad \textbf{(13--1)}$$

Thus, a two-pole, 60 Hz induction motor has a synchronous speed of 3600 rpm, a four-pole, 60 Hz motor has a synchronous speed of 1800 rpm, and so on. Note that the synchronous speed of the motor can be changed by varying the frequency of the applied stator voltage.

As the magnetic field in the stator rotates, it "cuts" across the rotor bars mounted in the rotor. In most motors, these rotor bars are connected to each other at each end of the rotor to form what is referred to as a *squirrel cage rotor.* The rotating stator flux cutting across the rotor bars causes a voltage to be induced in the rotor bars. Since the rotor bars are short circuited at each end, the induced rotor voltage causes a rotor current to flow. This induced rotor current produces a magnetic field that interacts with the magnetic field produced by the stator current. The result is a magnetic force of attraction between the rotor and stator producing torque in the motor. The end result is rotation of the rotor at a speed slightly less than the synchronous speed of the motor. The difference between the synchronous speed and the actual speed of the motor is referred to as *slip.* Slip is often expressed as a percentage or per-unit of the synchronous speed as follows:

$$\text{Slip} = \frac{\text{Synchronous speed} - \text{Actual speed}}{\text{Synchronous speed}} \qquad \textbf{(13--2)}$$

Typically, the full-load slip of an induction motor is approximately 0.03, or 3%. Thus, a four-pole, 60 Hz, squirrel cage induction motor having a synchronous speed of 1800 rpm and a slip at full load of 3%, will have a full-load speed of 1746 rpm.

A less common type of three-phase induction motor is the wound-rotor induction motor. The stator construction of the wound-rotor induction motor is the same as that of the squirrel cage induction motor. Unlike the squirrel cage motor, the wound-rotor induction motor has insulated three-phase windings placed in the rotor rather than rotor bars. This rotor winding is commonly referred to as the *wound rotor secondary.* This secondary winding is commonly connected to a variable external resistor, or resistance steps, by means of slip rings and brushes. The addition of the external resistance allows for varying the effective resistance of the rotor circuit, enabling control of the torque and speed of the motor. With the advent of variable frequency motor drives, the wound-rotor induction motor is not as common as it once was.

Single-Phase Induction Motor

The construction features of the single-phase induction motor are shown in Figure 13–1(B). The rotor construction of the single-phase induction motor is similar to that of the squirrel cage induction motor. The stator winding construction consists of a start winding and a run winding. The windings are identifiable by their physical construction. The conductors used in the start winding are smaller in cross section than the conductors used in the run winding. The result is a difference in resistance and reactance between the start and run windings. Also, the start and run windings are placed 90 electrical degrees apart from each other in the stator. The stator construction shown in Figure 13–1(B) is representative of a two-pole machine.

Recall that in the three-phase motor, a rotating magnetic field was produced as a result of the 120° displacement between the three phase currents in the stator. To produce a rotating magnetic field in the single-phase motor during starting, a phase displacement between the currents in the start and run windings must be produced. This phase displacement is accomplished by addition of an external resistance or capacitance in series with the start winding. The motor shown in Figure 13–1(B) utilizes a capacitor to produce the required phase shift.

As previously mentioned, the start winding is necessary to produce a rotating magnetic field in the stator during starting. Once the motor is up to speed, the start winding may be disconnected. The motor will continue to run with only the run winding energized. To facilitate switching of the start winding, a start switch is used. This switch may be a centrifugal switch mounted on the shaft of the motor or a current-sensing relay that monitors the current in the motor. During starting, the start switch is closed, thereby inserting the start capacitor and start winding in the circuit. Once the motor starts and approaches normal speed, the start switch opens to disconnect the start winding from the supply. The motor continues to operate with only the run winding in the circuit.

13–2 MOTOR RATINGS

Electric motors are required to have at least the following information stamped on the nameplate: voltage, number of phases, horsepower, speed, full-load current, code letter, design-type letter, temperature rise, and service factor. This nameplate information is of importance when designing circuits to supply and control electric motors. Other information may also be stamped on the motor nameplate. A brief description of several of these ratings is presented here. The locked rotor code letter is discussed in Section 13–4.

The nameplate voltage rating of the motor is expressed in terms of the rated line-to-line voltage of the motor. Typical voltages are 115 V, 200 V, 230 V, 460 V, and 575 V. The rated motor voltage is usually slightly less than the nominal system voltage to which the motor would be applied. For example, a three-phase motor rated 460 V would be applied to a 480 V, three-phase system, a 230 V, single-phase motor would be applied to a 240 V supply, and so on. The number of phases will indicate whether the motor is single phase or three phase.

The horsepower rating of the motor indicates the maximum mechanical load that can be applied continuously to the motor without exceeding the allowable temperature rise. The service factor also indicates the amount of mechanical overload that can be applied to the motor without exceeding the allowable temperature rise. Typical service factors are 1.0, 1.15, 1.25, and 1.35. The motor nameplate horsepower multiplied by the service factor gives the maximum permissible loading of the motor.

The speed rating of the motor is expressed in revolutions per minute (rpm) or radians per second (rad/s). This rating indicates the speed of the motor when supplying rated mechanical load (nameplate HP) and with rated terminal voltage applied. The full-load current rating of the motor indicates the line current that the motor will draw when supplying rated load under rated conditions. The temperature rise of the motor is the expected increase in motor temperature above ambient when the motor is supplying rated load under rated conditions. The increase in temperature is due to the mechanical and electrical losses in the motor.

The design-type letter of the motor is an indication of the torque–speed characteristic of the motor, a characteristic determined by the size and placement of the rotor bars in the rotor. Most common applications use design A or B motors. Design C and D motors are designed for high starting torque and are used in hoists, elevators, and so on. The design E motor is a premium efficiency motor having lower losses and higher nameplate efficiency than a standard motor. The design E motor does have higher inrush current than designs A or B. This higher inrush current may affect the rating of motor circuit short circuit protection devices.

13–3   TERMINAL CONNECTIONS

Terminal connections for single-phase and three-phase motors are shown in Figure 13–2. Motors having a single voltage rating are designed to be connected to a system having a nominal voltage slightly greater than the motor voltage rating. For three-phase motors, the windings may be wye or delta, connected as shown in Figure 13–2(A). The supply leads are connected directly to the motor terminals labeled T1, T2, and T3 (or simply 1, 2, and 3), as shown.

For reasons of economics, many three-phase motors are available with dual-voltage ratings. A typical voltage rating for a dual-voltage, three-phase motor would be 230/460 V. The three-phase windings may be wye connected, as shown in Figure 13–2(B), or delta connected, as shown in Figure 13–2(C). In either the delta or wye connection, the motor windings are split—two per phase. For low-voltage connection, the windings are placed in parallel; for a high-voltage connection, the windings are series connected. The supply leads are connected to terminals 1, 2, and 3 as before.

Single-phase motors are also available with either a single or dual voltage rating. For single-phase motors with a single voltage rating, the connection is made directly to the supply leads. Single-phase, dual-voltage motors have split windings that are to be connected in parallel for low voltage and in series for high voltage. Figure 13–2(D) shows the connections for a single-phase, dual-voltage motor.

13–4   LOCKED-ROTOR CURRENT

When a motor is initially energized, the current that flows into the motor will be several times the full-load current rating of the motor. This current is referred to as the *locked-rotor current*, since the rotor is not turning at the instant of starting. The locked-rotor current can be determined by use of the code letter indicating the locked-rotor current of the motor. The code letter expresses the locked-rotor quantities in terms of kVA per horsepower. Therefore, the code letter and motor horsepower can be used to determine the locked-rotor kVA according to the following:

$$\text{Locked-rotor kVA} = \text{Code letter (kVA/hp)} \times \text{Motor horsepower (hp)} \quad \textbf{(13–3)}$$

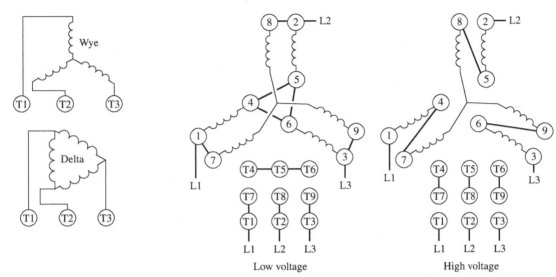

A. Three-Phase, Single Voltage

B. Three-Phase, Dual-Voltage,
Wye-Connected Stator

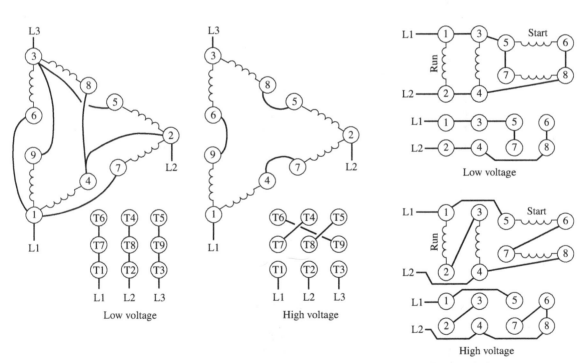

C. Three-Phase, Dual-Voltage,
Delta-Connected Stator

D. Single-Phase, Motor,
Dual Voltage

FIGURE 13–2
Motor Terminal Connections

Table 430.7(B), of the *NEC* shown in Table 13–1, lists the code letters for the locked-rotor current for single-phase and three-phase motors.

For many applications, it is more convenient to express the locked-rotor quantities in terms of amperes rather than kVA. For single-phase motors, the locked-rotor kVA can be converted to amperes according to the following:

$$I_{LR} = \frac{\text{Locked-rotor kVA} \times 1000}{\text{Motor line voltage}} \tag{13–4}$$

Likewise, for three-phase motors, the locked-rotor current is

$$I_{LR} = \frac{\text{Locked-rotor kVA} \times 1000}{\sqrt{3} \times \text{Motor line voltage}} \tag{13–5}$$

If the code letter of a motor is not known, it is common to assume that the locked-rotor current will be approximately 6 times the full-load rated current of the motor.

TABLE 13–1
Table 430.7(B) Locked-Rotor Indicating
Code Letters

Code Letter	Kilovolt-Amperes per Horsepower with Locked Rotor
A	0–3.14
B	3.15–3.54
C	3.55–3.99
D	4.0–4.49
E	4.5–4.99
F	5.0–5.59
G	5.6–6.29
H	6.3–7.09
J	7.1–7.99
K	8.0–8.99
L	9.0–9.99
M	10.0–11.19
N	11.2–12.49
P	12.5–13.99
R	14.0–15.99
S	16.0–17.99
T	18.0–19.99
U	20.0–22.39
V	22.4 and up

Source: Reprinted with permission from NFPA 70 *The National Electric Code* © 2002, National Fire Protection Association, Quincy, MA 02269. This reprinted material is not the referenced subject which is represented only by the standard in its entirety.

EXAMPLE 13–1

Determine the locked-rotor current expressed in amperes for the following motors:

a) 5 hp, 230 V, code letter H
b) 50 hp, 460 V, code letter G

Solution:

a) From Table 13–1, the appropriate multiplier has a range of 6.3 to 7.09 kVA/hp. Using the value of 7.09 kVA/hp results in

$$\text{Locked-rotor kVA} = (7.09 \text{ kVA/hp}) \times (5 \text{ hp}) = 35.45 \text{ kVA}$$

The locked-rotor current is given by Equation (13–4):

$$I_{LR} = \frac{35.45 \text{ kVA} \times 1000}{230 \text{ V}} = 154.1 \text{ A}$$

b) From Table 13–1, the appropriate multiplier has a range of 5.6 to 6.29 kVA/hp. Using the value of 6.29 kVA/hp results in

$$\text{Locked-rotor kVA} = (6.29 \text{ kVA/hp}) \times (50 \text{ hp}) = 314.5 \text{ kVA}$$

The locked-rotor current is given by Equation (13–5):

$$I_{LR} = \frac{314.5 \text{ kVA} \times 1000}{\sqrt{3} \times 460 \text{ V}} = 394.7 \text{ A}$$

As the motor comes up to speed, a countervoltage or back-emf is produced in the motor. This countervoltage has a polarity that opposes the applied line voltage. As a result, the input current to the motor will decrease as the motor comes up to speed. The input line current of the motor during starting is shown in Figure 13–3. Note that at time $t = 0$, the value of the motor current is equal to the locked-rotor current, I_{LR}. As the motor accelerates and comes up to speed, the motor current drops to the full-load current value, as shown in the curve. The stall point assumes that the motor is prevented from turning, resulting in the motor current remaining equal to the locked-rotor current. The actual time that it takes for a motor to accelerate is governed by the starting torque produced by the motor and the moment of inertia of the load.

13–5   BASIC MOTOR CIRCUIT

The basic components of a motor circuit supplying a single motor are shown in Figure 13–4. The motor circuit is connected to the source by means of a disconnecting device and overcurrent protection device. The motor controller is equipped with a contactor to provide the ON-OFF switching action of the motor and a set of overload elements that monitor motor current to provide overload protection. Figure 13–5 shows a typical motor installation.

FIGURE 13–3
Motor Starting Current

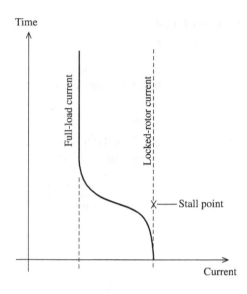

Motor Circuit Conductor Sizing

The motor branch circuit conductors connect the motor to the supply, as shown in Figure 13–4. For a single motor installation, Section 430.22 of the *NEC* requires that these conductors have an ampacity of at least 125% of the full-load current of the motor. The ampacity is determined by applying the ambient temperature correction factors and raceway fill adjustment factors and consideration of device terminal temperature ratings. The

FIGURE 13–4
Motor Branch Circuit

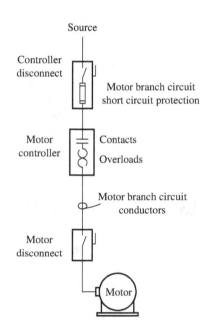

FIGURE 13–5
Motor Installation *Source:* Courtesy of Youngstown State University.

full-load current of the motor used for the purpose of conductor sizing is not the same as the nameplate full-load current. This full-load current must be taken from the tables shown in Table 13–2.

EXAMPLE 13–2

What size THW copper conductor is required to supply a 30 hp, 460 V, three-phase squirrel cage induction motor? Assume 30°C ambient, three current-carrying conductors in the raceway, and a device terminal temperature rating of 75°C.

Solution: From Table 13–2, the motor full-load current is 40 A. The minimum conductor ampacity is 125% × 40 A = 50 A. From Table 310.16, a #8 AWG copper THW conductor is required.

Motor Branch Circuit Short Circuit Protection

The motor branch circuit short circuit protective device is sized to protect the motor branch circuit conductors against damage due to short circuits. This device is not intended to protect the motor against overload. Section 430.52 of the *NEC* specifies that the maximum

TABLE 13–2
Table 430.148 Full-Load Currents in Amperes, Single-Phase Alternating-Current Motors

The following values of full-load currents are for motors running at usual speeds and motors with normal torque characteristics. Motors built for especially low speeds or high torques may have higher full-load currents, and multispeed motors will have full-load current varying with speed, in which case the nameplate current ratings shall be used.
The voltages listed are rated motor voltages. The currents listed shall be permitted for system voltage ranges of 110 to 120 and 220 to 240 volts.

Horsepower	115 Volts	200 Volts	208 Volts	230 Volts
1/6	4.4	2.5	2.4	2.2
1/4	5.8	3.3	3.2	2.9
1/3	7.2	4.1	4.0	3.6
1/2	9.8	5.6	5.4	4.9
3/4	13.8	7.9	7.6	6.9
1	16	9.2	8.8	8.0
1½	20	11.5	11.0	10
2	24	13.8	13.2	12
3	34	19.6	18.7	17
5	56	32.2	30.8	28
7½	80	46.0	44.0	40
10	100	57.5	55.0	50

Table 430.150 Full-Load Current, Three-Phase Alternating-Current Motors

The following values of full-load currents are typical for motors running at speeds usual for belted motors and motors with normal torque characteristics.
Motors built for low speeds (1200 rpm or less) or high torque may require more running current, and multispeed motors will have full-load current varying with speed. In these cases, the nameplate current rating shall be used.
The voltages listed are rated motor voltages. The currents listed shall be permitted for system voltage ranges of 110 to 120, 220 to 240, 440 to 480, and 550 to 600 volts.

Horsepower	Induction-Type Squirrel Cage and Wound Rotor (Amperes)							Synchronous-Type Unity Power Factor* (Amperes)			
	115 Volts	200 Volts	208 Volts	230 Volts	460 Volts	575 Volts	2300 Volts	230 Volts	460 Volts	575 Volts	2300 Volts
1/2	4.4	2.5	2.4	2.2	1.1	0.9	—	—	—	—	—
3/4	6.4	3.7	3.5	3.2	1.6	1.3	—	—	—	—	—
1	8.4	4.8	4.6	4.2	2.1	1.7	—	—	—	—	—
1½	12.0	6.9	6.6	6.0	3.0	2.4	—	—	—	—	—
2	13.6	7.8	7.5	6.8	3.4	2.7	—	—	—	—	—
3	—	11.0	10.6	9.6	4.8	3.9	—	—	—	—	—
5	—	17.5	16.7	15.2	7.6	6.1	—	—	—	—	—
7½	—	25.3	24.2	22	11	9	—	—	—	—	—
10	—	32.2	30.8	28	14	11	—	—	—	—	—
15	—	48.3	46.2	42	21	17	—	—	—	—	—
20	—	62.1	59.4	54	27	22	—	—	—	—	—
25	—	78.2	74.8	68	34	27	—	53	26	21	—

TABLE 13–2
Continued

Horsepower	Induction-Type Squirrel Cage and Wound Rotor (Amperes)							Synchronous-Type Unity Power Factor* (Amperes)			
	115 Volts	200 Volts	208 Volts	230 Volts	460 Volts	575 Volts	2300 Volts	230 Volts	460 Volts	575 Volts	2300 Volts
30	—	92	88	80	40	32	—	63	32	26	—
40	—	120	114	104	52	41	—	83	41	33	—
50	—	150	143	130	65	52	—	104	52	42	—
60	—	177	169	154	77	62	16	123	61	49	12
75	—	221	211	192	96	77	20	155	78	62	15
100	—	285	273	248	124	99	26	202	101	81	20
125	—	359	343	312	156	125	31	253	126	101	25
150	—	414	396	360	180	144	37	302	151	121	30
200		552	528	480	240	192	49	400	201	161	40
250	—	—	—	—	302	242	60	—	—	—	—
300	—	—	—	—	361	289	72	—	—	—	—
350	—	—	—	—	414	336	83	—	—	—	—
400	—	—	—	—	477	382	95	—	—	—	—
450	—	—	—	—	515	412	103	—	—	—	—
500	—	—	—	—	590	472	118	—	—	—	—

*For 90 and 80 percent power factor, the figures shall be multiplied by 1.1 and 1.25, respectively.
Source: Reprinted with permission from NFPA 70 *The National Electric Code* © 2002, National Fire Protection Association, Quincy, MA 02269. This reprinted material is not the referenced subject which is represented only by the standard in its entirety.

rating permitted for the short circuit overcurrent protection device shall not exceed the values listed in Table 430.152, which is shown in Table 13–3. Note that the rating is a function of the type of motor and the type of overcurrent device used. In most cases, the rating of the short circuit protection device selected will exceed the ampacity of the conductor. Keep in mind, however, that this is a motor circuit, not a general-purpose branch circuit. Thus, the load on the circuit is well known and predictable. Also keep in mind that the overload protection for the motor is typically provided by other devices.

If the device ratings as determined by application of the percentages listed in Table 13–3 do not correspond to a standard rated device, the *NEC* permits selection of the next-higher rating. In addition, the device ratings may be increased to allow for starting of the motor in accordance with Section 430.52 of the *NEC*.

EXAMPLE 13–3

Determine the rating of the short circuit protection device for the motor circuit of Example 13–2 for the following devices:

a) Non-time-delay fuse
b) Dual-element time-delay fuse

TABLE 13–3
Table 430.52 Maximum Rating or Setting of Motor Branch-Circuit Short-Circuit and Ground-Fault Protective Devices

	Percentage of Full-Load Current			
Type of Motor	Nontime Delay Fuse[1]	Dual Element (Time-Delay) Fuse[1]	Instantaneous Trip Breaker	Inverse Time Breaker[2]
Single-phase motors	300	175	800	250
AC polyphase motors other than wound-rotor				
Squirrel cage—other than Design E or Design B energy efficient	300	175	800	250
Design E or Design B energy efficient	300	175	1100	250
Synchronous[3]	300	175	800	250
Wound rotor	150	150	800	150
Direct current (constant voltage)	150	150	250	150

Note: For certain exceptions to the values specified, see 430.54.

[1]The values in the Nontime Delay Fuse column apply to Time-Delay Class CC fuses.

[2]The values given in the last column also cover the ratings of nonadjustable inverse time types of circuit breakers that may be modified as in 430.52(C), Exception No. 1 and 2.

[3]Synchronous motors of the low-torque, low-speed type (usually 450 rpm or lower), such as are used to drive reciprocating compressors, pumps, and so forth, that start unloaded, do not require a fuse rating or circuit-breaker setting in excess of 200 percent of full-load current.

Source: Reprinted with permission from NFPA 70 *The National Electric Code* © 2002, National Fire Protection Association, Quincy, MA 02269. This reprinted material is not the referenced subject which is represented only by the standard in its entirety.

    c) Instantaneous-trip breaker
    d) Inverse-time-trip (thermal) breaker

Solution: From Example 13–2, the motor full-load current was 40 A.

    a) For a non-time-delay fuse, the percentage is 300%. The device rating is 300% × 40 A = 120 A. Since this does not correspond to a standard rating, a 125 A fuse (next larger) may be used.

    b) For a dual-element time-delay fuse, the percentage is 175%. The device rating is 175% × 40 A = 70 A. Therefore, a 70 A fuse may be used. Note that several fuse manufacturers recommend use of time-delay fuses sized at 125% of the full-load current. When sized at 125%, the time-delay fuse may provide backup overload protection for the motor in addition to short circuit protection of the motor circuit conductors.

    c) For an instantaneous-trip circuit breaker, the percentage is 800%. The device rating is 800% × 40 A = 320 A. Since this does not correspond to a standard rating, a 350 A breaker (next larger) may be used.

d) For an inverse-time circuit breaker, the percentage is 250%. The device rating is 250% × 40 A = 100 A. Therefore, a 100 A breaker may be used.

Motor Controller

Energizing and deenergizing of the motor is performed by the motor controller or starter. The starter is typically either manual or magnetic. A manual starter is essentially a set of switched contacts equipped with thermal overload elements. The overload elements monitor the motor current, thereby sensing the load on the motor. In the event of an overload condition, the overload elements will operate to deenergize the motor. A magnetic starter uses an electromagnetic coil to open and close the starter contacts. In the event of low voltage on the system, the electromagnetic armature will "drop out" and deenergize the motor.

Section 430.83(C)(2) of the *NEC* permits the use of a toggle switch rated for ac use only to serve as the controller for stationary alternating current motors rated 2 hp or less. The toggle switch must have an ampere rating not less than 125% of the full-load current rating of the motor. In other words, the motor full-load current rating cannot exceed 80% of the ampere rating of the switch.

Sizing of the motor starter is based on NEMA or IEC standards. The starter contacts must be rated for the motor horsepower, system voltage, and motor duty (nonplugging, plugging, jogging, etc.). Section 430.83(A)(1) of the *NEC* requires that controllers used on design E premium-efficiency motors rated more than 2 hp must be marked as rated for use with design E motors. In lieu of this marking, standard controllers may be used for the control of design E motors provided the controller has a hp rating at least 1.4 times the hp rating for motors rated 3 through 100 hp, and at least 1.3 times the hp rating for motors above 100 hp. NEMA specifies starter sizes from size 00 to size 9, with size 9 being the largest. The application charts shown in Table 13–4 can be used to select the proper size.

EXAMPLE 13–4

Determine the appropriate NEMA starter for the following motors:

a) 50 hp, 460 V, design B, nonplugging, nonjogging duty
b) 50 hp, 460 V, design E, nonplugging, nonjogging duty

Solution:

a) Since this is not a design E motor, the starter size is read directly from Table 13–4. Therefore, a size 3 starter is required.
b) The standard starter rating must be at least 1.4 times the hp rating for this design E motor. The minimum hp rating is 1.4 × 50 hp = 70 hp. Therefore, a size 4 starter is required. Note that the design E motor requires a larger starter than the design B motor of part (a). This is due to the higher starting currents associated with design E motors.

As previously mentioned, overload protection of the motor is provided by a set of overload elements or other overload-sensing device. The overload elements are sized

TABLE 13–4
Motor Starter Data
Full-Voltage Contactors and Starters—NEMA
Application Data—Class 8502, 8536

NEMA Size	Load Volts	Maximum Horsepower Rating—Nonplugging and Nonjogging Duty		Maximum Horsepower Rating—Plugging and Jogging duty		Continuous Current Rating, Amperes—600 Volt Max.	Service-Limit Current Rating, Amperes	Tungsten and Infrared Lamp Load, Amperes—250 Volts Max.	Resistance Heating Loads, KW—Other Than Infrared Lamp Loads		Transformers Having Inrush Currents (Worst Case Peak) of Not More Than 20 Times Peak of Continuous Current Rating		Transformers Having Inrush Currents (Worst Case Peak) of Over 20 Through 40 Times Peak of Continuous Current Rating		3 Phase Rating for Switching Capacitors
		Single Phase	Poly-Phase	Single Phase	Poly-Phase				Single Phase	Poly-Phase	Single Phase	Poly-Phase	Single Phase	Poly-Phase	kvar
00	115	½	…	…	…	9	11	5	…	…	…	…	…	…	…
	200	…	1½	…	…	9	11	5	…	…	…	…	…	…	…
	230	1	1½	…	…	9	11	5	…	…	…	…	…	…	…
	380	…	1½	…	…	9	11	…	…	…	…	…	…	…	…
	460	…	2	…	…	9	11	…	…	…	…	…	…	…	…
	575	…	2	…	…	9	11	…	…	…	…	…	…	…	…
0	115	1	…	½	…	18	21	10	…	…	0.6	…	0.3	…	…
	200	…	3	…	1½	18	21	10	…	…	…	1.8	…	0.9	…
	230	2	3	1	1½	18	21	10	…	…	1.2	2.1	0.6	1.0	…
	380	…	5	…	1½	18	21	…	…	…	…	…	…	…	…
	460	…	5	…	2	18	21	…	…	…	2.4	4.2	1.2	2.1	…
	575	…	5	…	2	18	21	…	…	…	3.0	5.2	1.5	2.6	…
1	115	2	…	1	…	27	32	15	3	5	1.2	…	0.6	…	…
	200	…	7½	…	3	27	32	15	…	9.1	…	3.6	…	1.8	…
	230	3	7½	2	3	27	32	15	6	10	2.4	4.3	1.2	2.1	…
	380	…	10	…	5	27	32	…	…	16.5	…	…	…	…	…
	460	…	10	…	5	27	32	…	12	20	4.9	8.5	2.5	4.3	…
	575	…	10	…	5	27	32	…	15	25	6.2	11.0	3.1	5.3	…

Poles	Volts														
1P	115	3		1½		36	42	24							
	230	5		3		36	42	24							
2	115	3		2		45	52	30	5	8.5	2.1				
	200		10		7½	45	52	30		15.4		6.3	1.0	3.1	
	230	7½	15	5	10	45	52	30	10	17	4.1	7.2	2.1	3.6	8
	380		25		15	45	52			28					
	460		25		15	45	52		20	34	8.3	14	4.2	7.2	16
	575		25		15	45	52		25	43	10.0	18	5.2	8.9	20
3	115					90	104	60	10	17	4.1				
	200		25		15	90	104	60		31		12	2.0	6.1	
	230		30		20	90	104	60	20	34	8.1	14	4.1	7.0	27
	380		50		30	90	104			56					
	460		50		30	90	104		40	68	16	28	8.1	14	53
	575		50		30	90	104		50	86	20	35	10	18	67
4	200		40		25	135	156	120		45		20		10	
	230		50		30	135	156	120	30	52	14	23	6.8	12	40
	380		75		50	135	156			86.7					
	460		100		60	135	156		60	105	27	47	14	23	80
	575		100		60	135	156		75	130	34	59	17	29	100
5	200		75		60	270	311	240		91		41		20	
	230		100		75	270	311	240	60	105	27	47	14	24	80
	380		150		125	270	311			173					
	460		200		150	270	311		120	210	54	94	27	47	160
	575		200		150	270	311		150	260	68	117	34	59	200
6+	200		150		125	540	621	480		182		81		41	
	230		200		150	540	621	480	120	210	54	94	27	47	160
	380		300		250	540	621			342					
	460		400		300	540	621		240	415	108	188	54	94	320
	575		400		300	540	621		300	515	135	234	68	117	400
7+	230		300			810	932		180	315					240
	460		600			810	932		360	625					480
	575		600			810	932		450	775					600

Source: Square D/Schneider Electric.

based on the full-load nameplate current rating of the motor, not the full-load current of the motor as determined from Table 13–2. For continuous-duty motors exceeding 1 hp, and for motors 1 hp or less that are automatically started, Section 430.32 of the *NEC* requires separate overload protection not exceeding the following percentages of the motor full-load current rating:

Service factor not less than 1.15:	125%
Temperature rise not over 40°C:	125%
All other motors:	115%

In some applications, motors may be equipped with integral thermal and overload protection devices. The rating of these devices is selected to match the motor performance. The reader is referred to the Section 430.32 of the *NEC* for maximum ratings and settings of these integral devices.

The number of overload elements required depends on the type of motor and the supply system. These requirements are stated in Section 430.37 of the *NEC*. For single-phase, 115 V motors connected between the ungrounded and grounded conductor of the supply, one overload element is required in the ungrounded conductor. Single-phase, 230 V motors connected between two ungrounded conductors are required to have at least one overload element in either of the ungrounded conductors. Three-phase motors are required to have overload protection in all three of the ungrounded conductors.

EXAMPLE 13–5

Determine the appropriate rating of overload elements for the following motors:

a) 30 hp, 460 V, nameplate full-load amperes (FLA) = 38 A, service factor of 1.15
b) 30 hp, 460 V, nameplate FLA = 38 A, service factor of 1.0
c) 30 hp, 460 V, nameplate FLA = 38 A, temperature rise = 50°C

Solution:

a) The required overload cannot exceed 125% of the full-load current rating of the motor, or 125% × 38 A = 47.5 A. An overload element with a current rating not exceeding 47.5 A would be selected.
b) For a 1.0 service factor, the overload element cannot exceed 115% of the FLA rating of the motor. Therefore, the maximum rating of the overload element is 115% × 38 A = 43.7 A.
c) For a temperature rise exceeding 40°C, the overload element cannot exceed 115% of the FLA rating of the motor. Therefore, the maximum rating of the overload element is 115% × 38 A = 43.7 A.

Controller and Motor Disconnects

The controller disconnect is required to physically disconnect the motor controller from the supply. Section 430.102(A) of the *NEC* requires the controller disconnect to be within sight of the controller and not more than 50 feet away. The disconnect must simultaneously open all ungrounded conductors supplying the controller.

The motor disconnect is required to disconnect the motor from the branch circuit for maintenance purposes. As with the controller disconnect, Section 430.102(B) of the *NEC* requires the motor disconnect be within sight of the motor and located within 50 feet. The motor disconnect is not required if the controller disconnect is capable of being locked in the open position, as permitted by the exception to Section 430.102(B) of the *NEC*.

Section 430.110 of the *NEC* requires the ampere rating of the disconnect switch to be at least 115% of the full-load current rating of the motor. The disconnect must also have a hp rating equal to or greater than the hp rating of the motor. Section 430.109(A)(1) requires that disconnects used on design E premium-efficiency motors rated more than 2 hp must be marked as rated for use with design E motors. In lieu of this marking, standard disconnects may be used for the control of design E motors provided the disconnect has a hp rating at least 1.4 times the hp rating for motors rated 3 through 100 hp and at least 1.3 times the hp rating for motors above 100 hp.

Another aspect to keep in mind is that if a fused disconnect switch is used, the rating of the switch must be sufficient to accommodate the fuse. For example, specifying a 100 A fused disconnect switch with a 125 A fuse would be in error. The 125 A fuse would not fit into the fuseholder of the 100 A disconnect in this case. The next-larger size disconnect rating of 200 A would be specified to allow for mounting of the fuse.

Listed molded-case circuit breakers and listed molded-case switches may also be used as disconnects. As previously discussed, the *NEC* allows toggle switches rated for ac use only to serve as the disconnect for stationary motors rated 2 hp or less. The toggle switch must have an ampere rating not less than 125% of the full-load current rating of the motor. Also, Section 430.109(F) of the *NEC* permits the use of a horsepower-rated attachment plug and receptacle as the disconnecting means for general-purpose motors and design E motors rated 2 hp or less. For design E motors rated more than 2 hp, the horsepower rating of the plug and receptacle must be at least 1.4 times the hp rating of the motor.

EXAMPLE 13–6

What is the required rating of a standard disconnect used for a 50 hp, 460 V, design E motor having a nameplate FLA of 63 A?

Solution: The minimum ampere rating of the disconnect must be 115% × 63 A, or 72.5 A. The next-higher standard rating is 100 A. For a design E motor, the hp rating of the disconnect must be at least 1.4 times the horsepower rating of the motor, or 70 hp. Therefore, a 100 A, 70 hp disconnect rating must be specified.

13–6   MULTIPLE MOTOR CIRCUIT

In many installations, it is necessary to supply several motors from a single feeder. An example of this type of multiple motor circuit is shown in Figure 13–6. The main motor feeder is shown supplying three motors through a disconnect switch and motor feeder short circuit protection device. The individual motor branch circuits are tapped from the motor

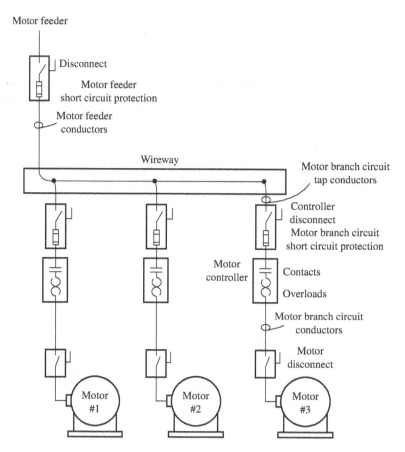

FIGURE 13–6
Multiple Motor Circuit Installation

feeder conductors in the wireway, as shown. Each motor branch circuit is protected by a disconnect switch and motor branch circuit protection device. In this installation, the motor branch circuit disconnect switch also serves as the motor controller disconnect. Each motor has a separate motor controller with separate contacts and overload elements. The motor branch circuit conductors are connected to each motor through a motor disconnect, as shown.

The sizing of the motor branch circuit conductors, controller disconnect, motor branch circuit short circuit protection, controller contacts, overloads, and motor disconnect follows the same procedure as the single motor installation discussed in the previous section. The motor branch circuit tap conductors from the motor feeder conductors to the motor branch circuit short circuit protection devices require special consideration. The minimum ampacity of the tap conductors must be sufficient to supply the motor and is based on the full-load current of the motor. Typically, the minimum ampacity of the tap conductor is based on 125% of the full-load current of the motor as determined from tables. Section 430.28 of the *NEC* requires that the tap conductors must terminate in a fused switch, circuit breaker, or other branch circuit protection device, as shown. The tap conductors must be protected from physical damage by routing in a suitable raceway system. Section 430.28 requires the ampacity of the tap conductors to be at least one-tenth the rating or setting of the motor feeder overcurrent protection device for taps not exceeding 10 ft in length. The length of the tap may be increased to 25 ft if the ampacity of the tap conductors exceeds one-third the ampacity of the motor feeder conductors. The taps can be any length if the tap conductors have the same ampacity as the motor feeder conductors.

Section 430.24 of the *NEC* requires the ampacity of the motor feeder conductors to be equal to or greater than the sum of the full-load currents of all motor loads, plus 25% of the full-load current of the largest motor in the group, plus the rated-load current of other loads supplied by the feeder.

The rating of the motor feeder short circuit protection device is determined in accordance with Section 430.62 of the *NEC*. This rating is determined by first calculating the maximum rating permitted for a single motor in the group. Rounding up to the next-higher standard rating is permitted at this point in the calculations. Next, the full-load current rating of other motors and loads is added to the maximum rating of the device permitted for a single motor in the group. The rating of the feeder device cannot exceed the results of this calculation; that is, rounding up is not permitted.

The ampere rating of the motor feeder disconnect is sized based on the full-load currents of all motors, plus the rated current of other loads supplied. Section 430.110(C)(2) of the *NEC* requires that the ampere rating of the disconnect switch must be at least 115% of this total load current. Also, keep in mind that the ampere rating of the motor feeder disconnect switch must be sufficient to accommodate the motor feeder short circuit protection device.

The horsepower rating of the disconnect switch is determined by calculating an equivalent horsepower rating of the loads supplied by the disconnect switch. Section 430.110(C)(1) of the *NEC* requires that the locked-rotor current of each motor must be determined from the tables shown in Table 13–5. The locked-rotor currents of all motors that may be started simultaneously are added together along with the rated-load current of other loads supplied by the feeder. The equivalent horsepower rating of the switch corresponding to this total current is determined from the appropriate table shown in Table 13–5.

EXAMPLE 13–7

A 480 V, three-phase motor feeder supplies a 50 hp motor, a 20 hp motor, and a 25 kW electric heating element. For the motor feeder only, determine the appropriate-size THW copper conductor, the horsepower and ampere rating of the disconnect switch, and the time-delay fuse rating. All motors are design B and may be started simultaneously. Assume 75°C device terminal ratings.

Solution: The motor full-load currents are 65 A and 27 A, respectively. The full-load current of the 25 kW, 480 V resistance heater is calculated as 30 A. The minimum feeder conductor ampacity is determined as

$$\text{Minimum ampacity} = 125\% \times (65 \text{ A}) + 27 \text{ A} + 30 \text{ A} = 138.3 \text{ A}$$

TABLE 13–5

Table 430.151(A) Conversion Table of Single-Phase Locked-Rotor Currents for Selection of Disconnecting Means and Controllers as Determined from Horsepower and Voltage Rating

For use only with 430.110, 440.12, 440.41 and 455.8(C).

Rated Horsepower	Maximum Locked-Rotor Current in Amperes, Single Phase		
	115 Volts	208 Volts	230 Volts
½	58.8	32.5	29.4
¾	82.8	45.8	41.4
1	96	53	48
1½	120	66	60
2	144	80	72
3	204	113	102
5	336	186	168
7½	480	265	240
10	600	332	300

Table 430.151(B) Conversion Table of Polyphase Design B, C, D, and E Maximum Locked-Rotor Currents for Selection of Disconnecting Means and Controllers as Determined from Horsepower and Voltage Rating and Design Letter

For use only with 430.110, 440.12*, 440.41* and 455.8(C).

Rated Horsepower	Maximum Motor Locked-Rotor Current in Amperes, Two- and Three-Phase, Design B, C, D, and E											
	115 Volts		200 Volts		208 Volts		230 Volts		460 Volts		575 Volts	
	B, C, D	E	B, C, D	E	B, C, D	E	B, C, D	E	B, C, D	E	B, C, D	E
½	40	40	23	23	22.1	22.1	20	20	10	10	8	8
¾	50	50	28.8	28.8	27.6	27.6	25	25	12.5	12.5	10	10
1	60	60	34.5	34.5	33	33	30	30	15	15	12	12
1½	80	80	46	46	44	44	40	40	20	20	16	16
2	100	100	57.5	57.5	55	55	50	50	25	25	20	20
3	—	—	73.6	84	71	81	64	73	32	36.5	25.6	29.2
5	—	—	105.8	140	102	135	92	122	46	61	36.8	48.8
7½	—	—	146	210	140	202	127	183	63.5	91.5	50.8	73.2

	—	186.3	259	179	249	162	225	81	113	64.8	90
10	—	186.3	259	179	249	162	225	81	113	64.8	90
15	—	267	388	257	373	232	337	116	169	93	135
20	—	334	516	321	497	290	449	145	225	116	180
25	—	420	646	404	621	365	562	183	281	146	225
30	—	500	775	481	745	435	674	218	337	174	270
40	—	667	948	641	911	580	824	290	412	232	330
50	—	834	1185	802	1139	725	1030	363	515	290	412
60	—	1001	1421	962	1367	870	1236	435	618	348	494
75	—	1248	1777	1200	1708	1085	1545	543	773	434	618
100	—	1668	2154	1603	2071	1450	1873	725	937	580	749
125	—	2087	2692	2007	2589	1815	2341	908	1171	726	936
150	—	2496	3230	2400	3106	2170	2809	1085	1405	868	1124
200	—	3335	4307	3207	4141	2900	3745	1450	1873	1160	1498
250	—	—	—	—	—	—	—	1825	2344	1460	1875
300	—	—	—	—	—	—	—	2200	2809	1760	2247
350	—	—	—	—	—	—	—	2550	3277	2040	2622
400	—	—	—	—	—	—	—	2900	3745	2320	2996
450	—	—	—	—	—	—	—	3250	4214	2600	3371
500	—	—	—	—	—	—	—	3625	4682	2900	3746

*In determining compliance with 440.12 and 440.41, the values in the B, C, D columns shall be used.

Source: Reprinted with permission from NFPA 70 *The National Electric Code* © 2002, National Fire Protection Association, Quincy, MA 02269. This reprinted material is not the referenced subject which is represented only by the standard in its entirety.

From the ampacity tables, a minimum-size #1/0 AWG THW copper conductor having a table-rated ampacity of 150 A is required.

The largest overcurrent protection device rating permitted for any of the three loads taken individually is that of a time-delay fuse applied to the 50 hp motor. The maximum rating permitted is based on 175% of the full-load current of the motor, or $175\% \times (65\ A) = 113.8\ A$. The next-higher standard rating is a 125 A fuse. The full-load currents of the 25 hp motor and the 25 kW resistance heater are added to the 125 A fuse rating, resulting in $125\ A + 27\ A + 30\ A = 182\ A$. The feeder overcurrent protection cannot exceed 182 A in this case. Therefore, a 175 A fuse would be appropriate for the motor feeder.

The minimum ampere rating of the switch is 115% of the full-load current of all loads:

$$\text{Minimum switch ampere rating} = 115\% \times (65\ A + 27\ A + 30\ A) = 140.3\ A$$

Therefore, a 200 A switch rating is required. The locked-rotor currents of the motors are determined as 363 A and 145 A, respectively. The sum of the locked-rotor currents and the full-load current of the resistive heater is $363 + 145 + 30 = 538\ A$. This equivalent locked-rotor current of 538 A corresponds to a 75 hp motor, as determined from Table 13–5. Therefore, a 200 A, 75 hp disconnect switch is required as a minimum. The fuse-holder of the 200 A disconnect switch is sufficient to accommodate the 175 A feeder fuse.

The use of wireway and individual motor controllers to serve a multiple motor arrangement, as shown in Figure 13–6, becomes impractical for installations required to serve a large number of motors. For installations supplying several motors, a motor control center may be more appropriate. Motor control centers have a layout similar to a main distribution panel. The individual units mounted in a motor control center incorporate the motor branch circuit disconnect and short circuit protection device and the motor starter. The sizing of the disconnect, short circuit protection, and motor starter components follows the methods previously discussed. A layout of the motor control center is then developed based on the physical dimensions of the individual units in a manner similar to that used to lay out the main distribution panel. With the proper equipment, many motor control centers may be configured as service entrance equipment.

PROBLEMS

1. What is the synchronous speed of a six-pole, 60 Hz motor?

2. A four-pole, 60 Hz motor has a nameplate speed of 1735 rpm. What is the slip in rpm?

3. How does a wound-rotor induction motor differ from a squirrel cage induction motor?

4. How are single-phase motors started?

5. What is the maximum load in hp permitted on a 50 hp motor having a service factor of 1.15?

6. What is a design E motor? How does the starting current of a design E motor differ from that of a design B motor?

7. Sketch the terminal connections of a nine-lead, dual-voltage motor for (a) low-voltage and (b) high-voltage operation.

8. Determine the locked-rotor current of a 75 hp, 460 V, three-phase, code letter G motor.

9. What size THW copper conductor is required to supply a 75 hp, 460 V, three-phase squirrel cage induction motor?

10. What is the maximum permitted rating of a dual-element, time-delay fuse used to protect the circuit conductors of a 100 hp, 460 V, three-phase motor?

11. What size NEMA-rated starter is required for a 75 hp, design B, 460 V, three-phase induction motor?

12. Repeat Problem 11 for a design E motor.

13. What maximum-size overload protection is permitted for a 30 hp, 460 V, three-phase motor having a full-load current rating of 35 A and a service factor of 1.15?

14. Determine the current and horsepower rating for the disconnect required for a 100 hp, 460 V, design B, three-phase motor having a rated current of 120 A.

15. Repeat Problem 14 for a design E motor.

16. A 480 V, multiple motor installation similar to Figure 13–6 supplies a 5 hp, 10 hp, 30 hp, and 50 hp motor. Sketch the system. Determine the conductor size for each motor tap, the motor controller size, overload rating, motor and controller disconnect rating, time-delay fuse rating, and motor branch circuit conductor size. Also, determine the motor feeder disconnect rating, motor feeder time-delay fuse rating, and motor feeder conductor size.

14

Transformers

INTRODUCTION

This chapter will discuss the application of transformers in electrical power systems. A review of the basic theory of operation is presented to provide the necessary background. Also presented are transformer loading guidelines, connections, voltage taps, transformer impedances, calculation of rated line current, and the selection of standard apparent power and voltage ratings. Basic transformer construction for both overhead and underground transformers used to supply electrical services will also be discussed. Last, the chapter presents the selection of transformer overcurrent protection device ratings and primary and secondary conductor sizing for low-voltage transformers.

OBJECTIVES

Upon completion of this chapter, you will:

- Understand the basic theory of transformer operation
- Understand the basic design and construction of utility distribution transformers
- Have knowledge of the standard ratings and connections of transformers
- Be able to properly size transformers
- Be able to calculate transformer impedance from nameplate data
- Be able to calculate transformer-rated line currents
- Be able to properly size overcurrent protection for low-voltage transformers
- Be able to properly size primary and secondary conductors supplying transformers

14-1 BASIC THEORY OF OPERATION

The basic theory of transformer operation can be understood by examination of the simplified single-phase transformer shown in Figure 14–1(A). The basic components of the transformer consist of a primary winding, secondary winding, and iron core. The primary winding is the winding that is connected to the source; the secondary winding is connected to the load. For the purposes of this discussion, it is assumed that the transformer is to be used for step-down operation. Therefore, the primary winding is the higher-voltage winding, and the secondary is the lower-voltage winding.

Physically, the high-voltage winding contains several hundred turns of small, cross-sectional-area conductor. The secondary winding consists of fewer turns of larger cross-sectional-area conductor. These windings may use copper or aluminum conductor,

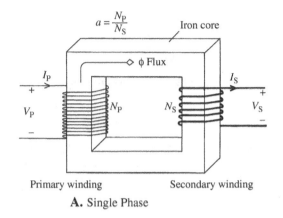

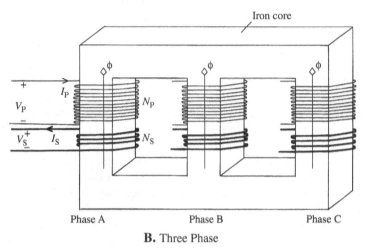

Primary winding   Secondary winding

A. Single Phase

Phase A   Phase B   Phase C

B. Three Phase

FIGURE 14–1
Basic Transformer Construction

depending on the design. Application of an alternating voltage to the primary winding of
the transformer results in an alternating magnetic flux, $\varnothing$, being produced in the iron core
of the transformer. As a result of this alternating flux, an alternating voltage is induced in
the secondary winding. The magnitude of the voltage induced in the secondary is a function of the turns ratio of the transformer. The turns ratio is defined as

$$a = \frac{N_P}{N_S} \tag{14–1}$$

where N_P is the number of turns on the primary and N_S is the number of turns on the secondary. In practice, the turns ratio is also equal to the voltage ratio of the transformer.

Therefore,

$$a = \frac{\text{Voltage rating of primary}}{\text{Voltage rating of secondary}} = \frac{V_P}{V_S} \qquad (14\text{--}2)$$

The primary and secondary currents are related by the turns ratio as follows:

$$\frac{I_S}{I_P} = \frac{N_P}{N_S} = a = \frac{V_P}{V_S} \qquad (14\text{--}3)$$

Note that the relation between primary and secondary current is the inverse of the relation between primary and secondary voltage. Simplification of Equation (14–3) results in the following:

$$\frac{I_S}{I_P} = \frac{V_P}{V_S}$$

which results in

$$V_P I_P = V_S I_S \qquad (14\text{--}4)$$

Equation (14–4) states that the input power is equal to the output power in an ideal transformer.

The simplified construction of a three-phase transformer is shown in Figure 14–1(B). Note that there are three phases—A, B, and C—each having a primary and secondary winding. Each of these three phases can be thought of as having the same characteristics as a single-phase transformer; that is, the turns ratio and voltage and current relationships are given by Equations (14–1) through (14–4) for each phase. In a three-phase transformer, the three primary phase windings may be connected in either wye or delta, with the delta connection being more common. Likewise, the three secondary phase windings may be connected in wye or delta, with the wye connection being more common. For many calculations involving three-phase transformers, it is common to define the primary-to-secondary voltage ratio of the transformer. This ratio is defined to be the ratio of the primary line voltage to secondary line voltage as follows:

$$\text{Primary-to-secondary voltage ratio} = \frac{\text{Line voltage rating of primary}}{\text{Line voltage rating of secondary}} \qquad (14\text{--}5)$$

Note that the primary-to-secondary voltage ratio is not necessarily the same as the turns ratio of the individual phases.

The equivalent circuit diagrams for a single-phase transformer is shown in Figure 14–2(A). The primary voltage and current are designated V_P and I_P, as in Figure 14–1(A). The equivalent circuit diagram for a delta–wye-connected, three-phase transformer is shown in Figure 14–2(B). When performing calculations involving three-phase transformers, the line voltage and phase voltage are usually of interest. For a delta connection, the line voltage and phase voltage are the same. These voltages are designated V_L and V_ϕ, as shown. Also, in the delta connection, the line current is equal to $\sqrt{3}$ times the phase current. In the wye connection, the line voltage is equal to $\sqrt{3}$ times the phase voltage, and the line current is equal to the phase current. In either the delta or wye connection, the turns ratio is equal to the ratio of the phase voltages.

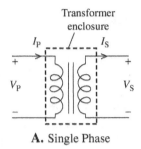

A. Single Phase

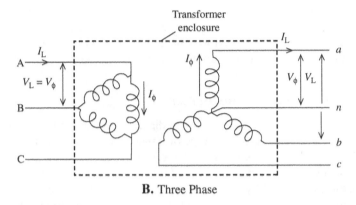

B. Three Phase

FIGURE 14–2
Transformer Equivalent Circuit Diagrams

EXAMPLE 14–1

Determine the turns ratio and primary-to-secondary voltage ratio of a 480–208Y/120 V transformer. The transformer is delta connected on the high-voltage side and wye connected on the low-voltage side.

Solution: The line and phase voltages are equal in magnitude on the high-voltage side, 480 V. On the low-voltage side, the phase voltage is 120 V and the line voltage is 208 V. Therefore, the turns ratio is the ratio of phase voltages as follows:

$$a = \frac{480 \text{ V}}{120 \text{ V}} = 4$$

The primary-to-secondary voltage ratio is the ratio of the primary-to-secondary line voltage as follows:

$$\text{Primary-to-secondary voltage ratio} = \frac{480 \text{ V}}{208 \text{ V}} = 2.31$$

It is interesting to note that the turns ratio divided by the primary-to-secondary line voltage ratio is equal to $\sqrt{3}$.

14–2   SERVICE TRANSFORMERS

The basic construction of power and distribution transformers used to supply electric services can be separated into two major groups: overhead and underground. Overhead transformers are designed primarily for pole mounting, while underground transformers are designed for either pad mounting or installation in underground vaults. The high-side or low-side terminals on underground transformers may be designed for either live or dead front connectors. The dead-front high-voltage connection typically uses insulated separable connectors such as load break elbows for connection to the high-voltage bushings.

Overhead distribution transformers are available in standard apparent power ratings of 500 kVA and less. The voltage rating of the high-side winding for distribution transformers is 34,500 volts and less. The low-voltage rating is limited to 7,970 volts and less. Transformers that do not fall into this broad category are classified as power transformers.

Single-Phase Overhead Transformer

The basic construction features and schematic diagram of a single-phase overhead transformer are shown in Figure 14–3. This type of transformer has one high-voltage bushing, designated H1. This bushing is located on the left-hand side of the transformer when viewed from the low-voltage side. This type of transformer is to be connected between the phase conductor and the solidly grounded neutral. The H2 terminal of the high-voltage winding is connected to the tank ground internally by the manufacturer to complete the electrical circuit. The multigrounded system neutral (MGN) would be externally connected to the tank ground. Figure 14–4 shows a typical single-phase overhead transformer installation.

If the transformer is to be connected between phases, such as in a delta connection, or in a floating wye configuration, two high-voltage bushings (H1 and H2) would be required. The H2 bushing would be located to the right of H1 as viewed from the low-voltage side. The construction features and schematic diagram of this type of transformer are shown in Figure 14–5.

In Figure 14–3, the low-voltage bushings are designated X1, X2, and X3. This low-voltage bushing configuration would apply to transformers that have center-tapped secondary windings for single-phase three-wire services. Transformers that have a single-voltage secondary would have two secondary bushings marked X1 and X2. Figure 14–3 shows the low-voltage terminal arrangements for additive polarity. If the transformer has subtractive polarity, the low-voltage bushings would be designated X1, X2, and X3, left to right, as viewed from the low-voltage side. In accordance with American National Standards Institute (ANSI) standards, distribution transformers rated 200 kVA and less with a high-voltage rating of 8660 V and below would have additive polarity. All other distribution transformers will have subtractive polarity. The secondary ground strap is used to connect the X2 low-voltage bushing to ground. This is the common connection for a single-phase, 120/240 V, three-wire service requirement. In certain three-phase connections, the grounding strap would need to be removed from one or two of the transformers in the bank.

FIGURE 14-3

Single-Phase, Single-Bushing Overhead
Transformer

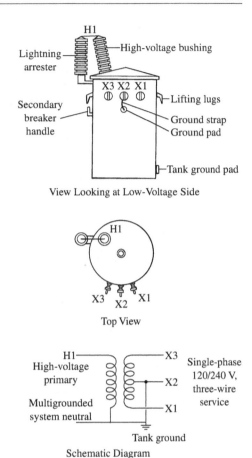

View Looking at Low-Voltage Side

Top View

Schematic Diagram

The single-phase overhead transformers shown in Figures 14-3 and 14-5 are equipped with a high-voltage lightning arrester, low-voltage circuit breaker, and an internal high-voltage fuse link (not shown). This type of transformer is referred to as a completely self-protected (CSP) transformer. A conventional transformer would not have any of these protective devices. Usually, a high-voltage fused cutout and lightning arrester would be supplied and installed by the user to protect the conventional transformer.

Three-Phase Overhead Transformers

Three-phase overhead transformers are also available to supply overhead three-phase services. Typically, overhead three-phase services would be supplied by connecting two or three single-phase overhead transformers in a "bank," rather than by one three-phase overhead transformer. For additional information regarding three-phase overhead transformers,

FIGURE 14-4
Single-Phase Overhead Transformer Installation *Source:* Courtesy of Ohio Edison Company.

the reader is referred to American National Standards Institute publication C57-12.20. Figure 14–6 shows three single-phase transformers connected in a "bank" to serve a three-phase load.

Single-Phase, Pad-Mount Transformers

Single-phase underground pad-mount transformers are designed for installation on a multigrounded neutral primary system. These transformers are typically used in new residential developments where an underground primary distribution system is required by law. Construction features and a schematic diagram of this type of transformer are shown in Figure 14–7. Note that the transformer high-voltage bushings are designated H1A and H1B and are located in the left-hand side of the transformer compartment. For safety, a high-voltage barrier is often placed between the high-voltage and low-voltage compartments.

High-voltage bushings H1A and H1B connect to the same end of the high-voltage coil. The other end of the high-voltage coil is connected to the multigrounded primary neutral, which is typically the concentric neutral of the high-voltage cable. The two high-voltage bushings allow for the loop feed capability of these transformers. The incoming

FIGURE 14–5
Single-Phase, Dual-Bushing Overhead
Transformer

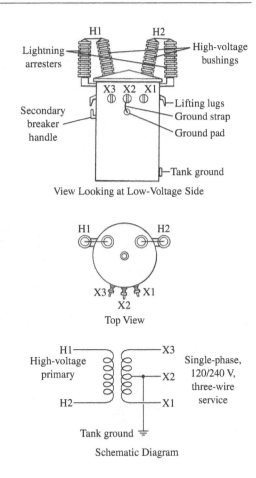

View Looking at Low-Voltage Side

Top View

Schematic Diagram

cable from the source typically terminates on the H1A bushing. Connection to transformers on the load side is made through a high-voltage cable connected to the H1B bushing. It is therefore possible to daisy-chain these transformers together to form an underground loop system. A parking stand is available to terminate a high-voltage cable where it is desirable to form an open in the loop. The high-voltage cable remains energized but does not connect to the high-voltage winding of the transformer when connected to the cable parking stand.

The low-voltage terminals may be either spade type or eyebolt and are designated X1, X2, and X3, in a manner similar to those in overhead transformers. These low-voltage terminals are located on the right-hand side of the transformer compartment. The X2 terminal is normally connected to a ground rod and the concentric neutral of the high-voltage cable. This ground establishes the neutral for a 120/240 V, single-phase, three-wire service. Figure 14–8 shows a typical single-phase, pad-mount transformer installation.

FIGURE 14–6
Three Single-Phase Transformers Connected to Supply a Three-Phase Service *Source:* Courtesy of Ohio Edison Company.

Three-Phase, Pad-Mount Transformers

The construction features of a three-phase, pad-mounted transformer are similar to the single-phase, pad-mounted transformer previously discussed. Three-phase, pad-mount transformers are available with either radial- or loop-feed capability. Figures 14–9 and 14–10 show features and schematic diagrams for three-phase, pad-mounted transformers having radial- and loop-feed capability.

Three-phase, underground, pad-mounted transformers with loop-feed capability can be used to form an underground loop similar to the single-phase, pad-mounted units. This underground loop is desirable in a commercial or industrial area where reliability and

FIGURE 14–7
Single-Phase, Pad-Mounted
Transformer

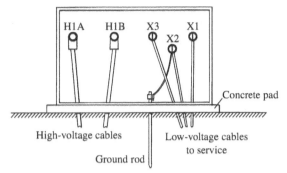

Front View Looking into Compartment

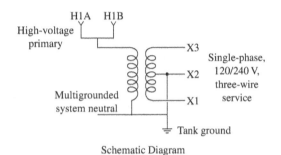

Schematic Diagram

FIGURE 14–8
Single-Phase, Pad-Mounted Transformer Installation *Source:* Courtesy of Ohio Edison Company.

FIGURE 14–9

Three-Phase, Radial-Feed, Pad-Mounted Transformer

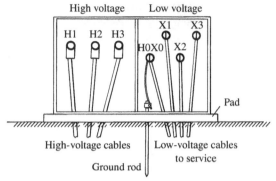

Front View Looking into Compartment

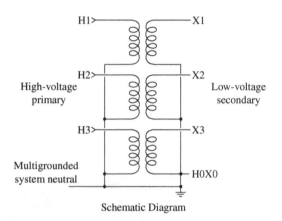

Schematic Diagram

operating flexibility are preferred. Parking stands are provided for each single-phase power cable entering the high-voltage cable compartment. If a cable fault develops in a loop-feed system, the faulted section of cable can be isolated for repair while maintaining continuity of service to other installations on the system.

In both single- and three-phase, pad-mount transformers, a high-voltage under-oil fuse link may be provided by the manufacturer for overcurrent protection. It is also possible to have an under-oil lightning arrester to protect the transformer against overvoltages. Figure 14–11 shows a typical three-phase, pad-mount transformer installation.

14–3   LOW-VOLTAGE TRANSFORMERS

Low-voltage transformers are rated less than 600 V on both primary and secondary windings. A common application of this type of transformer is to step down voltage from 480 V to 120 V to supply 120 V receptacle outlets. Typically, transformers of this rating used in building systems are either single phase or three phase, with voltage ratings of 480–120/240 V, or 480–208Y/120 V, respectively. These transformers are generally

FIGURE 14–10

Three-Phase, Loop-Feed, Pad-
Mounted Transformer

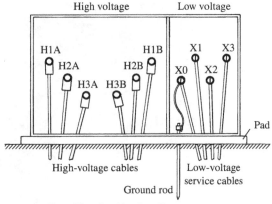

Front View Looking into Compartment

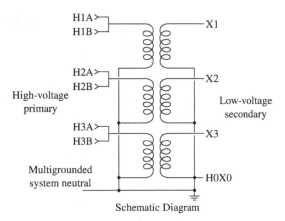

Schematic Diagram

designed for indoor installation and are of dry-type construction to eliminate the need to provide for oil-spill containment. Figure 14–12 shows a typical low-voltage, dry-type transformer installation.

14–4   CONNECTIONS AND WINDING VOLTAGE DESIGNATIONS

Single-Phase Winding Voltage Designations

Single-phase overhead transformers may be connected either as a single unit to supply single-phase loads or in a three-phase bank to supply three-phase loads. In general, there are only two ways that a transformer winding can be connected in a three-phase system: phase-to-neutral or phase-to-phase. The first step in determining the proper voltage designation is to determine what the applied voltage to the winding will be. It is then necessary to determine how the transformer high side will be connected, that is, single phase, wye grounded, floating wye, open wye, open delta, or delta.

FIGURE 14–11
Three-Phase, Pad-Mounted Transformer Installation *Source:* Courtesy of Ohio Edison Company.

A high-voltage winding with a voltage designation of E volts would be suitable for phase-to-phase connection on an E volt system. This transformer would have two high-voltage bushings and two lightning arresters if of the CSP type. Figure 14–13 shows examples of the high-voltage connections for this designation.

The $E/E_1 Y$ designation is for a winding rated at E volts. This transformer may be connected phase-to-phase on an E volt system or phase-to-neutral on an E_1 volt system. This transformer would have two high-voltage bushings for connection to the primary. If the transformer is a CSP transformer to be connected phase-to-phase, then two high-voltage lightning arresters and two high-voltage fuse links would be required. For a floating wye connection, only one high-voltage lightning arrester and one high-voltage fuse link would be required on the H1 bushing. Examples of the high-voltage connections for this winding designation are shown in Figure 14–14.

The $E_1 GRDY/E$ is the designation for a winding rated at E volts with reduced insulation at the neutral end. It is designed to be installed phase-to-neutral, on an E_1 volt system, where the neutral is solidly grounded. This transformer would have a single high-voltage bushing for the phase connection. Normally, the H2 lead of the high-voltage winding would be connected to the tank ground internally by the manufacturer. Standard connections are shown in Figure 14–15.

FIGURE 14–12
Dry-Type, Low-Voltage, Step-Down Transformer Installation *Source:* Courtesy Youngstown State University.

A winding voltage designation of E/2E indicates a two-section winding, with each section rated at E volts. The two sections may be connected in parallel for operation at E volts or in series for operation at 2E volts. In addition, the windings may be placed in series with a center point tap between the windings for single-phase, three-wire operation. The center point would normally be connected to ground and forms the neutral of the three-wire system. The currents in the individual winding sections may be unbalanced. This is the common voltage designation used in the low-voltage windings for single-phase, three-wire, 120/240 volt services. The two winding sections would be connected in parallel for a 208Y/120, three-phase, four-wire grounded wye connection. Figure 14–16 shows common connections for this winding voltage designation.

The 2E/E designation indicates a center-tapped winding that has 2E volts across the coil and E volts from the extreme terminals to the center tap. This is the common designation used in single-phase, pad-mounted transformers to supply single-phase, three-wire services. Each section of this winding has half the full-rated kVA of the entire winding. As in the previous winding designation, the currents in each half of this winding may be unbalanced. The individual coil sections cannot be connected in parallel. Figure 14–17 shows the coil connection for this designation.

The EXE_1 designation indicates a two-section winding in which the sections may be connected in series for 2E volt operation or in parallel for E volt operation. This winding is

FIGURE 14–13
High-Voltage Connections
for E Winding Voltage
Designation

A. Single
Phase

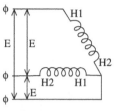

B. Open Delta

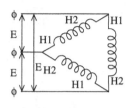

C. Delta

FIGURE 14–14
High-Voltage Connections for
E/E$_1$Y Winding Voltage
Designation

A. Single
Phase

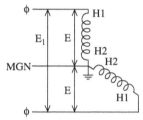

B. Open Wye

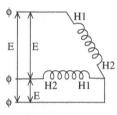

C. Open Delta

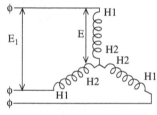

D. Floating Wye

FIGURE 14–15
High-Voltage Connections for E$_1$GRDY/E
Winding Voltage Designation

A. Single
Phase

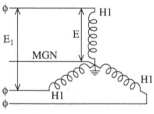

B. Grounded Wye

FIGURE 14–16
Connections for E/2E Winding
Voltage Designation

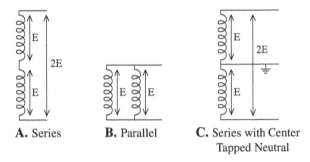

A. Series   **B.** Parallel   **C.** Series with Center
                                                        Tapped Neutral

FIGURE 14–17
Connections for 2E/E Winding Voltage Designation

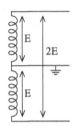

not suitable for three-wire, center-tapped operation. The currents in the two coil sections must be balanced. Figure 14–18 shows the coil connections for this designation.

Three-Phase Transformer Winding Voltage Designations

Three-phase transformers may have their high- and/or low-voltage windings connected in wye or delta. Windings suitable for floating wye connection have a neutral that is fully insulated and brought out to a bushing for external connection if desired. In a winding specifically designed for a grounded wye connection, reduced winding insulation may be used. The neutral may be connected to the tank ground internally or may be brought out to a neutral bushing for permanent connection to ground.

The E volt designation as applied to three-phase transformers designates a permanently delta-connected winding for use on an E volt system. The rated coil voltage for each of the three coils is E volts.

FIGURE 14–18
Connections for EXE₁ Winding Voltage Designation

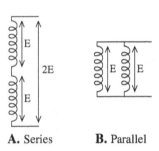

A. Series   **B.** Parallel

The E_1Y designation is for a permanently connected floating wye winding suitable for use on an E_1 volt system. Each coil would have a rated voltage of $E_1/\sqrt{3}$. There is no connection to the neutral.

The E_1Y/E designation is for a permanently wye-connected winding with a fully insulated neutral connection. Each coil has a voltage rating of E volts for connection on an E_1 volt system.

The E_1GRDY/E volt designation is for a permanently connected grounded wye winding suitable for use on an E_1 volt system. Each coil has a voltage rating of E volts. The neutral connection of the winding is brought out to a bushing and permanently grounded. This type of winding also may have a reduced insulation system.

14–5   STANDARD RATINGS

Overhead Pole Transformers

Standard apparent power ratings for single-phase and three-phase pole-type transformers are shown in Table 14–1. Voltage ratings for pole-type transformers are shown in Table 14–2.

Pad-Mounted Transformers

The standard kVA ratings for single-phase and three-phase, pad-mounted distribution transformers are shown in Table 14–3. Standard voltage ratings for single-phase and three-phase, pad-mounted distribution transformers are shown in Table 14–4.

TABLE 14–1
Standard KVA Ratings for
Overhead Transformers

Single Phase	Three Phase
10	30
15	45
25	75
37.5	112.5
50	150
75	225
100	300
167	500
250	
333	
500	

Source: Reprinted from American National
Standard C57.12.20-1988 by permission of the
National Electrical Manufacturers Association.

TABLE 14–2
Standard Voltage Ratings for Overhead Transformers

Single Phase	Three Phase
2400/4160Y	2400
4800/8320Y	4160Y/2400
7200/12,470Y	4160Y
12,470GRDY/7200	4160
7620/13,200Y	4800
13,200GRDY/7620	8320Y/4800
12,000	7200
13,200/22,860Y	12,000
13,200	12,470Y/7200
13,800GRDY/7970	12,470Y
13,800/23,900Y	13,200Y/7620
13,800	13,200Y
14,400/24,940Y	13,200
24,940GRDY/14,400	13,800
16,340	13,800GRDY/7970
34,500GRDY/19,920	24,940GRDY/14,400
34,500	35,400GRDY/19,920
120/240	208Y/120
277	240
240/480	480
	240X480
	480Y/277

Source: Reprinted from American National Standard C57.12.20-1988 by permission of the National Electrical Manufacturers Association.

Low-Voltage, Dry-Type Transformers

Standard kVA and voltage ratings for low-voltage, dry-type transformers are shown in Table 14–5.

Cooling Class

Virtually all of the transformers used in utility power systems to supply electric services are immersed in liquid. The liquid is usually some form of insulating oil or silicone fluid. The temperature rise above ambient for most liquid-immersed transformers is 65°C. In some instances, dry-type transformers may be employed that have a temperature rise of up to 180°C above ambient. In either case, the temperature rise is limited by the amount of heat the insulating material can withstand. The

TABLE 14–3
Standard kVA Ratings for Pad-Mounted Transformers

Single Phase	Three Phase
25	75
37.5	112.5
50	150
75	225
100	300
167	500
	750
	1000
	1500
	2000
	2500

Source: Reprinted from American National Standard C57.12.21-1980 by permission of the National Electrical Manufacturers Association.

TABLE 14–4
Standard Voltage Ratings for Pad-Mounted Transformers

Single Phase	Three Phase
4160GRDY/2400	2400
8320GRDY/4800	4160
12,000GRDY/6930	4800
12,470GRDY/7200	7200
13,200GRDY/7620	12,000
13,800GRDY/7970	12,470
16,430GRDY/9430	13,200
22,860GRDY/13,200	13,800
23,900GRDY/13,800	16,340
34,500GRDY/19,920	22,860GRDY/13,200
	23,900GRDY/13,800
	24,940GRDY/14,400
	34,500GRDY/19,920
240/120	208Y/120
	240
	480
	480Y/277

Source: Reprinted from American National Standard C57.12.21-1980 by permission of the National Electrical Manufacturers Association.

TABLE 14–5
Standard kVA and Voltage Ratings for Dry-Type Transformers

VOLTAGE RATINGS

Single Phase	Three Phase
240X480 V primary	480 V delta primary
120/240 V secondary	208Y/120 V secondary
480 V primary	480 V delta primary
120/240 V secondary	240 V delta secondary
600 V primary	480 V delta primary
120/240 V secondary	240/120 V secondary
	480 V delta primary
	480Y/277 V secondary
	480 V delta primary
	380Y/220 V secondary

kVA RATINGS

Single Phase	Three Phase
0.050	3
0.100	6
0.150	9
0.250	15
0.500	30
0.750	45
1.0	75
1.5	112.5
2	150
3	225
5	300
7.5	500
10	750
15	1000
25	
37.5	
50	
75	
100	
167	

Source: Square D/Schneider Electric.

ANSI standards have specified the following cooling classes for liquid-immersed transformers:

Class OA—Self-Cooled
Class OA/FA—Self-Cooled/Forced-Air Cooled
Class OA/FA/FA—Self-Cooled/Forced-Air Cooled/Forced-Air Cooled
Class OA/FA/FOA—Self-Cooled/Forced-Air Cooled/Forced-Liquid Cooled
Class OA/FOA/FOA—Self-Cooled/Forced-Liquid Cooled/Forced-Liquid Cooled
Class OW—Water Cooled
Class OW/A—Water Cooled/Self-Cooled

The temperature rise for low-voltage, dry-type transformers is a function of the type of insulation system used. Temperature rises of 55°C, 80°C, 115°C, and 150°C are common for general-purpose, dry-type, standard-ventilated transformers. The amount of heat produced by losses in the transformer must be taken into account when designing transformer vaults. Section 450–45(C) of the *NEC* requires a minimum of 3 sq in. of ventilation opening per kVA of transformer capacity, and not less than 1 sq ft total ventilating opening for transformers rated less than 50 kVA.

As a result of the alternating magnetic flux produced in the transformer core, all transformers produce audible sound, predominantly in the 120 Hz range. When installed indoors, this sound may become objectionable. Standard sound levels have been established by the National Electrical Manufacturers Association (NEMA) and are shown in Table 14–6. Several transformer manufacturers offer transformers with reduced sound level.

14–6   LOADING CALCULATIONS AND SIZING

Loading calculations are necessary to determine the actual apparent power load to be expected so that the proper kVA rating may be specified. In the case of single-phase, three-wire services, the transformer loading is determined by summing the connected loads and applying the appropriate demand factors, as discussed in Chapter 3. For three-phase, four-wire wye services, the loading on the transformer(s) is easily determined since the three-phase load is assumed to be balanced. Load calculations for the three-phase, four-wire

TABLE 14–6
Sound Levels for Transformers

kVA	NEMA Sound Level
0–9	40 dB
10–50	45 dB
51–150	50 dB
151–300	55 dB
301–500	60 dB

Source: Square D/Schneider Electric.

delta secondary connections are much more difficult. This section will present methods that can be used to calculate the apparent power loading on transformers in single-phase and three-phase connections. In addition, "rules of thumb" will be introduced that will enable approximate but rapid determination of transformer loading for most situations.

Single Phase

Single-phase overhead or underground transformers may be used to supply single-phase, three-wire services. Figure 14–19 shows the schematic diagram and connections required to supply a single-phase, three-wire service. In reference to Figure 14–19, the single-phase loads are assumed to be balanced from each phase to neutral. This being the case, the current in the neutral conductor will be zero. The total loading on the transformer will then be equal to the estimated total connected load (demand) multiplied by the appropriate demand factor. Recall from Chapter 3 that the demand factor is a function of the total number of individual loads connected to the transformer. The required kVA rating of the transformer used to supply these loads will be the next-larger standard size available.

Grounded Wye–Grounded Wye Connection

The grounded wye–grounded wye connection may be used to supply a three-phase, four-wire service from a three-phase, four-wire primary distribution system. Single-phase loads may be connected from line to neutral on the low-voltage side. Three-phase loads would involve connection to all three phases. In performing loading calculations, the single-phase loads are assumed to be divided equally among the three phases and the three-phase load is assumed to be balanced. Thus, each transformer in the bank will be loaded equally. The loading on each transformer will be equal to one-third of the total three-phase load plus one-third of the total single-phase load. Figure 14–20 shows the schematic and connection diagrams for the grounded wye–grounded wye connection.

EXAMPLE 14–2

A commercial establishment is to be supplied service at 208Y/120 V, three-phase, four-wire. The utility primary distribution circuit is a 12.47 kV, three-phase MGN system. The total estimated single-phase load is 30 kW at 0.95 lagging power factor. The total estimated three-phase load is 150 kW at 0.8 lagging power factor. A grounded wye–grounded wye connection of three single-phase transformers is to be used to supply this service. Determine the apparent power ratings and winding voltage designations for each of the three transformers in the bank.

FIGURE 14–19
Schematic Diagram of Single-Phase, Three-Wire Connection

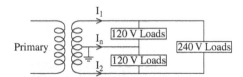

FIGURE 14–20
Schematic Diagram of
Grounded Wye–Grounded Wye
Connection

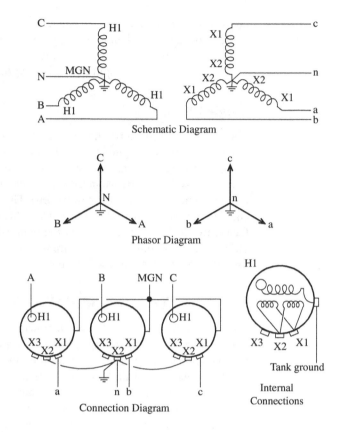

Schematic Diagram

Phasor Diagram

Connection Diagram

Internal
Connections

Solution: Since the power factors of the three-phase and single-phase loads are different, each of these loads must be expressed in terms of real and reactive power, then added together.

Single-phase load = 30 kW, 9.9 kvar
Three-phase load = 150 kW, 112.5 kvar

The loading on each transformer will be

$$\text{Loading} = \left(\frac{1}{3}\right)(30 + 150) + j\left(\frac{1}{3}\right)(9.9 + 112.5)\,\text{kVA}$$

$$= 60 + j40.8$$

$$= 72.6 \angle 34.2° \,\text{kVA}$$

Therefore, three 75 kVA transformers are required. The winding voltage designations for each of the three transformers will be 12,470GRDY/7,200–120/240 volts. As an alternative, a winding voltage designation of 7200/12470Y V may be used (two HV bushings).

EXAMPLE 14–3

An industrial plant is to be supplied service at 480Y/277 V, three-phase, four-wire. The utility primary distribution circuit is a 24.94 kV, three-phase MGN system. The total estimated single-phase load is 30 kW at 0.95 lagging power factor. The total estimated three-phase load is 300 kW at 0.7 lagging power factor. A grounded wye–grounded wye connection of three single-phase transformers is to be used to supply this service. Determine the apparent power ratings and winding voltage designations for each of the three transformers in the bank.

Solution: Expressing the loads in terms of real and reactive powers:

Single-phase load $= 30 + j9.9$ kVA
Three-phase load $= 300 + j306.1$ kVA
Total load $= 330 + j316.0$ kVA

The loading on each transformer is

$$\text{Loading} = \left(\frac{1}{3}\right)(330) + j\left(\frac{1}{3}\right)(316) \text{ kVA}$$
$$= 110 + j105.3$$
$$= 152.3 \text{ kVA}$$

Therefore, three 167 kVA transformers are required. The winding voltage designations for each of the three transformers will be 24,940GRDY/14,400–277 Volts. As an alternative, a winding voltage designation of 14400/24940Y V may be used (two HV bushings).

Delta–Grounded Wye Connection

The loading calculations for the delta–grounded wye connection are the same as for the grounded wye–grounded wye connection. Figure 14–21 shows the schematic and connection diagrams for the delta–grounded wye connection. For the connection shown in the figure, the high voltage leads the low voltage by 210°.

EXAMPLE 14–4

Repeat Example 14–3 for a utility primary distribution circuit consisting of a 13.2 kV, three-phase MGN system. A delta–grounded wye connection of three single-phase transformers is to be used to supply this service. Determine the apparent power ratings and winding voltage designations for each of the three transformers in the bank.

Solution: The loading on each transformer is 152.3 kVA as calculated in Example 14–3. Therefore, three 167 kVA transformers are required. The winding voltage designations for each of the three transformers will be 13,200–277 volts. Each transformer would have two fully insulated HV bushings since it will be connected line-to-line. The primary system neutral would be connected to the secondary neutral in this case.

FIGURE 14–21
Schematic Diagram of
Delta–Grounded Wye
Connection

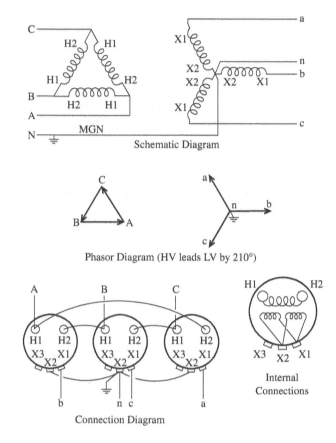

Schematic Diagram

Phasor Diagram (HV leads LV by 210°)

Connection Diagram

Internal
Connections

Floating Wye–Delta Connection

In the floating wye–delta connection, the transformer high-voltage sides are connected in a
wye configuration with the transformer bank neutral floating, that is, not connected to the
primary system neutral. The transformer low-voltage sides are connected in a delta configuration. This connection can be used to supply both 120/240 V, single-phase, three-wire
loads and 240 V, delta, three-phase, three-wire loads. The schematic and connection diagrams are shown in Figure 14–22. For the connection shown in the figure, the high-side
line voltages lead the low-side line voltages by 210°.

A rule of thumb is applicable in the determination of transformer loading in banks
where the secondaries are connected in a closed delta configuration. As an approximation,
the lighting leg transformer will carry two-thirds of the single-phase load plus one-third of
the three-phase load. The power leg transformers will each carry one-third of the single-
phase load plus one-third of the three-phase load. When calculating transformer loading in
the delta–delta or floating wye–delta connections, this rule can be applied to determine
approximate transformer ratings. Detailed calculations to determine the actual loading on
the transformers are beyond the scope of this text.

FIGURE 14–22
Schematic Diagram of Floating
Wye–Delta Connection

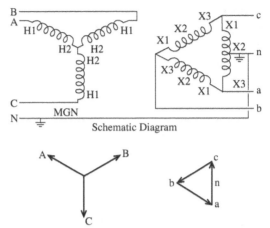

Schematic Diagram

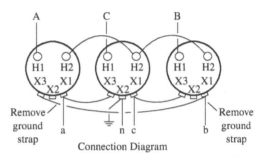

Phasor Diagram (HV leads LV by 210°)

Connection Diagram

EXAMPLE 14–5

Three single-phase transformers are to be connected floating wye–delta to supply the following loads:

Single-phase load: 30 kW, 0.95 lagging PF, 120/240 V, 3W
Three-phase load: 100 kW, 0.8 lagging PF, 240 V, 3W

The utility primary distribution circuit is a 4.16 kV MGN system. Determine the apparent power ratings and winding voltage designations for each of the three transformers in the bank.

Solution: To determine the loading on the transformers, the rule of thumb will be applied. The three-phase load is equal to $100/0.8 = 125$ kVA, and the single-phase load is equal to $30/0.95 = 31.6$ kVA. Therefore, the lighting leg transformer will carry approximately 94.3 kVA, and the two power leg transformers will carry approximately 52.2 kVA each. The apparent power rating of the lighting leg transformer will be selected as 100 kVA, and the two power leg transformers will each have a rating of 75 kVA for this load condition.

The winding voltage designation for all three transformers is: 2400/4160Y–120/240 volts. Each transformer would have two fully insulated HV bushings.

FIGURE 14–23
Schematic Diagram of Delta–Delta
Connection

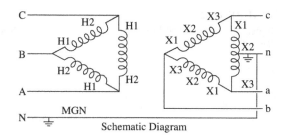

Schematic Diagram

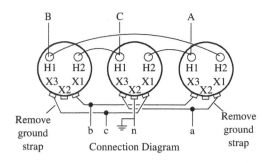

Phasor Diagram (HV in phase with LV)

Connection Diagram

Delta–Delta Connection

The schematic and connection diagrams for the delta–delta connection are shown in Figure
14–23. Note that both the transformer high-voltage and low-voltage sides are connected in
delta.

EXAMPLE 14–6

Three single-phase transformers are to be connected delta–delta to supply the following
loads:

Single-phase load: 50 kW, 0.95 lagging PF, 120/240 V, 3W
Three-phase load: 120 kW, 0.8 lagging PF, 240 V, 3W

The utility primary distribution circuit is a 13.8 kV MGN system. Determine the apparent
power ratings and winding voltage designations for each of the three transformers in the
bank.

Solution: To determine the loading on the transformers, the rule of thumb will be applied. The three-phase load is equal to $120/0.8 = 150$ kVA, and the single-phase load is equal to $50/0.95 = 52.6$ kVA. Therefore, the lighting leg transformer will carry approximately 85 kVA, and the two power leg transformers will carry approximately 67.5 kVA. The apparent power rating of the lighting leg transformer will be selected as 100 kVA, and the two power leg transformers will have a rating of 75 kVA for this load condition.

The winding voltage designation for all three transformers is 13,800–120/240 volts. Each transformer would have two fully insulated HV bushings. In addition, two HV fuse links and two lightning arresters would be required if CSP-type transformers are used.

Open Delta–Open Delta and Open Wye–Open Delta Connections

The loading equations for the open delta–open delta and open wye–open delta are identical. Obviously, the connections on the transformer high side are different for the two connections; the connections on the low-voltage side are identical. In the loading calculations, the single-phase and three-phase loads are assumed to be balanced. The schematic and connection diagrams for the open delta–open delta transformer connection are shown in Figure 14–24, and the schematic and connection diagrams for the open wye–open delta connection are shown in Figure 14–25.

When distribution transformers are connected in either the open wye–open delta or open delta–open delta configuration, a rule of thumb can be applied to determine the approximate apparent power loadings on the two transformers in the bank. The lighting leg transformer will carry 100% of the single-phase load, plus 58% of the total three-phase load. The power leg transformer will carry approximately 58% of the total three-phase load.

EXAMPLE 14–7

A commercial establishment is to be supplied service from an open wye–open delta leading transformer bank. The single-phase and three-phase loads are

Single-phase load: 100 kW, 0.90 lagging PF, 120/240 V, 3W
Three-phase load: 20 kW, 0.85 lagging PF, 240V, 3W

The utility primary distribution circuit consists of two phases of a 12.47 kV, three-phase MGN system. Determine the apparent power and voltage ratings for the transformers required to serve this load.

Solution: The single-phase load kVA is equal to 100 kW$/0.9 = 111.1$ kVA. The three-phase load kVA is equal to 20 kW$/0.85 = 23.5$ kVA. Therefore, the lighting transformer will carry approximately 125 kVA and the power transformer will carry approximately 13.6 kVA. Standard apparent power ratings of 167 kVA and 15 kVA are selected.

The appropriate winding voltage designation for both transformers would be 12,470GRDY/7,200–120/240 volts. Each transformer would have one high-voltage bushing. As an alternative, a winding voltage designation of 7,200/12,470Y V may be used.

FIGURE 14–24
Schematic Diagram of Open Delta–Open
Delta Connection

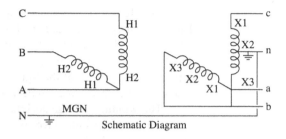

Schematic Diagram

Phasor Diagram (HV in phase with LV)

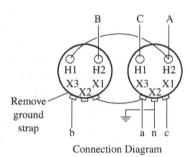

Connection Diagram

14–7   TRANSFORMER VOLTAGE TAPS

Distribution transformers designed for utility applications to provide single-phase and three-phase services generally have a fixed voltage rating. As a result, it is not possible to adjust the voltage ratio of the transformer to allow for applications in which the system voltage is slightly off the nominal values. In situations where the system voltage differs from nominal, it is possible to specify transformers with voltage taps. Adjustment of the transformer turns ratio is accomplished by connection of the supply conductors to the appropriate taps on the transformer or by adjustment of the tap-setting mechanism. In either case, tap setting is normally accomplished with the transformer deenergized.

The taps are usually made to the high-voltage winding to adjust for the variation in supply voltage. Common tap arrangements for single-phase and three-phase, dry-type, low-voltage transformers are shown in Figure 14–26. The single-phase transformer shown in Figure 14–26(A) typically has a primary winding that may be connected in parallel for a nominal voltage rating of 240 V or in series for a nominal voltage rating of 480 V. Connection of the high-voltage supply conductors to the various terminals labeled 1 through 8 adjust the voltage ratio of the transformer. Figure 14–26(B) shows a delta–wye-

FIGURE 14–25
Schematic Diagram of Open
Wye–Open Delta Connection

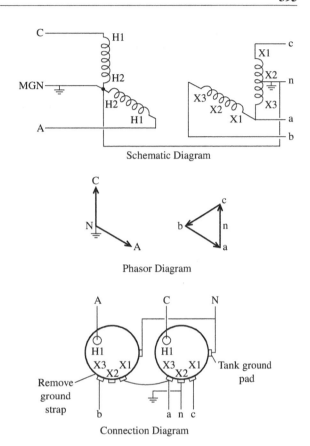

Schematic Diagram

Phasor Diagram

Connection Diagram

connected, three-phase transformer with a nominal voltage rating of 480–208 Y/120 V. The taps are designated 1 through 7, with the corresponding voltage rating as shown.

The resulting secondary voltage present under no-load conditions is given by the following:

$$V_S = \text{Applied primary voltage} \times \left[\frac{\text{Rated secondary voltage}}{\text{Primary tap voltage}}\right] \quad \textbf{(14–6)}$$

Typically, the primary tap voltage is given on the nameplate of the transformer. In most manufacturers' catalog information, the taps are usually expressed in percent of nominal. For example, the taps may be specified as 6—2.5% 2+ 4−. This designation means that there are six taps in addition to nominal, or a total of seven possible tap settings. Each tap will adjust the voltage 2.5% per step, with two taps above nominal and four taps below nominal. Thus, the taps will allow for voltage settings at +5%, +2.5%, nominal, −2.5%, −5%, −7.5%, and −10%. Also, the designation FCBN means that the transformer has Full Capacity Below Nominal. In other words, the transformer can supply rated current at the voltage taps below the nominal setting.

FIGURE 14–26
Common Tap Arrangements for Low-Voltage,
Dry-Type Transformers

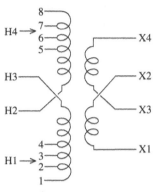

A. Single Phase

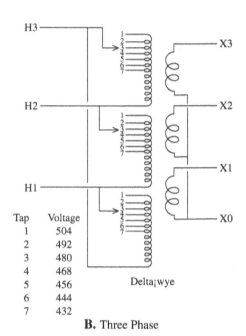

Tap	Voltage
1	504
2	492
3	480
4	468
5	456
6	444
7	432

Delta¦wye

B. Three Phase

EXAMPLE 14–8

A 75 kVA, 480–208Y/120 V, three-phase transformer is equipped with taps as shown in Figure 14–26(B). Determine the actual secondary voltage at no load if the tap is set at #6 for the following actual applied primary voltages:

a) 480 V

b) 460 V

c) 440 V

Solution: Tap #6 corresponds to a voltage of 7.5% below nominal, or 444 V.

a) Application of Equation (14–6) results in

$$V_S = 480 \text{ V} \times \left[\frac{208 \text{ V}}{444 \text{ V}} \right] = 224.9 \text{ V} \qquad 108\% \text{ of nominal}$$

b)
$$V_S = 460 \text{ V} \times \left[\frac{208 \text{ V}}{444 \text{ V}} \right] = 215.5 \text{ V} \qquad 103.6\% \text{ of nominal}$$

c)
$$V_S = 440 \text{ V} \times \left[\frac{208 \text{ V}}{444 \text{ V}} \right] = 206.1 \text{ V} \qquad 99.1\% \text{ of nominal}$$

EXAMPLE 14–9

A 25 kVA, 480–120/240 V, single-phase transformer is equipped with two taps at −5% each. Determine (a) the tap voltage ratings and (b) the secondary voltages for each tap setting if the actual voltage is 465 V.

Solution:

a) Nominal tap voltage = 1.00(480 V) = 480 V
−5% tap voltage   = 0.95(480 V) = 456 V
−10% tap voltage   = 0.90(480 V) = 432 V

b) Nominal tap: $V_S = 465 \text{ V} \times \left[\dfrac{240 \text{ V}}{480 \text{ V}} \right] = 232.5 \text{ V} \qquad 97\%$ of nominal

−5% tap: $V_S = 465 \text{ V} \times \left[\dfrac{240 \text{ V}}{456 \text{ V}} \right] = 244.7 \text{ V} \qquad 102\%$ of nominal

−10% tap: $V_S = 465 \text{ V} \times \left[\dfrac{240 \text{ V}}{432 \text{ V}} \right] = 258.3 \text{ V} \qquad 107.6\%$ of nominal

Note that in this case, the most desirable tap setting is the −5% tap, resulting in a secondary voltage of 102% of nominal at no load. Setting the tap at nominal results in a voltage of 97% at no load, while setting at −10% results in an excessively high voltage. Generally, the tap setting selected should be as close as possible to the actual primary system voltage without producing an excessively high secondary voltage at no load.

14–8   TRANSFORMER IMPEDANCES

In reality, the primary and secondary windings of a transformer have a finite value of resistance that is a function of the cross-sectional area and length of the conductors used to make up the primary and secondary windings. Typically, the resistances of the transformer windings are lumped together to form a single resistance, referred to as the *transformer*

FIGURE 14-27

Transformer Impedances Referred
to Secondary

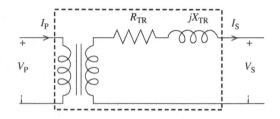

winding resistance. In most instances, the winding resistance of the primary is reflected to the secondary and added directly to the secondary winding resistance. The transformer winding resistance is shown as R_{TR} in Figure 14-27.

As discussed in previous sections, the application of ac voltage to the primary winding produces an alternating magnetic flux in the transformer core. This alternating flux passes through the window formed by the secondary winding, thereby inducing a voltage in the secondary winding. In a real transformer, not all of the flux produced by the primary winding links with the secondary winding. The portion of flux that does not link both the primary and secondary coils is referred to as the *leakage flux.* The effect of this leakage flux is to produce a voltage drop in the transformer, which is modeled by including a leakage reactance in the equivalent circuit model. The voltage drop that appears across this leakage reactance is the same as that produced internally by the leakage flux. As with the transformer winding resistances, a single leakage reactance is defined for both the primary and secondary windings. This leakage reactance is designated as X_{TR} in Figure 14-27.

The transformer impedance is the vector sum of the resistance and reactance as given by

$$Z_{TR} = R_{TR} + jX_{TR} \qquad (14\text{-}7)$$

The values of transformer resistance and reactance are often expressed in percents by the manufacturer. These percent impedance values are based on the transformer rated kVA and rated voltage. The actual ohmic impedance values are given by

$$R_{TR} = \frac{1}{100}\left[\frac{(\% \, R)(\text{Transformer line voltage})^2}{\text{Transformer VA}}\right] \qquad (14\text{-}8)$$

$$X_{TR} = \frac{1}{100}\left[\frac{(\% \, X)(\text{Transformer line voltage})^2}{\text{Transformer VA}}\right] \qquad (14\text{-}9)$$

EXAMPLE 14-10

A 75 kVA, 480–208Y/120 V, three-phase transformer has a winding resistance of 3% and a leakage reactance of 4.22%. Determine the ohmic impedances referred to the low-voltage side.

Solution: Since the impedance is to be calculated as referred to the low-voltage side, the rated line voltage is 208 V. Applying Equations (14–8) and (14–9) results in

$$R_{TR} = \frac{1}{100}\left[\frac{(3\%)(208\text{ V})^2}{75{,}000\text{ VA}}\right] = 0.0173\ \Omega$$

$$X_{TR} = \frac{1}{100}\left[\frac{(4.22\%)(208\text{ V})^2}{75{,}000\text{ VA}}\right] = 0.0243\ \Omega$$

In some instances, the manufacturer may specify the total impedance, Z, and the X/R ratio. In this instance, the transformer resistance and reactance are determined by first calculating the impedance angle as follows:

$$\theta = \tan^{-1}(X/R) \qquad\qquad\qquad \textbf{(14–10)}$$

The resistance and reactance are then given by

$$R_{TR} = \frac{1}{100}\left[\frac{(\%\ Z)(\text{Transformer line voltage})^2}{\text{Transformer VA}}\right] \times \cos(\theta) \qquad \textbf{(14–11)}$$

$$X_{TR} = \frac{1}{100}\left[\frac{(\%\ Z)(\text{Transformer line voltage})^2}{\text{Transformer VA}}\right] \times \sin(\theta) \qquad \textbf{(14–12)}$$

EXAMPLE 14–11

A 5 kVA, 480–120/240 V, single-phase transformer has an impedance $Z = 3.8\%$, and an X/R ratio of 0.74. Determine the ohmic values of winding resistance and leakage reactance.

Solution: Application of Equations (14–10) through (14–12) results in

$$\theta = \tan^{-1}(0.74) = 36.5°$$

$$R_{TR} = \frac{1}{100}\left[\frac{(3.8)(240\text{ V})^2}{5000\text{ VA}}\right] \times \cos(36.5°) = 0.3519\ \Omega$$

$$X_{TR} = \frac{1}{100}\left[\frac{(3.8)(240\text{ V})^2}{5000\text{ VA}}\right] \times \sin(36.5°) = 0.2604\ \Omega$$

Typical impedance values for low-voltage transformers are shown in Table 14–7.

14–9   TRANSFORMER RATED LINE CURRENTS

The calculation of transformer rated line current is the first step in designing overcurrent protection for transformers. The rated line current is also necessary to properly size primary and secondary circuit conductors for transformer circuits. For single-phase transformers, the line current is given by

$$I_L = \frac{\text{Transformer volt} - \text{Ampere rating}}{\text{Line voltage}} \qquad \textbf{(14–13)}$$

For three-phase transformers, the line current is given by

$$I_L = \frac{\text{Transformer volt} - \text{Ampere rating}}{\sqrt{3}\ \text{Line voltage}} \qquad \textbf{(14–14)}$$

EXAMPLE 14–12

Calculate the rated primary and secondary line currents for the following transformers:

a) 5 kVA, 480–120/240 V, single phase
b) 75 kVA, 480–208Y/120 V, three phase

TABLE 14–7
Typical Impedances for Low-Voltage,
Dry-Type Transformers

SINGLE PHASE		
kVA	% Impedance	X/R Ratio
3	4.4	0.41
5	3.8	0.74
7.5	2.5	0.66
10	2.5	0.62
15	5.2	0.71
25	6.0	0.99
37.5	6.5	1.29
50	5.2	1.06
75	6.1	1.66
100	6.5	1.75
167	7.0	2.22

THREE PHASE		
kVA	% Impedance	X/R Ratio
15	5.0	0.75
30	5.5	0.72
45	5.7	0.93
75	5.2	1.39
112.5	6.9	1.67
150	6.7	1.90
225	6.6	2.00
300	3.7	1.72
500	6.2	2.27
750	5.0	1.98
1000	5.8	2.38

Solution:

a) Application of Equation (14–13) on the high-voltage primary side results in

$$I_P = \frac{5000 \text{ VA}}{480 \text{ V}} = 10.42 \text{ A}$$

Applying Equation (14–13) to the low-voltage secondary side results in

$$I_S = \frac{5000 \text{ VA}}{240 \text{ V}} = 20.83 \text{ A}$$

b) Application of Equation (14–14) on the high-voltage primary side results in

$$I_P = \frac{75,000 \text{ VA}}{\sqrt{3}\ 480 \text{ V}} = 90.2 \text{ A}$$

Applying Equation (14–14) to the low-voltage secondary side results in

$$I_S = \frac{75,000 \text{ VA}}{\sqrt{3}\ 208 \text{ V}} = 208.2 \text{ A}$$

14–10 TRANSFORMER CIRCUIT DESIGN

Transformers must be protected against overcurrents due to overloads and short circuits. The required protection usually consists of an overcurrent protection device on both the primary side of the transformer and on the secondary. The rating of the overcurrent protection devices is based on the full-load rated current of the transformer. Separate calculations must be performed for the primary and secondary sides of the transformer. Article 450 of the *NEC* presents the requirements for transformer installations in detail. This section discusses transformer circuit design for transformers having primary and secondary ratings of 600 V and below.

Once the overcurrent protection device ratings have been selected, the transformer primary and secondary circuit conductors can be determined. In most cases, the ampacity of the primary and secondary conductors will be selected such that the conductors are protected within their ampacity. However, there are instances where tap conductors may be used to supply transformer circuits. The rules applicable to tap conductors supplying transformer circuits are described next.

Single-Voltage, Two-Wire Secondary

Transformers having a single-voltage, two-wire secondary may be protected against overload by the overcurrent device installed in the primary, as shown in Figure 14–28(A). Section 450.3(B) of the *NEC* permits the rating of the primary overcurrent protection device to be a maximum of 125% of the full-load rated current of the transformer. The next-higher standard rating may be used if the rated primary current of the transformer is 9 A or more. In addition, Section 450.3(B) permits the maximum rating for the primary OCPD to be not more than 167% of the rated current for a rated primary current of less

FIGURE 14–28
Transformer Circuits

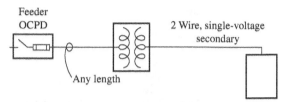

A. Secondary Conductors Protected by Primary OCPD

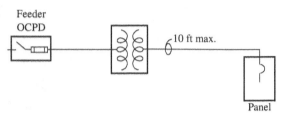

B. 10 ft Tap Rule

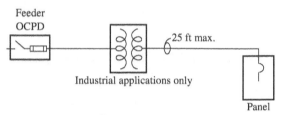

C. 25 ft Tap Rule

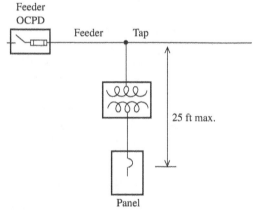

D. Primary Plus Secondary Not Over 25 ft

than 9 A and not more than 300% of the rated primary current for rated primary currents less than 2 A.

The primary circuit conductors must have an ampacity that is at least equal to the rating of the primary overcurrent device. Section 240.21(C)(1) of the *NEC* requires the secondary conductors to have an ampacity that is at least equal to the rating of the primary overcurrent device multiplied by the transformer voltage ratio. Sizing the secondary conductors in this fashion allows the conductors to be protected against overcurrents by the primary OCPD.

10 ft Tap Rule

Section 240.21(C)(2) of the *NEC* discusses the requirements for application of the 10 ft tap rule as applied to transformer secondaries. The conditions for application of the 10 ft tap rule are shown in Figure 14–28(B). The conductors from the transformer secondary terminals to the panel OCPD are considered to be tap conductors. As such, these conductors are not required to have overcurrent protection at their point of supply. To apply the tap rules, the secondary conductors must be protected from physical damage between the transformer secondary terminals and the OCPD located in the panel and cannot exceed 10 ft in length. The ampacity of the secondary conductors must equal or exceed both the rating of the secondary overcurrent protection device (panel OCPD) and the computed load on the panel. The ampacity of the primary circuit conductors is selected to be equal to or greater than the rating of the primary feeder OCPD. Since the primary circuit conductors are protected within their ampacity at the point of supply, they are not considered tap conductors.

Protection of the transformer secondary is achieved by the proper sizing of the OCPD in the panel. To provide overcurrent protection for the transformer, Section 450.3(B) of the *NEC* requires that the panel OCPD must not exceed 125% of the rated secondary current of the transformer. The next-higher standard rating may be selected if this does not correspond to a standard rated device for transformers having a rated secondary current of 9 A or more. The secondary OCPD cannot exceed 167% of the rated secondary current for transformers having a rated secondary current less than 9 A. To provide protection for the panel, the panel OCPD must be sized equal to or less than the rating of the panelboard busbars. With the secondary protected as just described, Section 450.3(B) allows the primary overcurrent protection to be rated at up to 250% of the full-load current rating of the transformer primary. Note that the primary OCPD rating cannot exceed 250% of the full-load current rating of the transformer, for most transformer installations. Section 450.3(B) allows an increase in the rating of the primary OCPD if the transformer is equipped with integral overload protection by the manufacturer. The reader is referred to Section 450.3(B) for specific details.

EXAMPLE 14–13

The 5 kVA, 480–120/240 V, single-phase transformer of Example 14–12 is to be protected on both the primary and the secondary. Determine the appropriate ratings for the primary and secondary OCPD.

Solution: The secondary rated current was determined to be 20.83 A. The secondary OCPD rating is based on 125% of the rated secondary current: 125% × 20.83 A = 26 A. A standard rating of 25 A will be selected, although the next-higher standard rating of 30 A is allowed.

   The rated primary current was calculated as 10.42 A. The primary OCPD rating is not to exceed 250% of the rated primary current: 250% × 10.42 A = 26 A. Therefore, a standard rating of 25 A is selected for the primary OCPD.

EXAMPLE 14–14

The 75 kVA, 480–208Y/120 V, three-phase transformer of Example 14–12 is to be protected on both the primary and the secondary. Determine the appropriate ratings for the primary and secondary OCPD.

Solution: The secondary rated current was determined to be 208.2 A. The secondary OCPD rating is based on 125% of the rated secondary current: 125% × 208.2 A = 260.3 A. A standard rating of 250 A will be selected, although the next-higher standard rating of 300 A is allowed.

   The rated primary current was calculated as 90.2 A. The primary OCPD rating is not to exceed 250% of the rated primary current: 250% × 90.2 A = 225.5 A. Therefore, a standard rating of 225 A is selected for the primary OCPD.

EXAMPLE 14–15

THW copper conductors for the primary and secondary of the 5 kVA, 480–120/240 V, single-phase transformer of Example 14–12 are to be selected. Determine the appropriate-size conductor, assuming the use of 60°C terminals. In addition, the secondary conductors do not exceed 10 ft in length.

Solution: Based on the secondary OCPD rating of 25 A, a #10 AWG THW copper conductor is selected. The required ampacity of the primary circuit conductors is determined based on the rating of the primary overcurrent protection device. For a primary OCPD rating of 25 A, the appropriate-sized conductor is #10 AWG THW copper. Note that the primary conductors are protected against overload and short circuit by the primary OCPD.

EXAMPLE 14–16

A 45 kVA, 480–208Y/120 V, three-phase transformer supplies a panelboard equipped with a main breaker. The distance from the transformer secondary terminals to the panel OCPD is less than 10 ft. The panel OCPD is used to protect both the panelboard and the transformer secondary conductors. The transformer feeder is protected by a fused disconnect switch. Assume the use of 75°C conductors. Determine the following:

a) Maximum rating of the OCPD to protect the panel and transformer secondary conductors

b) THW copper secondary conductor size between the transformer and panel

c) Maximum rating of the OCPD to protect the transformer primary

d) THW copper primary circuit conductor size

Solution:

a) The rated transformer secondary current is

$$I_S = \frac{45,000 \text{ VA}}{\sqrt{3}\ 208 \text{ V}} = 124.9 \text{ A}$$

The maximum secondary OCPD rating is 125% × 124.9 A = 156.1 A. Although it is permissible to round up, a standard rating of 150 A will be used. Note that if this breaker is to protect the panelboard as well as the transformer secondary, the panelboard main busbars must be rated at least 150 A. A standard 225 A panel would most likely be used.

b) The secondary conductor size is based on the 150 A OCPD rating. Therefore, a #1/0 AWG THW copper conductor is selected.

c) The rated transformer primary current is

$$I_P = \frac{45,000 \text{ VA}}{\sqrt{3}\ 480 \text{ V}} = 54.1 \text{ A}$$

The maximum primary OCPD rating is 250% × 54.1 A = 135.3 A. The next-lower standard rating is 125 A. Therefore, a 125 A rating is selected for the transformer primary protection.

d) The minimum ampacity required for the primary conductors is based on the primary OCPD rating of 125 A. Therefore, a #1 AWG THW copper conductor is selected with a table-rated ampacity of 130 A.

25 ft Tap Rule—Industrial Locations

Section 240.21(C)(3) of the *NEC* discusses the requirements for application of the 25 ft tap rule as applied to transformer secondaries in industrial installations. The conditions applicable to the 25 ft tap rule for supervised industrial locations are shown in Figure 14–28(C). The length of the secondary conductors between the transformer secondary terminals and the panel OCPD cannot exceed 25 ft. In addition, the conductors must be protected from physical damage. As indicated in Section 450.3(B) of the *NEC*, the OCPD may consist of up to six separate devices. The sum of the ratings for all the devices cannot exceed that permitted for a single device. In this situation, the ampacity of the secondary conductors must be equal to or greater than the transformer secondary rated current and the sum of the ratings of all OCPDs in the panel. The ampacity of the primary circuit conductors must be equal to or greater than the rating of the primary feeder OCPD. Otherwise, the primary circuit conductors will be considered tap conductors.

As in the 10 ft tap rule, protection of the transformer secondary is achieved by the proper sizing of the OCPDs in the panel. To provide overcurrent protection for the transformer, Section 450.3(B) of the *NEC* requires that the panel OCPD rating (or the sum of the ratings of all OCPDs if multiple OCPDs are used) must not exceed 125% of the rated secondary current of the transformer. The next-higher standard rating may be selected if this does not correspond to a standard rated device for transformers having a rated secondary current of 9 A or more. The secondary OCPD cannot exceed 167% of the rated secondary current for transformers having a rated secondary current less than 9 A. To provide protection for the panel, the panel OCPD must be sized equal to or less than the rating of the panelboard busbars. With the secondary protected as just described, the primary overcurrent protection may be rated at up to 250% of the full-load current rating of the transformer primary, for most transformer installations.

Primary Plus Secondary Not Over 25 ft

The conditions shown in Figure 14–28(D) are perhaps the most common for transformer installations. The primary circuit conductors to the transformer are tapped from a feeder. The secondary conductors terminate in a panel containing a main overcurrent device. The rating of the overcurrent device on the secondary is selected to provide protection for both the panelboard and the transformer secondary. As required by Section 240.21(B)(3) of the *NEC,* the total length of the primary plus secondary conductors cannot exceed 25 ft, and the conductors must be protected from physical damage by a suitable raceway.

The feeder conductors are protected within their ampacity by the feeder overcurrent device. Section 240.21(B)(3) requires that the ampacity of the tap conductors between the tap point and the transformer primary terminals be equal to or greater than one-third the ampere rating of the feeder OCPD. In addition, to protect the tap conductors against overload, the minimum ampacity of the tap conductors must be greater than or equal to the secondary OCPD rating reflected to the primary. In effect, the primary tap conductors will be protected against overload by the secondary OCPD, and against short circuit current by the feeder OCPD.

Section 240.21(B)(3) requires that the ampacity of the transformer secondary conductors must be equal to or greater than one-third times the ampere rating of the feeder OCPD rating multiplied by the reciprocal of the transformer voltage ratio. In addition, the ampacity of the transformer secondary conductors must be equal to or greater than the rating of the secondary OCPD.

Protection of the transformer secondary is achieved by the proper sizing of the OCPD in the panel. As in the previous cases, the required protection is specified by Section 450.3(B) of the *NEC.* To provide overcurrent protection for the transformer, the panel OCPD rating must not exceed 125% of the rated secondary current of the transformer. The next-higher standard rating may be selected if this does not correspond to a standard rated device for transformers having a rated secondary current of 9 A or more. The secondary OCPD cannot exceed 167% of the rated secondary current for transformers having a rated secondary current less than 9 A. To provide protection for the panel, the panel OCPD must be sized equal to or less than the rating of the panelboard busbars. With the secondary protected as just described, the primary overcurrent protection may be rated at up to 250% of the full-load current rating of the transformer primary. Again, note that the protection cannot exceed 250% for most transformer installations. If the rating of the feeder OCPD does not exceed 250% of the rated primary current of the transformer, the feeder OCPD may also be used as primary overcurrent protection for the transformer.

EXAMPLE 14–17

A 112.5 kVA, 480–208Y/120 V, three-phase transformer is to be supplied from a feeder by means of tap conductors, similar to Figure 14–28(D). The transformer secondary conductors terminate in a panel equipped with a main circuit breaker. The total length of the primary and secondary conductors is less than 25 ft. Determine the following:

a) Secondary OCPD rating and the panel main busbar rating
b) Primary feeder OCPD rating if the feeder OCPD is to protect the transformer primary
c) Tap conductor size on the primary
d) Secondary conductor size

Solution: The transformer primary and secondary currents are determined to be 135.3 A and 312.3 A, respectively.

a) The secondary OCPD rating is 125% of the transformer rated secondary current:

$$\text{Secondary OCPD rating} = (125\%)(312.3) = 390.4 \text{ A}$$

The next-higher standard rating of 400 A will be used. The three-phase panel on the secondary side must have a main busbar rating of 400 A minimum.

b) To protect the transformer primary, the maximum rating of the feeder OCPD cannot exceed 250% of the rated primary current:

$$\text{Maximum feeder OCPD rating} = (250\%)(135.3 \text{ A}) = 338.3 \text{ A}$$

Since this is an absolute maximum permissible rating, the next-lower standard rating of 300 A is selected.

c) The ampacity of the primary tap conductor must be sufficient to carry the rated primary current of the transformer. In addition, the minimum tap conductor ampacity must be greater than or equal to $\frac{1}{3}$ times the feeder OCPD rating and greater than or equal to the secondary OCPD rating reflected to the primary. Therefore, a comparison must be made to determine the larger of the rated primary current, $\frac{1}{3}$ times the feeder OCPD rating, and the secondary OCPD rating reflected to the primary. The results are

Transformer rated primary current = 135.3 A
$\frac{1}{3}$ times feeder OCPD rating = $(\frac{1}{3})(300 \text{ A})$ = 100 A
Secondary OCPD rating reflected to primary = (400 A)(208 V ÷ 480 V) = 173.3 A

The largest value of current results from reflecting the secondary OCPD rating to the primary. Therefore, the primary tap conductors must have a minimum ampacity of 173.3 A to be properly protected against overload. A #2/0 AWG THW copper conductor having a table-rated ampacity of 175 A is selected for the primary tap.

d) The secondary conductor must have an ampacity greater than or equal to $\frac{1}{3}$ times the primary feeder OCPD times the reciprocal of the transformer voltage ratio. Also, the secondary conductors must have an ampacity greater than or equal to the rating of the secondary OCPD. The results are

($\frac{1}{3}$)(Feeder OCPD rating)(Voltage ratio) = ($\frac{1}{3}$)(300 A)(480 V ÷ 208 V) = 230.8 A
Secondary OCPD rating = 400 A

Therefore, the secondary conductors must have an ampacity equal to or greater than 400 A. A 600 kcmil THW copper conductor having a table-rated ampacity of 420 A is selected for the secondary conductors. Note it would also be permissible to install parallel conductors if conditions warranted.

PROBLEMS

1. A commercial office building is to be supplied service at 208Y/120 V from the utility company 12.47 kV distribution feeder (12.47 kV line-to-line and 7.2 kV line-to-neutral). The estimated demand load is 85 kW at 0.9 lagging power factor. Determine the appropriate apparent power rating and voltage rating of the three-phase, pad-mounted transformer required to serve this load. The transformer is connected delta–grounded wye. Assume the load is continuous and allow a 25% factor for load growth.

2. Repeat Problem 1 if the service is supplied from a bank of three single-phase overhead transformers connected in a grounded wye–grounded wye configuration. Assume single-bushing transformers.

3. An industrial facility is to be supplied service at 480Y/277 V from the utility company 24.94 kV distribution feeder (24.94 kV line-to-line and 14.4 kV line-to-neutral). The estimated demand load is 290 kW at 0.85 lagging power factor. Determine the appropriate apparent power rating and voltage rating of the three-phase, pad-mounted transformer required to serve this load. The transformer is connected delta–grounded wye. Assume the load is continuous and allow a 25% factor for load growth.

4. Repeat Problem 3 if the service is supplied from a bank of three single-phase overhead transformers connected in a grounded wye–grounded wye configuration. Assume single-bushing transformers.

5. A four-unit residential apartment building is to be supplied service at 120/240 V from the utility company 4.16 kV distribution feeder. The estimated demand load is 35 kW at 0.95 lagging power factor. Determine the appropriate apparent power rating and voltage ratings of the single-phase transformer required to serve this load. Assume the load is continuous and allow a 25% factor for load growth.

6. The estimated load for 120 V loads in an industrial facility is 28 kVA. The facility is supplied with a 480Y/277 V service. Determine the required apparent power and voltage rating of the three-phase step-down transformer required to serve this load. Assume the load is continuous and allow for 25% load growth.

7. Repeat Problem 6 if a single-phase step-down transformer is used.

8. A 25 kVA, 7200–120/240 V, single-phase distribution transformer has an impedance of $R = 1.9\%$ and $X = 1.5\%$. Determine the ohmic resistance and reactance of the transformer referred to the low-voltage side.

9. A 112.5 kVA, 12.47 kV–208/120 V, three-phase transformer has an impedance of $R = 2.5\%$ and $X = 3.5\%$. Determine the ohmic resistance and reactance of the transformer referred to the low-voltage side.

10. A 225 kVA, 12.47 kV–480Y/277 V, three-phase transformer has an impedance of 2.5% and an X/R ratio of 1.5. Determine the ohmic resistance and reactance of the transformer referred to the low-voltage side.

11. A single-phase, dry-type, step-down transformer has a voltage rating of 480–120/240 V. The actual voltage applied to the primary is 490 V. Determine the resulting secondary voltage at no load.

12. A three-phase, dry-type transformer has a voltage rating of 480–208Y/120 V. The voltage applied to the transformer primary is 470 V. Determine the resulting secondary voltage at no load.

13. A 225 kVA, three-phase transformer has a voltage rating of 480–208Y/120 V. The voltage applied to the transformer primary is 470 V. The transformer is equipped with taps as follows: 2 @ 2.5% above nominal, and 4 @ 2.5% below nominal. Determine the resulting secondary voltage at no load for each of the primary tap settings. Which tap setting yields the most acceptable secondary voltage?

14. What is the acceptable sound level for a 225 kVA transformer?

15. A 225 kVA, three-phase transformer has a voltage rating of 480–208Y/120 V. The transformer is supplied by a dedicated feeder from the main distribution panel. The secondary of the transformer terminates in a three-phase panelboard located adjacent to the transformer. Determine the required overcurrent protection and THW copper conductor size required on the primary and secondary.

16. A 25 kVA, single-phase transformer having a voltage rating of 480–120/240 V is supplied by a dedicated feeder from the main distribution panel. The secondary of the transformer terminates in a single-phase panelboard located adjacent to the transformer. Determine the required overcurrent protection and THW copper conductor size required on the primary and secondary.

17. A 75 kVA, three-phase transformer has a voltage rating of 480–208Y/120 V. The transformer primary supply is tapped from a 400 A feeder that originates in the main distribution panel. The total length of the transformer primary plus secondary conductors does not exceed 25 ft. The secondary of the transformer terminates in a three-phase panelboard located adjacent to the transformer. Determine the required overcurrent protection and THW copper conductor size required on the primary and secondary.

15

Capacitor Applications

INTRODUCTION

The application of capacitors to electrical power systems can produce several desirable effects. Improved voltage regulation, power factor correction, reduced line losses, and released system capacity are a few of the advantages. Capacitors are usually installed on a power system in a three-phase configuration rather than single-phase. The individual capacitor units making up a bank may be either three phase or single phase. Capacitors are typically installed in the service entrance switchgear or at the terminals of individual motor installations.

The primary function of capacitors is to supply reactive power to the system. As a result, the capacitors will supply a portion of the reactive power required by various lagging power factor loads in the system. A reduction in line current magnitude, reduced apparent power loading, and reduced I^2R line losses are obtained. In addition, voltage drop is reduced due to the decrease in line current magnitude and improvement in power factor.

OBJECTIVES

Upon completion of this chapter, you will;

- Understand the ratings of capacitors
- Understand power factor improvement
- Be able to size a capacitor to improve power factor
- Be able to calculate voltage rise due to capacitor installation
- Be able to calculate inrush current into a capacitor
- Be able to properly size a conductor for capacitor banks

15–1   CONSTRUCTION AND RATINGS

Low-voltage (less then 1000 V), capacitor units may be either single phase or three phase. The low-voltage, single-phase units typically have two terminals for connection to the line. Three-phase, low-voltage units are typically supplied with three terminals for connection to all three-phase conductors on a three-phase system. Low-voltage capacitors are usually connected in a delta configuration.

Section 460.6 of the *NEC* requires all capacitor units to be supplied with a means to reduce the trapped residual voltage on the capacitor after disconnecting from the supply. Typically, an internal discharge resistor is connected in parallel with the capacitor unit to provide a path for current to flow in the event the capacitor is disconnected from the source. The residual voltage trapped on the capacitor unit must decrease to less than 50 volts within one minute after deenergizing.

Standard voltage ratings for low-voltage capacitor units are 240 V, 480 V, and 600 V. Standard kvar ratings for low-voltage capacitor units are too numerous to list here. The reader is referred to manufacturers' product literature.

15–2   POWER FACTOR IMPROVEMENT

The ability of capacitors to improve the power factor can be understood by examining the one-line diagram for an industrial plant shown in Figure 15–1. The load is assumed to be operating at a lagging power factor. As such, the load will absorb active power, P_{LOAD} and reactive power, Q_{LOAD} from the system. A capacitor bank added to the bus will supply reactive power, Q_{CAP}. This results in a decrease in the reactive power supplied by the source, Q_{SYS}, and consequently an improved power factor. Unity power factor occurs if the reactive power supplied by the capacitor is equal to the reactive power consumed by the load. Under unity power factor conditions, the source does not supply any reactive power to the load.

If the reactive power supplied by the capacitor is less than the reactive power consumed by the load, the overall plant power factor will improve but remain lagging. If the reactive power supplied by the capacitor bank exceeds the reactive power consumed by the load, a leading power factor will result. This condition is sometimes referred to as *overcompensation*. It is generally undesirable to operate a system at a leading power factor.

The expressions for the apparent, active, and reactive powers for balanced three-phase loads are

$$S_{3\phi} = \sqrt{3}V_{LL}I_{LL} \tag{15–1}$$

$$P_{3\phi} = \sqrt{3}V_{LL}I_{LL}\cos(\theta) \tag{15–2}$$

$$Q_{3\phi} = \sqrt{3}V_{LL}I_{LL}\sin(\theta) \tag{15–3}$$

The angle θ is the power factor angle of the load and is assumed to be positive for leading power factor loads. The quantity $\cos(\theta)$ is the load power factor (PF), and the term $\sin(\theta)$ is the reactive factor (RF).

Equations (15–1), (15–2), and (15–3) can be used to express the complex form of the apparent power:

$$S_{3\phi} = P_{3\phi} + jQ_{3\phi} \tag{15–4}$$

FIGURE 15–1
Power Flow Diagram of Industrial Plant

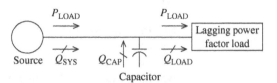

FIGURE 15–2
Power Triangle to Illustrate Power
Factor Correction

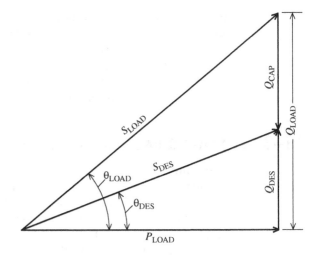

For actual and desired load conditions, a power triangle can be constructed in the complex plane based on Equation (15–4), as shown in Figure 15–2. In reference to Figure 15–2, the following variables are defined:

S_{LOAD} = apparent power consumed by the load before adding capacitors
S_{DES} = apparent power supplied by the source after adding capacitors
Q_{LOAD} = reactive power consumed by the load before adding capacitors
Q_{DES} = reactive power supplied by the source after adding capacitors
P_{LOAD} = active power consumed by the load

In the analysis that follows, it is assumed that the active power consumed by the load will remain constant both before and after the addition of capacitors. The amount of reactive compensation supplied by the capacitor bank is

$$Q_{CAP} = Q_{LOAD} - Q_{DES} \qquad (15\text{–}5)$$

The apparent power for the actual and desired power factor conditions can be expressed in terms of the active power demand and actual and desired power factors as follows:

$$S_{LOAD} = \frac{P_{LOAD}}{PF_{LOAD}} \qquad (15\text{–}6)$$

$$S_{DES} = \frac{P_{LOAD}}{PF_{DES}} \qquad (15\text{–}7)$$

where $PF_{LOAD,}$ and PF_{DES} are the actual load and desired system power factors, respectively.

The reactive power can be expressed in terms of the apparent power and active power for the actual and desired power factor conditions as follows:

$$Q_{\text{LOAD}} = \sqrt{S_{\text{LOAD}}^2 - P_{\text{LOAD}}^2} \qquad (15\text{–}8)$$

$$Q_{\text{DES}} = \sqrt{S_{\text{DES}}^2 - P_{\text{LOAD}}^2} \qquad (15\text{–}9)$$

Substituting Equation (15–6) into (15–8) and Equation (15–7) into (15–9), results in the following:

$$Q_{\text{LOAD}} = \sqrt{\left(\frac{P_{\text{LOAD}}}{PF_{\text{LOAD}}}\right)^2 - P_{\text{LOAD}}^2} \qquad (15\text{–}10)$$

$$Q_{\text{DES}} = \sqrt{\left(\frac{P_{\text{LOAD}}}{PF_{\text{DES}}}\right)^2 - P_{\text{LOAD}}^2} \qquad (15\text{–}11)$$

Substituting Equations (15–10) and (15–11) into Equation (15–5) results in

$$Q_{\text{CAP}} = \sqrt{\left(\frac{P_{\text{LOAD}}}{PF_{\text{LOAD}}}\right)^2 - P_{\text{LOAD}}^2} - \sqrt{\left(\frac{P_{\text{LOAD}}}{PF_{\text{DES}}}\right)^2 - P_{\text{LOAD}}^2}$$

$$= P_{\text{LOAD}} \times \left[\sqrt{\left(\frac{1}{PF_{\text{LOAD}}^2}\right) - 1} - \sqrt{\left(\frac{1}{PF_{\text{DES}}^2}\right) - 1}\right] \qquad (15\text{–}12)$$

Equation (15–12) can be used to determine the reactive power rating of a capacitor bank required to improve the power factor to a desired level.

EXAMPLE 15–1

An industrial plant has an active power demand of 500 kW at a power factor of 0.76 lagging. Determine the reactive power rating of the capacitor bank required to improve the power factor to the following:

a) 0.8 lagging
b) 0.85 lagging
c) 0.9 lagging
d) 0.95 lagging
e) unity

Assume that capacitor steps are available in 50 kvar increments.

Solution: Direct application of Equation (15–12) results in the following:

a) $Q_{\text{CAP}} = 500 \text{ kW} \times \left[\sqrt{\left(\frac{1}{0.76^2}\right) - 1} - \sqrt{\left(\frac{1}{0.80^2}\right) - 1}\right] = 52.6 \text{ kvar} \approx 50 \text{ kvar}$

b) $Q_{\text{CAP}} = 500 \text{ kW} \times \left[\sqrt{\left(\frac{1}{0.76^2}\right) - 1} - \sqrt{\left(\frac{1}{0.85^2}\right) - 1}\right] = 117.7 \text{ kvar} \approx 100 \text{ kvar}$

c) $Q_{\text{CAP}} = 500 \text{ kW} \times \left[\sqrt{\left(\frac{1}{0.76^2}\right) - 1} - \sqrt{\left(\frac{1}{0.90^2}\right) - 1}\right] = 185.4 \text{ kvar} \approx 200 \text{ kvar}$

d) $Q_{CAP} = 500 \text{ kW} \times \left[\sqrt{\left(\dfrac{1}{0.76^2} \right) - 1} - \sqrt{\left(\dfrac{1}{0.95^2} \right) - 1} \right] = 263.2 \text{ kvar} \approx 250 \text{ kvar}$

e) $Q_{CAP} = 500 \text{ kW} \times \left[\sqrt{\left(\dfrac{1}{0.76^2} \right) - 1} - \sqrt{\left(\dfrac{1}{1.0^2} \right) - 1} \right] = 427.6 \text{ kvar} \approx 400 \text{ kvar}$

Notice that in order to improve the power factor to 0.95 power factor, a capacitor bank rating of approximately 250 kvar is required. However, to improve the power factor to unity requires a capacitor bank rating of 400 kvar.

15–3   VOLTAGE IMPROVEMENT

In addition to improved power factor, capacitors will produce a voltage rise on the bus that they are connected to. This voltage rise is due to the leading current of the capacitor being supplied through the inductive reactance of the source. When connected to the low side of a service transformer, the inductive reactance is due primarily to the leakage reactance of the transformer windings.

To understand the voltage rise produced by a capacitor, consider the circuit shown in Figure 15–3. The rated capacitor current is given by

$$I_C = \frac{Q_{CAP}}{\sqrt{3} \times V_{LL}} \qquad (15\text{–}13)$$

where:

Q_{CAP} = Three-phase reactive power rating of the capacitor (var)
V_{LL} = Rated line-to-line voltage of the capacitor bank (V)

The voltage rise produced by the capacitor is equal to

$$V_{RISE} = X_L \times I_c \qquad (15\text{–}14)$$

where X_L is the inductive reactance of the source, and I_C is the rated capacitor current. Substituting Equation (15–13) into (15–14) results in the following:

$$V_{RISE} = X_L \left[\frac{Q_{CAP}}{\sqrt{3} \times V_{LL}} \right] \qquad (15\text{–}15)$$

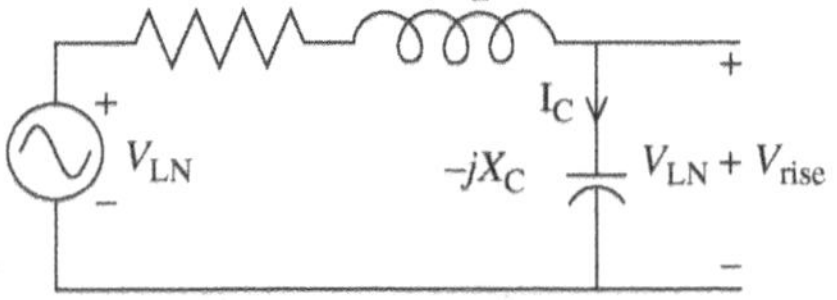

FIGURE 15–3
Equivalent Circuit to Determine Voltage Rise

Line-to-Neutral Equivalent Circuit

The percent voltage rise produced by the capacitor is equal to the actual voltage rise in volts, as given by Equation (15–15), divided by the nominal line-to-neutral system voltage, multiplied by 100. In the form of an equation:

$$\%V_{\text{RISE}} = \frac{V_{\text{RISE}}}{V_{\text{LN}}} \times 100 \qquad (15\text{–}16)$$

Substituting Equation (15–15) into (15–16) results in

$$\%V_{\text{RISE}} = \frac{X_{\text{L}}\left[\dfrac{Q_{\text{CAP}}}{\sqrt{3} \times V_{\text{LL}}}\right]}{V_{\text{LN}}} \times 100 \qquad (15\text{–}17)$$

Recall that for balanced three-phase operation,

$$V_{\text{LN}} = \frac{V_{\text{LL}}}{\sqrt{3}} \qquad (15\text{–}18)$$

Substituting Equation (15–18) into (15–17) results in a simplified expression for the voltage rise due to capacitor installation:

$$\%V_{\text{RISE}} = X_{\text{L}}\left[\frac{Q_{\text{CAP}}}{V_{\text{LL}}^2}\right] \times 100 \qquad (15\text{–}19)$$

EXAMPLE 15–2

A 300 kvar, 480V, three-phase capacitor bank is to be installed at the main switchgear of a 1200 A service. The service transformer is rated 1000 kVA, 4.16 kV–480Y/277V, and has an impedance referred to the low side of $0.0023 + j0.01244$ Ω/phase. Calculate the percentage voltage rise due to this capacitor installation.

Solution: The inductive reactance of the transformer is 0.01244 Ω as given in the problem statement. Direct application of Equation (15–19) results in

$$\%V_{\text{RISE}} = 0.01244\left[\frac{300{,}000 \text{ var}}{(480 \text{ V})^2}\right] \times 100 = 1.6\%$$

15–4   SWITCHING CONSIDERATIONS

In many instances, it is desirable to install several steps of switched capacitor units rather than one large, fixed bank. This is particularly true if the load reactive power requirements fluctuate by a substantial amount during the day. When a deenergized capacitor is energized, the capacitor essentially behaves as an electrical short. A large inrush current will flow into the capacitor bank under these conditions. The inductance of the source will tend to limit the magnitude of the current flowing into the capacitor bank when energized. Energizing a single bank is referred to as *isolated bank switching*.

Likewise, when energizing one step of a multistepped capacitor bank, a high-magnitude current will result as the energized steps discharge into the step being energized. This type of switching is referred to as *back-to-back switching*. Generally, back-to-back switching results in higher-magnitude inrush currents than isolated bank switching.

The calculation of currents during capacitor switching is an extremely important consideration in capacitor applications. Contactors and circuit breakers used for capacitor switching are limited in the amount of momentary current the contacts can safely withstand. The momentary current rating is specified by the switch or breaker manufacturer. Failure to limit momentary inrush current to below specified values will result in contact welding, increased pitting of the contacts, or severe damage to the switch.

Limiting of the inrush current is done by installation of current-limiting inductors. The inductors used for current limiting are typically air core in design. Iron core inductors are not recommended for current-limiting purposes since the iron would saturate under high current conditions. The result of core saturation would be a reduction in the inductance of the inductor; therefore, the effectiveness of the iron core inductor to limit switching currents would be greatly reduced. The continuous-current rating of the inductors must be equal to the continuous-current rating of the capacitor bank.

The high-magnitude currents that occur during capacitor switching are also of relatively high frequency compared to the system frequency. These high-frequency currents will produce high-frequency voltage spikes on the system that may interfere with the operation of various control circuits. When switching large capacitor banks, it is important to consider providing overvoltage protection or isolated power supplies for proper operation of the control circuitry.

Isolated Bank Switching

Exact calculations of capacitor switching currents are extremely difficult to perform manually. In order to provide some basic guidelines, the following assumptions will be made:

1. The system will be analyzed on a single-phase, line-to-neutral equivalent basis.
2. The source will be modeled as a dc voltage source.
3. The magnitude of the dc voltage source model will be constant.
4. The dc voltage source model will have a magnitude equal to the peak line-to-neutral system voltage.
5. Resistance in the system will be neglected.

The validity of these assumptions lies in the fact that the transient period of interest usually occurs in much less than one cycle of the nominal system frequency. As such, the magnitude of the source voltage will not change substantially during the period of interest.

Based on the preceding assumptions, the peak magnitude of the source voltage is

$$V_O = \sqrt{2}\left[\frac{V_{LL}}{\sqrt{3}}\right] \qquad (15\text{--}20)$$

An approximate value of source inductance is given by

$$L_S = \frac{1}{2\pi f} \times \frac{V_{LL}^2}{VA_{SC}}$$ (15–21)

where:

f = system frequency
V_{LL} = line-to-line system voltage
VA_{SC} = three-phase short circuit expressed in volt-amperes

The capacitance per phase of the capacitor bank is given by

$$C = \frac{Q_{CAP}}{2\pi f(V_{LL})^2}$$ (15–22)

The detailed solution for the maximum instantaneous peak inrush current is beyond the scope of this text. The maximum instantaneous peak value of the inrush current is given by the following:

$$I_{MAX} = V_O\sqrt{\frac{C}{L_S}}$$ (15–23)

EXAMPLE 15–3

Determine the peak instantaneous switching current for the capacitor bank of the previous example.

Solution: The system inductance is assumed to be equal to the inductance of the transformer winding. The inductive reactance was given as 0.01244 Ω. The corresponding inductance is $0.01244 \div (2\pi 60) = 33 \times 10^{-6}$ H. The capacitance is determined by application of Equation (15–22):

$$C = \frac{300,000 \text{ var}}{2\pi 60(480 \text{ V})^2} = 3.45 \times 10^{-3} \text{ F}$$

The peak instantaneous system voltage is given by Equation (15–20):

$$V_O = \sqrt{2}\left[\frac{480 \text{ V}}{\sqrt{3}}\right] = 392 \text{ V}$$

The maximum peak instantaneous current is given by Equation (15–23):

$$I_{MAX} = 392 \text{ V}\sqrt{\frac{3.45 \times 10^{-3} \text{ F}}{33 \times 10^{-6} \text{ H}}} = 4008 \text{ A}$$

Back-to-Back Switching

The inrush current that flows between the steps in a capacitor bank consisting of several steps is also of concern. The most severe switching duty will arise when the last step is being energized, with all other steps energized, and the system voltage is at maximum peak value. Under these conditions, the energized steps will discharge into the step being switched on. For the purposes of this analysis, the source contribution of current will be neglected.

To determine the inrush current that flows when capacitors are switched back-to-back, it will be assumed that all steps in the bank are of equal rating. Each step has a capacitance C and an inductance L. Let N represent the number of steps of capacitance that may be switched on and off as reactive power demands dictate. The maximum peak instantaneous current flowing into the last step to be switched is given by

$$I_{MAX} = V_O \left[\frac{N-1}{N} \right] \sqrt{\frac{C}{L}} \qquad (15\text{--}24)$$

EXAMPLE 15–4

A 500 kvar, 480 V, three-step capacitor bank is comprised of ten steps of 50 kvar each. The lead inductance of the cabling between steps is 5 μH. Determine the inrush current into the last step to become energized.

Solution: The capacitance per step is calculated by applying Equation (15–22):

$$C = \frac{50,000 \text{ var}}{2\pi 60(480 \text{ V})^2} = 575.6 \times 10^{-6} \text{ F}$$

Application of Equation (15–24) results in

$$I_{MAX} = 392 \text{ V} \left[\frac{10-1}{10} \right] \sqrt{\frac{575.6 \times 10^{-6} \text{ F}}{5 \times 10^{-6} \text{ H}}} = 3785 \text{ A}$$

Note that the full-load current of the 50 kvar step is 60.1 A. Thus, the inrush current represents approximately 63 times rated current.

15–5   CONTROLS

Capacitor banks may be permanently connected (fixed) or switched as reactive power demands dictate. Fixed capacitors are generally sized to supply reactive power equal to the minimum reactive power demands of the system. Switched capacitors are used to supply the variable amount of reactive power needed as the reactive power demands of the load fluctuate. Switching of the capacitor banks may be done either manually or automatically. There are several types of automatic control that can be used to initiate switching of capacitor banks. These include time clock, power factor, and voltage. The type of control selected will be dependent on the primary function of the capacitor bank itself.

Time clocks can be used where the reactive power demand is a predictable function of time. Examination of the reactive load profile at a given bus will indicate the desired switching times. The reactive power consumption of industrial plant loads may also be a predictable function of time based on manufacturing and shift schedules. It must be understood that capacitor switching based on time ignores the actual load conditions and may produce undesirable results. However, capacitor switching based on time of day is the most economical of all automatic switching schemes.

If the primary function of the capacitor bank is to control the load power factor to a specified value, a controller that senses the load power factor is the most desirable. This type of control will operate independently of time and generally produces the most desirable effect. Typically, a set of current and/or voltage transformers may be needed to provide the appropriate electrical quantities to the controller. The costs associated with controllers based on load power factor are generally higher than time-based control. This is due to the increased complexity of the controller itself, as well as the need for voltage and current transformers.

Control based on voltage is used where the primary function of the capacitor bank is to provide voltage improvement. The capacitor will be switched on and off based on the magnitude of the system voltage. An increase in the reactive power demand of a lagging power factor load will cause a reduction in the bus voltage. The decrease in voltage is sensed by the controller and switching action initiated. Conversely, as the reactive power demand of the load decreases, the bus voltage will tend to increase. Under these conditions, the controller will switch the capacitor steps off to prevent excessive bus voltages from occurring.

Switching of multistep capacitor banks is usually performed one step at a time. A time delay between step switching is often included to allow the system to adjust to the new conditions. The amount of time delay is often adjustable by the user. Also, an adjustable reactive power bandwidth is provided to prevent excessive hunting of the controller, thereby minimizing switching operations. Excessive switching will cause premature wear of the switch contacts and control mechanism.

15–6   CONDUCTOR SIZING

Section 460.8 of the *NEC* requires the ampacity of conductors supplying capacitor circuits to be at least 135% of the full-load rated current of the capacitor. In addition, tap conductors supplying capacitors connected to motor terminals must have an ampacity of at least one-third the ampacity of the motor circuit conductors.

Overcurrent protection must be provided in each ungrounded conductor supplying a capacitor bank. For capacitors installed at motor terminals, the motor overload device may serve as the overload protective device for the capacitor bank. The overcurrent protective device must be rated as low as possible to protect the capacitor without operating. A disconnect must be provided to isolate the capacitor bank from the supply. For capacitors installed at motor terminals, the motor or motor controller disconnect may serve as the required disconnecting device. Section 460.8(C) of the *NEC* requires that the rating of the disconnect be at least 135% of the rated current of the capacitor.

EXAMPLE 15–5

What size THW copper conductor is required to supply a 300 kvar, 480 V, fixed capacitor bank? Use 75°C terminations.

Solution: The rated current of the capacitor bank is

$$I_C = \frac{300,000 \text{ var}}{\sqrt{3} \times 480 \text{ V}} = 361 \text{ A}$$

The minimum conductor ampacity is 135% of 361 A, or 487 A. Therefore, a parallel arrangement of two 250 kcmil, THW copper conductors per phase would be required. The table-rated ampacity is 255 A per conductor, or 510 A for the two conductors in parallel per phase.

EXAMPLE 15–6

A 20 kvar, 480 V, three-phase capacitor is connected to the terminals of a 50 hp, 460 V, three-phase induction motor. The motor feeder consists of #4 THW copper conductor. Determine the required tap conductor size for the capacitor tap.

Solution: The table-rated ampacity of the #4 THW copper conductor is 85 A. The full-load current of the capacitor bank is

$$I_C = \frac{20,000 \text{ var}}{\sqrt{3} \times 480 \text{ V}} = 24.1 \text{ A}$$

The minimum required ampacity of the tap conductor based on 135% of the capacitor rated current is (24.1A)(135%) = 32.5 A. From the ampacity tables, a #10 THW copper conductor having a table-rated ampacity of 30 A is selected.

In addition, the tap conductor must have an ampacity at least one-third the ampacity of the motor feeder conductor, or ($\frac{1}{3}$)(85 A) = 28.33 A. Since the tap conductor has an ampacity exceeding one-third the ampacity of the motor feeder conductor, this installation meets *NEC* requirements.

PROBLEMS

1. An industrial plant is supplied service at 480Y/277 V, three-phase, four-wire. The plant has an active power demand of 1200 kW at a power factor of 0.72 lagging. Determine the following:
   a) apparent power demand
   b) reactive power demand
   c) line current magnitude
   d) rating of capacitor bank required to improve the plant power factor to 0.95 lagging
   e) active, reactive, and apparent power demands after addition of the capacitors
   f) line current magnitude after addition of the capacitors

2. A 480Y/277 V, three-phase, four-wire service is supplied by a 500 kVA transformer. The transformer impedance is 0.006 + j0.0287 Ω/phase. A 200 kvar, 480 V capacitor bank is installed at the main distribution switchgear. Calculate the percentage voltage rise due to the installation of this capacitor bank.

3. A 200 kvar, 480 V capacitor bank is installed on a plant bus supplied from a 750 kVA, 12.47 kV–480Y/277 V transformer having a nameplate impedance of 6.8%. Neglecting the impedance of the 12.47 kV source and transformer resistance, determine the maximum instantaneous value of the transient inrush current when the capacitor bank is switched on.

4. A four-step, 480 kV capacitor bank consists of four steps of 100 kvar each. The lead inductance of the connecting leads between the steps is 10 μH. Determine the maximum peak instantaneous inrush current when the last step is switched on.

5. Determine the THW copper conductor required to supply the capacitor bank of Problem 3.

6. A 25 kvar, 480 V capacitor is connected to the terminals of a 75 hp, 460 V, three-phase induction motor. The motor feeder consists of #1 THW copper conductor. Determine the required tap conductor size for this installation.

16

Voltage Drop Calculations

INTRODUCTION

This chapter discusses the calculation of voltage drop on electrical power distribution systems. Voltage drop occurs when load current flows through a conductor or transformer having a finite impedance. This voltage drop may result in lower-than-normal system voltage at a given point in the power system. Normal system voltage is defined to be within a certain tolerance of nominal system voltage. Lower-than-normal voltage on a system will result in motor failures, dropout of motor starters, and dimming of lamps. Higher-than-normal system voltage will cause motor failures due to insulation stress, saturation of transformers, and so on. The total allowable voltage drop between the service and the utilization device should not exceed 5% of nominal system voltage.

The actual voltage present on the power system lines will differ from the nominal values due to voltage drops across line and transformer impedances. The ability to calculate voltage drops in a power system is of prime importance to the system designer. Selection of conductor size is often determined with consideration of voltage drop as well as current-carrying capability. This is particularly true for branch circuits with long home runs between the panel and the first utilization device or outlet on the circuit.

OBJECTIVES

Upon completion of the chapter, you will:

- Understand the allowable voltage range permitted for services
- Understand the approximate method of voltage drop calculation
- Be able to calculate the voltage drop along single-phase and three-phase conductors
- Be able to calculate voltage drop along parallel conductors
- Be able to calculate voltage drop across single-phase and three-phase transformers
- Be able to calculate voltage drop due to motor starting
- Be able to perform voltage drop calculations on simple three-phase and single-phase systems

16–1   VOLTAGE RANGES

As previously stated, the actual voltage present in any part of a power distribution system will deviate from nominal due to voltage drops on the system. ANSI Standard C84 specifies the allowable tolerances for various nominal voltage levels. For low-voltage systems (<1000 V), the actual service voltage must lie within ±5% of nominal for continuous operation. On medium-voltage systems up to 35 kV, the service voltage must lie within −2.5% and +5% of nominal for continuous operation. Any voltage deviations beyond these tolerances must be corrected. On high-voltage transmission systems, the voltage range is generally the same as for medium-voltage systems.

EXAMPLE 16–1

Calculate the allowable service voltage range for a 120/240 V, single-phase, three-wire service.

Solution: The lower end of the range is

$$V = 240 \times 0.95 = 228 \text{ V line-to-line}$$
$$V = 120 \times 0.95 = 114 \text{ V line-to-neutral}$$

The upper end of the range is

$$V = 240 \times 1.05 = 252 \text{ V}$$
$$V = 120 \times 1.05 = 126 \text{ V}$$

Therefore, the allowable range for line-to-neutral voltage is 114 V to 126 V. The allowable range for the phase-to-phase voltage is 228 V to 256 V.

EXAMPLE 16–2

Calculate the allowable service voltage range for a 480Y/277 V, three-phase, four-wire service.

Solution: The lower end of the range is

$$V = 480 \times 0.95 = 456 \text{ V line-to-line}$$
$$V = 277 \times 0.95 = 263.2 \text{ V line-to-neutral}$$

The upper end of the range is

$$V = 480 \times 1.05 = 504 \text{ V}$$
$$V = 277 \times 1.05 = 291 \text{ V}$$

Therefore, the allowable range for line-to-neutral voltage is 263.2 V to 291 V. The allowable range for the phase-to-phase voltage is 456 V to 504 V.

Examples 16–1 and 16–2 illustrate the calculation of allowable voltage ranges for service voltage. The electrical system designer is responsible for designing the system to provide adequate voltage within the specified range.

16–2   VOLTAGE DROP DEFINED

The voltage drop that occurs in three-phase and single-phase systems can be calculated by assuming balanced conditions. Balanced conditions on a three-phase system implies that the three line currents are equal in magnitude and displaced 120° in phase from each other. Also, the source voltage is assumed to be balanced, as are the impedances of the cables in each phase. For single-phase, three-wire and three-phase, four-wire systems, balanced conditions assume the neutral current is zero. As a result, there is no voltage drop across the neutral conductor. However, when calculating the voltage drop on a branch circuit consisting of the ungrounded and grounded (neutral) conductor of a system, the neutral current is not zero and the voltage drop across the neutral conductor must be taken into account.

The voltage drop is determined by multiplying the complex line current by the impedance of the line. Typically, the line-to-neutral voltage at the source end of the cable segment is selected as a reference. The line current is then determined with respect to the reference voltage. The voltage at the end of the cable segment is then equal to the voltage at the sending end minus the impedance voltage drop in the cable. The equivalent circuit is shown in Figure 16–1(A). In reference to Figure 16–1(A), the line current is designated as

FIGURE 16–1
Equivalent Circuit for Voltage Drop
Calculations

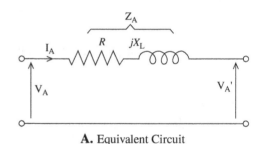

A. Equivalent Circuit

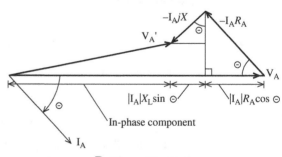

B. Phasor Diagram

I_A, the source end voltage as V_A, the voltage at the end of the cable as $V_{A'}$, and the cable impedance as Z_A. The voltage at the end of the cable segment is found by applying Kirchoff's voltage law to the circuit shown in Figure 16–1(A):

$$\mathbf{V}_{A'} = \mathbf{V}_A - \mathbf{I}_A \times \mathbf{Z}_A \tag{16–1}$$

The magnitude of the voltage drop that occurs along the line is defined as being equal to the magnitude of the sending-end voltage minus the magnitude of the receiving-end voltage:

$$|V_{DROP}| = |\mathbf{V}_A - \mathbf{V}_{A'}| \tag{16–2}$$

The phasor diagram shown in Figure 16–1(B) represents the source- and load-end conditions. As an approximation, the magnitude of the voltage drop can be determined by subtracting the in-phase component of the voltage drop from the sending-end voltage. The result is

$$|V_{DROP}| \approx |\mathbf{I}_A| \times [R_L \times \cos(\theta) - X_L \times \sin(\theta)] \tag{16–3}$$

where:

R_L = circuit resistance in ohms
X_L = circuit reactance in ohms
θ = phase angle of line current

The voltage drop is usually expressed as a percentage of nominal, as follows:

$$\% \, V_{DROP} = \frac{|V_{DROP}|}{|\mathbf{V}_A|} \times 100\% \tag{16–4}$$

16–3   CABLE IMPEDANCES

The cable impedance values are determined from Table 16–1. Note that the data shown in Table 16–1 represents the impedance, in ohms, to neutral for three-phase systems. Also, the impedance is expressed in both ohms per kilometer and ohms per 1000 ft of cable.

Three Phase

Since the three-phase voltage drop calculation assumes a balanced loading condition, no neutral current flows back to the source. Thus, the impedance to be used for three-phase voltage drop calculations is sometimes referred to as the "*one-way*" impedance. The ohmic cable impedances are calculated as

$$R_L = \frac{\text{Resistance in ohms/1000 ft}}{1000} \times (\text{Cable length in ft}) \tag{16–5}$$

$$X_L = \frac{\text{Reactance in ohms/1000 ft}}{1000} \times (\text{Cable length in ft}) \tag{16–6}$$

TABLE 16-1
Table 9 Alternating-Current Resistance and Reactance for 600-Volt Cables, 3-Phase, 60 Hz, 75°C (167°F)—Three Single Conductors in Conduit

Ohms to Neutral per Kilometer / Ohms to Neutral per 1000 Feet

Size (AWG or kcmil)	X_L (Reactance) for All Wires — PVC, Aluminum Conduits	X_L (Reactance) for All Wires — Steel Conduit	AC Resistance Uncoated Copper — PVC Conduit	AC Resistance Uncoated Copper — Aluminum Conduit	AC Resistance Uncoated Copper — Steel Conduit	AC Resistance Aluminum — PVC Conduit	AC Resistance Aluminum — Aluminum Conduit	AC Resistance Aluminum — Steel Conduit	Effective Z at 0.85 PF Uncoated Copper — PVC Conduit	Effective Z at 0.85 PF Uncoated Copper — Aluminum Conduit	Effective Z at 0.85 PF Uncoated Copper — Steel Conduit	Effective Z at 0.85 PF Aluminum — PVC Conduit	Effective Z at 0.85 PF Aluminum — Aluminum Conduit	Effective Z at 0.85 PF Aluminum — Steel Conduit	Size (AWG or kcmil)
14	0.190 / 0.058	0.240 / 0.073	10.2 / 3.1	10.2 / 3.1	10.2 / 3.1	— / —	— / —	— / —	8.9 / 2.7	8.9 / 2.7	8.9 / 2.7	— / —	— / —	— / —	14
12	0.177 / 0.054	0.223 / 0.068	6.6 / 2.0	6.6 / 2.0	6.6 / 2.0	10.5 / 3.2	10.5 / 3.2	10.5 / 3.2	5.6 / 1.7	5.6 / 1.7	5.6 / 1.7	9.2 / 2.8	9.2 / 2.8	9.2 / 2.8	12
10	0.164 / 0.050	0.207 / 0.063	3.9 / 1.2	3.9 / 1.2	3.9 / 1.2	6.6 / 2.0	6.6 / 2.0	6.6 / 2.0	3.6 / 1.1	3.6 / 1.1	3.6 / 1.1	5.9 / 1.8	5.9 / 1.8	5.9 / 1.8	10
8	0.171 / 0.052	0.213 / 0.065	2.56 / 0.78	2.56 / 0.78	2.56 / 0.78	4.3 / 1.3	4.3 / 1.3	4.3 / 1.3	2.26 / 0.69	2.26 / 0.69	2.30 / 0.70	3.6 / 1.1	3.6 / 1.1	3.6 / 1.1	8
6	0.167 / 0.051	0.210 / 0.064	1.61 / 0.49	1.61 / 0.49	1.61 / 0.49	2.66 / 0.81	2.66 / 0.81	2.66 / 0.81	1.44 / 0.44	1.48 / 0.45	1.48 / 0.45	2.33 / 0.71	2.36 / 0.72	2.36 / 0.72	6
4	0.157 / 0.048	0.197 / 0.060	1.02 / 0.31	1.02 / 0.31	1.02 / 0.31	1.67 / 0.51	1.67 / 0.51	1.67 / 0.51	0.95 / 0.29	0.95 / 0.29	0.98 / 0.30	1.51 / 0.46	1.51 / 0.46	1.51 / 0.46	4
3	0.154 / 0.047	0.194 / 0.059	0.82 / 0.25	0.82 / 0.25	0.82 / 0.25	1.31 / 0.40	1.35 / 0.41	1.31 / 0.40	0.75 / 0.23	0.79 / 0.24	0.79 / 0.24	1.21 / 0.37	1.21 / 0.37	1.21 / 0.37	3

			2	1	1/0	2/0	3/0	4/0	250	300	350	400	500	600
2	0.148 / 0.045	0.187 / 0.057	0.62 / 0.19	0.66 / 0.20	0.66 / 0.20	1.05 / 0.32	1.05 / 0.32	1.05 / 0.32	0.62 / 0.19	0.62 / 0.19	0.66 / 0.20	0.98 / 0.30	0.98 / 0.30	0.98 / 0.30
1	0.151 / 0.046	0.187 / 0.057	0.49 / 0.15	0.52 / 0.16	0.52 / 0.16	0.82 / 0.25	0.85 / 0.26	0.82 / 0.25	0.52 / 0.16	0.52 / 0.16	0.52 / 0.16	0.79 / 0.24	0.79 / 0.24	0.82 / 0.25
1/0	0.144 / 0.044	0.180 / 0.055	0.39 / 0.12	0.43 / 0.13	0.39 / 0.12	0.66 / 0.20	0.69 / 0.21	0.66 / 0.20	0.43 / 0.13	0.43 / 0.13	0.43 / 0.13	0.62 / 0.19	0.66 / 0.20	0.66 / 0.20
2/0	0.141 / 0.043	0.177 / 0.054	0.33 / 0.10	0.33 / 0.10	0.33 / 0.10	0.52 / 0.16	0.52 / 0.16	0.52 / 0.16	0.36 / 0.11	0.36 / 0.11	0.36 / 0.11	0.52 / 0.16	0.52 / 0.16	0.52 / 0.16
3/0	0.138 / 0.042	0.171 / 0.052	0.253 / 0.077	0.269 / 0.082	0.259 / 0.079	0.43 / 0.13	0.43 / 0.13	0.43 / 0.13	0.289 / 0.088	0.302 / 0.092	0.308 / 0.094	0.43 / 0.13	0.43 / 0.13	0.46 / 0.14
4/0	0.135 / 0.041	0.167 / 0.051	0.203 / 0.062	0.220 / 0.067	0.207 / 0.063	0.33 / 0.10	0.36 / 0.11	0.33 / 0.10	0.243 / 0.074	0.256 / 0.078	0.262 / 0.080	0.36 / 0.11	0.36 / 0.11	0.36 / 0.11
250	0.135 / 0.041	0.171 / 0.052	0.171 / 0.052	0.187 / 0.057	0.177 / 0.054	0.279 / 0.085	0.295 / 0.090	0.282 / 0.086	0.217 / 0.066	0.230 / 0.070	0.240 / 0.073	0.308 / 0.094	0.322 / 0.098	0.33 / 0.10
300	0.135 / 0.041	0.167 / 0.051	0.144 / 0.044	0.161 / 0.049	0.148 / 0.045	0.233 / 0.071	0.249 / 0.076	0.236 / 0.072	0.194 / 0.059	0.207 / 0.063	0.213 / 0.065	0.269 / 0.082	0.282 / 0.086	0.289 / 0.088
350	0.131 / 0.040	0.164 / 0.050	0.125 / 0.038	0.141 / 0.043	0.128 / 0.039	0.200 / 0.061	0.217 / 0.066	0.207 / 0.063	0.174 / 0.053	0.190 / 0.058	0.197 / 0.060	0.240 / 0.073	0.253 / 0.077	0.262 / 0.080
400	0.131 / 0.040	0.161 / 0.049	0.108 / 0.033	0.125 / 0.038	0.115 / 0.035	0.177 / 0.054	0.194 / 0.059	0.180 / 0.055	0.161 / 0.049	0.174 / 0.053	0.184 / 0.056	0.217 / 0.066	0.233 / 0.071	0.240 / 0.073
500	0.128 / 0.039	0.157 / 0.048	0.089 / 0.027	0.105 / 0.032	0.095 / 0.029	0.141 / 0.043	0.157 / 0.048	0.148 / 0.045	0.141 / 0.043	0.157 / 0.048	0.164 / 0.050	0.187 / 0.057	0.200 / 0.061	0.210 / 0.064
600	0.128 / 0.039	0.157 / 0.048	0.075 / 0.023	0.092 / 0.028	0.082 / 0.025	0.118 / 0.036	0.135 / 0.041	0.125 / 0.038	0.131 / 0.040	0.144 / 0.044	0.154 / 0.047	0.167 / 0.051	0.180 / 0.055	0.190 / 0.058

Source: Reprinted with permission from NFPA 70 *The National Electric Code* © 2002, National Fire Protection Association, Quincy, MA 02269. This reprinted material is not the referenced subject which is represented only by the standard in its entirety.

Parallel Conductors

For installations involving parallel conductors, the voltage drop can be calculated in one of two ways. The first method involves calculating the equivalent impedance of the parallel conductors and multiplying by the total current flowing in the conductors. The equivalent impedance of the parallel conductors is equal to the table value divided by the number of parallel conductors per phase.

The second method involves calculating the current flowing in an individual conductor of the parallel group, which is simply the table value. This current is equal to the total current flowing divided by the number of parallel conductors per phase. The voltage drop is then calculated by multiplying the current in an individual conductor by the current flowing in that conductor. Since the conductors making up the parallel installation are of the same length, type, and so on, the voltage drop is the same in each conductor.

EXAMPLE 16–3

Determine the percent voltage drop along a 480 V, three-phase feeder, 75 ft in length, consisting of one 500 kcmil THW copper conductor per phase. The current is 300 $\angle -30°$ A. Assume steel conduit.

Solution: From Table 16–1, the resistance is 0.029 Ω/1000 ft and the reactance is 0.048 Ω per 1000 ft. Applying Equations (16–5) and (16–6) results in

$$R_L = \frac{0.029 \ \Omega/1000 \ ft}{1000} \times (75 \ ft) = 0.002175 \ \Omega$$

$$X_L = \frac{0.048 \ \Omega/1000 \ ft}{1000} \times (75 \ ft) = 0.0036 \ \Omega$$

The voltage drop is given by Equation (16–3):

$$|V_{DROP}| \approx 300 \ A \times [0.002175 \ \Omega \times \cos(-30°) - 0.0036 \ \Omega \times \sin(-30°)] = 1.105 \ V$$

The line-to-neutral voltage is 277 V. Therefore, the percent voltage drop is given by Equation (16–4):

$$\% \ V_{DROP} = \frac{1.105 \ V}{277 \ V} \times 100\% = 0.4\%$$

EXAMPLE 16–4

Determine the voltage drop along a 480 V, three-phase feeder, 75 ft in length, consisting of three 500 kcmil THW copper conductors in parallel per phase. The load current is 950 $\angle -30°$ A. Assume steel conduit.

Solution: From Table 16–1, the resistance is 0.029 Ω/1000 ft and the reactance is 0.048 Ω per 1000 ft. Note that these values are for a single conductor. For three conductors in parallel per phase, the resistance is ($\frac{1}{3}$)(0.029 Ω/1000 ft) = 0.00967 Ω/1000 ft. Likewise, the reactance is $(\frac{1}{3})(0.048 \ \Omega/1000 \ \text{ft}) = 0.016 \ \Omega/1000 \ \text{ft}$. Applying Equations (16–5) and (16–6) results in

$$R_L = \frac{0.00967 \ \Omega/1000 \ \text{ft}}{1000} \times (75 \ \text{ft}) = 0.000732 \ \Omega$$

$$X_L = \frac{0.016 \ \Omega/1000 \ \text{ft}}{1000} \times (75 \ \text{ft}) = 0.0012 \ \Omega$$

The voltage drop is given by Equation (16–3):

$$|V_{\text{DROP}}| \approx 950 \ \text{A} \times [0.000732 \ \Omega \times \cos(-30°) - 0.0012 \ \Omega \times \sin(-30°)] = 1.172 \ \text{V}$$

The line-to-neutral voltage is 277 V. Therefore, the percent voltage drop is given by Equation (16–4):

$$\% \ V_{\text{DROP}} = \frac{1.172 \ \text{V}}{277 \ \text{V}} \times 100\% = 0.423\%$$

Single Phase

When calculating the voltage drop in a single-phase system, the load current will flow from the source to the load and back to the source. Thus, unlike the voltage drop calculations in a three-phase system, the cable impedance between the source and load must be taken as twice that shown in Table 16–1. The ohmic cable impedances are calculated as

$$R_L = 2 \times \frac{\text{Resistance in ohms/1000 ft}}{1000} \times (\text{Cable length in ft}) \qquad \textbf{(16–7)}$$

$$X_L = 2 \times \frac{\text{Reactance in ohms/1000 ft}}{1000} \times (\text{Cable length in ft}) \qquad \textbf{(16–8)}$$

EXAMPLE 16–5

Determine the voltage drop along a 120 V, single-phase branch circuit 100 ft in length, consisting of #12 AWG THW copper conductor. The load current is $15 \angle -20°$ A. Assume steel conduit.

Solution: From the impedance tables, the resistance and reactance are 2.0 Ω/1000 ft and 0.068 Ω/1000 ft, respectively. Application of Equations (16–7) and (16–8) results in

$$R_L = 2 \times \frac{2.0 \ \Omega/1000 \ \text{ft}}{1000} \times (100 \ \text{ft}) = 0.4 \ \Omega$$

$$X_L = 2 \times \frac{0.068 \ \Omega/1000 \ \text{ft}}{1000} \times (100 \ \text{ft}) = 0.0136 \ \Omega$$

The voltage drop is given by Equation (16–3):

$$|V_{\text{DROP}}| \approx 15 \ \text{A} \times [0.4 \ \Omega \times \cos(-20°) - 0.0136 \ \Omega \times \sin(-20°)] = 5.708 \ \text{V}$$

The line-to-neutral voltage is 120 V. Therefore, the percent voltage drop is given by Equation (16–4):

$$\% \ V_{\text{DROP}} = \frac{5.708 \ V}{120 \ V} \times 100\% = 4.757\%$$

16–4   TRANSFORMER VOLTAGE DROP

Another significant source of voltage drop in a power system is the voltage drop through transformers. The voltage drop through a transformer can be calculated using the percent resistance and percent inductive reactance. The resistance and reactance can be referred to either the high-voltage or low-voltage side. However, care must be taken to ensure that all calculations are done on either the high side or the low side. For example, if the transformer impedances are determined on the low side, then the load current referred to the low side must be used. Typically, the excitation branch of the transformer equivalent circuit is neglected when performing voltage drop calculations. Voltage drop calculations for three-phase and single-phase transformers are presented in this section.

The voltage drop for a three-phase transformer will be calculated assuming the resistance and inductive reactance are equal in all three phases. Therefore, the voltage drop can be calculated on a single-phase, line-to-neutral equivalent basis, using phase A as a reference. The method presented also applies to three identical single-phase transformers connected in a bank to supply balanced three-phase loads and to single-phase, three-wire transformers supplying a balanced single-phase load.

The single-phase equivalent circuit with all parameters referred to the low-voltage side is shown in Figure 16–2. Assuming a constant-current representation for the load and applying Kirchoff's voltage law around the secondary results in

$$\mathbf{E}_{\text{LS}} = \mathbf{V}_{\text{LS}} + \mathbf{I}_{\text{LS}} \times [R_{\text{TR}} + jX_{\text{TR}}] \qquad \textbf{(16–9)}$$

where:

$\mathbf{E}_{\text{LS}}$ = induced voltage on low-voltage side
$\mathbf{V}_{\text{LS}}$ = terminal voltage on low-voltage side
$\mathbf{I}_{\text{LS}}$ = load current on low-voltage side
R_{TR} = equivalent resistance referred to low-voltage side
X_{TR} = equivalent reactance referred to low-voltage side

FIGURE 16–2
Transformer Equivalent Circuit

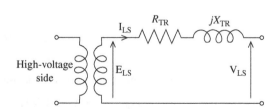

For the purposes of this text, the approximate method of voltage drop calculations will be used for transformers. The rated line-to-neutral terminal voltage on the low-voltage side will be selected as reference. Also, the load current must be calculated on the low-voltage side of the transformer. The voltage drop through the transformer using the approximate method is

$$|V_{\text{DROP}}| \approx |\mathbf{I}_{\text{LS}}| \times [R_{\text{TR}} \times \cos(\theta) - X_{\text{TR}} \times \sin(\theta)] \qquad (16\text{--}10)$$

The voltage drop expressed as a percentage of rated voltage is equal to

$$\% \ V_{\text{DROP}} = \frac{|V_{\text{DROP}}|}{|\mathbf{V}_{\text{LS}}|} \times 100\% \qquad (16\text{--}11)$$

Three-Phase Transformer Impedance

As presented in Chapter 14, the transformer impedances are generally specified in percents based on the nameplate apparent power and voltage rating of the transformer. When performing voltage drop calculations, it is common to refer the transformer impedances to the low-voltage side of the transformer. The ohmic impedances reflected to the low-voltage side are given by

$$R_{\text{TR}} = \frac{1}{100} \left[\frac{(\% \ R)(\text{Secondary line voltage})^2}{\text{Transformer voltampere rating}} \right] \qquad (16\text{--}12)$$

$$X_{\text{TR}} = \frac{1}{100} \left[\frac{(\% \ X)(\text{Secondary line voltage})^2}{\text{Transformer voltampere rating}} \right] \qquad (16\text{--}13)$$

If the transformer percent impedance $\% \ Z_{\text{TR}}$, and X/R ratio are given, the resistance and reactance can be determined by first calculating the transformer impedance angle according to

$$\theta = \tan^{-1}(X/R) \qquad (16\text{--}14)$$

The impedance angle together with the impedance magnitude are then used to calculate the transformer percent resistance and reactance as follows:

$$\% \ R_{\text{TR}} = \% \ Z_{\text{TR}} \times \cos(\theta) \qquad (16\text{--}15)$$

$$\% \ X_{\text{TR}} = \% \ Z_{\text{TR}} \times \sin(\theta) \qquad (16\text{--}16)$$

Equations (16–12) and (16–13) are then used to determine the ohmic impedance of the transformer referred to the low-voltage side.

EXAMPLE 16–6

Determine the voltage drop through a 112.5 kVA, 480–208Y/120 V, three-phase transformer having an impedance of 3%, and an X/R ratio of 1.5. The transformer is operating at full load, 0.8 lagging power factor.

Solution: The impedance angle is given by Equation (16–14):

$$\theta = \tan^{-1}(1.5) = 56.3°$$

The transformer percent resistance and percent reactance according to Equations (16–15) and (16–16) are

$$\% R_{TR} = 3\% \times \cos(56.3°) = 1.66\%$$

$$\% X_{TR} = 3\% \times \sin(56.3°) = 2.5\%$$

The ohmic resistance and reactance are given by Equations (16–12) and (16–13):

$$R_{TR} = \frac{1}{100}\left[\frac{(1.66\%)(208\ \text{V})^2}{112,500\ \text{VA}}\right] = 0.00638\ \Omega$$

$$X_{TR} = \frac{1}{100}\left[\frac{(2.5\%)(208\ \text{V})^2}{112,500\ \text{VA}}\right] = 0.00961\ \Omega$$

The full-load current of the transformer is

$$I_{LS} = \frac{112,500\ \text{VA}}{\sqrt{3} \times 208\ \text{V}} = 312.3\ \text{A}$$

The phase angle of the load current is $\theta = -\cos^{-1}(0.8) = -36.87°$. Note the negative phase angle due to lagging power factor. The approximate voltage drop is

$$|V_{DROP}| \approx 312.3\ \text{A} \times [0.00638\ \Omega \times \cos(-36.87°) - 0.00961\ \Omega \times \sin(-36.87°)] = 3.395\ \text{V}$$

The voltage drop expressed as a percentage of rated line-to-neutral voltage is equal to

$$\% V_{DROP} = \frac{3.395\ \text{V}}{120\ \text{V}} \times 100\% = 2.83\%$$

Single-Phase Transformer Impedances

The single-phase, center-tapped transformer is commonly used to provide single-phase, three-wire systems both at the service and inside the building. When performing voltage drop calculations involving single-phase, three-wire transformers, the single-phase load is assumed to be balanced. As a result, the full winding impedance as calculated using Equations (16–12) and (16–13) is used.

EXAMPLE 16–7

Determine the percent voltage drop for a 50 kVA, 480–120/240 V, single-phase transformer having a resistance of 1.3% and a reactance of 1.7%. Calculate for the following load conditions:

a) full-load unity power factor
b) full-load 0.8 lagging power factor
c) full-load 0.8 leading power factor

Solution: For all three load conditions, the equivalent resistance and reactance will be expressed in ohms referred to the low-voltage side. The ohmic resistance and reactance are given by Equations (16–12) and (16–13):

$$R_{TR} = \frac{1}{100}\left[\frac{(1.3\%)(240\text{ V})^2}{50,000\text{ VA}}\right] = 0.014976\text{ }\Omega$$

$$X_{TR} = \frac{1}{100}\left[\frac{(1.7\%)(240\text{ V})^2}{50,000\text{ VA}}\right] = 0.019584\text{ }\Omega$$

The full-load current of the transformer is

$$I_{LS} = \frac{50,000\text{ VA}}{240\text{ V}} = 208.3\text{ A}$$

a) The phase angle of the load current is $\theta = \cos^{-1}(1.0) = 0°$. The approximate voltage drop is

$$|V_{DROP}| \approx 208.3\text{ A} \times [0.014976\text{ }\Omega \times \cos(0°) - 0.019584\text{ }\Omega \times \sin(0°)] = 3.12\text{ V}$$

The voltage drop expressed as a percentage of rated voltage is equal to

$$\%\ V_{DROP} = \frac{3.12\text{ V}}{240\text{ V}} \times 100\% = 1.3\%$$

b) The phase angle of the load current is $\theta = -\cos^{-1}(0.8) = -36.87°$. The approximate voltage drop is

$$|V_{DROP}| \approx 208.3\text{ A} \times [0.014976\text{ }\Omega \times \cos(-36.87°) - 0.019584\text{ }\Omega \times \sin(-36.87°)] = 4.94\text{ V}$$

The voltage drop expressed as a percentage of rated voltage is equal to

$$\%\ V_{DROP} = \frac{4.94\text{ V}}{240\text{ V}} \times 100\% = 2.06\%$$

c) The phase angle of the load current is $\theta = \cos^{-1}(0.8) = +36.87°$. The approximate voltage drop is

$$|V_{DROP}| \approx 208.3\text{ A} \times [0.014976\text{ }\Omega \times \cos(+36.87°) - 0.019584\text{ }\Omega \times \sin(+36.87°)] = 0.048\text{ V}$$

The voltage drop expressed as a percentage of rated voltage is equal to

$$\%\ V_{DROP} = \frac{0.048\text{ V}}{240\text{ V}} \times 100\% = 0.02\%$$

The results of Example 16–7 indicate that the voltage drop is a function of both power factor and load on the transformer. Note also that for a leading power factor, the voltage drop is very small. Under certain leading power factor loading conditions, voltage actually rises as load is applied to the transformer, resulting in a negative voltage drop. A negative voltage drop implies an actual rise in voltage.

16–5   TRANSFORMER TAPS

Pad-mount service transformers and larger dry-type, general-purpose transformers are commonly manufactured with taps on the high-voltage winding. The tap ratings are usually specified as a percentage above or below the nominal voltage rating of the winding. The taps may be fixed or adjustable by a load tap changing mechanism.

The presence of taps on a transformer winding essentially means that the transformer turns ratio is adjustable to the amount specified by the tap rating. As such, the output voltage of the transformer is adjustable by changing the tap setting. From Chapter 14, the transformer turns ratio was defined as

$$a = \frac{\text{Voltage rating of primary}}{\text{Voltage rating of secondary}} = \frac{V_P}{V_S} \qquad \textbf{(14–2)}$$

For transformers with tapped windings, the rated high-side or low-side voltage will vary depending on the tap setting. The actual voltage on the low-voltage side under no-load conditions is

$$V_S = \text{Applied primary voltage} \times \left[\frac{\text{Rated secondary voltage}}{\text{Primary tap voltage}} \right] \qquad \textbf{(14–6)}$$

The primary tap voltage is set to compensate for low voltage applied to the primary of the transformer. This will adjust the secondary voltage to an acceptable level. The reader is referred to Examples 14–8 and 14–9. The voltage in systems with excessive voltage drop may be raised to an acceptable level by proper selection of the primary tap voltage of the transformer.

16–6   VOLTAGE DROP DUE TO MOTOR STARTING

Special consideration must be given to the voltage drop or flicker that occurs on a power system due to large motor starting. As discussed in Chapter 13, the locked-rotor kVA of a motor during starting is several times the normal full-load kVA. This large inrush current will cause a momentary dip in voltage as the motor comes up to speed. Voltage drop is especially large when starting large motors applied to systems having a relatively high source impedance. The voltage drop may be severe enough to cause control relay and motor start coils to drop out, television and CRT flicker, and so on. There are several methods of determining the magnitude of voltage drop due to motor starting.

The motor may be represented as a constant impedance load during starting, as shown in Figure 16–3(A). The voltage at any point in the system may be calculated by applying the voltage divider rule to the equivalent circuit.

A more common method is to represent the motor as a constant current load during starting, as shown in Figure 16–3(B). The voltage drop due to starting is then calculated in a manner similar to that discussed in Section 16–3. The following example illustrates the methods previously discussed.

FIGURE 16–3
Motor Equivalent Circuit for Voltage Drop
Calculations

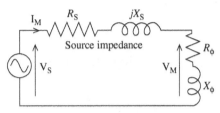

A. Constant Impedance

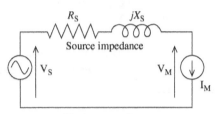

B. Constant Current

EXAMPLE 16–8

A 50 hp, 460 V, code letter G induction motor is to be started with full voltage applied from a 480Y/277 V system whose equivalent impedance is $0.01 + j0.02$ ohms/phase. Assume a locked-rotor power factor of 35% lagging. Calculate the percent voltage drop during starting using (a) the constant impedance and (b) the constant current representations.

Solution:

a) The locked-rotor kVA/hp is between 5.6 and 6.3. For worst-case voltage drop, a value of 6.3 will be used. The locked-rotor kVA during starting is

$$kVA_{LR} = 6.3 \text{ kVA/hp} \times 50 \text{ hp} = 315 \text{ kVA}$$

The locked-rotor current is

$$I_{LR} = \frac{315{,}000 \text{ VA}}{\sqrt{3} \times 460 \text{ V}} = 395.4 \text{ A}$$

The active and reactive power during starting are

$$P_{3\phi} = (315 \text{ kVA}) \times (0.35) = 110.25 \text{ kW}$$

$$Q_{3\phi} = (315 \text{ kVA}) \times (1 - 0.35^2)^{1/2} = 295.1 \text{ kvar}$$

The locked-rotor resistance and reactance are determined as

$$R_\varphi = \left(\frac{1}{3}\right)\left(\frac{110{,}250 \text{ W}}{395.4^2}\right) = 0.2351 \text{ }\Omega$$

$$X_\varphi = \left(\frac{1}{3}\right)\left(\frac{295{,}000 \text{ var}}{395.4^2}\right) = 0.6292 \ \Omega$$

The voltage at the motor terminals is determined by applying the voltage divider rule:

$$\mathbf{V_M} = 277 \ \angle 0° \left(\frac{0.2351 + j0.6292}{0.2351 + j0.6292 + 0.01 + j0.02}\right) = 268.1\angle - 0.2° \text{ V}$$

The percent voltage drop is

$$\% \ V_{\text{DROP}} = \frac{277 \text{ V} - 268.1 \text{ V}}{277 \text{ V}} \times 100\% = 3.213\%$$

b) The constant current representation of the motor is determined by selecting the A phase line-to-neutral voltage as a reference. Therefore,

$$\mathbf{I_M} = 395.4\angle - 69.7°$$

Using the approximate method, the voltage drop is

$$|V_{\text{DROP}}| \approx 395.4 \text{ A} \times [0.01 \ \Omega \times \cos(-69.7°) - 0.02 \ \Omega \times \sin(-69.7°)] = 8.8 \text{ V}$$

The percent voltage drop is

$$\% \ V_{\text{DROP}} = \frac{8.8 \text{ V}}{277 \text{ V}} \times 100\% = 3.173\%$$

Note the close agreement between parts (a) and (b).

Approximate Method of Voltage Drop Due to Motor Starting

In some instances, the locked-rotor power factor of the motor may not be known. In these cases, it is possible to calculate the voltage drop by assuming that the voltage drop is in phase with the source voltage. For the previous example, the magnitude of drop across the source impedance is

$$\mathbf{I} \times \mathbf{Z} = (395.4 \text{ A})|0.01 + j0.02| = 8.84 \text{ V}$$

This corresponds to a percent voltage drop of

$$\% \ V_{\text{DROP}} = \frac{8.84 \text{ V}}{277 \text{ V}} \times 100\% = 3.19\%$$

Note the close agreement with Example 16–8.

Use of the Flicker Curve

In addition to the magnitude of the voltage drop produced by motor starting, the frequency of occurrence of the voltage drop will also determine the severity of the drop. For example, a large voltage drop that occurs infrequently may be acceptable. Likewise, smaller voltage

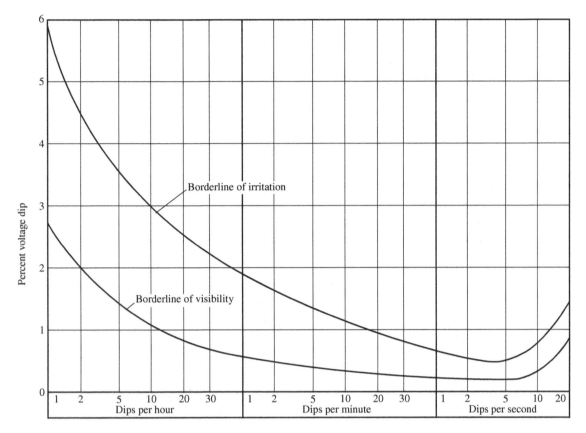

FIGURE 16–4

Flicker Curve *Source:* IEEE Standard 141-1993, IEEE Recommended Practice for Electric Power Distribution for Industrial Plants, IEEE Red Book, Copyright © 1994 IEEE. All rights reserved.

drops may be tolerated on a more frequent basis. The flicker curve shown in Figure 16–4 illustrates the borderline of objectionable voltage dips. As shown in the curve, the maximum permissible voltage drop is a function of the frequency of occurrence.

EXAMPLE 16–9

Determine the maximum number of motor starts permitted for the following voltage drops:

a) 2.0%
b) 3.0%
c) 4.0%
d) 5.0%
e) 6.0%

Solution: Examination of the flicker curve indicates the following permissible number of motor starts:

a) 45 starts per hour
b) 10 starts per hour
c) 4 starts per hour
d) 2 starts per hour
e) 1 start per hour

16–7   EXAMPLES OF VOLTAGE DROP STUDIES

This section presents the method used to perform voltage drop studies on power distribution systems. Calculations for three-phase and single-phase systems are presented. The general procedure for voltage drop calculations can be summarized as

Step 1. Determine all system impedances in ohms.

Step 2. Determine the load supplied at the end of each segment or portion of the system.

Step 3. Determine the load current magnitude and phase angle using the load data from Step 2.

Step 4. Calculate the percent voltage drop along each segment of the circuit, starting at the source.

Step 5. Add the percent voltage drops along each segment, starting at the source, to the point of interest.

Single-Phase System

Determine the voltage drop at the service panel for the system shown in Figure 16–5. The total load is 17 kVA @ 0.95 lagging power factor.

Step 1. Determine all system impedances in ohms.

$$\text{Transformer: } R_{TR} = \frac{1}{100}\left[\frac{(1.8\%)(240\text{ V})^2}{25,000\text{ VA}}\right] = 0.041472\ \Omega$$

$$X_{TR} = \frac{1}{100}\left[\frac{(1.5\%)(240\text{ V})^2}{25,000\text{ VA}}\right] = 0.03456\ \Omega$$

Note that the transformer impedances are referred to the 240 V side of the transformer.

$$\#4/0\text{ AWG: } R_L = 2 \times \frac{0.1\ \Omega/1000\text{ ft}}{1000} \times (150\text{ ft}) = 0.03\ \Omega$$

$$X_L = 2 \times \frac{0.041\ \Omega/1000\text{ ft}}{1000} \times (150\text{ ft}) = 0.0123\ \Omega$$

FIGURE 16–5
System for Single-Phase Voltage Drop Study

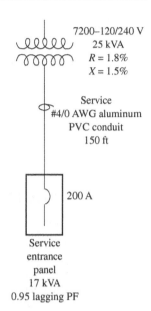

7200–120/240 V
25 kVA
$R = 1.8\%$
$X = 1.5\%$

Service
#4/0 AWG aluminum
PVC conduit
150 ft

200 A

Service
entrance
panel
17 kVA
0.95 lagging PF

Step 2. Determine load supplied at the end of each segment or portion of the system. The loading is given as 17 kVA @ 0.95 lagging power factor.

Step 3. Determine the load current magnitude and phase angle using the load data from Step 2.

The magnitude and phase angle of the load current through the transformer and #4/0 AWG service cable is

$$I = \frac{17{,}000 \text{ VA}}{240 \text{ V}} = 70.83 \text{ A} \quad \theta = -\cos^{-1}(0.95) = -18.2°$$

Step 4. Calculate the percent voltage drop along each segment of the circuit, starting at the source.

The approximate method is used.

Transformer:

$|V_{\text{DROP}}| \approx 70.83 \text{ A} \times [0.041472 \ \Omega \times \cos(-18.2°) - 0.03456 \ \Omega \times \sin(-18.2°)] = 3.56 \text{ V}$

$\%V_{\text{DROP}} = \dfrac{3.56 \text{ V}}{240 \text{ V}} \times 100\% = 1.48\%$

#4/0 AWG Service:

$|V_{\text{DROP}}| \approx 70.83 \text{ A} \times [0.03 \ \Omega \times \cos(-18.2°) - 0.0123 \ \Omega \times \sin(-18.2°)] = 2.29 \text{ V}$

$\% \ V_{\text{DROP}} = \dfrac{2.29 \text{ V}}{240 \text{ V}} \times 100\% = 0.95\%$

Note that the percent voltage drops were calculated based on the line-to-line voltage of 240 V.

Step 5. Add the percent voltage drops along each segment, starting at the source, to the point of interest.

The total voltage drop at the panel is

Transformer:	1.48%
#4/0 AWG Service:	0.95%
Total	2.43%

Three-Phase System

Determine the percent voltage drop at the MDP, panel RP, and at the end of the single-phase branch circuit for the system shown in Figure 16–6. The load on the single-phase

FIGURE 16–6
System for Three-Phase Voltage
Drop Study

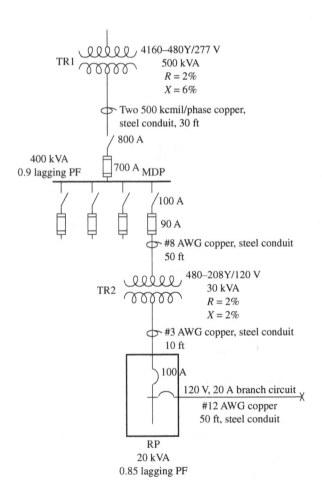

branch circuit is 12 A @ 0.85 lagging power factor. The total load on panel RP has been determined to be 20 kVA @ 0.85 lagging power factor. The loading on the MDP is 400 kVA @ 0.9 lagging power factor.

Step 1. Determine all system impedances in ohms.

$$\text{Transformer TR1: } R_{TR} = \frac{1}{100}\left[\frac{(2\%)(480 \text{ V})^2}{500,000 \text{ VA}}\right] = 0.009216 \text{ }\Omega$$

$$X_{TR} = \frac{1}{100}\left[\frac{(6\%)(480 \text{ V})^2}{500,000 \text{ VA}}\right] = 0.027648 \text{ }\Omega$$

Note that transformer TR1 impedances are referred to the 480 V side of the transformer.

$$\text{Parallel 500 kcmil: } R_L = \frac{0.029 \text{ }\Omega/1000 \text{ ft}}{1000} \times (30 \text{ ft}) = 0.00087 \text{ }\Omega$$

$$X_L = \frac{0.048 \text{ }\Omega/1000 \text{ ft}}{1000} \times (30 \text{ ft}) = 0.00144 \text{ }\Omega$$

Note that the cable impedance is for one conductor of the parallel group.

$$\text{\#8 AWG: } R_L = \frac{0.78 \text{ }\Omega/1000 \text{ ft}}{1000} \times (50 \text{ ft}) = 0.039 \text{ }\Omega$$

$$X_L = \frac{0.065 \text{ }\Omega/1000 \text{ ft}}{1000} \times (50 \text{ ft}) = 0.00325 \text{ }\Omega$$

$$\text{Transformer TR2: } R_{TR} = \frac{1}{100}\left[\frac{(2\%)(208 \text{ V})^2}{30,000 \text{ VA}}\right] = 0.02884 \text{ }\Omega$$

$$X_{TR} = \frac{1}{100}\left[\frac{(2\%)(208 \text{ V})^2}{30,000 \text{ VA}}\right] = 0.02884 \text{ }\Omega$$

Note that transformer TR2 impedances are referred to the 208 V side.

$$\text{\#3 AWG: } R_L = \frac{0.25 \text{ }\Omega/1000 \text{ ft}}{1000} \times (10 \text{ ft}) = 0.0025 \text{ }\Omega$$

$$X_L = \frac{0.059 \text{ }\Omega/1000 \text{ ft}}{1000} \times (10 \text{ ft}) = 0.00059 \text{ }\Omega$$

$$\text{\#12 AWG: } R_L = 2 \times \frac{2.0 \text{ }\Omega/1000 \text{ ft}}{1000} \times (50 \text{ ft}) = 0.2 \text{ }\Omega$$

$$X_L = 2 \times \frac{0.068\Omega/1000 \text{ ft}}{1000} \times (50 \text{ ft}) = 0.0068 \text{ }\Omega$$

Step 2. Determine load supplied at the end of each segment or portion of the system.

The loading on transformer TR1, the parallel 500 kcmil service cable, and the MDP is 400 kVA @ 0.9 lagging power factor. The loading on the 50 ft #8 AWG feeder to transformer TR2, transformer TR2, and the 10 ft #3 AWG feeder to panel

RP is 20 kVA @ 0.85 lagging power factor. Last, the loading on the 50 ft #12 AWG branch circuit is 12 A @ 0.85 lagging power factor.

Step 3. Determine the load current magnitude and phase angle using the load data from Step 2.

To determine the corresponding line current magnitude, the voltage at which the circuit operates must be determined. Since the impedances of transformer TR1 were determined on the 480 V side, the load current will be calculated at 480 V. Likewise, the parallel 500 kcmil service conductors and the 50 ft #8 AWG feeder to transformer TR2 operate at 480 V. The magnitude and phase angle of the load current through transformer TR1 is

$$I = \frac{400,000 \text{ VA}}{\sqrt{3} \ 480 \text{ V}} = 481.1 \text{ A} \qquad \theta = -\cos^{-1}(0.9) = -25.84°$$

The current in one conductor of the parallel 500 kcmil service conductors is the total current of 481.1 A divided by the number of conductors in parallel per phase. Thus, for two parallel conductors per phase, 240.6 A per conductor will flow.

The current through the 50 ft #8 AWG feeder to transformer TR2 is based on 20 kVA @ 480 V, 0.85 lagging power factor:

$$I = \frac{20,000 \text{ VA}}{\sqrt{3} \ 480 \text{ V}} = 24.1 \text{ A} \qquad \theta = -\cos^{-1}(0.85) = -31.8°$$

Since the impedances of transformer TR2 were determined on the 208 V side, the load current will be calculated at 208 V. Likewise, the 10 ft #3 AWG feeder from transformer TR2 to panel RP operates at 208 V. The magnitude and phase angle of the load current through transformer TR2 is

$$I = \frac{20,000 \text{ VA}}{\sqrt{3} \ 208 \text{ V}} = 55.5 \text{ A} \qquad \theta = -\cos^{-1}(0.85) = -31.8°$$

The current through the single-phase branch circuit was given in the problem statement as 12 A. The phase angle of this current is $-31.8°$, corresponding to 0.85 lagging power factor.

The load currents are summarized as

Transformer TR1: $I = 481.1\angle-25.84°$ A
500 kcmil service: $I = 240.6\angle-25.84°$ A (per conductor)
#8 AWG feeder: $I = 24.1\angle-31.8°$ A
Transformer TR2: $I = 55.5\angle-31.8°$ A
#3 AWG feeder: $I = 55.5\angle-31.8°$ A
#12 AWG branch: $I = 12\angle-31.8°$ A

Step 4. Calculate the percent voltage drop along each segment of the circuit, starting at the source.

The approximate method is used.

Transformer TR1:

$$|V_{\text{DROP}}| \approx 481.1 \text{ A} \times [0.009216 \ \Omega \times \cos(-25.84°) - 0.027648 \ \Omega \times \sin(-25.84°)] = 9.79 \text{ V}$$

$$\%V_{\text{DROP}} = \frac{9.79 \text{ V}}{277 \text{ V}} \times 100\% = 3.53\%$$

500 kcmil service:

$$|V_{\text{DROP}}| \approx 240.6 \text{ A} \times [0.00087 \ \Omega \times \cos(-25.84°) - 0.00144 \ \Omega \times \sin(-25.84°)] = 0.34 \text{ V}$$

$$\% \ V_{\text{DROP}} = \frac{0.34 \text{ V}}{277 \text{ V}} \times 100\% = 0.12\%$$

#8 AWG Feeder:

$$|V_{\text{DROP}}| \approx 24.1 \text{ A} \times [0.039 \ \Omega \times \cos(-31.8°) - 0.00325 \ \Omega \times \sin(-31.8°)] = 0.84 \text{ V}$$

$$\% \ V_{\text{DROP}} = \frac{0.84 \text{ V}}{277 \text{ V}} \times 100\% = 0.3\%$$

Transformer TR2:

$$|V_{\text{DROP}}| \approx 55.5 \text{ A} \times [0.02884 \ \Omega \times \cos(-31.8°) - 0.02884 \ \Omega \times \sin(-31.8°)] = 2.2 \text{ V}$$

$$\% \ V_{\text{DROP}} = \frac{2.2 \text{ V}}{120 \text{ V}} \times 100\% = 1.84\%$$

Note that the percent voltage drop is now calculated with respect to 120 V line-to-neutral rather than 277 V.

3 AWG Feeder:

$$|V_{\text{DROP}}| \approx 55.5 \text{ A} \times [0.0025 \ \Omega \times \cos(-31.8°) - 0.00059 \ \Omega \times \sin(-31.8°)] = 0.14 \text{ V}$$

$$\% \ V_{\text{DROP}} = \frac{0.14 \text{ V}}{120 \text{ V}} \times 100\% = 0.11\%$$

#12 AWG Branch:

$$|V_{\text{DROP}}| \approx 12.0 \text{ A} \times [0.2 \ \Omega \times \cos(-31.8°) - 0.0068 \ \Omega \times \sin(-31.8°)] = 2.1 \text{ V}$$

$$\% \ V_{\text{DROP}} = \frac{2.1 \text{ V}}{120 \text{ V}} \times 100\% = 1.74\%$$

Step 5. Add the percent voltage drops along each segment, starting at the source, to the point of interest.

The total voltage drop at the MDP is

TR1:	3.53%
500 kcmil:	0.12%
Total	3.65%

The voltage drop at panel RP is

Drop @ MDP:	3.65%
#8 AWG feeder:	0.30%
TR2:	1.84%
#3 AWG feeder:	0.11%
Total	5.90%

The voltage drop at the end of the #12 AWG branch circuit is

Drop @ RP:	5.90%
#12 AWG branch:	1.74%
Total	7.64%

Therefore, the total voltage drop from the source to the end of the #12 AWG branch circuit is 7.64%. Note that this is a percentage of nominal. To compensate for this large voltage drop, transformer TR1 or TR2 may be specified with taps to raise the voltage to an acceptable level. For example, setting the high side of TR1 at the −5% tap would reduce all percent voltage drops by 5% on the load side of TR1. The voltage at the end of the branch circuit would be 7.64% − 5% = 2.64%. Note, however, that under light-load conditions, the system voltages on the load side of TR1 would be approximately 5% above nominal, which is still in the acceptable range of ±5%. The voltage drop at panel RP would be 5.9% − 5% = 0.9% under the specified load conditions.

PROBLEMS

1. Why is determination of voltage drop important?
2. Explain the method used to calculate voltage drop in parallel feeder conductors.
3. What is the maximum allowable percent voltage drop permissible in a power distribution system?
4. Is voltage drop a function of power factor?
5. Explain how transformer taps can be used to adjust the voltage in a system.
6. Determine the voltage drop on a 480 V, three-phase feeder consisting of 300 kcmil THW copper conductor. The feeder is 150 ft in length. The loading on the feeder is 150 kVA @ 0.85 lagging power factor. Express the voltage drop in volts and percent.
7. A 480 V, three-phase, 1600 A service consists of four 600 kcmil XHHW copper conductors per phase. The length of the conductor is 100 ft and the load is 900 kVA @ 0.9 lagging power factor. Determine the voltage drop in volts and percent.
8. A 120/240 V, single-phase, 200 A service consists of #4/0 AWG XHHW aluminum conductor. The length of the service conductor is 150 ft and the load is 25 kVA @ 0.95 lagging power factor. Determine the voltage drop in volts and percent.

9. A 50 kVA, 480–120/240 V, single-phase transformer has a resistance of 1.8% and a reactance of 2.2%. The actual load on the transformer is 40 kVA @ 0.9 lagging power factor. Determine the voltage drop at the specified load condition in volts and percent.

10. A 225 kVA, 480–208Y/120 V, three-phase transformer has a resistance of 2.3% and a reactance of 3.5%. The actual load on the transformer is 150 kVA @ 0.9 lagging power factor. Determine the voltage drop at the specified load condition in volts and percent.

11. Determine the voltage drop in volts and percent for a 120 V branch circuit consisting of #14 AWG copper conductor 100 ft in length. The loading on the circuit is 10 A @ 0.8 lagging power factor.

12. Determine the voltage drop in volts and percent for a 480 V, single-phase feeder consisting of #10 AWG copper conductor 75 ft in length. The loading on the circuit is 22 A @ 0.9 lagging power factor.

13. Determine the voltage drop in volts and percent for a 277 V, single-phase feeder consisting of #12 AWG copper conductor 50 ft in length. The loading on the circuit is 18 A at 0.95 lagging power factor.

14. Determine the maximum circuit length permitted for a 120 V, single-phase branch circuit consisting of #12 AWG copper conductor if the voltage drop is not to exceed 3%. The loading on the circuit is 16 A @ 0.95 lagging power factor.

15. Repeat Problem 9 for a 277 V, single-phase branch circuit.

16. A residential dwelling is supplied by a 10 kVA, 2400–120/240 V, single-phase transformer having a resistance of 1.9% and a reactance of 2.1%. The utility source is a distribution feeder having a line-to-line voltage of 4160 V and a line-to-neutral voltage of 2400 V. The line-to-ground fault current on the utility feeder is 4000 A with an X/R ratio of 3:1. The service consists of 125 ft of #2/0 AWG XHHW aluminum conductor. The loading on the service panel is 8 kVA @ 0.95 lagging power factor. The longest branch circuit is 120 V and consists of #14 AWG THW copper conductor with a load of 10 A @ 0.9 lagging power factor. Sketch the one-line diagram of this system and determine the percent voltage drop at the service panel and at the end of the 120 V branch circuit.

17. An industrial facility is supplied from the utility distribution feeder having a line-to-line voltage of 12,470 V and a line-to-neutral voltage of 7200 V. The short circuit data for the utility feeder is three-phase 45 MVA, X/R = 1:1; single phase: I_{LG} = 1500 A, X/R = 0.8:1. The service transformer is rated 12.47 kV–480Y/277 V, 1000 kVA, Z = 6%, X/R = 4:1. The 1600 A service consists of four 600 kcmil XHHW copper conductors per phase. The service conductors terminate in an MDP with a total load of 900 kVA @ 0.9 lagging power factor. A three-phase, 480 V feeder from the MDP to a step-down transformer consists of #2/0 AWG THW copper conductor and is 50 ft in length. The step-down transformer is rated 480–208Y/120 V, 112.5 kVA, R = 2.2%, X = 2.5%. The feeder from the step-down transformer to panel RP consists of 500 kcmil THW copper conductor and is 10 ft in length. The total loading on panel RP is 80 kVA @ 0.9 lagging power factor. The longest branch circuit from panel RP is #12 AWG THW copper having a length of 60 ft and a loading of 16 A @ 0.9 lagging power factor. There is also a 480 V, 100 A, three-phase feeder from the MDP to a

60 hp motor consisting of #3 AWG THW copper conductor 175 ft in length. The loading on this motor feeder is 70 A @ 0.85 lagging power factor. Sketch the one-line diagram of this system and determine the percent voltage drop at (a) the MDP, (b) the 60 hp motor terminals, (c) panel RP, and (d) the tag end of the 120 V branch circuit off panel RP.

18. If the service transformer of Problem 17 is equipped with four taps at -2.5% FCBN and two taps at $+2.5\%$, recommend a tap setting to allow satisfactory system voltage if required.

19. It has been suggested that the conductor used for the 100 A, 480 V motor feeder of Problem 17 be increased in size to reduce voltage drop along this feeder. What is the percent drop at the motor terminals if the feeder is increased to #1 AWG THW copper?

20. A 50 hp, 460 V, code letter G, three-phase motor is to be started with full voltage. The system impedance is $0.02 + j0.03$ ohms. Determine the percent voltage drop when starting the motor at full voltage. Also, determine the maximum number of starts permitted if full-voltage starting is employed.

17

Short Circuit Calculations

INTRODUCTION

This chapter will discuss the methods used to calculate short circuit currents on electrical power systems. The chapter begins with a discussion of the actual fault current waveform and the effect of system resistance and inductance on the shape of the waveform. Of particular interest is the amount of "dc offset" present in the waveform immediately after the initiation of the fault. A significant dc offset will result in much higher maximum-peak instantaneous current levels than would be encountered if there were no dc offset. Knowledge of the maximum-peak instantaneous value of the waveform is necessary when specifying momentary duties of various electrical equipment.

The procedures for calculating short circuit currents for three-phase faults on three-phase systems and single-phase faults on single-phase systems will be discussed. The ohmic method will be used to calculate the magnitude of the fault currents on both three-phase and single-phase systems. Equivalent system impedance, transformer impedance, and cable impedances to be used in short circuit calculations will be discussed, along with the method used to reflect impedance from the primary to the secondary of transformers. The contribution of short circuit current from motor loads will also be included in the determination of the short circuit current levels.

OBJECTIVES

Upon completion of this chapter, you will:

- Understand the importance of short circuit calculations
- Understand what is meant by the X/R ratio of the system
- Be able to determine the peak asymmetrical fault current
- Be able to determine the equivalent system impedance
- Be able to calculate the appropriate transformer impedance to be used in short circuit calculations
- Be able to reflect impedance from primary to secondary of a transformer for the purposes of short circuit calculation
- Be able to calculate short circuit currents in three-phase and single-phase systems
- Understand the importance of motor contribution to short circuit current

17–1   SYMMETRICAL AND ASYMMETRICAL FAULT CURRENTS

The actual short circuit currents that initially flow in a power system upon inception of a fault will not be sinusoidal. Rather, the current waveforms will be offset from the time axis due to the inductance of the system between the source and the location of the fault. In general, the larger the source inductance with respect to the source resistance, the greater the amount of offset. The actual current that flows during a fault condition is referred to as the *asymmetrical fault current.*

When performing power system short circuit calculations, it is easier to apply sinusoidal steady-state circuit analysis techniques rather than work in the time domain. The short circuit currents calculated using sinusoidal steady-state (phasor) analysis will be the steady-state values after all transients have decayed. Since the asymmetrical fault current is a function of the system inductance and resistance, it is convenient to determine multipliers to be applied to the symmetrical values of fault current in order to determine the asymmetrical values.

In order to determine the asymmetrical multipliers, consider the circuit shown in Figure 17–1. The asymmetrical factors will be derived by assuming a balanced three-phase fault occurs on the system. As such, the three-phase power system can be represented using the line-to-neutral equivalent circuit. The resistance and inductance of all system components between the source and the fault location are designated as R and L, respectively. The source is represented as a sinusoidal voltage source, with a frequency of ω rad/s. The angle θ is included to allow the voltage source to have any value at time $t = 0$ s, when the fault occurs.

Applying Kirchoff's voltage law to the circuit of Figure 17–1 results in the following:

$$V_{m} \sin (\omega T + \theta) = R \cdot i(t) + L \cdot \frac{di(t)}{dt} \tag{17–1}$$

Rearranging and simplifying Equation (17–1) results in

$$\frac{di(t)}{dt} + \frac{R}{L} \cdot i(t) = \frac{V_{m}}{L} \sin (\omega t + \theta) \tag{17–2}$$

Equation (17–2) is in the standard form required for solution by use of the integrating factor method from differential equations. The solution of Equation (17–2) for the current $i(t)$ is beyond the scope of this text.

Rather than using the inductance of the system when performing short circuit calculations, it is more convenient to refer to the X/R ("X over R") ratio of the system impedance

FIGURE 17–1
Equivalent Circuit for Short Circuit Calculation

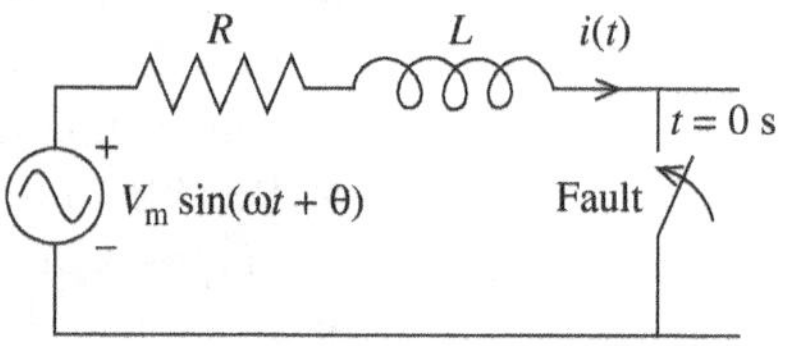

Line-to-Neutral Equivalent Circuit

when discussing asymmetrical fault current. Equations (17–1) and (17–2) used the inductance rather than the inductive reactance of the system. Recall that the inductance and inductive reactance are related by the following:

$$L = \frac{X}{\omega} \tag{17-3}$$

where X is the inductive reactance and ω is the frequency in rad/s.

In terms of the system resistance R and inductive reactance X, the solution to Equation (17–2) is

$$i(t) = \sqrt{2} \cdot I_{\text{rms}}\left[\sin(\omega t - \theta_Z) + \sin(\theta_Z) \cdot e^{-(\omega R/X)t}\right] \tag{17-4}$$

where:

$$I_{\text{rms}} = \frac{V_m}{\sqrt{2} \cdot Z_s}$$

$$\theta_Z = \tan^{-1}\left[\frac{\omega L}{R}\right]$$

$$Z_S = \sqrt{R^2 + X^2}$$

A plot of Equation (17–4) is shown in Figure 17–2 for X/R equal to infinity and zero. Notice that the dc offset is maximum for an X/R ratio equal to infinity. With X/R equal to zero, there is no dc offset, and the waveform represents a sine wave.

The bracketed term in Equation (17–4) multiplied by the $\sqrt{2}$ represents a multiplier that can be applied to the rms value of fault current to determine the instantaneous value of fault current at any time t. When specifying the momentary short circuit withstand capability of electrical equipment, the maximum peak instantaneous value of fault current is of major importance. The multiplying factor that is used to determine the maximum peak instantaneous fault current can be obtained by taking the derivative of the bracketed term of Equation (17–4) with respect to time and equating to zero. The result is then solved for the time of maximum peak, t_p. The time of maximum peak is then substituted into

FIGURE 17–2
Short Circuit Current Waveforms

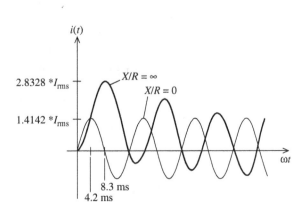

TABLE 17–1
Asymmetrical Current Factors

System X/R Ratio	Instantaneous Peak Factor	Half-Cycle Factor	Time of Peak t_p(ms)
0.0	1.4142	1.000	4.2
0.1	1.4142	1.000	4.4
0.2	1.4142	1.000	4.7
0.3	1.4149	1.000	4.9
0.4	1.4181	1.000	5.2
0.5	1.4250	1.000	5.4
0.6	1.4362	1.000	5.5
0.7	1.4511	1.000	5.7
0.8	1.4692	1.001	5.8
0.9	1.4897	1.002	5.9
1.0	1.5122	1.002	6.1
2.0	1.7560	1.042	6.8
3.0	1.9495	1.115	7.1
4.0	2.0892	1.191	7.4
5.0	2.1924	1.263	7.5
6.0	2.2708	1.304	7.6
7.0	2.3323	1.347	7.7
8.0	2.3817	1.381	7.8
9.0	2.4222	1.412	7.8
10.0	2.4561	1.438	7.9
20.0	2.6256	1.570	8.1
30.0	2.6890	1.618	8.2
40.0	2.7224	1.643	8.2
50.0	2.7427	1.662	8.2
100.0	2.7848	1.697	8.3
infinity	2.8284	1.732	8.3

Equation (17–4) to determine the appropriate multiplying factor. Table 17–1 summarizes the results for various system X/R ratios.

In addition to the peak value of the asymmetrical current waveform, the rms value of the waveform over the first half-cycle is also of interest. This first half-cycle rms value is determined by multiplying the rms symmetrical short circuit current by the first half-cycle rms multiplying factor. This multiplying factor is obtained by calculating the square root of the mean squared value of the waveform over the first half-cycle using the integral form of the definition of rms and dividing by the symmetrical rms value of the short circuit current:

$$\text{First half-cycle rms multiplying factor} = \frac{\sqrt{\dfrac{1}{T}\displaystyle\int_{O}^{T} i^2(t)\, dt}}{\text{rms Symmetrical short circuit current}}$$

As with the peak instantaneous multiplying factor, the half-cycle rms multiplying factor is a function of the X/R ratio of the system. Table 17–1 lists the half-cycle rms multipliers for various system X/R ratios for conditions of maximum rms values.

EXAMPLE 17–1

The source impedance at a 12.47 kV distribution substation bus is $0.4 + j1.5$ ohms per phase. Calculate (a) the rms fault current, (b) the maximum peak instantaneous value of fault current, and (c) the rms value of the half-cycle fault current if a balanced three-phase fault occurs.

Solution:

a) The line-to-neutral equivalent representation is used. The line-to-neutral voltage is

$$V_{LN} = 12,470 \div \sqrt{3}$$
$$= 7,200 \text{ V}$$

The rms symmetrical fault current is

$$I_{rms} = \frac{7,200 \text{ V}}{\sqrt{(0.4^2 + 1.5^2)}} = 4638 \text{ A}$$

b) The system X/R ratio is

$$X/R = 1.5 \div 0.4 = 3.75$$

From Table 17–1, the instantaneous peak factor is determined by interpolation:

$$\text{Asymmetrical factor} = (2.0892 - 1.9495)(3.75 - 3.0) + 1.9495$$
$$= 2.0543$$

The maximum peak instantaneous value of fault current is

$$I_p = (2.0543)(4638 \text{ A}) = 9528 \text{ A}$$

c) With an X/R ratio of 3.75, the rms half-cycle multiplying factor is determined by interpolation from Table 17–1:

$$\text{rms half-cycle factor} = (1.191 - 1.115)(3.75 - 3.0) + 1.115$$
$$= 1.172$$

The rms value of the first half-cycle asymmetrical fault current is

$$I_{rms,1/2} = (1.172)(4638 \text{ A}) = 5436 \text{ A}$$

17–2   EQUIVALENT SYSTEM IMPEDANCE

When performing short circuit calculations on distribution feeders or industrial plants, it is common practice to obtain the short circuit availability at the substation bus. This short circuit data is usually specified in terms of an apparent power at a certain voltage level for three-phase faults. In addition, the system X/R ratio at the point of fault is typically specified. The line-to-ground short circuit current magnitude and X/R ratio may also be specified. This data can be used to calculate the impedances of the source for the purposes of determining the three-phase and single-phase fault current levels.

Equivalent System Impedance for Three-Phase Faults

If the three-phase short circuit MVA and reference voltage for the system are specified, the fault current magnitude can be calculated as

$$I_{SC} = \frac{\text{Short circuit MVA} \times 10^6}{\sqrt{3} \times \text{Line-to-line system voltage}} \tag{17–5}$$

The impedance is equal to the line-to-neutral system voltage divided by the short circuit current as given by Equation (17–5):

$$Z_{SYS} = \frac{\text{Line-to-neutral voltage}}{I_{SC}} \tag{17–6}$$

Recall that for a three-phase system, the line-to-neutral voltage is equal to the line-to-line voltage divided by $\sqrt{3}$. Substituting Equation (17–5) into (17–6) and simplifying results in

$$Z_{SYS} = \frac{\text{Line-to-neutral voltage}}{\left(\dfrac{\text{Short circuit MVA} \times 10^6}{\sqrt{3} \times \text{Line-to-line voltage}}\right)} \tag{17–7}$$

$$= \frac{\left(\dfrac{\text{Line-to-line voltage}}{\sqrt{3}}\right)}{\left(\dfrac{\text{Short circuit MVA} \times 10^6}{\sqrt{3} \times \text{Line-to-line voltage}}\right)}$$

$$= \frac{(\text{Line-to-line voltage})^2}{\text{Short circuit MVA} \times 10^6}$$

The system X/R ratio is used to determine the impedance angle according to

$$\theta = \tan^{-1}(X/R) \tag{17–8}$$

The impedance angle together with the impedance magnitude are used to calculate the equivalent system resistance and reactance as follows:

$$R_{SYS} = Z_{SYS} \times \cos(\theta) \tag{17–9}$$

$$X_{SYS} = Z_{SYS} \times \sin(\theta) \tag{17–10}$$

Equivalent System Impedance for Line-to-Ground Faults

The line-to-ground fault current magnitude and system voltage can be used to determine the equivalent impedance of the system for line-to-ground or single-phase faults. Typically, the line-to-ground fault current is given in amperes with the X/R ratio specified. Note that the X/R ratio for line-to-ground faults differs from the X/R ratio for three-phase faults. In the absence of line-to-ground impedance data, it is sometimes assumed that the equivalent system impedance for line-to-ground faults is 2 times the impedance for a three-phase fault.

The equivalent system impedance for a line-to-ground fault is given by

$$Z_{SYS,1\phi} = \frac{\text{Line-to-neutral system voltage}}{\text{Line-to-ground fault current}} \qquad (17–11)$$

The equivalent system resistance and reactance for a single-phase fault are given by

$$R_{SYS,1\phi} = Z_{SYS,1\phi} \times \cos(\theta) \qquad (17–12)$$

$$X_{SYS,1\phi} = Z_{SYS,1\phi} \times \sin(\theta) \qquad (17–13)$$

EXAMPLE 17–2

The following system short circuit data is available for the HV bus of a 12.47 kV–480Y/277 V service transformer:

Three-phase fault = 100 MVA, X/R = 3.1 @ 12.47 kV
Line-to-ground fault = 3 kA, X/R = 4.7 @ 12.47 kV

Determine the equivalent system impedances for (a) the three-phase fault and (b) the single-phase fault.

Solution:

a) From Equation (17–7), the system impedance is

$$Z_{SYS} = \frac{(12,470 \text{ V})^2}{100 \text{ MVA} \times 10^6} = 1.555 \ \Omega$$

The impedance angle is

$$\theta = \tan^{-1}(3.1) = 72.1°$$

The equivalent system resistance and reactance are

$$R_{SYS} = 1.555 \times \cos(72.1°) = 0.4779 \ \Omega$$

$$X_{SYS} = 1.555 \times \sin(72.1°) = 1.4797 \ \Omega$$

b) From Equation (17–11), the equivalent system impedance for a single-phase fault is

$$Z_{SYS,1\phi} = \frac{7200 \text{ V}}{3000 \text{ A}} = 2.4 \ \Omega$$

The impedance angle is

$$\theta = \tan^{-1}(4.7) = 78°$$

The equivalent system resistance and reactance for a single phase fault is

$$R_{SYS,1\phi} = 2.4 \times \cos(78°) = 0.4990 \; \Omega$$

$$X_{SYS,1\phi} = 2.4 \times \sin(78°) = 2.348 \; \Omega$$

17–3   TRANSFORMER IMPEDANCES

Three-Phase Transformers

As presented in Chapter 14, the transformer impedances are generally specified in percent based on the nameplate apparent power rating and voltage rating of the transformer. When performing short circuit calculations, it is common to refer the transformer impedances to the low-voltage side of the transformer. The ohmic impedances reflected to the low-voltage side are given by

$$R_{TR} = \frac{1}{100} \left[\frac{(\% \; R)(\text{Secondary line voltage})^2}{\text{Transformer voltampere rating}} \right] \tag{17–14}$$

$$X_{TR} = \frac{1}{100} \left[\frac{(\% \; X)(\text{Secondary line voltage})^2}{\text{Transformer voltampere rating}} \right] \tag{17–15}$$

Single-Phase, Center-Tapped Transformers

The single-phase, center-tapped transformer is commonly used to provide single-phase, three-wire systems both at the service and inside the building. When performing short circuit calculations involving single-phase, three-wire transformer secondaries, the full winding impedance is used for faults between the ungrounded conductors (240 V). For faults between the ungrounded and grounded conductors (120 V), the half-winding impedance is used. Due to the nature of transformer construction, the half-winding impedance is not equal to one-half of the full winding impedance. For the purposes of this text, the half-winding impedance will be assumed to be equal to one-third of the full winding impedance. This assumption results in a short circuit current from line to ground being equal to 1.5 times the line-to-line short circuit current. The full winding impedance of single-phase transformers is calculated using Equations (17–14) and (17–15) directly. The half-winding impedances are then taken as $\frac{1}{3}$ times the full winding impedances.

EXAMPLE 17–3

Determine the full winding and half-winding resistance and reactance of a 10 kVA, 7200–120/240 V, single-phase transformer, having a resistance of 1.5% and a reactance of 1.9%.

Solution: The full winding impedances are

$$R_{TR} = \frac{1}{100}\left[\frac{(1.5\%)(240\text{ V})^2}{10{,}000\text{ VA}}\right] = 0.0864\ \Omega$$

$$X_{TR} = \frac{1}{100}\left[\frac{(1.9\%)(240\text{ V})^2}{10{,}000\text{ VA}}\right] = 0.1094\ \Omega$$

The half-winding impedances are

$$R_{TR,1/2} = (\tfrac{1}{3})(0.0864\ \Omega) = 0.0288\ \Omega$$

$$X_{TR,1/2} = (\tfrac{1}{3})(0.1094\ \Omega) = 0.0365\ \Omega$$

17–4   REFLECTING IMPEDANCES THROUGH THE TRANSFORMER

The fault current at any given point in the system is equal to the voltage divided by the impedance. In systems involving transformers, it is often necessary to reflect impedances from the high side to the low side of the transformer. For example, the equivalent system impedance must be reflected to the low side of the service transformer to determine the short circuit current on the low side of the transformer.

The general form of the equations for reflecting high-side impedances to the low side are given by

$$R_{LS} = R_{HS}\left(\frac{\text{Low-side line voltage}}{\text{High-side line voltage}}\right)^2 \qquad\qquad \textbf{(17–16)}$$

$$X_{LS} = X_{HS}\left(\frac{\text{Low-side line voltage}}{\text{High-side line voltage}}\right)^2 \qquad\qquad \textbf{(17–17)}$$

When performing three-phase short circuit calculations, the system impedance that is to be reflected to the low voltage side is the equivalent system impedance for a three-phase fault.

EXAMPLE 17–4

The equivalent system impedance for three-phase faults on the high side of a 112.5 kVA, 12.47 kV–480Y/277 V transformer is $0.3 + j1.2\ \Omega$. Determine the equivalent system impedance referred to the low-voltage side of the transformer.

Solution: Application of Equations (17–16) and (17–7) results in

$$R_{LS} = (0.3\ \Omega)\left(\frac{480\text{ V}}{12{,}470\text{ V}}\right)^2 = 0.000444\ \Omega$$

$$X_{LS} = (1.2\ \Omega)\left(\frac{480\text{ V}}{12{,}470\text{ V}}\right)^2 = 0.001778\ \Omega$$

For single-phase faults, the system impedance that is to be reflected to the low-voltage side is the system impedance for a single-phase fault. Also, the secondary voltage to be used when reflecting the impedance is either 240 V or 120 V, depending on the particular short circuit of interest.

EXAMPLE 17–5

The equivalent system impedance for single-phase fault current calculation has been calculated as $2.0 + j4.0$ Ω. A 25 kVA, 7200–120/240 V, single-phase transformer supplies the service. Determine the system impedance reflected to the secondary for (a) line-to-line faults, and (b) line-to-ground faults.

Solution:

a) The appropriate secondary voltage is 240 V for the line-to-line fault. The reflected impedances are

$$R_{LS} = (2.0 \ \Omega)\left(\frac{240 \text{ V}}{7200 \text{ V}}\right)^2 = 0.00222 \ \Omega$$

$$X_{LS} = (4.0 \ \Omega)\left(\frac{240 \text{ V}}{7200 \text{ V}}\right)^2 = 0.00444 \ \Omega$$

b) The appropriate secondary voltage is 120 V for the line-to-ground fault. The reflected impedances are

$$R_{LS} = (2.0 \ \Omega)\left(\frac{120 \text{ V}}{7200 \text{ V}}\right)^2 = 0.000556 \ \Omega$$

$$X_{LS} = (4.0 \ \Omega)\left(\frac{120 \text{ V}}{7200 \text{ V}}\right)^2 = 0.00111 \ \Omega$$

17–5   CABLE IMPEDANCES

The cable impedance values are determined from Table 17–2. Note that the data shown in Table 17–2 represents the impedance in ohms to neutral for three-phase systems. Also, the impedance is expressed in ohms per kilometer and ohms per 1000 ft of cable.

Three Phase

Since the three-phase fault involves a balanced condition, there is no flow of neutral current back to the source. Thus, the impedance to be used for three-phase fault calculations is sometimes referred to as the "one-way" impedance. The ohmic cable impedances are calculated as

$$R_C = \frac{\text{Resistance in ohms/1000 ft}}{1000} \times (\text{Cable length in ft}) \qquad \textbf{(17–18)}$$

$$X_C = \frac{\text{Reactance in ohms/1000 ft}}{1000} \times (\text{Cable length in ft}) \qquad (17\text{–}19)$$

For parallel conductors, the impedance is equal to the table value divided by the number of parallel conductors per phase.

EXAMPLE 17–6

Determine the impedance of a 480 V, three-phase feeder, 75 ft in length, consisting of one 500 kcmil THW copper conductor per phase. Assume steel conduit.

Solution: From Table 17–2, the resistance is 0.029 Ω/1000 ft and the reactance is 0.048 Ω/1000 ft. Applying Equations (17–18) and (17–19) results in

$$R_C = \frac{0.029 \ \Omega/1000 \ \text{ft}}{1000} \times (75 \ \text{ft}) = 0.002175 \ \Omega$$

$$X_C = \frac{0.048 \ \Omega/1000 \ \text{ft}}{1000} \times (75 \ \text{ft}) = 0.0036 \ \Omega$$

EXAMPLE 17–7

Determine the impedance of a 480 V, three-phase feeder, 75 ft in length, consisting of three 500 kcmil THW copper conductors in parallel per phase. Assume steel conduit.

Solution: From Table 17–2, the resistance is 0.029 Ω/1000 ft and the reactance is 0.048 Ω/1000 ft. Note that these values are for a single conductor. For three conductors in parallel per phase, the resistance is ($\frac{1}{3}$)(0.029 Ω/1000 ft) = 0.00967 Ω/1000 ft. The reactance is ($\frac{1}{3}$)(0.048 Ω/1000 ft) = 0.016 Ω/1000 ft. Applying Equations (17–18) and (17–19) results in

$$R_C = \frac{0.00967 \ \Omega/1000 \ \text{ft}}{1000} \times (75 \ \text{ft}) = 0.000732 \ \Omega$$

$$X_C = \frac{0.016 \ \Omega/1000 \ \text{ft}}{1000} \times (75 \ \text{ft}) = 0.0012 \ \Omega$$

Single Phase

When a single-phase fault occurs on a system, the short circuit current will flow from the source to the point of fault and back to the source. Thus, unlike the three-phase fault in a three-phase system, the cable impedance to the fault must be taken as twice that shown in Table 17–2. The ohmic cable impedances for single-phase faults are thus calculated as

$$R_C = 2 \times \frac{\text{Resistance in ohms/1000 ft}}{1000} \times (\text{Cable length in ft}) \qquad (17\text{–}20)$$

TABLE 17–2
Table 9 Alternating-Current Resistance and Reactance for 600-Volt Cables, 3-Phase, 60 Hz, 75°C (167°F)
Three Single Conductors in Conduit

Ohms to Neutral per Kilometer
Ohms to Neutral per 1000 Feet

Size (AWG or kcmil)	X_L (Reactance) for All Wires		Alternating-Current Resistance for Uncoated Copper Wires			Alternating-Current Resistance for Aluminum Wires			Effective Z at 0.85 PF for Uncoated Copper Wires			Effective Z at 0.85 PF for Aluminum Wires			Size (AWG or kcmil)
	PVC, Aluminum Conduits	Steel Conduit	PVC Conduit	Aluminum Conduit	Steel Conduit	PVC Conduit	Aluminum Conduit	Steel Conduit	PVC Conduit	Aluminum Conduit	Steel Conduit	PVC Conduit	Aluminum Conduit	Steel Conduit	
14	0.190 / 0.058	0.240 / 0.073	10.2 / 3.1	10.2 / 3.1	10.2 / 3.1	— / —	— / —	— / —	8.9 / 2.7	8.9 / 2.7	8.9 / 2.7	— / —	— / —	— / —	14
12	0.177 / 0.054	0.223 / 0.068	6.6 / 2.0	6.6 / 2.0	6.6 / 2.0	10.5 / 3.2	10.5 / 3.2	10.5 / 3.2	5.6 / 1.7	5.6 / 1.7	5.6 / 1.7	9.2 / 2.8	9.2 / 2.8	9.2 / 2.8	12
10	0.164 / 0.050	0.207 / 0.063	3.9 / 1.2	3.9 / 1.2	3.9 / 1.2	6.6 / 2.0	6.6 / 2.0	6.6 / 2.0	3.6 / 1.1	3.6 / 1.1	3.6 / 1.1	5.9 / 1.8	5.9 / 1.8	5.9 / 1.8	10
8	0.171 / 0.052	0.213 / 0.065	2.56 / 0.78	2.56 / 0.78	2.56 / 0.78	4.3 / 1.3	4.3 / 1.3	4.3 / 1.3	2.26 / 0.69	2.26 / 0.69	2.30 / 0.70	3.6 / 1.1	3.6 / 1.1	3.6 / 1.1	8
6	0.167 / 0.051	0.210 / 0.064	1.61 / 0.49	1.61 / 0.49	1.61 / 0.49	2.66 / 0.81	2.66 / 0.81	2.66 / 0.81	1.44 / 0.44	1.48 / 0.45	1.48 / 0.45	2.33 / 0.71	2.36 / 0.72	2.36 / 0.72	6
4	0.157 / 0.048	0.197 / 0.060	1.02 / 0.31	1.02 / 0.31	1.02 / 0.31	1.67 / 0.51	1.67 / 0.51	1.67 / 0.51	0.95 / 0.29	0.95 / 0.29	0.98 / 0.30	1.51 / 0.46	1.51 / 0.46	1.51 / 0.46	4
3	0.154 / 0.047	0.194 / 0.059	0.82 / 0.25	0.82 / 0.25	0.82 / 0.25	1.31 / 0.40	1.35 / 0.41	1.31 / 0.40	0.75 / 0.23	0.79 / 0.24	0.79 / 0.24	1.21 / 0.37	1.21 / 0.37	1.21 / 0.37	3

2															2
0.98 0.30	0.98 0.30	0.98 0.30	0.66 0.20	0.62 0.19	0.62 0.19	1.05 0.32	1.05 0.32	1.05 0.32	0.66 0.20	0.66 0.20	0.62 0.19	0.187 0.057	0.148 0.045		2
0.82 0.25	0.79 0.24	0.79 0.24	0.52 0.16	0.52 0.16	0.52 0.16	0.82 0.25	0.85 0.26	0.82 0.25	0.52 0.16	0.52 0.16	0.49 0.15	0.187 0.057	0.151 0.046		1
0.66 0.20	0.66 0.20	0.62 0.19	0.43 0.13	0.43 0.13	0.43 0.13	0.66 0.20	0.69 0.21	0.66 0.20	0.39 0.12	0.43 0.13	0.39 0.12	0.180 0.055	0.144 0.044		1/0
0.52 0.16	0.52 0.16	0.52 0.16	0.36 0.11	0.36 0.11	0.36 0.11	0.52 0.16	0.52 0.16	0.52 0.16	0.33 0.10	0.33 0.10	0.33 0.10	0.177 0.054	0.141 0.043		2/0
0.46 0.14	0.43 0.13	0.43 0.13	0.308 0.094	0.302 0.092	0.289 0.088	0.43 0.13	0.43 0.13	0.43 0.13	0.259 0.079	0.269 0.082	0.253 0.077	0.171 0.052	0.138 0.042		3/0
0.36 0.11	0.36 0.11	0.36 0.11	0.262 0.080	0.256 0.078	0.243 0.074	0.33 0.10	0.36 0.11	0.33 0.10	0.207 0.063	0.220 0.067	0.203 0.062	0.167 0.051	0.135 0.041		4/0
0.33 0.10	0.322 0.098	0.308 0.094	0.240 0.073	0.230 0.070	0.217 0.066	0.282 0.086	0.295 0.090	0.279 0.085	0.177 0.054	0.187 0.057	0.171 0.052	0.171 0.052	0.135 0.041		250
0.289 0.088	0.282 0.086	0.269 0.082	0.213 0.065	0.207 0.063	0.194 0.059	0.236 0.072	0.249 0.076	0.233 0.071	0.148 0.045	0.161 0.049	0.144 0.044	0.167 0.051	0.135 0.041		300
0.262 0.080	0.253 0.077	0.240 0.073	0.197 0.060	0.190 0.058	0.174 0.053	0.207 0.063	0.217 0.066	0.200 0.061	0.128 0.039	0.141 0.043	0.125 0.038	0.164 0.050	0.131 0.040		350
0.240 0.073	0.233 0.071	0.217 0.066	0.184 0.056	0.174 0.053	0.161 0.049	0.180 0.055	0.194 0.059	0.177 0.054	0.115 0.035	0.125 0.038	0.108 0.033	0.161 0.049	0.131 0.040		400
0.210 0.064	0.200 0.061	0.187 0.057	0.164 0.050	0.157 0.048	0.141 0.043	0.148 0.045	0.157 0.048	0.141 0.043	0.095 0.029	0.105 0.032	0.089 0.027	0.157 0.048	0.128 0.039		500
0.190 0.058	0.180 0.055	0.167 0.051	0.154 0.047	0.144 0.044	0.131 0.040	0.125 0.038	0.135 0.041	0.118 0.036	0.082 0.025	0.092 0.028	0.075 0.023	0.157 0.048	0.128 0.039		600

Source: Reprinted with permission from NFPA 70 *The National Electric Code* © 2002, National Fire Protection Association, Quincy, MA 02269. This reprinted material is not the referenced subject which is represented only by the standard in its entirety.

$$X_C = 2 \times \frac{\text{Reactance in ohms/1000 ft}}{1000} \times (\text{Cable length in ft}) \qquad \textbf{(17–21)}$$

EXAMPLE 17–8

Determine the impedance of a 120 V, single-phase branch circuit 100 ft in length consisting of #12 AWG THW copper conductor. Assume steel conduit.

Solution: From the impedance tables, the resistance and reactance are 2.0 Ω/1000 ft and 0.068 Ω/1000 ft, respectively. Application of Equations (17–20) and (17–21) results in

$$R_C = 2 \times \frac{2.0 \ \Omega/1000 \ \text{ft}}{1000} \times (100 \ \text{ft}) = 0.4 \ \Omega$$

$$X_C = 2 \times \frac{0.068 \ \Omega/1000 \ \text{ft}}{1000} \times (100 \ \text{ft}) = 0.0136 \ \Omega$$

17–6   MOTOR CONTRIBUTION

When a short circuit occurs on the power system, short circuit current will flow from the source to the point of fault. In addition, motors and generators connected to the system will also contribute to the total fault current. Typically, the motor contribution to the rms symmetrical short circuit current is approximately 6 times the full-load current rating of the motor. In addition, the motor contribution to the rms asymmetrical half-cycle current may also be considered as 6 times the full-load current rating of the motor. Where there are multiple motors in a system, the total equivalent motor load is used.

EXAMPLE 17–9

A three-phase power system has a short circuit current of 10,000 A rms symmetrical and 12,000 rms asymmetrical supplied from the source. In addition, a total of five 100 hp, 480 V motors, each having a full-load current rating of 120 A, are connected to the system. Determine the rms symmetrical and rms asymmetrical short circuit current, including the contribution from the motors.

Solution: The sum of the full-load currents for all five motors is 600 A. The short circuit contribution is assumed to be 6 times the sum of the full-load current ratings of all motors, or 3,600 A. Therefore, the total rms symmetrical short circuit current is 10,000 A + 3,600 A = 13,600 A. The rms asymmetrical short circuit current is 12,000 A + 3,600 A = 15,600 A.

17–7   THREE-PHASE SYSTEMS

When dealing with three-phase systems, there are several different ways in which a fault can occur. The three-phase fault occurs when all three ungrounded conductors come in contact with each other. The result is a balanced condition in which the three line currents are equal in magnitude and displaced 120° and 240° from each other. Other types of faults include the line-to-line fault, line-to-ground fault, and line-to-line-to-ground fault. In systems where the low-voltage bus is supplied by a delta–wye-connected transformer, the line-to-ground fault current magnitude may exceed the three-phase fault current. For most practical situations, the line-to-ground fault current seldom exceeds 125% of the three-phase fault current magnitude. The discussion in this section is limited to three-phase faults.

To determine the short circuit current, the total impedance to the fault point must be determined. This total impedance will include impedances of all electrical components, including the system impedance, transformer impedances, line and cable impedances, and so on. These impedances must be reflected to the point of fault, as previously mentioned.

Recall that the three-phase fault condition results in a balanced set of short circuit currents. As a result, it is sufficient to use the line-to-neutral equivalent system representation to calculate the short circuit current. The short circuit current is calculated by dividing the line-to-neutral system voltage by the magnitude of the total impedance to the fault point. In the form of an equation:

$$I_{\text{rms}} = \frac{\text{Line-to-neutral voltage}}{|Z_{\text{TOTAL}}|} \qquad (17\text{--}22)$$

The system X/R ratio is determined as the ratio of the total reactance to the fault point divided by the total resistance to the fault point. The X/R ratio is then used to determine the asymmetrical factors.

EXAMPLE 17–10

Determine the rms symmetrical, rms asymmetrical, and peak short circuit current magnitudes for a three-phase fault occurring at (a) F1 and (b) F2 for the power system shown in Figure 17–3.

Solution:

a) Fault at F1. To determine the short circuit current at F1, all impedances must be referred to the low-voltage (480 V) side of transformer TR1. The equivalent system impedance referred to the 480 V side of TR1 is given by Equation (17–7):

$$Z_{\text{SYS}} = \frac{(4160 \text{ V})^2}{65 \text{ MVA} \times 10^6} = 0.26624 \text{ } \Omega$$

The impedance angle of the equivalent system impedance is given by Equation (17–8):

$$\theta = \tan^{-1}(3) = 71.6°$$

The equivalent system resistance and reactance are given by Equations (17–9) and (17–10):

$$R_{\text{SYS}} = 0.26624 \times \cos(71.6°) = 0.0840 \text{ } \Omega$$

$$X_{\text{SYS}} = 0.26624 \times \sin(71.6°) = 0.2526 \text{ } \Omega$$

FIGURE 17–3

System for Three-Phase Short Circuit Study

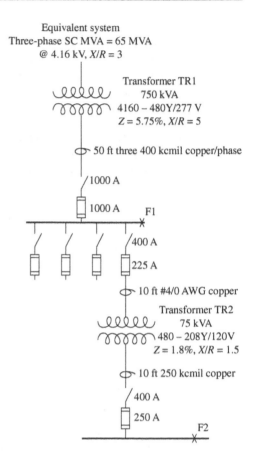

Equivalent system
Three-phase SC MVA = 65 MVA
@ 4.16 kV, $X/R = 3$

Transformer TR1
750 kVA
4160 – 480Y/277 V
$Z = 5.75\%$, $X/R = 5$

50 ft three 400 kcmil copper/phase

1000 A

1000 A   F1

400 A

225 A

10 ft #4/0 AWG copper

Transformer TR2
75 kVA
480 – 208Y/120V
$Z = 1.8\%$, $X/R = 1.5$

10 ft 250 kcmil copper

400 A

250 A

F2

The equivalent system resistance and reactance referred to the low-voltage side of TR1 are determined by application of Equations (17–16) and (17–17):

$$R_{\text{SYS,LS}} = 0.0840\left(\frac{480\text{ V}}{4160\text{ V}}\right)^2 = 0.00112\ \Omega$$

$$X_{\text{SYS,LS}} = 0.2526\left(\frac{480\text{ V}}{4160\text{ V}}\right)^2 = 0.00336\ \Omega$$

The percent resistance and percent reactance of transformer TR1 are determined as follows:

$$\theta_{\text{TR1}} = \tan^{-1}(5) = 78.7°$$

$$\%\ R_{\text{TR1}} = 5.75\% \times \cos(78.7°) = 1.13\%$$

$$\%\ X_{\text{TR1}} = 5.75\% \times \sin(78.7°) = 5.64\%$$

The ohmic resistance and reactance of transformer TR1 referred to the 480 V side are determined by applying Equations (17–14) and (17–15):

$$R_{TR} = \frac{1}{100}\left[\frac{(1.13\%)(480\ V)^2}{750,000\ VA}\right] = 0.00347\ \Omega$$

$$X_{TR} = \frac{1}{100}\left[\frac{(5.64\%)(480\ V)^2}{750,000\ VA}\right] = 0.01733\ \Omega$$

The resistance and reactance of the 50 foot service from TR1 to the 480 V switchgear are given by Equations (17–18) and (17–19). In addition, the resistance and reactance of a single conductor must be divided by 3 since there are three conductors in parallel per phase.

$$R_C = \left(\frac{1}{3}\right)\frac{0.035\ \Omega/1000\ ft}{1000} \times 50\ ft = 0.00058\ \Omega$$

$$X_C = \left(\frac{1}{3}\right)\frac{0.049\ \Omega/1000\ ft}{1000} \times 50\ ft = 0.00082\ \Omega$$

The total impedance to fault point F1 is

Equivalent system:	$0.001120 + j0.003360\ \Omega$
Transformer TR1:	$0.003470 + j0.017330\ \Omega$
50 ft 400 kcmil:	$0.000580 + j0.000820\ \Omega$
Total:	$0.005170 + j0.021510\ \Omega$

Therefore, $Z = 0.022123\ \Omega$ and the system X/R ratio at point F1 is 4.16.

The three-phase short circuit current at F1 is given by Equation (17–22):

$$I_{rms} = \frac{277\ V}{0.022123\ \Omega} = 12,521\ A$$

The instantaneous peak factor is 2.1057 as determined by interpolation from Table 17–1. The half-cycle rms factor is 1.2025. Therefore, the peak instantaneous current is

$$I_p = 2.1057(12,521\ A) = 26,365\ A$$

The half-cycle rms asymmetrical current is

$$I_{rms,1/2} = 1.2025(12,521\ A) = 15,057\ A$$

b) Fault at F2. To determine the short circuit current at F2, the total system impedance up to point F1 plus the impedance of the #4/0 AWG feeder to TR2, must be reflected to the low-voltage 208 V side of TR2. The resistance and reactance of the #4/0 AWG feeder are

$$R_C = \frac{0.063\ \Omega/1000\ ft}{1000} \times 10\ ft = 0.00063\ \Omega$$

$$X_C = \frac{0.051\ \Omega/1000\ ft}{1000} \times 10\ ft = 0.00051\ \Omega$$

The total resistance and reactance up to point F1 reflected to the low-voltage side of TR2 are

$$R_{\text{SYS,LS}} = 0.00517 \left(\frac{208 \text{ V}}{480 \text{ V}} \right)^2 = 0.000971 \; \Omega$$

$$X_{\text{SYS,LS}} = 0.02151 \left(\frac{208 \text{ V}}{480 \text{ V}} \right)^2 = 0.004039 \; \Omega$$

The #4/0 AWG cable resistance and reactance reflected to the low-voltage side of TR2 are

$$R_{4/0,\text{LS}} = 0.00063 \left(\frac{208 \text{ V}}{480 \text{ V}} \right)^2 = 0.000118 \; \Omega$$

$$X_{4/0,\text{LS}} = 0.00051 \left(\frac{208 \text{ V}}{480 \text{ V}} \right)^2 = 0.000096 \; \Omega$$

The percent resistance and percent reactance of transformer TR2 are determined as follows:

$$\theta_{\text{TR2}} = \tan^{-1}(1.5) = 56.3°$$

$$\% \, R_{\text{TR2}} = 1.8\% \times \cos(56.3°) = 1.0\%$$

$$\% \, X_{\text{TR2}} = 1.8\% \times \sin(56.3°) = 1.5\%$$

The ohmic resistance and reactance of transformer TR2 referred to the 208 V side are determined by applying Equations (17–14) and (17–15):

$$R_{\text{TR2}} = \frac{1}{100} \left[\frac{(1.0\%)(208 \text{ V})^2}{75,000 \text{ VA}} \right] = 0.005768 \; \Omega$$

$$X_{\text{TR2}} = \frac{1}{100} \left[\frac{(1.5\%)(208 \text{ V})^2}{75,000 \text{ VA}} \right] = 0.008653 \; \Omega$$

The resistance and reactance of the 250 kcmil AWG feeder are

$$R_{\text{C}} = \frac{0.054 \; \Omega/1000 \text{ ft}}{1000} \times 10 \text{ ft} = 0.00054 \; \Omega$$

$$X_{\text{C}} = \frac{0.052 \; \Omega/1000 \text{ ft}}{1000} \times 10 \text{ ft} = 0.00052 \; \Omega$$

The total impedance to fault point F2 is

Equivalent system:	$0.000971 + j0.004039 \; \Omega$
#4/0 cable:	$0.000118 + j0.000096 \; \Omega$
Transformer TR2:	$0.005768 + j0.008653 \; \Omega$
250 kcmil cable:	$0.000540 + j0.000520 \; \Omega$
Total:	$0.007397 + j0.013308 \; \Omega$

Therefore, $Z = 0.01522 \; \Omega$ and the system X/R ratio at point F2 is 1.8.

The three-phase short circuit current at F2 is given by Equation (17–22):

$$I_{rms} = \frac{120 \text{ V}}{0.01522 \ \Omega} = 7884 \text{ A}$$

The instantaneous peak factor is 1.7072, as determined by interpolation from Table 17–1. The half-cycle rms factor is 1.034. Therefore, the peak instantaneous current is

$$I_p = 1.7072(7884 \text{ A}) = 13,460 \text{ A}$$

The half-cycle rms asymmetrical current is

$$I_{rms,1/2} = 1.034(7884 \text{ A}) = 8152 \text{ A}$$

TABLE 17–3

	rms Symmetrical Current	rms Asymmetrical Current	Peak Current
Fault at F1:	12,521 A	15,057 A	26,365 A
Fault at F2:	7884 A	8152 A	13,460 A
Summary:			

17–8   SINGLE-PHASE SYSTEMS

In single-phase, three-wire systems, the two possible faults are line to line across 240 V and line to ground across 120 V. The short circuit current that flow as a result of a fault between the two ungrounded conductors (240 V) is calculated by dividing the line-to-line voltage by the total equivalent impedance to the point of the fault:

$$I_{rms,240 \text{ V}} = \frac{\text{Line-to-line voltage}}{|Z_{TOTAL}|} = \frac{240 \text{ V}}{|Z_{TOTAL}|} \qquad (17\text{–}23)$$

The short circuit current that flow as a result of a fault between an ungrounded conductor and the grounded conductor (120 V) is calculated by dividing the line-to-neutral voltage by the total equivalent impedance to the point of the fault:

$$I_{rms,120 \text{ V}} = \frac{\text{Line-to-neutral voltage}}{|Z_{TOTAL}|} = \frac{120 \text{ V}}{|Z_{TOTAL}|} \qquad (17\text{–}24)$$

EXAMPLE 17–11

Determine the rms symmetrical, rms asymmetrical, and peak short circuit current magnitudes for a single-phase, line-to-line (240 V) fault occurring at points (a) F1 and (b) F2 for

FIGURE 17–4
System for Single-Phase Short
Circuit Study

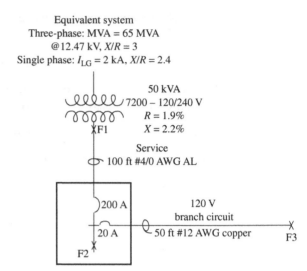

Equivalent system
Three-phase: MVA = 65 MVA
@12.47 kV, $X/R = 3$
Single phase: $I_{LG} = 2$ kA, $X/R = 2.4$

50 kVA
7200 – 120/240 V
$R = 1.9\%$
$X = 2.2\%$
F1

Service
100 ft #4/0 AWG AL

200 A

120 V
branch circuit
50 ft #12 AWG copper

20 A

F3

F2

the power system shown in Figure 17–4. Note that fault current calculation for a line-to-line fault is not possible at F3 since this branch circuit is 120 V.

Solution:

a) The equivalent system impedance is calculated based on the line-to-ground short circuit current and X/R ratio of the system. From Equation (17–11):

$$Z_{SYS,1\phi} = \frac{7200 \text{ V}}{2000 \text{ A}} = 3.6 \text{ } \Omega$$

$\theta = \tan^{-1}(2.4) = 67.4°$
$R_{SYS,1\phi} = 3.6 \times \cos(67.4°) = 1.3835 \text{ } \Omega$
$X_{SYS,1\phi} = 3.6 \times \sin(67.4°) = 3.3236 \text{ } \Omega$

Reflect system resistance and reactance to the 240 V side:

$$R'_{SYS,1\phi} = 1.3835 \text{ } \Omega \times \left(\frac{240 \text{ V}}{7200 \text{ V}}\right)^2 = 0.001537 \text{ } \Omega$$

$$X'_{SYS,1\phi} = 3.3236 \text{ } \Omega \times \left(\frac{240 \text{ V}}{7200 \text{ V}}\right)^2 = 0.003692 \text{ } \Omega$$

The transformer resistance and reactance referred to the low-voltage side are

$$R_{TR} = \frac{1}{100}\left[\frac{(1.9\%)(240 \text{ V})^2}{50,000 \text{ VA}}\right] = 0.02189 \text{ } \Omega$$

$$X_{TR} = \frac{1}{100}\left[\frac{(2.2\%)(240 \text{ V})^2}{50,000 \text{ VA}}\right] = 0.025344 \text{ } \Omega$$

The total impedance to F1 is

System: $0.001537 + j0.003692\ \Omega$
Transformer: $0.021890 + j0.025344\ \Omega$
    Total: $0.023427 + j0.029036$

The magnitude of the total impedance is $0.03731\ \Omega$ and the X/R ratio is 1.24. The peak factor and half-cycle rms factor are determined by interpolation from Table 17–1 as 1.5732 and 1.0116, respectively. The rms symmetrical short circuit current is

$$I_{rms} = \frac{240\ \text{V}}{0.03731\ \Omega} = 6433\ \text{A}$$

The peak current is

$$I_p = 1.5732(6433\ \text{A}) = 10{,}120\ \text{A}$$

The rms value of the first half-cycle asymmetrical current is

$$I_{rms,1/2} = 1.0116(6433\ \text{A}) = 6508\ \text{A}$$

b) Fault at F2. The resistance and reactance of the #4/0 AWG aluminum service entrance conductor is

$$R_C = 2 \times \frac{0.1\ \Omega/1000\ \text{ft}}{1000} \times 100\ \text{ft} = 0.02\ \Omega$$

$$X_C = 2 \times \frac{0.041\ \Omega/1000\ \text{ft}}{1000} \times 100\ \text{ft} = 0.0082\ \Omega$$

The total impedance to F2 is

Total to F1: $0.023427 + j0.029036\ \Omega$
#4/0 Cable: $0.02 + j0.0082\ \Omega$
    Total: $0.043427 + j0.037236\ \Omega$

The magnitude of the total impedance is $0.05721\ \Omega$ and the X/R ratio is 0.8574. The peak factor and half-cycle rms factor are determined by interpolation from Table 17–1 as 1.48 and 1.002, respectively. The rms symmetrical short circuit current is

$$I_{rms} = \frac{240\ \text{V}}{0.05721\ \Omega} = 4195\ \text{A}$$

The peak current is

$$I_p = 1.48(4195\ \text{A}) = 6209\ \text{A}$$

The rms value of the first half-cycle asymmetrical current is

$$I_{rms,1/2} = 1.002(4195\ \text{A}) = 4203\ \text{A}$$

Summary:

TABLE 17–4

	rms Symmetrical Current	rms Asymmetrical Current	Peak Current
Fault at F1:	6433 A	6508 A	10,120 A
Fault at F2:	4195 A	4203 A	6209 A

EXAMPLE 17–12

Repeat Example 17–11 for single-phase, line-to-ground (120 V) faults at points (a) F1, (b) F2, and (c) F3 for the power system shown in Figure 17–4.

Solution:

a) The equivalent system impedance is the same as in Example 17–11. However, when reflecting to the low-voltage side, the low-voltage rating of 120 V will be used rather than 240 V, since line-to-ground short circuit current is of interest. The result is

$$R'_{SYS,1\phi} = 1.3835 \ \Omega \times \left(\frac{120 \text{ V}}{7200 \text{ V}}\right)^2 = 0.0003843 \ \Omega$$

$$X'_{SYS,1\phi} = 3.3236 \ \Omega \times \left(\frac{120 \text{ V}}{7200 \text{ V}}\right)^2 = 0.0009232 \ \Omega$$

The transformer resistance and reactance for the half-winding condition are

$$R_{TR} = (\tfrac{1}{3})(0.02189 \ \Omega) = 0.0072967 \ \Omega$$

$$X_{TR} = (\tfrac{1}{3})(0.02534 \ \Omega) = 0.0084467 \ \Omega$$

The total impedance to F1 is

System:	$0.0003843 + j0.009232 \ \Omega$
Transformer:	$0.0072967 + j0.0084467 \ \Omega$
Total:	$0.0076810 + j0.0093699 \ \Omega$

The magnitude of the total impedance is $0.0121158 \ \Omega$ and the X/R ratio is 1.22. The peak factor and half-cycle rms factor are determined by interpolation from Table 17–1 as 1.5658 and 1.0108, respectively. The rms symmetrical short circuit current is

$$I_{rms} = \frac{120 \text{ V}}{0.0121158 \ \Omega} = 9904 \text{ A}$$

The peak current is

$$I_p = 1.5658(9904 \text{ A}) = 15,508 \text{ A}$$

The rms value of the first half-cycle asymmetrical current is

$$I_{rms,1/2} = 1.0108(9904\ A) = 10,011\ A$$

b) Fault at F2. The resistance and reactance of the #4/0 AWG aluminum service entrance conductor are the same as in Example 17–11:

$R_C = 0.02\ \Omega$
$X_C = 0.0082\ \Omega$

The total impedance to F2 is

Total to F1:	$0.007681 + j0.0093699\ \Omega$
#4/0 Cable:	$0.02\ \ \ \ \ + j0.0082\ \Omega$
Total:	$0.027681 + j0.0175699\ \Omega$

The magnitude of the total impedance is 0.032786 Ω and the X/R ratio is 0.635. The peak factor and half-cycle rms factor are determined by interpolation from Table 17–1 as 1.4414 and 1.000, respectively. The rms symmetrical short circuit current is

$$I_{rms} = \frac{120\ V}{0.032786\ \Omega} = 3660\ A$$

The peak current is

$$I_p = 1.4414(3660\ A) = 5276\ A$$

The rms value of the first half-cycle asymmetrical current is

$$I_{rms,1/2} = 1.000(3660\ A) = 3660\ A$$

c) Fault at F3. The resistance and reactance of the #12 AWG copper branch circuit conductor are

$$R_C = 2 \times \frac{2.0\ \Omega/1000\ ft}{1000} \times 50\ ft = 0.2\ \Omega$$

$$X_C = 2 \times \frac{0.0541\ \Omega/1000\ ft}{1000} \times 50\ ft = 0.0054\ \Omega$$

The total impedance to F3 is

Total to F2:	$0.027681 + j0.0175699\ \Omega$
#12 Cable:	$0.2\ \ \ \ \ + j0.0054\ \Omega$
Total:	$0.227681 + j0.0229699\ \Omega$

The magnitude of the total impedance is 0.228837 Ω and the X/R ratio is 0.1. The peak factor and half-cycle rms factor are determined by interpolation from Table 17–1 as 1.4142 and 1.000, respectively. The rms symmetrical short circuit current is

$$I_{rms} = \frac{120\ V}{0.228837\ \Omega} = 524\ A$$

The peak current is

$$I_p = 1.4142(524\ A) = 741\ A$$

The rms value of the first half-cycle asymmetrical current is

$$I_{rms,1/2} = 1.000(524 \text{ A}) = 524 \text{ A}$$

Summary:

TABLE 17–5

	rms Symmetrical Current	rms Asymmetrical Current	Peak Current
Fault at F1:	9904 A	10011 A	15,508 A
Fault at F2:	3660 A	3660 A	5276 A
Fault at F3:	524 A	524 A	741 A

It is also interesting to compare the rms short circuit current for line-to-line and line-to-ground faults for the system shown in Figure 17–4. The following table summarizes the rms symmetrical short circuit current values:

TABLE 17–6

	Line-to-Line Fault (240 V)	Line-to-Ground Fault (120 V)
Fault at F1:	6433 A	9904 A
Fault at F2:	4195 A	3660 A
Fault at F3:	N/A	524 A

Note that close to the terminals of the transformer, the line-to-ground short circuit current exceeds the line-to-line short circuit current level. This is due to the half-winding resistance of the transformer not being equal to ½ times the full winding resistance. It is common for the line-to-ground short circuit current to be approximately 1.5 times the line-to-line short circuit current close to the transformer on 120/240 V, single-phase, three-wire systems.

PROBLEMS

1. Why is the determination of short circuit current important?
2. The system impedance at a 480 V, three-phase panel location is $0.008 + j0.02$ ohms. Determine the symmetrical short circuit current, asymmetrical peak current, and half-cycle rms short circuit current.
3. What is the approximate short circuit contribution from a 100 hp, 460 V, three-phase induction motor?

4. A utility 4.16 kV, three-phase distribution feeder has a three-phase short circuit MVA of 36 MVA with an X/R ratio of 2:1, the single-phase line-to-ground fault current is 2750 A with an X/R ratio of 1:1. Determine the equivalent system impedance in ohms referred to the low side of a 4.16 kV–480Y/277 V transformer.

5. Repeat Problem 4 if the transformer is rated 4.16 kV–208 Y/120 V.

6. Repeat Problem 4 if the transformer is rated 2400–120/240 V. Determine the system impedance for line-to-line and line-to-ground faults on the secondary.

7. Determine the short circuit current at the terminals of a 500 kVA, 4160–480Y/277 V, three-phase transformer having an impedance of 5.75% and an X/R ratio of 4:1. Neglect system impedance.

8. Determine the short circuit current at the terminals of a 500 kVA, 4160–208Y/120 V, three-phase transformer having an impedance of 5.75% and an X/R ratio of 4:1. Neglect system impedance. How does this value compare with the results of Problem 7?

9. Determine the line-to-line and line-to-ground short circuit current at the terminals of a 50 kVA, 2400–120/240 V, single-phase transformer having a resistance of 2.2% and reactance of 1.8%.

10. Determine the short circuit current for faults from line to line and line to ground at the terminals of the service transformer for the system of Problem 16 in Chapter 16.

11. Determine the short circuit current for faults from line to line and line to ground at the service panel for the system of Problem 16 in Chapter 16.

12. Determine the short circuit current at (a) the MDP, (b) the 60 hp motor terminals, (c) panel RP, and (d) the tag end of the 120 V branch circuit off panel RP for the industrial facility defined in Problem 17 in Chapter 16. The total motor load on the MDP is 400 kVA.

18

Coordination and Equipment Protection

INTRODUCTION

This chapter presents an introduction to overcurrent device coordination and protection of equipment under short circuit conditions. The most common form of short circuit protection applied to power distribution systems is time–overcurrent (TOC). The devices that employ a time–overcurrent operating characteristic include fuses, circuit breakers, motor overload elements, and time–overcurrent relays. The tripping characteristic of time–overcurrent devices is a function of the magnitude and the time duration of the short circuit current.

The chapter begins with a discussion of the coordination of overcurrent devices to isolate the fault section of the power distribution system while minimizing the total outage in the facility. Protection of components such as cables, motor starters, and transformers and the coordination of motor overload elements with the starting current of the motor are also presented, and reflecting overcurrent device characteristics from one side of a transformer to the other is also discussed.

OBJECTIVES

Upon completion of this chapter, you will:

- Understand the need for overcurrent device coordination
- Understand conductor-withstand characteristics under short circuit conditions
- Be able to coordinate motor overload relays with motor starting current
- Understand requirements for transformer protection against short circuits
- Be able to reflect overcurrent device characteristics from the primary to the secondary of a transformer
- Understand coordination of overcurrent devices on the primary and secondary side of a transformer

18–1   OVERCURRENT DEVICE COORDINATION

The purpose of overcurrent device coordination is to ensure that the device nearest to the fault operates to permanently isolate only the faulted section of the line or equipment. By properly coordinating the overcurrent devices in a system, blackouts within the system can be isolated to that section of the system experiencing the fault. For example, the branch circuit overcurrent device should clear for short circuits on the branch circuit before the main breaker. Also, overcurrent devices on the transformer primary should not operate before the overcurrent devices on the secondary for faults on the secondary of the transformer. This section deals with coordination of overcurrent devices applied on radial power distribution systems.

Fuse–Fuse Coordination

Coordination exists for two fuses installed in series if the fuse closest to the fault clears before the upstream fuses operate or become damaged. In reference to Figure 18–1, the fuse that is closest to the fault on the source side is referred to as the "protecting" fuse, and the next upstream fuse located on the source side of the protecting fuse is referred to as the "protected" fuse. In order to determine whether coordination exists for low-level fault currents and overloads, the minimum melt and total clearing curves for both the protecting and protected fuse are plotted on the same graph. In addition, it is common to replot the minimum melt characteristic of the protected fuse at 75% of the minimum melting time to allow for preload currents and high ambient temperatures. These adjusted fuse characteristics are shown in Figure 18–1.

In reference to Figure 18–1, the current where 75% of the minimum melt time of the protected fuse intersects the total clearing curve of the protecting fuse is designated I_{MAX}. Coordination exists for currents up to the level of I_{MAX}. If the actual magnitude of the fault current on the load side of the protecting fuse exceeds I_{MAX}, both fuses may blow or damage may occur to the protected fuse due to partial melting of the fuse element. Time–current characteristic curves (TCC) for 5.5 kV, E-rated fuses are shown in Figure 18–2.

If the fault current magnitudes are high, it may be desirable to install current-limiting fuses. Coordination between two current-limiting fuses in series is achieved if the total clearing I^2t of the protecting fuse is greater than the minimum melt I^2t of the protected fuse. This generally applies for high current levels when the fuses are operating in the current-limiting mode. Fuse manufacturers typically provide a fuse ratio selectivity chart to determine if coordination exists in the high-fault current region where fuses operate in the current-limiting region. An example of a fuse selectivity guide is shown in Table 18–1. For operation outside the current-limiting region, the coordination is determined by plotting the time–current characteristics as before.

EXAMPLE 18–1

Determine whether coordination exists between the following fuses:

a) 200 A FRS-R line-side (protected) fuse, 50 A LPS-RKSP load-side (protecting) fuse
b) 200 A LPS-RKSP line-side (protected) fuse, 50 A FRS-R load-side (protecting) fuse

Solution:

a) From the selectivity chart shown in Table 18–1, the minimum ratio for selectivity between an FRS-R line-side fuse and an LPS-RKSP load-side fuse is 1.5:1. The actual ratio of line side to load side is 200 A ÷ 50 A = 4:1. Since the actual ratio of 4:1 exceeds the minimum required ratio of 1.5:1, coordination is achieved. Therefore, the

A. One–Line Diagram

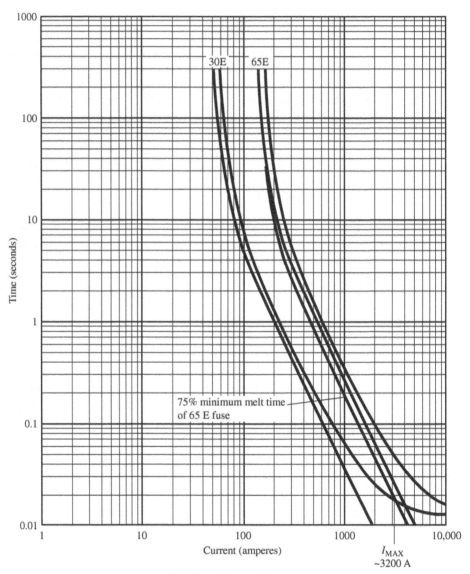

B. Time–Current Curves

FIGURE 18–1
Fuse–Fuse Coordination

A055F1DORO – 10E to 200E and A055F2DORO – 250E to 450E

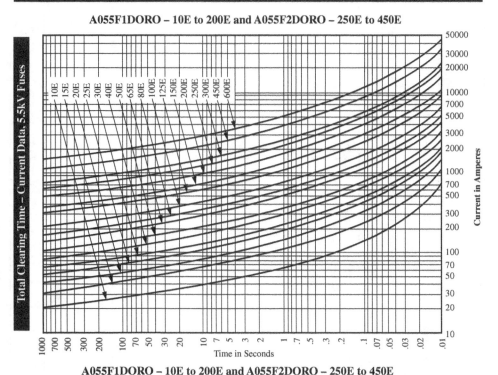

A055F1DORO – 10E to 200E and A055F2DORO – 250E to 450E

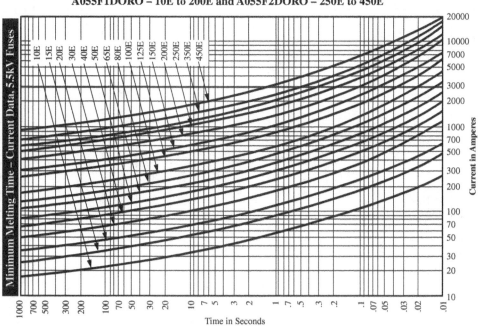

FIGURE 18–2
Time–Current Characteristics for E-Rated Medium-Voltage Fuses *Source:* Ferraz–Shawmut
Company.

TABLE 18-1
Fuse Selectivity Guide

*Selectivity Ratio Guide (Line-Side to Load-Side) for Blackout Prevention

Load-Side Fuse (columns)

Line-Side Fuse	601–6000A Time-Delay LOW-PEAK (L) KRP-CSP	601–4000A Time-Delay LIMITRON (L) KLU	0–600A Dual-Element Time-Delay LOW-PEAK (RK1) LPN-RKSP / LPS-RKSP	0–600A (J)** LPJSP	0–600A FUSETRON (RK5) FRN-R / FRS-R	601–6000A Fast-Acting LIMITRON (L) KTU	0–600A Fast-Acting LIMITRON (RK1) KTN-R / KTS-R	0–1200A T-TRON (T) JJN / JJS	0–600A LIMITRON (J) JKS	0–60A Time-Delay SC (G) SC
601 to 6000A — Time-Delay — LOW-PEAK (L) — KRP-CSP	2:1	2.5:1	2:1	2:1	4:1	2:1	2:1	2:1	2:1	N/A
601 to 4000A — Time-Delay — LIMITRON (L) — KLU	2:1	2:1	2:1	2:1	4:1	2:1	2:1	2:1	2:1	N/A
0 to 600A — Dual-Element — LOW-PEAK (RK1) — LPN-RKSP / LPS-RKSP	—	—	2:1	2:1	8:1	—	3:1	3:1	3:1	4:1
0 to 600A — Dual-Element — LPJSP** (J)	—	—	2:1	2:1	8:1	—	3:1	3:1	3:1	4:1
0 to 600A — Dual-Element — FUSETRON (RK5) — FRN-R / FRS-R	—	—	1.5:1	1.5:1	2:1	—	1.5:1	1.5:1	1.5:1	1.5:1
601 to 6000A — Fast-Acting — LIMITRON (L) — KTU	2:1	2.5:1	2:1	2:1	6:1	2:1	2:1	2:1	2:1	N/A
0 to 600A — Fast-Acting — LIMITRON (RK1) — KTN-R / KTS-R	—	—	3:1	3:1	8:1	—	3:1	3:1	3:1	4:1
0 to 1200A — T-TRON (T) — JJN / JJS	—	—	3:1	3:1	8:1	—	3:1	3:1	3:1	4:1
0 to 600A — LIMITRON (J) — JKS	—	—	2:1	2:1	8:1	—	3:1	3:1	3:1	4:1
0 to 60A — Time-Delay — SC (G) — SC	—	—	3:1	3:1	4:1	—	2:1	2:1	2:1	2:1

*Note: At some values of fault current, specified ratios may be lowered to permit closer fuse sizing. Plot fuse curves or consult with Bussmann.

General Notes: Ratios given in this Table apply only to Buss fuses. When fuses are within the same case size, consult Bussmann.

**Consult Bussmann for latest LPJSP ratios.

Source: Cooper Bussmann.

50 A fuse will clear any short circuit on its load side without the 200 A line-side fuse blowing.

b) From the selectivity chart shown in Table 18–1, the minimum ratio for selectivity between an LPS-RKSP line-side fuse and an FRS-R load-side fuse is 8:1. The actual ratio of line side to load side is 200 A ÷ 50 A = 4:1. Since the actual ratio of 4:1 does not exceed the minimum required ratio of 8:1, coordination is not achieved. Therefore, both the 200 A and the 50 A fuses will blow in the event of a short circuit on the load side of the 50 A fuse.

Breaker–Breaker Coordination

Coordination of two breakers in series for normal load and overload conditions is achieved when the characteristic (tripping) curve of the line-side breaker lies above and to the right of the load-side breaker. The maximum short circuit current that will allow coordination is the point at which the unlatching (lower) portion of the source-side breaker curve touches the total clearing (upper) portion of the load-side breaker curve. If the source-side breaker has an adjustable instantaneous trip setting, the maximum value of short circuit current for coordination purposes is affected by the instantaneous trip setting. For example, increasing the instantaneous trip setting results in an increase in the maximum value of short circuit current permitted for coordination purposes. In most instances, the maximum current for coordination of two circuit breakers in series is equal to the instantaneous setting of the source-side breaker. A representative time–current characteristic curve of two breakers in series is shown in Figure 18–3. Note that the source-side breaker has an adjustable instantaneous trip setting in this case.

EXAMPLE 18–2

Determine the maximum fault current for coordination between the breakers shown in Figure 18–3.

Solution: Examination of the curves indicates that coordination is achieved for short circuit current up to 1000 A. Note that this level of short circuit current is equal to the instantaneous trip level of the 100 A breaker. Any short circuit current level above this maximum point will result in both breakers tripping in the event of a short circuit.

Fuse–Breaker Coordination

Coordination of a source-side fuse in series with a load-side breaker is obtained for normal load and overload conditions if the characteristic (tripping) curve of the source-side fuse lies above and to the right of the load-side breaker curve. The maximum short circuit current that will allow coordination is the point at which the minimum melt curve of the source-side fuse touches the total clearing (upper) portion of the load-side breaker curve. As with fuse–fuse coordination, it may be necessary to adjust the minimum melt characteristic of the source-side fuse to allow for preloading. In some instances, coordination may occur for certain ranges of short circuit current levels. Figure 18–4 illustrates an example of fuse–breaker coordination.

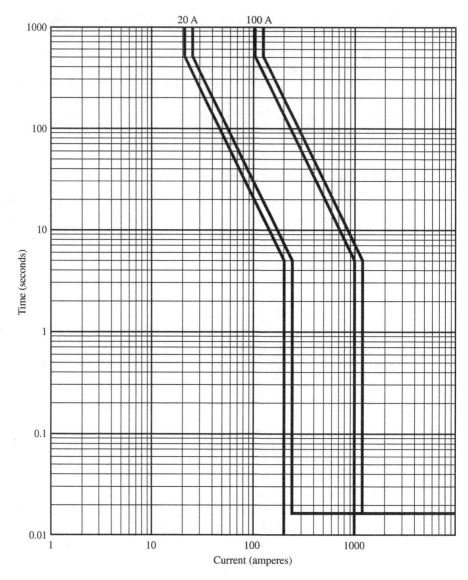

FIGURE 18–3
Breaker–Breaker Coordination

EXAMPLE 18–3

Determine the range of coordination between the following overcurrent devices. The time–current characteristic curves are shown in Figure 18–4.

a) 20 A breaker and 50 A fuse
b) 20 A breaker and 100 A fuse

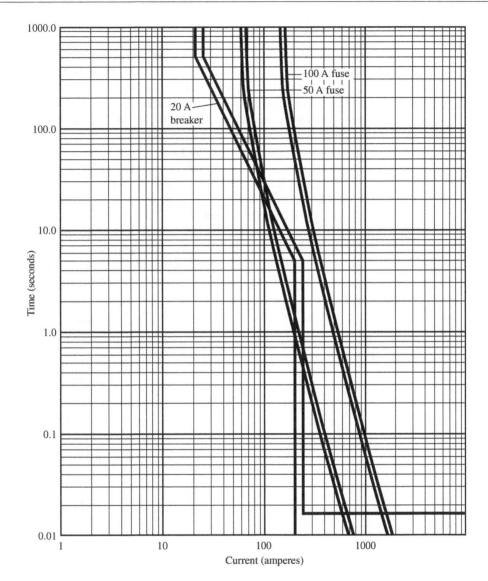

FIGURE 18–4
Fuse–Breaker Coordination

Solution:

a) Investigation of the TCC curves reveals that coordination occurs for short circuit current less than 90 A and between 150 A and 600 A. For short circuit currents in the range between 90 A and 200 A, coordination is not achieved. Also, high levels of short circuit current above 600 A result in tripping of both the 20 A breaker and the 50 A fuse.

b) Coordination is achieved for currents up to 1500 A. Levels of short circuit current above 1500 A result in tripping of both the 20 A breaker and 100 A fuse.

Series-Rated Systems

A series-rated system is one in which the load-side overcurrent device has an interrupting rating less than the source-side overcurrent device. An example of a series-rated system is shown in Figure 18–5(A). The interrupting rating of the source-side OCPD must be equal to or greater than the maximum fault current availability on the load side of the downstream OCPD. The interrupting rating of the load-side OCPD may be less than the available fault current. In the event of a short circuit on the load side of the load-side overcurrent device, both the source-side and load-side overcurrent devices will operate to clear the fault. However, it is the source-side device that will actually interrupt the short circuit current. The advantage of series-rated systems is that the load-side OCPDs can have a lower interrupting rating, resulting in less cost. The major disadvantage is the loss of coordination between the source and load OCPDs in the event of a short circuit. This loss of coordination can have a negative impact on critical circuits in a facility.

Section 240.86 of the *NEC* lists several requirements that must be met when applying series-rated systems. First, all panels must be labeled as being part of a series-rated system. The rating and type of OCPD permitted to be installed in both the source and load

FIGURE 18–5
Series-Rated System

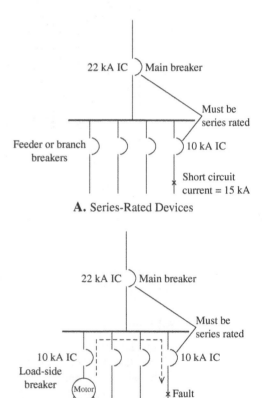

A. Series-Rated Devices

B. Motor Contribution

panels must be designated on each panel. The OCPD devices must be rated for series application. Motors are not permitted to be connected between the source-side and load-side OCPDs. Also, the sum of all motor full-load currents cannot exceed 1% of the interrupting rating of the load-side OCPD, as indicated in Figure 18–5(B).

18–2   CABLE PROTECTION

As previously discussed, fuse and breaker ratings are selected to protect conductors within their allowable ampacity. This selection process is designed to protect the conductors against normal overloads that may occur. Additional consideration must be given to the selection of overcurrent devices to protect the conductor during short circuit conditions.

When selecting fuse and breaker ratings, it is important to coordinate the time–current characteristics of these devices with the short circuit withstand characteristic curve of the conductor. The short circuit withstand curves for insulated conductors are based on the following equations:

$$\text{Copper conductor:} \quad \left[\frac{I}{A}\right]^2 T = 0.0297 \log\left[\frac{T_2 + 234}{T_1 + 234}\right] \qquad \textbf{(18–1a)}$$

$$\text{Aluminum conductor:} \quad \left[\frac{I}{A}\right]^2 T = 0.0125 \log\left[\frac{T_2 + 228}{T_1 + 228}\right] \qquad \textbf{(18–1b)}$$

where:

I = short circuit current in amperes
A = conductor cross-sectional area in circular mils
T = time duration of short circuit current in seconds
T_1 = maximum conductor temperature under normal operating conditions, °C
T_2 = maximum conductor temperature under short circuit conditions, °C

The maximum conductor temperature under normal operating conditions, T_1, is 75°C for thermoplastic and rubber insulation and 90°C for XLP and EPR insulation. The maximum conductor temperature under short circuit conditions is 150°C for thermoplastic, 200°C for rubber, and 250°C for XLP and EPR insulations. When plotted on a log–log scale, Equations (18–1a) and (18–1b) become straight lines. Withstand curves for other conductor and insulation types can be obtained by applying Equations (18–1a) and (18–1b).

For conductor protection, the overcurrent device characteristic curve must lie below and to the left of the conductor withstand characteristic curve. Generally, sizing the OCPD within the ampacity of the conductor provides overload protection and protection against short circuit currents. However, in situations such as motor circuits and tap conductors where it is permitted to size the OCPD at a value exceeding the ampacity of the conductor, the withstand characteristic of the conductor must be compared to the time–current characteristic of the OCPD to determine if the conductor is protected.

EXAMPLE 18–4

Determine the maximum short circuit withstand current of a #4 AWG THW copper conductor at times of (a) 0.01 s and (b) 10 s.

Solution: The cross-sectional area of the #4 AWG copper conductor is 41,740 circular mils. The conductor temperature for normal operation, T_1, is 75°C, and the maximum permitted conductor temperature under short circuit conditions, T_2, is 150°C. Solving Equation (18–1a) for the current I results in

$$I = \sqrt{\frac{0.0297 \log\left[\dfrac{T_2 + 234}{T_1 + 234}\right]}{T}} \times A$$

a) At $t = 0.01$ s,

$$I = \sqrt{\frac{0.0297 \log\left[\dfrac{150 + 234}{75 + 234}\right]}{0.01}} \times 41,740 = 21,418 \text{ A}$$

b) At $t = 10$ s,

$$I = \sqrt{\frac{0.0297 \log\left[\dfrac{150 + 234}{75 + 234}\right]}{10.0}} \times 41,740 = 699 \text{ A}$$

Plotting these two points on a log–log scale would result in a straight line, as shown in Figure 18–6.

18–3   MOTOR CIRCUITS

As discussed in Chapter 13, overload protection for motors is required. This protection is usually provided by an overload element rated according to the motor full-load current. When coordinating the overload protection for motor circuits, consideration must be given to the inrush current a motor draws when initially energized. When a motor is energized with full voltage, the initial inrush current is typically 6 times the full-load rated current of the motor. This inrush or locked-rotor current will flow until the motor comes up to full speed, at which point the motor current becomes equal to the full-load current of the motor. A typical motor starting time–current characteristic curve is shown in Figure 18–7. In addition to the starting current characteristic, the stall point is shown. The current at the stall point is the locked-rotor current of the motor. The time at the stall point is the maximum amount of time permitted for the locked-rotor current to flow without damaging the motor.

The overload element must allow the motor to start under normal conditions. Thus, the time–current characteristic curve of the overload element must lie above and to the right of the motor starting current curve. In addition, the overload element must protect the motor in the event the motor stalls. Protection during stall is accomplished by having the time–current characteristic of the overload element lie below the stall point of the motor, as shown in Figure 18–7. For the conditions shown in the figure, the Class 20 overload element provides the required protection. Note that Class 10 and Class 30 overload element characteristics are also shown. The overload relay class refers to the time in seconds that the overload element will carry 6 times rated current before operating. Thus, a

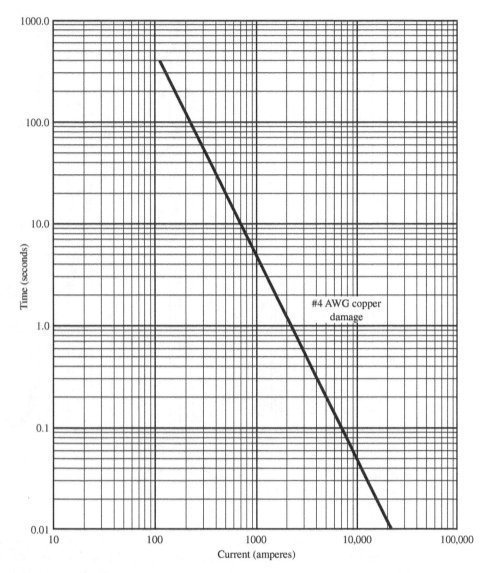

FIGURE 18–6
#4 AWG THW Copper Damage Curve

Class 10 overload element will carry 6 times rated current for 10 seconds, a Class 20 will carry 6 times rated current for 20 seconds, and so on.

Recall that the overload elements protect the motor and motor circuit conductors against overload conditions. Since the branch circuit overcurrent device is usually rated above the ampacity of the conductor, it provides short circuit protection only. To protect the motor starter contacts and overload elements from damage during short circuit conditions,

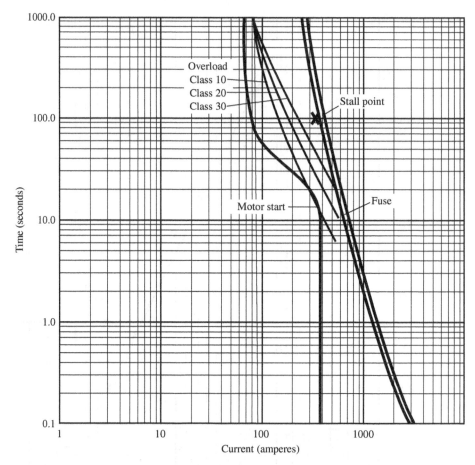

FIGURE 18–7
Motor Starting Coordination Curve

the time–current characteristic of the motor branch circuit or feeder short circuit protective device must be coordinated with the withstand rating of the motor controller. Most motor controller manufacturers will specify the maximum permitted branch circuit short circuit protective device permitted for their controller. In most instances, the use of current-limiting fuses in motor circuits is the only way of obtaining short circuit protection for motor controllers and overload relays.

18–4   TRANSFORMER PROTECTION

Transformers are required to be protected against both internal and through faults. Examples of internal transformer faults include insulation failures, bushing failures, tap changer contact welding, and so on. Through faults are faults that occur external to the transformer. An example would be a 1000 kVA transformer supplying 480 V switchgear from the 13.8 kV system. If a fault develops on the 480 V bus, fault current will flow through the transformer from the 13.8 kV system. Thus, while there is no internal transformer fault, the transformer does carry fault current. For a fault occurring on the secondary of a transformer, the maximum fault current that can possibly flow is equal to the system prefault voltage divided by the transformer impedance.

As in the case of insulated cables, it is necessary to consider the short circuit-withstand capability of the transformer. The withstand capability of dry-type transformers is specified according to the kVA rating of the transformer. ANSI C57.12.59-1989 lists two categories of dry-type transformer ratings:

TABLE 18–2

Category	Single-Phase kVA	Three-Phase kVA
I	>5–500	> 5–500
II	501–1667	501–5000

Time–current withstand curves are given for each category. Representative withstand curves are shown in Figure 18–8 for the various transformer categories. The withstand curves indicate the ability of the transformer windings to withstand short circuit currents for varying intervals of time after inception of the fault. In order for the primary overcurrent device to protect the transformer, its time–current characteristic curve must lie below and to the left of the transformer withstand curve.

Generally, the rating of the fuse, or setting of the overcurrent relay protecting the transformer primary, is approximately 150% to 200% of the full-load line current rating of the primary of the transformer. This range of percentages will allow the overcurrent device to carry inrush currents due to magnetizing inrush and load pickup after an outage occurs. In order to account for the heating effects of inrush currents, a value of 12 to 15 times the transformer full-load current rating for 0.1 seconds is typically assumed. This point is plotted on the transformer withstand curve. The primary overcurrent device characteristic curve must lie above the inrush point so that nuisance fuse blowing or relay operation will not occur during normal energizing of the transformer.

With the primary overcurrent protection device (OCPD) sized at 150% to 200% of the full-load primary current rating of the transformer, overload protection is not provided by the primary overcurrent device. Therefore, the primary overcurrent device will provide protection against short circuits only. Overload protection is typically provided by the overcurrent device on the transformer secondary. As discussed in Chapter 14, the rating or setting of the overcurrent device on the transformer secondary is typically 125% of the full-load current rating of the secondary.

In reference to Figure 18–8, note that the abscissa (x-axis) is specified in terms of multiples of the transformer normal base current. When applying protection to the primary side of the transformer, the transformer withstand characteristic curve must be plotted in

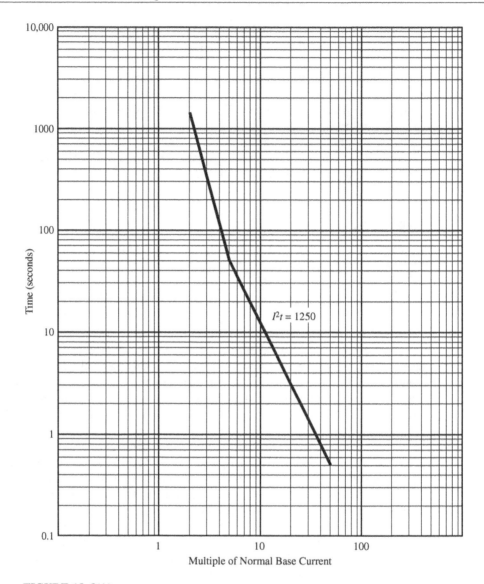

FIGURE 18–8(A)

Transformer Damage Curves for Category I Transformer *Source:* From IEEE Standard C37.91-1985, IEEE Guide for Protective Relay Applications to Power Transformers, Reaff. 1991. Copyright © 1985 IEEE. All rights reserved.

terms of actual amperes. The OCPD characteristic curve can then be plotted on the same graph as the transformer withstand characteristic.

As an initial starting point in the selection of fuse rating, the transformer withstand curve and inrush point are plotted. Next, a fuse rating equal to approximately 150% of the transformer rated full-load primary current is selected. The fuse characteristic is then plotted on the same graph as the transformer withstand curve and inrush point. The resulting

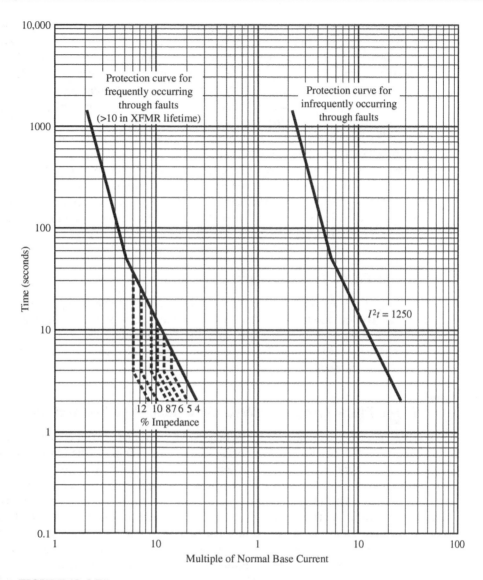

FIGURE 18–8(B)
Transformer Damage Curves for Category II Transformer

graph is then inspected to determine if the protection criteria have been met. If the protection criteria have not been met, it may be necessary to select the next-higher- or lower-rated over-current device. This process is repeated until the proper device rating or setting is selected.

Typically, overcurrent protection is located in series with the line terminations of the transformer. As such, the OCPD devices will carry the line current of the transformer primary or secondary. For a wye connection, the current flowing in the transformer phase winding is equal to the line current. Therefore, the fuse connected in the line will carry the same current as the transformer winding. In the delta connection, the current flowing in the transformer phase winding is equal to the line current divided by $\sqrt{3}$. Therefore, the line fuse carries $\sqrt{3}$ times the phase current under balanced conditions. Under balanced three-phase fault conditions, the transformer withstand curve may be used directly without modification. However, in the case of unbalanced fault conditions, the transformer withstand characteristic must be modified to account for the differences between the currents flowing through the line fuse and the transformer phase winding.

The modifications required to the transformer withstand characteristic curve will be discussed for single-phase, three-phase wye–wye, three-phase delta–delta, and three-phase delta–wye transformers. Three-phase line-to-line and line-to-ground fault conditions will be addressed for three-phase transformers. To simplify the analysis, step-down operation on a radial system, with transformer overcurrent (short circuit) protection provided on the high-voltage side, is assumed. Also, the turns ratio between the high-voltage and low-voltage phase windings is assumed to be 1:1.

Single-Phase Transformers

For single-phase transformers, the withstand curves shown in Figure 18–8 can be used directly without modification. The fuse characteristic is plotted on the withstand curve to ensure that the fuse characteristic curve lies below and to the left of the withstand curve and above the inrush point. The inrush point is generally assumed to be 12 times rated current for 0.1 seconds.

Three-Phase Grounded Wye–Grounded Wye Connection

The schematic diagrams for the grounded wye–grounded wye connection are shown in Figure 18–9. Since the transformer withstand curves apply to the transformer windings, it is necessary to determine the relationship between the transformer winding currents and line currents for all possible fault conditions on the transformer secondary.

Figure 18–9(A) shows the conditions for a three-phase fault on the transformer secondary. Since the three-phase fault represents a balanced fault condition, the transformer winding and line currents are equal. The transformer line and phase currents for phase-to-phase and phase-to-ground faults are shown in Figures 18–9(B) and 18–9(C), respectively.

Note that for all fault conditions on the secondary, the transformer winding currents are equal to the line currents. Therefore, it is not necessary to adjust or modify the withstand characteristic for a grounded wye–grounded wye transformer. The withstand curve can be used directly without modification.

Three-Phase Delta–Delta Connection

The schematic diagrams for the delta–delta connection are shown in Figure 18–10. As a result of the delta connection, the magnitude of the transformer winding currents will in general be different than the magnitude of the line currents. The relationship between the transformer winding currents and line currents will depend on the type of fault.

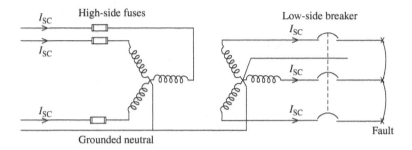

A. Three-Phase Fault

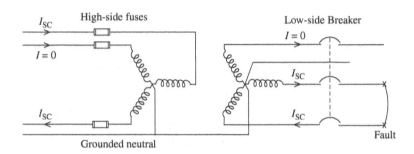

B. Phase-to-Phase Fault

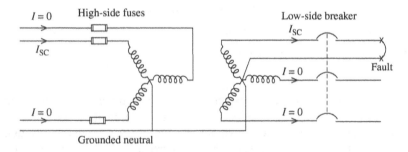

C. Phase-to-Ground Fault

FIGURE 18–9
Protection of Grounded Wye–Grounded Wye Transformer

For the three-phase fault conditions shown in Figure 18–10(A), the magnitude of the transformer winding currents is equal to the magnitude of the line current divided by $\sqrt{3}$. This is the same as the relation between line and phase currents for a balanced three-phase, delta-connected system. Therefore, the transformer withstand curve can be used directly, as in the case of the single-phase and grounded wye–grounded wye connections previously discussed.

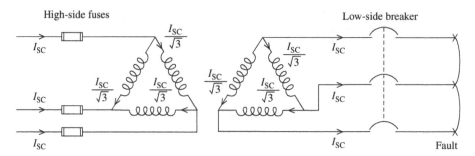

A. Three-Phase Fault

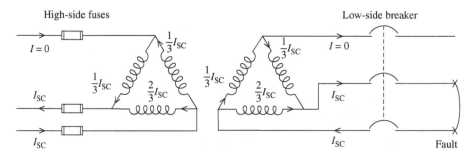

B. Phase-to-Phase Fault

FIGURE 18–10
Protection of Delta–Delta Transformer

The conditions for a phase-to-phase secondary fault are shown in Figure 18–10(B). This type of fault represents a single-phase condition on the transformer secondary. Since the impedance of each transformer winding is equal, the current in each winding will divide according to the current divider rule. The fault current flowing through the faulted winding will be equal to ⅔ times the short circuit current. Likewise, the fault current flowing through the other two windings will be equal to ⅓ times the short circuit current. These secondary currents will, of course, be reflected to the primary by means of the transformer turns ratio.

The ratio of winding current for the phase-to-phase fault to winding current for the three-phase fault is

$$\text{Ratio} = \frac{(1/3)I_{SC}}{\left(1/\sqrt{3}\right)I_{SC}} = \frac{2/3}{1/\sqrt{3}} = 1.1547$$

The correction factor to be applied to the transformer withstand curve is obtained by dividing the magnitude of the highest line current by the ratio just defined. The result is

$$\text{Correction factor} = 1.0 \div 1.1547 = 0.866$$

The transformer withstand curve is modified by multiplying each value of current on the curve by this correction factor of 0.866. The fuse characteristic curve should lie below and to the left of the modified withstand curve for all probable values of short circuit current. Note that by multiplying each current on the withstand curve by 0.866, the curve will shift to the left. The result may be a lower-rated fuse for a delta–delta transformer as compared to a grounded wye–grounded wye transformer with the same ratings.

Three-Phase Delta–Grounded Wye Connection

The schematic diagrams for the delta–grounded wye connection are shown in Figure 18–11 for the three-phase, phase-to-phase, and phase-to-ground fault conditions. As in the case of the delta–delta connection, the relation between the transformer winding currents and line currents must be determined.

Figure 18–11(A) shows conditions for a three-phase fault. The magnitude of the transformer winding currents on the high-side delta connection is equal to the magnitude of the line currents divided by $\sqrt{3}$. On the low-voltage side, the transformer winding currents are equal to the line currents. Again, since the three-phase fault represents a balanced fault condition, the transformer withstand curve does not need to be adjusted for the three-phase fault condition.

For the phase-to-phase secondary fault, the circuit shown in Figure 18–11(B) applies. The transformer winding currents on the low-voltage side are equal to the short circuit line current. On the high-voltage side, current will flow in only two of the three transformer windings due to the nature of the fault. The high-side line currents in two of the lines are equal to the transformer winding (phase) currents, as shown. However, the line current in the other phase is equal to twice the current in the transformer windings.

The ratio of winding current for the phase-to-phase fault to winding current for the three-phase fault is

$$\text{Ratio} = \frac{I_{\text{SC}}}{(1/\sqrt{3})I_{\text{SC}}} = \sqrt{3}$$

The correction factor to be applied to the transformer withstand curve is obtained by dividing the magnitude of the highest line current by this ratio. The result is

$$\text{Correction factor} = \frac{2}{\sqrt{3}} = 1.1547$$

The transformer withstand curve is modified by multiplying each point on the curve by 1.1547 for the phase-to-phase fault. This will result in the transformer withstand curve shifting toward the right.

Conditions for the phase-to-ground fault are shown in Figure 18–11(C). On both the high-voltage and low-voltage sides, only one transformer winding carries fault current; the other two windings carrying no fault current. However, due to the delta connection on the high-voltage side, fault current equal to the transformer winding current will flow in two of the lines.

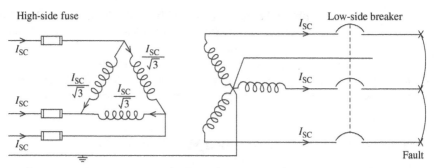

A. Three-Phase Fault

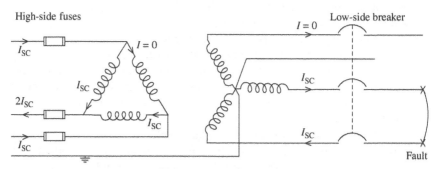

B. Phase-to-Phase Fault

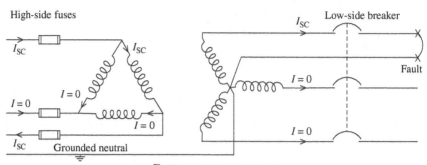

C. Phase-to-Ground Fault

FIGURE 18–11
Protection of Delta–Grounded Wye Transformer

The ratio of winding current for the phase-to-ground fault to winding current for the three-phase fault is

$$\text{Ratio} = \frac{I_{SC}}{(1/\sqrt{3})I_{SC}} = \sqrt{3}$$

The correction factor to be applied to the transformer withstand curve is obtained by dividing the magnitude of the highest line current by this ratio. The result is

$$\text{Correction factor} = \frac{1}{\sqrt{3}} = 0.5774$$

The transformer withstand curve is modified by multiplying each point on the curve by 0.5774 for the phase-to-phase fault. This will result in the transformer withstand curve shifting toward the left.

The worst-case condition for the delta–grounded wye transformer is a phase-to-ground fault on the secondary. This will result in the withstand curve being shifted to the left, typically resulting in a smaller fuse size than for a grounded wye–grounded wye or delta–delta transformer having the same ratings.

EXAMPLE 18–5

Determine a suitable E-rated fuse to protect a 1000 kVA, 4.16 kV–480Y/277 V, delta–grounded wye-connected, 5.75% impedance, dry-type transformer. Assume that the faults will occur infrequently in the transformer lifetime.

Solution: As an initial selection, a fuse size equal to 150% of the transformer full-load rated current will be used. The full-load current rating of the transformer is

$$I = \frac{1000 \text{ kVA}}{\sqrt{3} \, (4.16 \text{ kV})} = 138.8 \text{ A}$$

The fuse rating is initially selected as 150% of the full-load current of the transformer:

$$\text{Fuse rating} = (150\%)(138.8 \text{ A}) = 208.2 \text{ A}$$

Therefore, a 200E fuse is initially selected.

Since this is a delta–grounded wye connection, the transformer withstand curve must be adjusted to account for worst-case conditions. Recall that worst-case conditions are for a phase-to-ground fault on the secondary, resulting in a correction factor of 0.5774 being applied to values of current on the withstand curve. The transformer withstand curve is plotted in amperes by applying the curve of Figure 18–8(B). Investigation of Figure 18–8(B) reveals that the transformer can withstand 5 times rated current (694 A) for 50 seconds and 25 times rated current (3470 A) for 2 seconds. These two points are used to plot the withstand characteristic curve.

The adjusted transformer withstand curve, inrush point, and 200E fuse characteristic are plotted in Figure 18–12. Note that the curves are plotted in terms of primary amperes at 4.16 kV. For comparison purposes, a 150E fuse characteristic is also plotted. Note that the fuse characteristic of the 200E fuse lies between the inrush point and the adjusted withstand curve for currents greater than approximately 500 A. The 150E fuse characteristic also lies between the inrush point and adjusted withstand curve for currents greater than 300 A.

18–5   TIME–OVERCURRENT RELAYS

Time–overcurrent (TOC) relays are commonly used on medium-voltage switchgear and low-voltage, high-ampere-rated switchgear to provide overcurrent protection. These relays are used in conjunction with current transformers and circuit breakers to sense the current flowing on a line. Upon detection of an overcurrent, the relay will operate, thereby opening or closing its contacts. These relay contacts will be used to energize the trip coil of the circuit breaker and possibly a reclosing or timing relay.

Relay operation will begin when the current flowing through the relay exceeds the pickup tap setting. The tap setting is adjustable either by means of plugs in electromechanical relays or electronically in solid-state relays. When current transformers are used, the relay current will be equal to the actual primary short circuit current divided by the CT ratio. For example, if a current transformer with a ratio of 400:5 were used, a fault current of 3000 amperes would be reflected to the CT secondary as

$$I_{RELAY} = \frac{3000 \text{ A}}{400/5} = 37.5 \text{ A}$$

If the relay tap was set at 5 A, then the actual relay current would correspond to 7.5 times the pickup of the relay.

The actual time that elapses between initiation and actual relay contact closure is adjustable by means of the time dial setting. Figure 18–13 shows a typical time–current characteristic curve for a time–overcurrent relay. Additional time–current curves for time–overcurrent relays are readily available from the manufacturer. Note that the current axis is labeled in multiples of the pickup value. The time axis may be specified in either seconds or cycles on a 60 Hz basis.

EXAMPLE 18–6

A circuit breaker equipped with bushing-mounted current transformers having a ratio of 600:5 is protecting a 4.16 kV distribution switchgear. The time–overcurrent relay characteristics are given in Figure 18–14. The relay is to operate when the load current on the feeder is 500 A. In addition, the available short circuit current is 5000 A at the breaker location and 2000 A at the far end of the circuit. Determine (a) the appropriate tap setting required for the relay to pick up at 500 A and (b) the required time dial setting to allow a time delay of 0.3 s at maximum fault current levels.

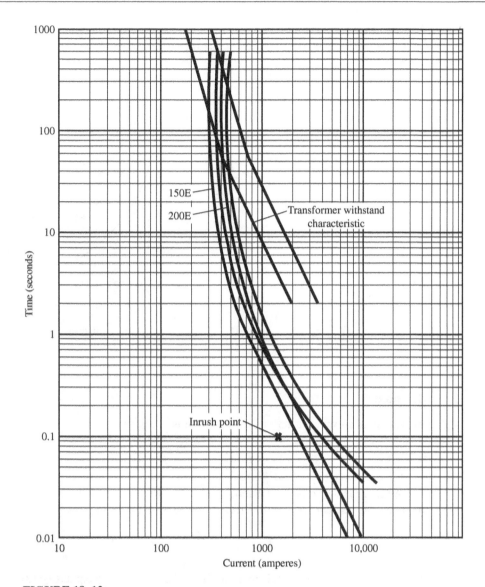

FIGURE 18–12
Coordination Curves for Transformer Protection Example

FIGURE 18–13
Time–Overcurrent Relay Time—
Current Curves

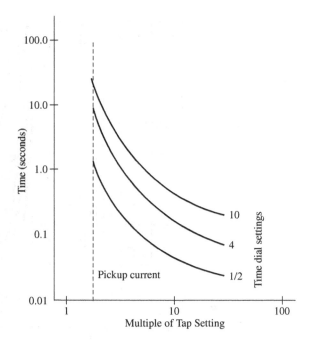

Solution:

a) The relay current for a 500 A load current is

$$I_{RELAY} = \frac{500 \text{ A}}{600/5} = 4.167 \text{ A}$$

Therefore, a tap setting of 4.0 is required.

b) The relay current for a fault current of 5000 A on the primary is equal to

$$I_{RELAY} = \frac{5000 \text{ A}}{600/5} = 41.67 \text{ A}$$

This relay current corresponds to a multiple of the tap setting equal to $41.67/4 = 10.4$. In order to obtain a time delay of 0.3 s, a time dial setting of approximately 5 is necessary.

18–6   REFLECTING OCPD CHARACTERISTICS

Single-Phase Transformers

When coordinating overcurrent protection devices on opposite sides of a transformer, it is necessary to reflect all overcurrent protection device characteristics to a common voltage. Often, the characteristics of the devices on the high-voltage side are reflected to the

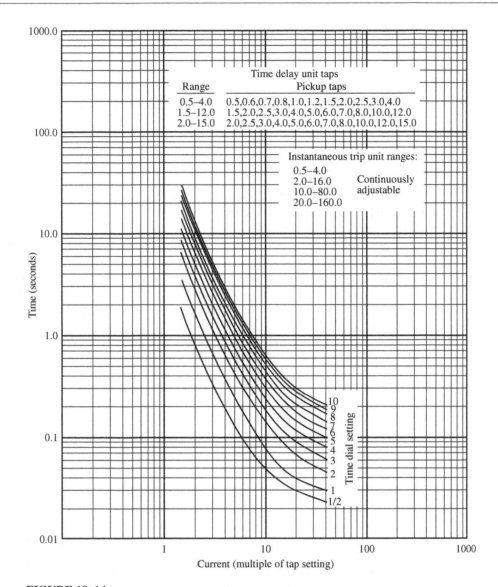

FIGURE 18–14
Time–Current Characteristics of IAC77 Time–Overcurrent Relay *Source:* Courtesy General Electric Company, Curve #GEK-34055.

low-voltage side to determine if coordination exists. Reflecting of device characteristics is accomplished by multiplying each value of the high-side device characteristic curve by the transformer turns ratio. The following results:

$$I'_{LS} = I_{HS} \times \left[\frac{\text{Transformer rated HS voltage}}{\text{Transformer rated LS voltage}} \right] \qquad (18\text{--}2)$$

where:

I'_{LS} = high-side current reflected to low side
I_{HS} = actual high-side current

Equation (18–2) is applied to several points on the high-side device characteristic curve in order to reflect the characteristic to the low side. The characteristic curves for the low-side device(s) are then plotted directly without modification.

For selective coordination, the reflected high-side device characteristic curve should lie above and to the right of the low-side characteristic curve. Both the reflected high-side device and low-side device characteristics should lie below and to the left of the reflected transformer damage curve to provide through-fault protection for the transformer. Backup protection should be provided by the high-side device in the event that the low-side device fails to clear the fault.

If the reflected high-side device characteristic curve was found to lie below and to the left of the low-side device characteristic curve, then the high-side device would operate before the low-side device. The result would be operation of the high-side device for virtually all low-side faults on the load side of the low-side protective device. Obviously, this miscoordination would be unacceptable.

Similarly, if either the reflected high-side device characteristic or low-side device characteristic curves were found to lie above and to the right of the reflected transformer withstand curve, the transformer would not be protected against through faults. Under these circumstances, the transformer would be severely damaged for all faults on the low side. Obviously, this is unacceptable.

EXAMPLE 18–7

Consider the single-phase transformer shown in Figure 18–15(A). The transformer is rated 50 kVA, 2400–120/240 V. The high-voltage side is protected by a 30E fuse, and the low-voltage side is connected to a low-voltage bus through a 250 A secondary main breaker. In addition, there are three 100 A feeder breakers connected to the bus. If a fault were to occur on the load side of one of the feeder breakers, only the feeder breaker should trip. The primary high-side fuse or secondary main breaker should not operate for any feeder faults. However, the secondary main breaker or transformer high-side fuse should provide backup protection in the event the feeder breaker fails. In order to selectively coordinate, the time-current characteristic curve of the feeder breakers must lie below and to the left of the reflected high-side fuse characteristic curve.

Solution: Selective coordination between secondary main overcurrent devices and high-side devices may be difficult to obtain. For example, if a fault were to occur on

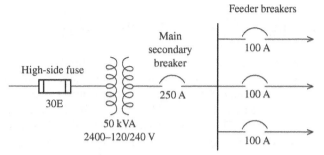

A. Schematic

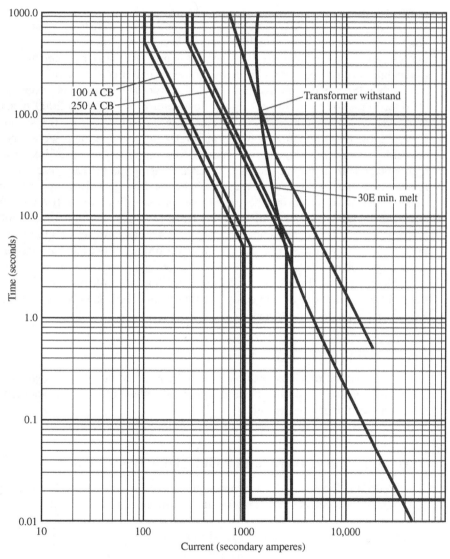

B. Time–Current Curves

FIGURE 18–15
Reflecting OCPD Characteristics, Single-Phase Transformer

the secondary bus, the secondary main breaker should trip before the primary fuse operates. Tripping of the secondary main breaker would result in the deenergizing of the entire low-voltage bus. Similarly, if the transformer high-side fuse were to blow, the transformer would be deenergized, resulting in the deenergizing of the entire low-voltage bus as well. Thus, the consequences of either the high-side device or low-side main device operating in the event of a fault are the same. The important point to remember is that coordination must be obtained between the highest-ampere-rated secondary feeder overcurrent protection device and the high-side primary overcurrent protection device.

Figure 18–15(B) shows the reflected transformer withstand, reflected 30E minimum melt characteristic, and low-voltage breaker trip curves plotted on the same log-log scale. Note that selective coordination is achieved between the low-voltage feeder breakers and the high-side fuse. However, note that the main secondary breaker and high-side fuse curves overlap each other for fault current between 2000 A and 3000 A. Thus, for fault currents on the low-voltage bus between 2000 A and 3000 A, it is likely that the transformer high-side fuse will blow before the secondary main breaker trips. If coordination between the high-side fuse and main secondary breaker is desirable, it may be advisable to increase the rating of the fuse link protecting the high-voltage side of the transformer. When increasing the primary fuse size, it must be remembered that the fuse curve must lie below and to the left of the transformer withstand curve. Also, increasing the transformer primary fuse size will reduce the protection margin that the fuse will provide. An alternative solution to the coordination problem is to lower, if possible, the instantaneous pickup level of the main secondary breaker. This may, however, cause coordination problems between the feeder and main secondary breakers.

Note also from Figure 18–15(B) that since both the 30E fuse and 250 A secondary main breaker characteristics lie below the transformer withstand characteristic curve, the transformer is properly protected.

Although the previous example involved coordination between high-side fuses and low-voltage breakers, the same basic procedure would be followed for other types of overcurrent protection devices as well.

Three-Phase Wye–Wye- and Delta–Delta Transformers

When reflecting the high-side overcurrent protective device characteristics on wye–wye or delta–delta transformers to the low side, the following equation is used:

$$I'_{\text{LS}} = I_{\text{HS}} \times \left[\frac{\text{Transformer rated HS line voltage}}{\text{Transformer rated LS line voltage}} \right] \qquad \textbf{(18–3)}$$

where I'_{LS} and I_{HS} are as previously defined. Equation (18–3) may be used for all types of faults that may occur on the low-voltage side.

Three-Phase Delta–Grounded Wye Transformers

The delta–wye three-phase transformer connection requires special consideration when reflecting high-side OCPD characteristics to the low side for coordination purposes. In particular, the type of fault is a significant factor in determining the multiplier to be used.

For a three-phase fault, the results of Equation (18–3) may be used directly. Recall that a three-phase fault represents a balanced fault condition.

In order to determine the appropriate multiplier to be applied in the event of a phase-to-phase fault, consider the equivalent circuit shown in Figure 18–16(A). A phase b-to-phase c fault is assumed. The voltage rating of each high-side coil is equal to the line-to-line voltage of the transformer high-voltage side. On the low-voltage side, the voltage rating of each coil is equal to the line-to-line voltage of the transformer low-voltage side divided by $\sqrt{3}$.

For the phase-to-phase fault shown in Figure 18–16(A), assume that the short circuit current is given as I_{SC}. The current I that flows in the high-voltage coils is given by

$$I = I_{SC} \times \left[\frac{\text{Transformer rated LS line voltage}/\sqrt{3}}{\text{Transformer rated HS line voltage}} \right] \qquad \textbf{(18–4)}$$

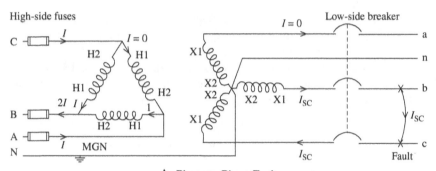

A. Phase-to-Phase Fault

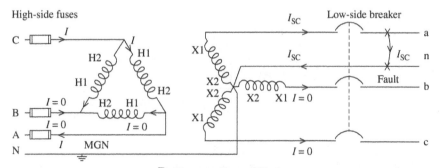

B. Phase-to-Ground Fault

FIGURE 18–16
Reflecting OCPD Characteristics on Delta–Grounded Wye-Connected Transformer

The line current magnitudes on the high-voltage side are given by

$$|I_A| = I \qquad \text{(18-5a)}$$

$$|I_B| = 2 \times I \qquad \text{(18-5b)}$$

$$|I_C| = I \qquad \text{(18-5c)}$$

The largest line current magnitude occurs in phase b.

Substituting Equation (18-4) into (18-5b) and simplifying results in

$$|I_B| = 2 \times I = I_{SC} \times \frac{2}{\sqrt{3}}\left[\frac{\text{Transformer rated LS line voltage}}{\text{Transformer rated HS line voltage}}\right] \qquad \text{(18-6)}$$

Equation (18-6) shows the relationship between the largest-magnitude line current on the high side as a function of the short circuit current on the low side. Therefore, when reflecting the high-side characteristic to the low side for phase-to-phase faults on the low side, Equation (18-6) must be solved for the reflected high-side current as follows:

$$|I'_{LS}| = I_{HS} \times \frac{\sqrt{3}}{2}\left[\frac{\text{Transformer rated HS line voltage}}{\text{Transformer rated LS line voltage}}\right] \qquad \text{(18-7)}$$

where I'_{LS} is the high-side current reflected to the low side and I_{HS} is the actual high-side current as read from the fuse curve. Note that Equation (18-7) is similar to Equation (18-3) with the exception of the ($\sqrt{3}/2$) factor.

For single line-to-ground faults, the circuit of Figure 18-16(B) applies. Here, a phase-to-ground fault on phase a is assumed to occur. The fault current on the low side is designated I_{SC}. The current I on the high side is given by

$$I = I_{SC} \times \left[\frac{\text{Transformer rated LS line voltage}/\sqrt{3}}{\text{Transformer rated HS line voltage}}\right] \qquad \text{(18-8)}$$

The line current magnitudes on the high-voltage side are

$$|I_A| = I \qquad \text{(18-9a)}$$

$$|I_B| = 0 \qquad \text{(18-9b)}$$

$$|I_C| = I \qquad \text{(18-9c)}$$

Note that the magnitude of the line currents in phases a and c are equal. Substituting Equation (18-8) into (18-9a) and (18-9c) results in

$$|I_A| = |I_C| = I_{SC} \times \frac{1}{\sqrt{3}}\left[\frac{\text{Transformer rated LS line voltage}}{\text{Transformer rated HS line voltage}}\right] \qquad \text{(18-10)}$$

Equation (18-10) shows the relationship between the largest-magnitude line current on the high side as a function of the short circuit current on the low side. Therefore, when reflecting the high-side characteristic to the low side for phase-to-ground faults on the low side, Equation (18-10) must be solved for the reflected high-side current as follows:

$$|I'_{LS}| = I_{HS} \times \sqrt{3} \times \left[\frac{\text{Transformer rated HS line voltage}}{\text{Transformer rated LS line voltage}} \right] \qquad \textbf{(18–11)}$$

where I'_{LS} is the high-side current reflected to the low side and I_{HS} is the actual high-side current as read from the fuse curve. Again, note the similarities between Equations (18–11) and (18–3).

EXAMPLE 18–8

A 300 kVA, 4,160–480Y/277 V, delta–grounded wye, 5% impedance transformer is protected on the high-voltage side by a 65E-rated power fuse. The low-voltage side is connected to a main distribution panel with a 500 A main circuit breaker. The main distribution panel contains four 100 A feeder breakers as well. The one-line diagram for the system is shown in Figure 18–17(A). On the same graph, sketch the transformer withstand characteristics, high-side power fuse characteristics, and low-voltage main and feeder breaker characteristics in terms of actual low-voltage-side amperes.

Solution: The transformer withstand curves are plotted in terms of low-side amperes by calculating the rated line current of the transformer, as follows:

$$I = \frac{300 \text{ kVA}}{\sqrt{3} \; 480 \text{ V}} = 360.8 \text{ A}$$

Two points on the transformer withstand characteristic curve can now be calculated:

5 × Rated current for 50 s = 5(360.8 A) = 1804 A
25 × Rated current for 2 s = 25(360.8 A) = 9020 A

Recall that the phase-to-ground fault on the secondary is the worst-case condition and results in a shifting of the transformer withstand curve to the left by a factor of 0.5774. Therefore, the following points are calculated to plot the withstand curve for the phase-to-ground fault:

50 s: 0.5774(1804 A) = 1041.6 A
5 s: 0.5774(9020 A) = 5208.1 A

In addition, the inrush point of 12 times rated current (4329.6 A) for 0.1 seconds must also be plotted. The withstand characteristic is plotted for both three-phase and phase-to-ground faults on the secondary.
    The 65E power fuse characteristic must be reflected to the low-voltage side and adjusted for a phase-to-phase fault by applying Equation (18–7). The high-voltage power fuse characteristic should lie between the adjusted transformer withstand curve for the phase-to-ground secondary fault and the inrush point. The low-voltage main and branch feeder breaker characteristics are plotted directly in terms of low-side amperes.
    The transformer withstand characteristics, 65E power fuse characteristic, and low-voltage main and feeder breaker characteristics are plotted in Figure 18–17(B). Note that

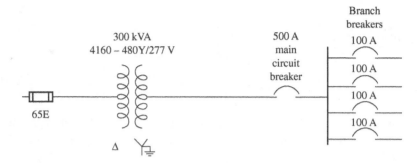

A. One-Line Diagram

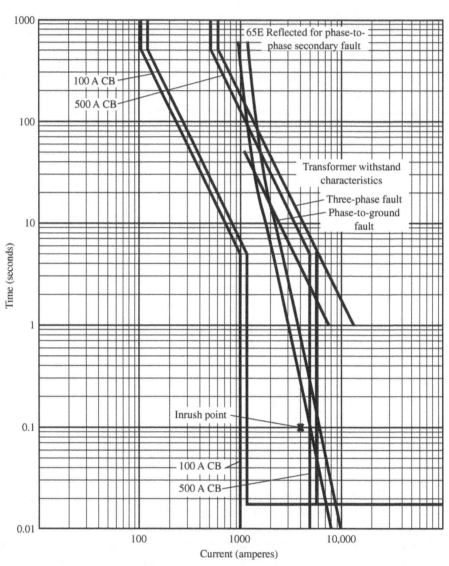

B. Time–Current Curves

FIGURE 18–17

Example of Coordination Between High-Side and Low-Side Devices on Delta–Grounded Wye-Connected Transformer

the 65E power fuse characteristic lies below the transformer withstand curve for a phase-to-ground fault for fault currents greater than approximately 1000 A referred to the secondary. In addition, the 65E power fuse characteristic lies above the inrush point. Therefore, the 65E power fuse should not blow due to inrush currents during energizing of the transformer.

The low-voltage feeder breaker characteristic curve lies below and to the left of the 65E power fuse characteristic for all values of fault current. However, the main secondary breaker characteristic curve lies above the reflected 65E fuse characteristic curve for fault currents between 1000 A and 5000 A. This situation would result in the 65E fuse blowing for short circuit currents between 1000 A and 5000 A on the secondary. This situation could be modified by either increasing the rating of the high-side fuse or decreasing the instantaneous trip setting of the main and branch secondary breakers, or both.

PROBLEMS

1. What is overcurrent device coordination and why is it important?

2. What is the minimum melt time at 1000 A of a 30E, 5.5 kV fuse?

3. What is the total clearing time of a 100E, 5.5 kV fuse at 700 A?

4. What is the selectivity ratio between a FRN-R load-side fuse and a FRN-R line-side fuse?

5. What is the minimum rating of a FRS-R line-side fuse for coordination with a 100A KTS-R load-side fuse?

6. Plot the minimum melt and total clearing time of a 40E, 5.5 kV protecting fuse and an 80E, 5.5 kV protected fuse on log-log scale. What is the maximum current for coordination?

7. Plot the withstand characteristic of a #4/0 AWG THW aluminum conductor on a log-log scale.

8. Plot the withstand characteristic of a #4/0 AWG THW copper conductor on a log-log scale.

9. Plot the time–current characteristic of a 50 A molded case circuit breaker.

10. Plot the starting characteristic of a 20 hp, 460 V, three-phase motor having a full-load current of 26 A. Assume that the motor takes 5 seconds to come up to full speed. Plot the time–current characteristic of a 40A FRS-R fuse. Is this system coordinated?

11. What is the appropriate multiplying factor to be applied to the TCC of a delta–grounded wye transformer when determining the protection requirements for the transformer?

12. Plot the withstand characteristic of a 500 kVA 4800–480Y/277 V transformer. Plot the characteristics of an 80E, 100E, and 125 E, 5.5 kV, Class E fuse link on the same graph. Include withstand characteristics for all fault conditions.

13. A time–overcurrent relay has a TCC as shown in Figure 18–14. The CT ratio is 400:5. If the relay pickup is set at 5 A, and the time dial setting is set at 4, determine the trip time for primary currents of 1000 A, 2500 A, 4000 A, and 6000 A.

14. A 400 A service is supplied by a 100 kVA, 4800–120/240 V, single-phase transformer. The transformer primary is protected by a 30E, 5.5 kV fuse. The main secondary breaker is rated 400 A. Plot the transformer withstand, reflected 30E fuse characteristic, and 400 A main secondary breaker characteristic curves. Comment on the coordination of this system.

15. What is the appropriate multiplying factor to be applied to the TCC of a delta–grounded wye transformer when reflecting the high-side device to the low side?

16. A 500 kVA, 4800–480Y/277 V, delta–grounded wye transformer is protected on the high side by a 100E, 5.5 kV fuse. The low-voltage side is connected to a main distribution panel with a 600 A main breaker. The MDP contains ten 100 A feeder breakers as well. Sketch the transformer withstand characteristic, high-side power fuse, and low-side breaker characteristics curves in terms of low-voltage-side amperes. Comment on the coordination of this system.

19

Power System Harmonics

INTRODUCTION

The topic of power system harmonics has received increased attention over the past several years. Although the presence of harmonic currents and voltages is not a new phenomenon, the increased use of harmonic-producing equipment has led to an increase in the amount of harmonic currents and voltages present. Advances in power electronic technology have made it possible to control larger amounts of power than previously possible. While the power electronic control equipment is more efficient than previous methods of power control, the increased use of this equipment has created new problems due to increased harmonic current levels. In addition, it is characteristic of this power electronic control equipment to operate at relatively low power factors. In order to improve the power factor, capacitors are often installed. The installation of these capacitors can result in a parallel resonance condition with the utility supply, thereby amplifying the harmonic currents. Amplification of the harmonic currents will result in increased voltage distortion, nuisance fuse blowing and breaker tripping, and overheating of equipment, to name a few of the problems.

This chapter begins with a discussion of the nature of harmonic currents and voltages and some of the more common sources of harmonic-producing equipment. Typical harmonic current levels for various equipment will be presented. Problems related to system resonance and the determination of resonance conditions are also discussed. The chapter concludes with a discussion of the design and specification of a detuned capacitor bank used for power factor correction and harmonic filtering, followed by an example of harmonic analysis and filter design.

OBJECTIVES

Upon completion of this chapter, you will:

- Understand voltage and current harmonic distortion
- Understand the sources of harmonics
- Understand the problem of resonance when installing capacitors in a harmonic environment
- Be able to calculate the total harmonic distortion of voltage and current waveforms
- Understand the application of IEEE Standard 519
- Be able to determine the required filter inductance for a detuned capacitor bank
- Understand derating of capacitors at off-nominal frequency and voltage
- Understand voltage rise on capacitors used in a filter bank

19–1   SOURCES OF HARMONICS

In order to fully understand the problems created by harmonic currents and voltages, it is first necessary to understand what is meant by the term *harmonic*. Any periodic, nonsinusoidal, time-varying waveform may be expressed as the sum of several sinusoidal, waveforms, referred to as *harmonic components*. Each of these harmonic components will have a certain amplitude, frequency, and phase shift. The amplitude and phase shift of the individual harmonic components is determined by means of Fourier analysis applied to the original waveform. The details of Fourier analysis are beyond the scope of this text.

Generally, the fundamental component of the waveform will have the same frequency as the waveform itself. The frequency of the other harmonic components is expressed as an integer multiple of the fundamental frequency. For example, if the fundamental frequency is 60 Hz, the 5th harmonic frequency will be 5 times 60 Hz, or 300 Hz. Likewise, the 7th harmonic frequency is 420 Hz, and so on. For typical harmonic voltages and currents encountered in electrical power systems, it is sufficient to consider up to about the 25th harmonic frequency when representing nonsinusoidal periodic waveforms. If the waveform of the voltage or current is a pure sinusoid, the waveform will contain only a fundamental component, with the higher-order harmonic terms being equal to zero.

A listing of the frequency, amplitude and phase angle of the individual harmonic components is referred to as the *harmonic spectrum* of the waveform. This information is critical in the design specifications of harmonic filtering equipment. Table 19–1 represents the harmonic spectrum of a typical square wave current waveform up to the 13th harmonic order. The actual waveform becomes more like a square wave in appearance as additional higher-order harmonic terms are added to the waveform expression. The actual waveform is shown in Figure 19–1.

In addition to the harmonic spectrum of the waveform, several terms are used to quantify the nature of harmonic waveforms. The root of the sum of the squares, or rss,

FIGURE 19–1
Harmonic Composition of Square Wave Waveform

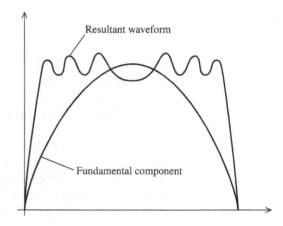

TABLE 19–1
Harmonic Content of Square Wave

Frequency	Harmonic Order	Magnitude	Phase Shift
60	Fundamental	1.000	0°
180	3	0.333	0°
300	5	0.200	0°
420	7	0.143	0°
660	11	0.091	0°
780	13	0.077	0°

value of the waveform represents the effective rms value of the waveform. The rss value is given by

$$\text{rss} = \sqrt{V_1^2 + V_2^2 + V_3^2 + \cdots + V_i^2} \qquad (19\text{–}1)$$

where:

V_1 = rms magnitude of the fundamental component
V_2 = rms magnitude of the 2nd harmonic component
V_3 = rms magnitude of the 3rd harmonic component
V_i = rms magnitude of the ith harmonic component.

The percent total harmonic distortion, or THD, of the waveform is a measure of how badly a waveform is distorted with respect to a pure sine wave. IEEE Standard 519-1992 specifies the maximum percentage THD permitted for both current distortion and voltage distortion. This standard is discussed in more detail in Section 19–4. The THD is given by

$$\text{THD} = \frac{\sqrt{V_2^2 + V_3^2 + \cdots + V_i^2}}{V_1} \times 100\% \qquad (19\text{–}2)$$

where the V_i are as defined above. Note that if a waveform is a pure sine wave, the rss value of the waveform is equal to the rms value of the fundamental component. Also, the THD of a pure sine wave is zero.

EXAMPLE 19–1

Determine the rss and THD for a voltage waveform with the following harmonic spectrum:

TABLE 19–2
Voltage Harmonic Spectrum

Frequency	Harmonic Order	Voltage Magnitude
60	1	277.0 V
300	5	25.0 V
420	7	12.0 V
660	11	5.0 V
780	13	2.0 V

All other harmonic components are equal to zero.

Solution: The rss value is given by Equation (19–1):

$$rss = \sqrt{277^2 + 25^2 + 12^2 + 5^2 + 2^2}$$
$$= 278.44 \text{ V}$$

The THD value is given by Equation (19–2):

$$THD = \frac{\sqrt{25^2 + 12^2 + 5^2 + 2^2}}{277} \times 100\% = 10.2\%$$

It is characteristic of most power electronic control equipment to draw line currents that are nonsinusoidal. As such, the most common representation for harmonic-producing loads is the current source or current sink models. Several sources of harmonic currents that may be found on electrical power systems are listed in Table 19–3. Typical harmonic spectrums of line current drawn from the supply by some three-phase, variable-speed motor drives and three-phase, full-wave rectifiers are listed in Table 19–4. Note that the percentages of harmonic content listed in Table 19–4 are typical values only and may be used only as a rough approximation to the actual harmonic currents that may be present. The manufacturer of the specific equipment should be consulted when precise information is desired in the planning stage of a filter design. In an existing installation, harmonic power analyzers should be used to sample the line currents to determine the actual harmonic content.

The magnitude of the harmonic components listed in Table 19–4 is expressed in percent of the rated fundamental current of the device. In order to determine the actual harmonic currents, it is necessary to multiply the fundamental current by the respective percentages shown in Table 19–4.

EXAMPLE 19–2

Using the theoretical values shown in Table 19–4, determine the following for a 500 kW, 480 V, three-phase, full-wave (6 pulse) rectifier:

a) Harmonic current spectrum
b) rss of the current waveform
c) THD of the current waveform

TABLE 19–3
Sources of Harmonics

Variable-speed motor drives
Rectifiers
Arc furnaces
Welders
Uninterruptible power supplies
Computer switched mode power supplies
HID Lighting ballasts

TABLE 19–4
Theoretical Harmonic Current Spectrum for Six-Pulse,
Three-Phase, Variable-Speed Motor Drives
and Three-Phase Full-Wave Rectifiers

Harmonic Order	Amplitude (% of Fundamental)
1	100.0%
5	20.0%
7	14.3%
11	9.1%
13	7.7%
17	5.9%
19	5.3%
23	4.3%
25	4.0%

Solution: The fundamental component of the line current is

$$I_L = \frac{500{,}000 \text{ VA}}{\sqrt{3} \, 480 \text{ V}} = 601.4 \text{ A}$$

a) The individual harmonic currents are calculated and tabulated as follows:

$I_1 = (601.4 \text{ A})(1.0) = 601.4 \text{ A}$
$I_5 = (601.4 \text{ A})(0.2) = 120.3 \text{ A}$
$I_7 = (601.4 \text{ A})(0.143) = 86.0 \text{ A}$
$I_{11} = (601.4 \text{ A})(0.091) = 54.7 \text{ A}$
$I_{13} = (601.4 \text{ A})(0.077) = 46.3 \text{ A}$
$I_{17} = (601.4 \text{ A})(0.059) = 35.5 \text{ A}$
$I_{19} = (601.4 \text{ A})(0.053) = 31.9 \text{ A}$
$I_{23} = (601.4 \text{ A})(0.043) = 25.9 \text{ A}$
$I_{25} = (601.4 \text{ A})(0.04) = 24.1 \text{ A}$

b) The rss value of the waveform is

$$\text{rss} = \sqrt{601.4^2 + 120.3^2 + 86.0^2 + 54.7^2 + 46.3^2 + 35.5^2 + 31.9^2 + 25.9^2 + 24.1^2}$$
$$= 626.2 \text{ A}$$

c) The THD of the waveform is

$$\text{THD} = \frac{\sqrt{120.3^2 + 86.0^2 + 54.7^2 + 46.3^2 + 35.5^2 + 31.9^2 + 25.9^2 + 24.1^2}}{601.4} \times 100\%$$
$$= 29.0\%$$

19–2   RESONANCE PROBLEMS

When applying power factor correction capacitors to a power system bus, a resonance condition will be created. This resonance takes place between the inductive reactance of the source and the capacitive reactance of the power factor correction capacitor bank. Since the power factor correction capacitor is connected in parallel with the source, an infinite parallel impedance will occur when the inductive reactance of the source is equal to the capacitive reactance of the capacitor bank. The parallel resonant frequency is the frequency at which the inductive reactance of the source and capacitive reactance of the capacitor bank are equal. If this parallel resonance frequency occurs at or near a harmonic current produced by the load, severe voltage distortion and harmonic current amplification may result. The increase in harmonic current is often large enough to cause nuisance fuse blowing and false breaker tripping. It is important to note that the application of capacitors to a bus will not create these harmonic currents but may cause amplification of these harmonic currents.

In order to determine the frequency at which parallel resonance will occur, consider the one-line diagram of a typical industrial plant substation shown in Figure 19–2. This one-line diagram is representative of the many industrial plant substations encountered. The plant is supplied from the utility system through a step-down transformer. The total plant load consists of both nonharmonic- and harmonic-producing loads. A capacitor bank is added to improve the overall plant power factor.

The equivalent system impedance, transformer impedance, and capacitor impedance must be calculated and referred to the transformer low-voltage side. The equivalent system resistance, R_{SYS}, and reactance, X_{SYS}, referred to the high-voltage side of the transformer are given by the following:

$$R_{\text{SYS}} = \left[\frac{kV_{\text{LL}}^2}{\text{MVA}_{\text{SC}}}\right]\cos\left\{\tan^{-1}(X/R \text{ ratio})\right\} \tag{19–3}$$

$$X_{\text{SYS}} = \left[\frac{kV_{\text{LL}}^2}{\text{MVA}_{\text{SC}}}\right]\sin\left\{\tan^{-1}(X/R \text{ ratio})\right\} \tag{19–4}$$

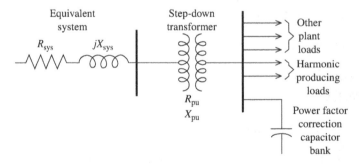

FIGURE 19–2
Basic One-Line Diagram of Industrial Plant

where:

kV_{LL} = line-to-line system voltage of utility source
MVA_{SC} = short circuit MVA of utility source
X/R ratio = ratio of inductive reactance to resistance of utility source

The equivalent system resistance and reactance referred to the low-voltage side of the step-down transformer are determined by dividing the values referred to the high-voltage side by the transformer turns ratio, as follows:

$$R'_{SYS} = \frac{R_{SYS}}{a^2} \qquad (19\text{--}5)$$

$$X'_{SYS} = \frac{X_{SYS}}{a^2} \qquad (19\text{--}6)$$

The equivalent transformer resistance and reactance referred to the low-voltage side are given by the following:

$$R_{TR} = R_{PU} \frac{1000\ (kV_{LL})^2}{kVA_{TR}} \qquad (19\text{--}7)$$

$$X_{TR} = X_{PU} \frac{1000\ (kV_{LL})^2}{kVA_{TR}} \qquad (19\text{--}8)$$

where:

R_{PU} = per-unit transformer resistance
X_{PU} = per-unit transformer reactance
kVA_{TR} = transformer rated apparent power
kV_{LL} = transformer rated line-to-line low voltage

The total system resistance is the sum of the equivalent system resistance plus the transformer resistance:

$$R_{TOT} = R'_{SYS} + R_{TR} \qquad (19\text{--}9)$$

Likewise, the total system reactance is the sum of the equivalent system reactance plus the transformer reactance:

$$X_{TOT} = X'_{SYS} + X_{TR} \qquad (19\text{--}10)$$

The equivalent reactance of the capacitor bank is given by the following:

$$X_{CAP} = \frac{1000\ (kV_{CAP})^2}{kVA_{CAP}} \qquad (19\text{--}11)$$

where:

kV_{CAP} = line-to-line voltage rating of the capacitor
kVA_{CAP} = three-phase reactive power rating of the capacitor

The inductance of the total source impedance is given by

$$L_{TOT} = \frac{X_{TOT}}{2\pi f_{SYS}} = \frac{X_{TOT}}{\omega_{SYS}} \qquad (19\text{--}12)$$

where f_{SYS} is the normal operating frequency of the system. The total system inductance as given by Equation (19–12) is constant. The inductive reactance at any other frequency is given by

$$X_L = (2\pi f_{ACT})L_{TOT} = \omega_{ACT}\, L_{TOT} \qquad (19\text{--}13)$$

where f_{ACT} is the actual operating frequency of the system.

Similarly, the capacitance of the capacitor bank is

$$C = \frac{1}{2\pi f_{SYS}X_{CAP}} = \frac{1}{\omega_{SYS}X_{CAP}} \qquad (19\text{--}14)$$

The capacitance of the capacitor bank is constant regardless of frequency. The capacitive reactance at other frequencies is given by

$$X_C = \frac{1}{2\pi f_{ACT}C} = \frac{1}{\omega_{ACT}C} \qquad (19\text{--}15)$$

The resulting equivalent circuit for the power system shown in Figure 19–2 is redrawn in Figure 19–3. The impedance looking into the system from the load bus consists of the source impedance connected in parallel with the capacitor impedance. Since both the inductive reactance of the system and the capacitive reactance of the capacitor bank are functions of frequency, the parallel impedance of the system will also be a function of frequency. This parallel impedance is given by the following:

$$\mathbf{Z}_{IN} = \frac{(R_{TOT} + j\omega L_{TOT}) \times [-j/(\omega_{ACT}C)]}{R_{TOT} + j\omega L_{TOT} - [j/(\omega_{ACT}C)]} \qquad (19\text{--}16)$$

Equation (19–16) can be used to determine the system impedance at any value of frequency. A frequency scan of the system may be performed by varying the frequency and calculating the magnitude of the system impedance. The magnitude of the impedance is then plotted as a function of frequency to locate the parallel resonant frequency. Parallel

FIGURE 19–3
Equivalent Circuit for the System of Figure 19–2

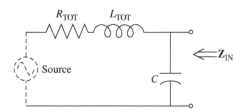

resonance occurs when the inductive reactance and capacitive reactance are equal. The frequency at which parallel resonance occurs is designated ω_0 (rad/s) or f_0 (Hz). Designating the parallel resonant frequency by ω_0 and equating the inductive and capacitive reactances results in the following:

$$\omega_0 L_{TOT} = \frac{1}{\omega_0 C} \qquad\qquad \text{(19–17)}$$

Solving Equation (19–17) for ω_0 results in the following:

$$\omega_0 = \frac{1}{\sqrt{L_{TOT}C}} \qquad\qquad \text{(19–18)}$$

The parallel resonant frequency in Hz is given by

$$f_0 = \frac{1}{2\pi\sqrt{L_{TOT}C}} \qquad\qquad \text{(19–19)}$$

EXAMPLE 19–3

An industrial plant is supplied from the utility 12.47 kV, three-phase, multigrounded neutral distribution feeder. The short circuit data from the utility indicate a three-phase short circuit MVA of 200 MVA and an X/R ratio of 2.4. The transformer supplying the plant is rated 1000 kVA, 12.47 kV–480Y/277 V, $R = 1.0\%$, $X = 6.0\%$. The system frequency is 60 Hz. Determine the parallel resonant frequencies for the following values of power factor correction capacitors applied to the 480 V bus:

a) 200 kvar
b) 400 kvar
c) 600 kvar
d) 800 kvar

The system one-line diagram is shown in Figure 19–4.

FIGURE 19–4
Example System for Parallel
Resonance Calculation

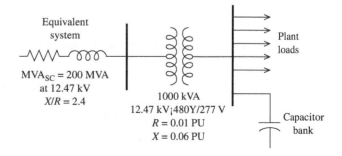

Solution: The equivalent system resistance and reactance are calculated by applying Equations (19–3) and (19–4):

$$R_{SYS} = \left[\frac{(12.47 \text{ kV})^2}{200 \text{ MVA}} \right] \cos\{\tan^{-1}(2.4)\} = 0.2990 \ \Omega$$

$$X_{SYS} = \left[\frac{(12.47 \text{ kV})^2}{200 \text{ MVA}} \right] \sin\{\tan^{-1}(2.4)\} = 0.7177 \ \Omega$$

The transformer turns ratio a is equal to

$$a = 12{,}470 \div 480 = 25.98$$

The equivalent system resistance and reactance referred to the low-voltage side are

$$R_{SYS} = 0.2990 \div (25.98)^2 = 0.000443 \ \Omega$$

$$X_{SYS} = 0.7177 \div (25.98)^2 = 0.001063 \ \Omega$$

The transformer resistance and reactance referred to the low-voltage side are

$$R_{TR} = 0.01 \left[\frac{1000 \ (0.48 \text{ kV})^2}{1000 \text{ kVA}} \right] = 0.002304 \ \Omega$$

$$X_{TR} = 0.06 \left[\frac{1000 \ (0.48 \text{ kV})^2}{1000 \text{ kVA}} \right] = 0.013824 \ \Omega$$

The total system resistance and inductance referred to the low-voltage side of the transformer are

$$R_{TOT} = 0.000443 + 0.002304 = 0.002747 \ \Omega$$

$$X_{TOT} = 0.001063 + 0.013824 = 0.014887 \ \Omega$$

The inductance of the system is given by Equation (19–12):

$$L_{TOT} = \frac{0.014887}{2\pi 60} = 39.5 \times 10^{-6} \text{ H}$$

a) The capacitive reactance for 200 kvar, 480 V is equal to

$$X_{CAP} = \frac{1000 \ (0.48 \text{ kV})^2}{200 \text{ kvar}} = 1.152 \ \Omega$$

The capacitance is calculated from Equation (19–14):

$$C = \frac{1}{2\pi(60)(1.152)} = 2.3026 \times 10^{-3} \text{ F}$$

The parallel resonant frequency is

$$f_0 = \frac{1}{2\pi \sqrt{39.5 \times 10^{-6} \times 2.3026 \times 10^{-3}}} = 527.7 \text{ Hz}$$

The harmonic order at which parallel resonance occurs is

$$h = 527.7 \div 60 = 8.8$$

b) The capacitive reactance for 400 kvar, 480 V is equal to

$$X_{CAP} = \frac{1000 \ (0.48 \ kV)^2}{400 \ kvar} = 0.576 \ \Omega$$

The capacitance is calculated from Equation (19–14):

$$C = \frac{1}{2\pi(60)(0.576)} = 4.6052 \times 10^{-3} \ F$$

The parallel resonant frequency is

$$f_0 = \frac{1}{2\pi\sqrt{39.5 \times 10^{-6} \times 4.6052 \times 10^{-3}}} = 373.2 \ Hz$$

The harmonic order at which parallel resonance occurs is

$$h = 373.2 \div 60 = 6.22$$

c) The capacitive reactance for 600 kvar, 480 V is equal to

$$X_{CAP} = \frac{1000(0.48 \ kV)^2}{600 \ kvar} = 0.384 \ \Omega$$

The capacitance is calculated from Equation (19–14):

$$C = \frac{1}{2\pi(60)(0.384)} = 6.9076 \times 10^{-3} \ F$$

The parallel resonant frequency is

$$f_0 = \frac{1}{2\pi\sqrt{39.5 \times 10^{-6} \times 6.9076 \times 10^{-3}}} = 304.7 \ Hz$$

The harmonic order at which parallel resonance occurs is

$$h = 304.7 \div 60 = 5.08$$

d) The capacitive reactance for 800 kvar, 480 V is equal to

$$X_{CAP} = \frac{1000 \ (0.48 \ kV)^2}{800 \ kvar} = 0.288 \ \Omega$$

The capacitance is calculated from Equation (19–14):

$$C = \frac{1}{2\pi(60)(0.288)} = 9.2101 \times 10^{-3} \ F$$

The parallel resonant frequency is

$$f_0 = \frac{1}{2\pi\sqrt{39.5 \times 10^{-6} \times 9.2101 \times 10^{-3}}} = 263.9 \text{ Hz}$$

The harmonic order at which parallel resonance occurs is

$$h = 263.9 \div 60 = 4.4$$

Note from Example 19–3 that there exists a parallel resonant frequency very close to the 5th harmonic order if a 600 kvar capacitor bank is placed on the system. If a harmonic load that produces a significant 5th harmonic current were to be connected to the bus, severe voltage distortion would result. The following example illustrates the calculation of voltage and current distortion for the power system of Example 19–3 with and without the 600 kvar capacitor bank connected.

EXAMPLE 19–4

The power system of Example 19–3 supplies a 200 kVA, 480 V, harmonic-producing load that has the following harmonic spectrum:

TABLE 19–5

Harmonic Spectrum for 200 kVA Load		
Frequency	Harmonic Order	Line Current Magnitude
300	5	50.0 A
420	7	30.0 A
660	11	15.0 A
780	13	7.0 A
1020	17	3.0 A

Determine the following:

a) The rss and THD of the source current and bus voltage without the 600 kvar capacitor connected.
b) The rss and THD of the bus voltage with the 600 kvar capacitor connected.
c) The rss and THD of the capacitor current with the capacitor connected.

Solution: The magnitude of the fundamental load current is

$$I_1 = \frac{200{,}000 \text{ VA}}{\sqrt{3}\,480 \text{ V}} = 240.6 \text{ A}$$

a) Without the capacitor connected, the system representation is a series RL circuit. The inductive reactance of the system is computed at each harmonic frequency according to Equation (19–13). The resulting inductive reactance is then combined with the system resistance to obtain the magnitude of the system impedance at each harmonic frequency. The voltage drop due to the harmonic load currents will be computed at each harmonic frequency by multiplying the harmonic load current magnitude by the magnitude of the system impedance. The following table summarizes the results:

TABLE 19–6

Frequency	R_{TOT}	X_{TOT}	$|Z_{OUT}|$	I_h	V_h
300	0.002747	0.074455	0.074486	50.0	3.72
420	0.002747	0.104209	0.104245	30.0	3.13
660	0.002747	0.163757	0.163780	15.0	2.46
780	0.002747	0.193531	0.193551	7.0	1.35
1020	0.002747	0.253079	0.253094	3.0	0.76

The rss and THD of the line current are

$$\text{rss current} = \sqrt{240.6^2 + 50.0^2 + 30.0^2 + 15.0^2 + 7.0^2 + 3.0^2}$$
$$= 248.1 \text{ A}$$

$$\text{THD current} = \frac{\sqrt{50.0^2 + 30.0^2 + 15.0^2 + 7.0^2 + 3.0^2}}{240.6} \times 100\%$$
$$= 25.22\%$$

The rss and THD of the load voltage are determined with respect to the nominal line-to-neutral voltage of the system:

$$\text{rss voltage} = \sqrt{277.0^2 + 3.72^2 + 3.13^2 + 2.46^2 + 1.35^2 + 0.76^2}$$
$$= 277.05 \text{ V}$$

$$\text{THD voltage} = \frac{\sqrt{3.72^2 + 3.13^2 + 2.46^2 + 1.35^2 + 0.76^2}}{277.0} \times 100\%$$
$$= 2.045\%$$

b) With the capacitor bank added, the magnitude of the system impedance includes the parallel combination of the capacitor and the system. Equation (19–16) can be used to calculate the magnitude of the parallel impedance at each harmonic order frequency. The voltage drop at each harmonic is equal to the harmonic load current multiplied by the magnitude of the impedance. The results are tabulated as follows:

TABLE 19–7

Frequency	$|Z_{IN}|$	I_h	V_h
300	1.5787 Ω	50.0 A	78.94 V
420	0.1157 Ω	30.0 A	3.47 V
660	0.0444 Ω	15.0 A	0.67 V
780	0.0349 Ω	7.0 A	0.24 V
1020	0.0248 Ω	3.0 A	0.07 V

The rss value of the bus voltage is

$$\text{rss voltage} = \sqrt{277.0^2 + 78.94^2 + 3.47^2 + 0.67^2 + 0.24^2 + 0.07^2}$$
$$= 288.1 \text{ V}$$

The percent THD of the bus voltage is

$$\text{THD voltage} = \frac{\sqrt{3.72^2 + 3.13^2 + 2.46^2 + 1.35^2 + 0.76^2}}{277.0} \times 100\%$$
$$= 28.5\%$$

Note that the percent THD of the bus voltage is 25.8% with the capacitor bank added, as opposed to 2.045% without the capacitor bank. In this instance, the capacitor bank has combined with the source inductance to create a parallel resonance condition very near the 5th harmonic. The amplification of the 5th harmonic has lead to an increase in the THD of the bus voltage to an unacceptable value.

c) The current through the capacitor bank at each harmonic frequency can be calculated by applying Ohm's law to the capacitor element. The bus voltage at each harmonic frequency has already been calculated and tabulated. The capacitive reactance of the 600 kvar, 480 V capacitor bank at 60 Hz is determined by applying Equation (19–11):

$$X_{CAP} = \frac{1000 \, (0.48 \text{ kV})^2}{600 \text{ kvar}} = 0.384 \, \Omega$$

The capacitance of the 600 kvar, 480 V capacitor bank is determined by applying Equation (19–14):

$$C = \frac{1}{2\pi(60)(0.384)} = 6.9078 \times 10^{-3} \text{ F}$$

The impedance of the capacitor can be calculated by applying Equation (19–15) for the harmonic frequencies of interest. The results are tabulated as follows:

TABLE 19–8

Frequency	X_{CAP}	V_h	I_{CAP}
300	0.0768 Ω	78.94 V	1027.9 A
420	0.0549 Ω	3.47 V	63.2 A
660	0.0349 Ω	0.67 V	19.2 A
780	0.0295 Ω	0.24 V	8.1 A
1020	0.0226 Ω	0.07 V	3.1 A

The fundamental value of the capacitor current is

$$I_1 = \frac{600,000 \text{ VA}}{\sqrt{3} \, 480 \text{ V}} = 721.7 \text{ A}$$

The rss value of the capacitor current is

$$\text{rss capacitor current} = \sqrt{721.7^2 + 1027.9^2 + 63.2^2 + 19.2^2 + 8.1^2 + 3.1^2}$$
$$= 1257.6 \text{ A}$$

Note that the capacitor current is approximately 175% of rated! This magnitude of current would likely cause the capacitor fuses to blow or capacitor breaker to trip. If the fuse or circuit breaker protecting the capacitor bank does not operate due to this overcurrent, damage to the capacitor would likely result.

19–3   DETUNED CAPACITOR HARMONIC FILTER DESIGN

Example 19–4 has illustrated the special consideration that must be given to the application of power factor correction capacitors to a power system that contains harmonic-producing equipment. Even though the actual harmonic currents produced by the load may be small, these currents can be amplified to unacceptable levels due to parallel resonance conditions.

The parallel resonance condition discussed in the previous section occurs at a frequency at which the capacitive reactance of the capacitor bank equals the inductive reactance of the system. If this resonance frequency occurs at or near one of the harmonics produced by the load equipment, severe amplification of the harmonic voltages and currents will result. If the parallel resonance frequency could be shifted or made to occur at a value less than the lowest-order harmonic term of the load equipment, then the amplification of the harmonic load currents could be minimized.

Shifting of the parallel resonance frequency is accomplished by placing an inductor in series with the capacitor bank. The series inductor/capacitor combination is referred to as a *harmonic filter bank* or *detuned capacitor bank*. These detuned capacitor banks may use capacitors that are delta connected, as in Figure 19–5(A), or wye connected, as in

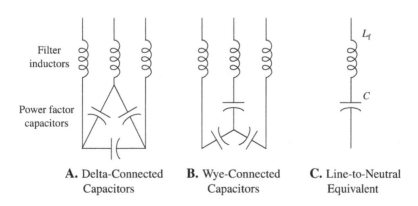

A. Delta-Connected Capacitors   **B.** Wye-Connected Capacitors   **C.** Line-to-Neutral Equivalent

FIGURE 19–5
Detuned Capacitor Filter Bank Configurations

Figure 19–5(B). In either the delta or wye connection, the analysis is based on the single-phase line-to-neutral equivalent circuit representation. The single-phase line-to-neutral equivalent representation of the capacitor bank with a tuning inductor is shown in Figure 19–5(C). The series resonant frequency or tuning frequency of the detuned capacitor bank is generally selected to be about 3% to 10% less than the lowest-order harmonic produced by the load equipment. For a typical six-pulse power converter, the lowest-order harmonic term is the 5th harmonic, which corresponds to a frequency of 300 Hz on a 60 Hz system. A detuned capacitor bank applied to this system would have a tuning frequency of between 270 and 290 Hz. Typically, the tuning frequency for a filter of this nature is 282 Hz, corresponding to the 4.7^{th} harmonic term.

In addition to shifting the parallel resonant frequency, the detuned capacitor will supply a portion of the harmonic current demanded by the load. The most significant portion of harmonic load current supplied will occur at the harmonic order closest to the tuning order of the filter. For example, a harmonic filter tuned to the 4.7^{th} harmonic will supply a major portion of the 5th harmonic current demanded by the load. The filter will also supply a significantly lower amount of the higher-order harmonic load currents as well. Therefore, since the filter bank will supply some of the load harmonic current, less harmonic current needs to be supplied by the source. This will result in a reduction in the THD of the load bus voltage. The series resonant frequency of the filter element is given by

$$f_0 = \frac{1}{2\pi\sqrt{L_f C}}\ \text{Hz} \tag{19–20}$$

where:

L_f = inductance of the tuning inductor
C = capacitance of the capacitor bank

Solving Equation (19–20) for L_f results in

$$L_f = \frac{1}{C(2\pi f_0)^2}\ \text{H} \tag{19–21}$$

Substituting Equation (19–14) into (19–21) results in

$$L_f = \frac{2\pi f_{SYS} X_{CAP}}{(2\pi f_0)^2}\ \text{H} \tag{19–22}$$

$$= \frac{f_{SYS} X_{CAP}}{2\pi (f_0)^2}\ \text{H}$$

Substituting Equation (19–11) into (19–22) results in

$$L_f = \frac{1000 f_{SYS}(kV_{CAP})^2}{2\pi (f_0)^2 \text{kvar}_{CAP}}\ \text{H} \tag{19–23}$$

Equation (19–23) can be used to determine the filter inductance required to tune the filter to a particular frequency.

EXAMPLE 19–5

Determine the value of filter inductance required to tune the following capacitor banks to 282 Hz (4.7^{th} harmonic). The nominal system frequency is 60 Hz.

a) 50 kvar, 480 V
b) 1200 kvar, 12.47 kV

Solution:

a) Direct application of Equation (19–23) results in the following:

$$L_f = \frac{1000 \times 60 \times (0.48)^2}{2\pi(282)^2\, 50} = 5.533 \times 10^{-4}\,H \quad \text{or} \quad 553.3\,\mu H$$

b) $L_f = \dfrac{1000 \times 60 \times (12.47)^2}{2\pi(282)^2\, 1200} = 1.5561 \times 10^{-2}\,H \quad \text{or} \quad 15.561\,mH$

The amount of load harmonic current supplied by the filter, and the resulting bus voltage THD can be determined by analyzing the equivalent circuit shown in Figure 19–6. The input impedance looking into the source from the harmonic load consists of the filter in parallel with the source. The input impedance is a function of frequency and is given by the following:

$$\mathbf{Z}_{IN} = \frac{(R_{TOT} + j\omega L_{TOT}) \times (j\omega L_f - j/(\omega C))}{R_{TOT} + j\omega L_{TOT} + j\omega L_f - j/(\omega C)} \quad (19\text{–}24)$$

$$= \frac{(R_{TOT} + j\omega L_{TOT}) \times (j\omega L_f - j/(\omega C))}{R_{TOT} + j[\omega L_{TOT} + \omega L_f - 1/(\omega C)]}$$

Parallel resonance occurs when the imaginary part of the denominator of Equation (19–24) is equal to zero:

$$\omega_0 L_{TOT} + \omega_0 L_f - \frac{1}{(\omega_0 C)} = 0 \quad (19\text{–}25)$$

FIGURE 19–6
Equivalent Circuit of System Employing a
Detuned Capacitor Filter Bank

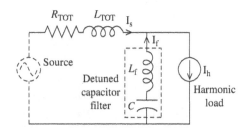

Solving Equation (19–25) for ω_0,

$$\omega_0 = \frac{1}{\sqrt{(L_{TOT} + L_f)C}} \qquad (19\text{–}26)$$

Similarly, the parallel resonant frequency in hertz is given by

$$f_0 = \frac{1}{2\pi\sqrt{(L_{TOT} + L_f)C}} \qquad (19\text{–}27)$$

Note the similarities between Equations (19–26) and (19–18).

EXAMPLE 19–6

The power factor correction capacitors of Example 19–3 have harmonic filter tuning inductors installed in series with the capacitor units. The resulting harmonic filter will be tuned to the 4.7th harmonic order. For each of the capacitor sizes listed in Example 19–3, determine the following:

a) tuning inductance required
b) parallel resonant frequency of the source and filter bank with the tuning inductors installed
c) The resonant frequencies with and without the tuning inductors installed

Solution:

a) The required inductance is determined by direct application of Equation (19–23). The results are:

200 kvar: $L_f = 1.3830 \times 10^{-4}$ H
400 kvar: $L_f = 6.9166 \times 10^{-5}$ H
600 kvar: $L_f = 4.6100 \times 10^{-5}$ H
800 kvar: $L_f = 3.4580 \times 10^{-5}$ H

b) The parallel resonant frequencies are determined by applying Equation (19–27). The total system inductance was determined in Example 19–3 as 39.5×10^{-6} H. The results are:

TABLE 19–9

kvar	Capacitance	Filter Inductance	Parallel Resonant Frequency	Harmonic Order
200 kvar	2.3026×10^{-3} F	1.3830×10^{-4} H	248.7 Hz	4.14
400 kvar	4.6052×10^{-3} F	6.9166×10^{-5} H	225.0 Hz	3.75
600 kvar	6.9076×10^{-3} F	4.6100×10^{-5} H	207.0 Hz	3.45
800 kvar	9.2101×10^{-3} F	3.4580×10^{-5} H	193.0 Hz	3.21

TABLE 19–10
Parallel Resonant Frequencies

Capacitance	Without Filter Inductors	With Filter Inductors
200 kvar	527.73 Hz	248.7 Hz
400 kvar	373.3 Hz	225.0 Hz
600 kvar	304.7 Hz	207.0 Hz
800 kvar	263.9 Hz	193.0 Hz

c) The parallel resonant frequencies with and without the tuning inductors are shown in Table 19–10.

Notice that the parallel resonant frequency has been shifted to a value below the tuning frequency of the filter.

In order to calculate the bus voltage distortion and filter harmonic duty, it is necessary to calculate the harmonic load current supplied from both the source and the harmonic filter bank. The division of current can be determined by applying the current divider rule to the circuit of Figure 19–6. The current supplied by the harmonic filter bank is given by the following:

$$\mathbf{I}_f = I_h \times \frac{(R_{TOT} + j\omega L_{TOT})}{R_{TOT} + j[\omega L_{TOT} + \omega L_f - 1/(\omega C)]} \qquad (19\text{–}28)$$

In a similar manner, the current supplied by the source is given by

$$\mathbf{I}_s = I_h \times \frac{j[(\omega L_f - 1/(\omega C)])}{R_{TOT} + j[\omega L_{TOT} + \omega L_f - 1/(\omega C)]} \qquad (19\text{–}29)$$

The bus voltage at each harmonic is determined by multiplying the source current by the source impedance, as follows:

$$\mathbf{V}_h = \mathbf{I}_s \times (R_{TOT} + j\omega L_{TOT}) \qquad (19\text{–}30)$$

Equations (19–28), (19–29), and (19–30) are evaluated at each harmonic frequency of interest to determine the harmonic duty of the filter and the resulting percent THD bus voltage distortion with the filter capacitors installed. Equations (19–28), (19–29), and (19–30) are applicable to all frequencies except the fundamental.

The magnitude of the fundamental component of the source current is equal to

$$I_{s,1} = \frac{\text{Total three-phase voltampere load}}{\sqrt{3} \times \text{Nominal line-to-line bus voltage}} \qquad (19\text{–}31)$$

The magnitude of the fundamental component of the filter bank line current is equal to

$$I_{f,1} = \frac{\text{Nominal line-to-neutral bus voltage}}{\omega_{SYS}L_f - 1/(\omega_{SYS}C)} \qquad (19\text{–}32)$$

The magnitude of the fundamental component of bus voltage is assumed to be equal to the nominal line-to-neutral bus voltage magnitude.

EXAMPLE 19–7

A 600 kvar harmonic filter bank has been installed on the power system of Example 19–3. The harmonic spectrum of the load current is given in Example 19–4. Determine the following:

a) filter harmonic current spectrum and rss of the filter current
b) bus voltage harmonic spectrum
c) percent THD and rss of the bus voltage

Solution: From Example 19–3, the source resistance and inductance are

$$R_{TOT} = 0.002747 \ \Omega, \ L_{TOT} = 39.5 \times 10^{-6} \ \text{H}$$

From Example 19–6, the tuning inductor required to tune a 600 kvar, 480 V, three-phase capacitor bank to the 4.7th harmonic was

$$L_f = 4.61 \times 10^{-5} \ \text{H}$$

The equivalent line-to-neutral capacitance for the 600 kvar, 480 V capacitor bank is $C = 6.9076 \times 10^{-3}$ F. The fundamental component of the load harmonic current was determined to be 240.6 A. The load harmonic current spectrum is repeated here for reference:

TABLE 19–11
Harmonic Spectrum for 200 kVA Load

Frequency	Harmonic Order	Line Current Magnitude
300	5	50.0 A
420	7	30.0 A
660	11	15.0 A
780	13	7.0 A
1020	17	3.0 A

a) The magnitude of the fundamental component of the filter bank current is determined by direct application of Equation (19–32):

$$I_{f,1} = \left| \frac{480/\sqrt{3}}{377.0 \times 4.61 \times 10^{-5} - 1/(377.0 \times 6.9076 \times 10^{-3})} \right| = 756.0 \ \text{A}$$

In order to determine the harmonic current spectrum of the filter, Equation (19–28) is evaluated at each of the load harmonic frequencies just listed. The results are:

TABLE 19–12

Frequency (Hz)	Harmonic Order	Filter Line Current
300	5	44.02 A
420	7	19.28 A
660	11	7.68 A
780	13	3.47 A
1020	17	1.44 A

The rss value of the filter bank line current is

$$\text{rss filter current} = \sqrt{756^2 + 44.02^2 + 19.28^2 + 7.68^2 + 3.47^2 + 1.44^2}$$
$$= 757.5 \text{ A}$$

The rated current of the capacitor bank is

$$I = \frac{600{,}000 \text{ VA}}{\sqrt{3} \, 480} = 721.7 \text{ A}$$

The rss filter current expressed as a percentage of rated is

$$I = \frac{757.5 \text{ A}}{721.7 \text{ A}} \times 100\% = 105\%$$

b) The bus voltage harmonic distortion is determined by first calculating the harmonic currents supplied from the source. This involves application of Equation (19–29) at each harmonic frequency of interest. The results are:

TABLE 19–13

Frequency (Hz)	Harmonic Order	Source Line Current
300	5	5.98 A
420	7	11.72 A
660	11	7.33 A
780	13	3.53 A
1020	17	1.56 A

The harmonic components of the bus voltage are determined by applying Equation (19–30) at each harmonic load frequency. The results are

TABLE 19–14

Frequency (Hz)	Harmonic Order	Bus Voltage
300	5	0.45 V
420	7	1.22 V
660	11	1.20 V
780	13	0.68 V
1020	17	0.39 V

The fundamental component of the bus voltage is

$$V_1 = \frac{480 \text{ V}}{\sqrt{3}} = 277.0 \text{ V}$$

c) The percent THD and rss values of the bus voltage are

$$\text{THD voltage} = \frac{\sqrt{0.45^2 + 1.22^2 + 1.2^2 + 0.68^2 + 0.39^2}}{277.0} \times 100\%$$

$$= 0.7\%$$

$$\text{rss bus voltage} = \sqrt{277.0^2 + 0.45^2 + 1.22^2 + 1.2^2 + 0.68^2 + 0.39^2}$$

$$= 277.01 \text{ V}$$

Note from Example 19–7 that the THD bus voltage distortion has been reduced from 2.045% without the capacitor/filter bank to 0.7% with the capacitor/filter bank. Also, the THD bus voltage has been reduced from 25.8% with 600 kvar of capacitors installed to 0.7% with the 600 kvar capacitor/filter bank. This reduction in THD bus voltage distortion has occurred because the parallel resonant frequency has been shifted to a value less than the lowest-order harmonic component of load current.

When tuning inductors are applied to a capacitor bank to create a harmonic filter, an overvoltage occurs on the individual capacitor units. This overvoltage may cause excessive stress in the dielectric of the capacitor units and lead to premature failure. In order to determine the voltage on the capacitor unit of a harmonic filter, consider the line-to-neutral equivalent circuit shown in Figure 19–7.

In reference to Figure 19–7, the magnitude of the voltage across the capacitor is given by

$$V_{C,h} = I_{f,h} \times \frac{1}{\omega C} \qquad \textbf{(19–33)}$$

FIGURE 19–7
Equivalent Circuit for Determining Voltage Duty of
Detuned Filter Bank Components

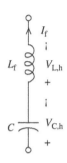

The magnitude of the voltage across the filter inductor is

$$V_{L,h} = I_{f,h} \times \omega L_f \tag{19-34}$$

where $I_{f,h}$ is the filter current at each of the harmonic frequencies of interest. These currents are obtained by analyzing the system according to Equation (19–28).

EXAMPLE 19–8

For the harmonic filter of Example 19–7, determine the magnitude of the harmonic voltages across the capacitor units and filter inductor.

Solution: Direct application of Equations (19–32) and (19–33) results in the following:

TABLE 19–15

Frequency (Hz)	Line to Neutral		
	$I_{f,h}$	$V_{L,h}$	$V_{C,h}$
300	44.02 A	3.83 V	3.38 V
420	18.28 A	2.22 V	1.00 V
660	7.68 A	1.47 V	0.27 V
780	3.47 A	0.79 V	0.10 V
1020	1.44 A	0.43 V	0.03 V

Note: If the capacitor units are delta connected, the equivalent line-to-neutral voltages must be multiplied by $\sqrt{3}$ to determine the actual voltage across the capacitor units.
The fundamental voltage across the capacitor units is

$$V_{C,1} = 756.0 \times \left[\frac{1}{377 \times 6.9076 \times 10^{-3}} \right] = 290.3 \text{ V}$$

The rss value of the voltage across the capacitor cells is

$$\text{rss capacitor voltage} = \sqrt{290.3^2 + 3.38^2 + 1.0^2 + 0.27^2 + 0.1^2 + 0.03^2}$$
$$= 290.32 \text{ V}$$

The actual capacitor voltage expressed as a percentage of rated capacitor voltage is

$$V_{\text{CAP}} = \frac{290.32 \text{ V}}{277.0 \text{ V}} \times 100\% = 104.8\%$$

As Example 19–8 illustrates, an overvoltage of about 5% above nominal will occur across the capacitor units of a capacitor bank tuned to operate as a harmonic filter. For example, if the system bus voltage is 5% above nominal, an overvoltage of approximately 110% will appear across the capacitor units. For this reason, it is common to specify the next-higher-standard voltage rating for the capacitor units used in a harmonic filter bank. Some capacitor manufacturers have "low-voltage stress" capacitor units available for harmonic filter applications. If the voltage rating of the capacitors is higher than the nominal bus voltage, the reactive power rating must be derated according to the following:

$$\text{kvar}_{\text{ACT}} = \text{kvar}_{\text{RATED}} \times \left[\frac{\text{Actual frequency}}{\text{Rated frequency}} \right] \times \left[\frac{\text{Actual line voltage}}{\text{Rated line voltage}} \right]^2 \quad \textbf{(19–35)}$$

19–4   IEEE STANDARD 519

The maximum allowable voltage and current distortion is specified in IEEE Standard 519-1992. The limits on current distortion apply to the amount of harmonic current to be supplied by the utility source to the harmonic load. By limiting the amount of harmonic current, the voltage THD at the point of common coupling (PCC) with the utility can be kept within specified limits. For most industrial power systems, the maximum permitted voltage THD is 5.0%, with the maximum percentage for any one harmonic component equal to 3%.

Table 19–16 shows the maximum percentages of current distortion for general distribution systems (120 V to 69 kV) at the point of common coupling with the utility. Note from the table that the maximum permitted current THD is a function of the I_{SC}/I_1, or short circuit ratio (SCR). I_{SC} is the magnitude of the short circuit current at the point of common coupling with the utility, and I_1 is the rated fundamental current of the total load at the point of common coupling. A high short circuit ratio indicates a low system impedance as compared to the load. This type of system is able to supply a higher amount of harmonic current than a system with a low SCR ratio.

Table 19.16 specifies limits on the total harmonic current distortion and maximum distortion for the individual harmonic components. These THD limits are given for specific ranges of harmonic currents. For example, a system with an SCR of 75 would be permitted to have a THD of 10.0% for harmonics less than the 11th harmonic order, a THD of

TABLE 19–16
Current Distortion Limits for General Distribution Systems

I_{SC}/I_1	<11	$11 \leq h < 17$	$17 \leq h < 23$	$23 \leq h < 35$	$35 < h$	THD
<20	4.0	2.0	1.5	0.6	0.3	5.0%
20 < 50	7.0	3.5	2.5	1.0	0.5	8.0%
50 < 100	10.0	4.5	4.0	1.5	0.7	12.0%
100 < 1000	12.0	5.5	5.0	2.0	1.0	15.0%
>1000	15.0	7.0	6.0	2.5	1.4	20.0%

Source: From IEEE Standard 519-1992 IEEE Recommended Practices and Requirements for Harmonic Control in Electric Power Systems. Copyright © 1993 IEEE. All rights reserved.

4.5% for harmonic currents between the 11th and 17th harmonic orders, and so on. The THD within a specified range is calculated by taking the square root of the sum of the squares of the harmonic currents within that range and dividing by the maximum fundamental load current at the PCC.

EXAMPLE 19–9

A load containing harmonic-generating equipment is connected through a step-down transformer to a 12.47 kV utility distribution feeder. A 5th harmonic filter has been added to the plant bus to filter out the majority of the 5th harmonic current. The point of common coupling is considered to be the 12.47 kV connection to the step-down transformer. The short circuit availability at the PCC is 55 MVA @ 12.47 kV. The maximum fundamental load current is 40 A @ 12.47 kV. The following harmonic currents are present on the utility system as a result of this load:

TABLE 19–17

Frequency (Hz)	Harmonic Order	Source Line Current
300	5	2.5 A
420	7	3.8 A
660	11	1.6 A
780	13	0.6 A
1020	17	0.4 A

Determine whether or not the requirements of IEEE 519 are met for this harmonic load.

Solution: The short circuit current at 12.47 kV is

$$I_{SC} = \frac{1000 \ (55 \ \text{MVA})}{\sqrt{3} \ 12.47 \ \text{kV}} = 2546.5 \ \text{A}$$

The SCR ratio is calculated as

$$SCR = 2546.5 \div 40 = 63.7$$

The THD for the harmonic current range less than the 11th is

$$THD_{<11} = \frac{\sqrt{2.5^2 + 3.8^2}}{40.0} \times 100\% = 11.4\%$$

According to Table 19–16, the maximum permissible THD for harmonics less than the 11th harmonic order is 10.0%. Therefore, IEEE 519 is violated in this range.

The THD for the harmonic current range between the 11th and 17th harmonic is

$$THD_{11; 17} = \frac{\sqrt{1.6^2 + 0.6^2}}{40.0} \times 100\% = 4.3\%$$

The maximum permissible THD for harmonics between the 11th and 17th harmonic order is 4.5%. Therefore, the requirements of IEEE Standard 519 are met within this range.

The THD for the harmonic current range between the 17th and 23rd harmonic is

$$THD_{17; 23} = \frac{\sqrt{0.4^2}}{40.0} \times 100\% = 1.0\%$$

The maximum permissible THD for harmonics between the 17th and 23rd harmonic order is 4.0%. Therefore, the requirements of IEEE Standard 519 are met within this range.

The THD including all harmonic terms is

$$THD = \frac{\sqrt{2.5^2 + 3.8^2 + 1.6^2 + 0.6^2 + 0.4^2}}{40.0} \times 100\% = 12.2\%$$

This value of THD slightly exceeds the maximum of 12.0% as specified by IEEE 519.

Example 19–9 has illustrated a situation where the requirements of IEEE 519 have not been met. The large amount of 7th harmonic current is most likely the cause of the violation. In order to reduce the amount of 7th harmonic current in the system, it may be necessary to install both a 5th and a 7th harmonic filter to the plant bus.

The details of the design and analysis of multiple tuned filters is beyond the scope of this text. However, when applying multiple tuned filters to a power system, it must be remembered that the lowest-order step must be energized first, followed by successively higher-order steps. Similarly, when deenergizing steps, the highest-order step is switched off first, followed by successively lower-order steps. For example, in a filter bank consisting of 5th-, 7th-, and 11th-order steps, the 5th-order step would be energized first, followed by the 7th-order then the 11th-order steps. With all steps energized, the 11th-order step would be deenergized first, followed by the 7th- and then the 5th-order steps in succession.

19–5   SUMMARY OF DETUNED HARMONIC FILTER DESIGN AND ANALYSIS

The examples of Section 19–3 have presented an introduction to the fundamental concepts of harmonic filter design. The basic procedure can be summarized by the following steps:

Step 1. Determine the amount of reactive compensation (kvar) required.

Step 2. Select a capacitor voltage rating equal to the next-higher-standard voltage rating available or use "low-stress" capacitor design.

Step 3. Determine the actual amount of reactive power supplied by the capacitors after derating.

Step 4. Calculate the rating of the filter inductor required to tune the capacitor/filter to the desired harmonic order frequency.

Step 5. Calculate the harmonic current spectrum of the filter bank.

Step 6. Calculate the harmonic spectrum, THD, and rss of the bus voltage after application of the harmonic filter.

Step 7. Calculate the harmonic spectrum, THD, and rss of the source current.

Step 8. Determine if the requirements of IEEE 519 are met.

PROBLEMS

1. Determine the THD and rss values of a current waveform having the following harmonic spectrum:

TABLE 19–18

Frequency (Hz)	Harmonic Order	Current (A)
60	Fundamental	100.0
300	5	17.0
420	7	12.0
660	11	7.5
780	13	4.8
1020	17	3.0
1140	19	2.3
1380	23	1.4
1500	25	0.8

2. Determine the THD and rss values of a voltage waveform having the following harmonic spectrum:

TABLE 19–19

Frequency (Hz)	Harmonic Order	Voltage (V)
60	Fundamental	120.0
300	5	5.0
420	7	2.3
660	11	1.2
780	13	0.3
1020	17	0.1

3. Determine a typical harmonic current spectrum for a 100 hp, 460 V, six-pulse, variable-speed motor drive. Assume 1 kVA per hp.

4. Determine the rss and THD of the current waveform for the variable-speed motor drive of Problem 3.

5. An industrial plant is supplied from the utility 24.94 kV, three-phase, MGN distribution feeder. The short circuit data on the 24.94 kV system indicate a three-phase short circuit availability of 105 MVA @ 24.94 kV, with an X/R ratio of 2.2. The step-down transformer is rated 2000 kVA, 24.94 kV–480Y/277 V, $R = 1.1\%$, $X = 6.5\%$. Determine the parallel resonant frequencies with the following capacitors connected to the 480 V bus:
   a) 400 kvar
   b) 800 kvar
   c) 1200 kvar

6. The industrial plant of Problem 5 supplies a total three-phase load of 1700 kVA. Included in the 1700 kVA of total load is a harmonic load having the following harmonic spectrum:

TABLE 19–20
Harmonic Spectrum

Frequency	Harmonic Order	Line Current Magnitude
300	5	250.0 A
420	7	130.0 A
660	11	60.0 A

It is proposed that a 1200 kvar capacitor bank be added to the 480 V bus to improve the plant power factor. Determine the following:
   a) rss and THD of the line current and bus voltage without the capacitor bank connected

b) rss and THD of the line current and bus voltage with the capacitor bank connected

c) rss and THD of the capacitor current with the capacitor bank connected

7. For the power system of Problems 5 and 6, it is now proposed that a 1200 kvar, 480 V, capacitor detuned to the 5th harmonic filter be installed. Assume that "low-stress" capacitors are available at a voltage rating of 480 V. Determine the following:

   a) value of tuning inductor required to tune the bank to the 4.7^{th} harmonic order

   b) rss and THD of the line current and bus voltage with the detuned capacitor bank installed

   c) rss and THD of the filter current with the filter connected

8. Determine if the requirements of IEEE 519 are met for the filter installation of Problem 7. Assume that the PCC is at the high side of the 2000 kVA step-down transformer.

Index

Active power, 31, 411
Ambient temperature correction
    factor, 116
American Wire Gauge (AWG),
    102
Angle of incidence, 309
Apparent power, 411
Appliance demand factor, 50
Arc fault circuit interruption, 149
    Description, 149
    Required locations, 150
Architectural responsibilities, 12
Asymmetrical factor, 87
Asymmetrical fault current, 448,
    450
Auxiliary gutter, 186

Backfill requirements, 191
Ballast, 300
    Constant wattage autotransformer
        HID, 303
    Electronic, 302
    Fluorescent preheat, 301
    Fluorescent rapid start, 301
    Fluorescent instant start, 302
    Reactor HID, 303
Ballast data, 333
Bathroom circuit, 152
Billing, 51
Bolted fault, 80
Bonding of service raceways, 230
Bonding of systems above 250 V to
    ground, 230
Branch circuits
    Loading, 41
    Number required, 150
Branch circuit requirements,
    150–153
Breaker ratings, 98

Cable and Conduit schedule, 199,
    200
Cable impedance, 425–427,
    458–459
    Three-phase circuit, 425, 456
    Parallel conductor, 428, 457
Cable insulation, 109
    Thermoplastic, 109
    Thermoset, 109
    Polyethylene PE, 109
    Polyvinylchloride, 109
Cable pulling, 192
    Allowable conductor stress, 193
    Coefficient of dynamic friction,
        193, 194
    Downward pull, 194
    Horizontal straight pull, 194
    Sidewall pressure, 195
    Sweeps, 195
    Upward pull, 194
    Weight correction factor, 194
Cable short circuit withstand, 481
Cable tray, 179
Cable types, 105
    AC, 105
    MC, 105
    Multiconductor, 105
    NM, 106
    NMC, 107
    SE, 107
    SER, 107
    SEU, 107
    Single conductor, 105
    UF, 107
    USE, 107
Cabling diagrams, 155–159
    Branch circuit designation, 156
    Conductor designations, 156
    Home run, 156

Candlepower, 305
Candlepower distribution curves,
    309, 325
    Across, 309
    Along, 309
    Vertical plane, 309
Capacitance, 18
Capacitive reactance, 25
Capacitor, 410
    Effect of frequency on rating, 530
    Effect of voltage on rating, 530
    Construction, 410
    Ratings, 410
Capacitor circuit conductor sizing,
    419
Capacitor controls, 418
Capacitor discharge resistor, 410
Capacitor switching, 415
    Back-to-back switching, 416, 417
    Current limiting inductor, 416
    Inrush current, 416
    Isolated bank switching, 415,
        416
    Single-phase circuit, 429, 457
Capacitor, voltage improvement,
    414
Cavity ratio, 315
Center-tap ground, 11
Circuit breaker, 90
    Molded case breaker, 90
    Tripping mechanism, 91
    Thermal trip, 91
    Magnetic trip, 92
    Thermal-magnetic trip, 91
    Electronic trip, 92
    Construction, 96
    Frame size, 97
Circuit breaker accessories, 94
Circular mil, 103

Civil engineering responsibilities, 12

Clearances, 239, 289
  Access to working space, 292
  Entrances, 292
  Final vertical clearance, 241
  From building opening, 240
  General, 239
  Over 600 V, 293
  Requirements, 291
  Working space, 290

Coefficient of thermal expansion, 178

Coefficient of utilization, 324

Color rendering index (CRI), 307, 308

Completely Self-Protected (CSP) transformer, 371

Complex conjugate, 27

Complex impedance, 23

Conductor ampacities, 110–115

Conductor considered outside of building, 242

Conductor dimensions, 176

Conductor resistance, 103

Conductor selection process, 123–126

Conductor weights, 196

Conduit dimensions, 174

Conduit types, 162
  Electrical Metallic Tubing (EMT), 165
  Electrical Nonmetallic Tubing (ENT), 168
  Flexible Metal Conduit (FMC), 168
  Intermediate Metallic Conduit (IMC), 164
  Liquidtight Flexible Metal Conduit (LFMC), 171
  Liquidtight Flexible Nonmetallic Conduit (LFNC), 172
  Rigid Metallic Conduit (RMC), 162
  Rigid Nonmetallic Conduit (RNC), 166

Continuous load, 122

Cooktop load, 43

Coordination, 472
  Breaker–breaker, 477
  Fuse–breaker, 477
  Fuse–fuse, 473, 474
  Fuse selectivity guide, 476

Cord and plug connected equipment loading, 142

Corner grounded delta, 10

Current interruption, 93
  Arc chutes, 93
  Current limiting, 93
  De-ionizing plates, 93
  Restrike, 93

Current transformer, 4
  Ratio, 494

DC offset, 449

Design team, 11

Demand factors, 47
  Fastened-in-place appliance, 50
  Lighting load, 49
  Non-dwelling receptacle load, 49

Demand meter, 257

Device terminal temperature ratings, 120

Diffuser, 304

Disconnect switches
  3PDT, 76
  3PST, 75
  4PDT, 76
  4PST, 75
  Applications, 76–77
  Construction, 73
  Contact arrangements, 75
  Enclosure types, 74
  Ratings, 73

Earth ground, 205, 207

Electric clothes dryer demand, 46

Electrical engineering responsibilities, 13

Environmental engineering responsibilities, 12

Equipment grounding conductor, 207, 215, 224
  Bonding jumper, 224, 226
  Compensation for voltage drop, 229

Definition, 9
  Parallel conductors, 228
  Raceway used for, 228, 229
  Routing, 228
  Sizing, 227

Equivalent low-side impedance, 455

Equivalent system impedance, 451
  Line-to-ground faults, 453
  Three-phase faults, 452

Estimated demand load, 38
  Dedicated branch circuit loading, 41
  General lighting load, 39
  General purpose receptacle load, 41
  Miscellaneous loads, 41

Expansion characteristics, 177

Expansion fitting, 178

Fixture mounting height, 334

Fixture whips, 170

Floor cavity correction factor, 326, 328–329

Footcandle, 307

Four-way switch, 59

Fuel cost adjustment factor, 52

Fuses
  Current limiting, 81
  Dimensions, 88
  Dual element, 82
  Non-current limiting, 81
  Non-time delay, 81
  Overload element, 82
  Physical construction, 88
  Short circuit element, 82
  Time delay, 81

Fuse Class designations, 99

Fuse derating curve, 85

Fuse peak let-through characteristic, 86

Fuse ratings, 98

Fuse time current characteristic, 83, 475
  Average melt, 83
  Minimum melt, 83, 473
  Total clear, 83, 473

Fuse types
   Edison base, 90
   Plug fuse, 90
   Type S, 90

Ground fault circuit interrupting
   receptacle, 63, 66
Ground fault circuit interruption
   requirements, 148
   Exception for dedicated
     appliances, 149
   Required receptacle location, 149
Ground fault protection of feeders,
   230
   Current transformer detector, 231
   Requirements, 230
   Trip setting, 231
   Window type detector, 231
Ground loops, 66
Grounded conductor, 9
Grounded service conductor, 205,
   216
   Sizing, 216, 217
Grounding, 203
   Equipment, 204
   Reasons for, 204
   Service, 204
   System, 203
Grounding electrode conductor, 209
   Sizing, 210–212
Grounding electrode system, 208
   Concrete encased electrode, 212
   Ground ring, 212
   Made electrode, 213
   Metal framework of building, 212
   Metal underground water pipe,
     209

Half-cycle factor, 450
Harmonic amplification, 521
Harmonic components, 508
   Harmonic order, 508
Harmonic filter, 521
   Configurations, 521
   Detuned filter bank, 521
   Filter inductor, 521
   Harmonic order, 522
   Multiple tuning frequencies, 532

   Summary of filter design, 533
   Tuning frequency, 522
   Voltage duty, 528
Harmonic resonance
   Parallel, 512, 515
   Series, 521, 522
Harmonic spectrum, 508
High-intensity discharge lamp
   starting, 303
High voltage under oil fuse link,
   376
High-voltage bushing, 370
Hospital-grade receptacle, 67

IEEE Standard 519, 530, 531
Illuminance, 307
Inductance, 18
Induction motor, 342
   Connections, 346, 347
   Construction, 342
   Design type letter, 346
   Full-load current, 352, 353
   Ratings, 345
   Run winding, 345
   Single phase, 344
   Start winding, 345
   Theory of operation, 343
   Three phase, 342
Inductive reactance, 24
Instantaneous peak factor, 450
Instrument transformer grounding,
   232
   Current transformers, 232
   Ground location, 233
   Voltage transformers, 232
Inverse square law, 308
Isofootcandle curve, 332, 334, 336
Isolated ground receptacle, 66
I^2t of fuse, 473

J operator, 18
Jamming ratio, 176
Junction boxes, 179

Key operated switch, 60
Kirchoff's current law, 32
Kirchoff's voltage law, 32

Lamp data, 333
Laundry circuit, 152
Light fixture distribution patterns,
   303–305, 325
Light fixture schedule, 339
Light levels, 327, 330
Light loss factors, 316
   Ballast factor (BF), 320
   Lamp burnout (LBO), 317
   Lamp lumen depreciation (LLD),
     317
   Luminaire ambient temperature
     (LAT), 320
   Luminaire dirt depreciation
     (LDD), 317, 320
   Luminaire surface depreciation
     (LSD), 320
   Room surface dirt depreciation
     (RSDD), 316, 318
   Voltage factor (VF), 320, 321
Light sources, 295
   Fluorescent, 296
   High-pressure sodium, 300
   Incandescent, 295
   Mercury vapor, 298
   Metal halide, 298
   Quartz restrike, 300
Lighted handle switch, 60
Lighting and appliance branch
   circuit panelboard, 273
   Definition, 273
   Main overcurrent protection
     requirements, 275, 276
Lighting circuits, 331, 332
Lighting control, 338
Lighting outlets, required locations,
   146–148
Lighting outlets, required switching,
   146–148
Lightning arrester, 204
Load current calculation, single
   phase, 34
Load current calculation, three
   phase, 34
Locked rotor current code letter,
   346, 348
Louver, 304
Low-voltage bushings, 370

Lumen, 306
Lumen method, 310
Luminous flux, 306
Lux, 307

Made electrode, 213
Main bonding jumper, 214
    Location, 214
    Sizing, 215
Main distribution panel, 283, 285
Mechanical engineering
    responsibilities, 12
Medium-voltage switchgear, 284,
    286
    Bus arrangements, 287
    Draw out rack, 286
    Metal clad, 284
Metal Oxide Varistor (MOV), 69
Metering, 257
    Connections, 261–265
    Induction disc meter, 257
    Meter class designation, 257
    Meter constant, 258
    Self-contained meter, 257
    Solid-state meter, 259
Minimum bending radius, conduit,
    163
Minimum cover requirements, 190
Momentary contact switch, 60
Motor circuit, 349
    Branch circuit short circuit
        protection, 351, 354
    Conductor sizing, 350
    Controller, 355
    Disconnect, 358, 359, 361
    Overload class, 482
    Overload coordination, 482
    Overload protection, 355, 358
Motor short circuit contribution, 460
Motor starter, 355–357
Motor starting switch, 60
Multigrounded system neutral
    (MGN), 370
Multi-outlet branch circuit, 140
Multiwire branch circuit, 153

National Electrical Code, 11
NEMA device configurations, 64, 65

Neutral counted as current carrying
    conductor, 118
Non-coincident loads, 50
Non-linear loads, 119

Ohm's law, 23
One-line diagram, 5
Open neutral, 72
Outlet and device boxes, 184
    Conductor allowance, 184
    Device allowance, 186
    Dimensions, 185
    Sizing, 184
Overcurrent protection, 79
Overload, defined, 80
Overvoltage, 204

Panel balancing, 282
Panel schedule, 278
    Single phase, 279
    Three phase, 280
Panel schematic, 270
Panelboard, 268
    Busbar arrangements, 268
    Ground bus, 280
    Main bus, 269
    Neutral bus, 269
    Phase designations, 271, 272
    Ratings, 274
    Spaces, 274
Parallel conductors, 131
    Ampacity calculation, 133
    Grouping to minimize inductive
        heating, 132
    Rules for installation, 131
Peak let-through current, 87
Phasor algebra, 18, 20
Phasor representation, 15
Photometrics, 305, 325
Pilot light switch, 60
Plan symbols, 7
Point ground, 66
Point of common coupling, 530
Power factor, 28, 30, 411
    Lagging, 30
    Leading, 30
Power factor improvement, 411
Power panelboard, 273

Protected fuse, 473
Protecting fuse, 473
Pull boxes, 179
    Sizing for angle pull, 182
    Sizing for straight pull, 181
    Sizing for U-pull, 182

Raceway fill, 173
Raceway fill adjustment factor,
    117
Raceway seals, 191, 244
Range load, 43
Rate schedule, 52
Reactive factor, 29
Reactive power, 31, 411
Real power, 31, 411
Receptacles
    Duplex, 61
    Locking, 62
    NEMA configurations, 62, 64,
        65
    Non-locking, 62
    Single, 61
Receptacle loading, 41, 142
Receptacle locations, required,
    143–145
Receptacle wiring, 70
Reflectances, 314, 321–323
Reflecting overcurrent device
    characteristics, 496
    Single-phase transformers, 496
    Three-phase delta – delta
        transformer, 500
    Three-phase delta – grounded
        wye transformer, 501
    Three-phase wye – wye
        transformer, 500
Rejection fuse, 74
Rejection slot, fuse, 89
Resistance, 18
Resistance to ground, 213
Resistivity, 103
Riser diagram, 2, 4

Schedule 40 conduit, 166
Schedule 80 conduit, 166
Self-contained meter, 2

Separately derived systems, 220
    Bonding jumper, 221, 222
    Definition, 220
    Grounding electrode conductor, 222, 223
    Grounding of, 220, 221
Series-rated systems, 480
Services, 236
    Basic elements, 237
    General requirements, 236
    Medium voltage, 239
    Number permitted, 237
    Overhead, 238
    Underground, 239
Service conductor protection, 242
    Burial depth, 242
    Raceway, 242
    Warning ribbon, 242
Service disconnect requirements, 248
    Ground fault protection of, 250
    Grouping of, 249
    Maximum number permitted, 248
    Multiple disconnects, 250
    Opening of ungrounded conductors, 248
Service entrance calculations, 253
Service entrance conductors, 244
    Nonlinear loads, 247
    Sizing, 245, 246
    Types permitted, 244
    Unbalanced load current, 247
Service grounding, 213
    Main bonding jumper, 214
    Multiple service disconnects, 217
    Service supplied from another building, 219
    Single service disconnect, 214
Service overcurrent protection, 251
    Location, 251
    Number required, 251
    Rating, 251
Service transformers, 370
    Loop feed, 374
    Radial feed, 374
    Single-phase overhead, 370
    Single-phase pad-mount, 372

Three-phase overhead, 371
    Three-phase pad-mount, 374
Shielding angle, 304
Short circuit calculation, three-phase system, 460
Short circuit calculation, single-phase system, 465
Short circuit contribution, motor, 460
Short circuit, defined, 80
Single receptacle, 140
Slip, 344
Small appliance branch circuits, 152
    Loading, 41
    Number required, 152
Split-wired receptacles, 71
Squirrel cage rotor, 343
Stator, 343
Symmetrical fault current, 448
Synchronous speed, 343
System grounding, 207, 208
System voltages, 8
    120 V, single phase two wire, 9
    120/240 V, single phase three wire, 9
    208Y/120 V, three phase four wire, 9
    240 V, three phase, three wire, 10
    240/120 V, three phase, four wire, 11
    480 V, three phase, three wire, 10
    480Y/277 V, three phase four wire, 10

Table listed ampacity, 124
Tamper-resistant receptacles, 68
Temperature coefficient of resistance, 104
Three-way switch, 57
Threshold current, 87
Time current curve
    Fuse, 83
    Breaker, 95
Time overcurrent relay, 494
    Pickup tap setting, 494
    Time dial, 494
    TOC curves, 496, 497

Toggle switches, 55
    Applications, 57
    Contact arrangements, 56–58
    DPDT, 57
    DPST, 56
    Ratings, 60
    SPDT, 57
    Special switches, 60
    SPST, 56
Total derating factor, 119
Total harmonic distortion
    Current, 509
    Voltage, 509
Total light loss factor, 321
Transfer switch, 5
Transformer, 366
    Primary, 366
    Secondary, 366
    Single phase, 367
    Theory of operation, 366
    Three phase, 367
    Turns ratio, 367
Transformer circuit design, 401
    10 ft tap rule, 403
    25 ft tap rule industrial locations, 405
    Primary plus secondary not over 25 ft, 406
    Single-voltage two-wire secondary, 401
Transformer connections, 377
    Single phase, 377
    Three phase, 381
Transformer, dry type, 376
Transformer equivalent circuit, 368
Transformer impedance, 397, 400
    Impedance angle, 399
    Leakage flux, 398
    Leakage reactance, 398, 454
    Single-phase center tapped, 454
    Winding resistance, 398, 454
Transformer load calculations, 387
    Delta – delta, 392
    Delta – grounded wye, 389
    Floating wye – delta, 390
    Grounded wye – grounded wye, 387

Transformer load calculations,
   (continued)
  Open delta – open delta, 393
  Open wye – open delta, 393
  Single phase, 387
Transformer, low voltage, 376
Transformer overcurrent protection,
  401–408
Transformer polarity, 370
Transformer rated currents, 399
Transformer ratings, 382
  Cooling class, 383, 386
  Low voltage, 383, 385
  Overhead, 382, 383
  Pad mount, 382, 384
  Sound levels, 386
  Temperature rise, 386
Transformer short circuit protection,
  484
  Category I, 485
  Category II, 485
  Inrush point, 485
  Single phase, 488
  Three-phase delta – delta, 488

Three-phase delta – grounded
  wye, 491
Three-phase grounded wye –
  grounded wye, 488
Withstand curves, 486, 487
Transformer voltage drop, 430
  Single-phase transformer
    impedance, 432
  Three-phase transformer
    impedance, 431
Transformer voltage taps, 394, 434
  FCBN, 395
  Schematic, 396
  Voltage improvement, 434
Transformer winding voltage
  designations, 377
  Single phase, 377
  Three phase, 381
Transient voltage surge suppressor
  receptacle, 68
Travellers, 59

Unit loading, 39
Unit substation, 284, 288

Voltage drop, 422
  Definition, 424
  In-phase component, 425
Voltage drop, motor starting, 434
  Equivalent circuit, 435
  Flicker curve, 436, 437
Voltage range, 423

Warning tape, 192
Wireway, 186
  Busbar ampacity, 188
  Conductor deflection, 188, 189
  Conductor fill allowance, 187
  Splice area allowance, 188
  Standard dimensions, 187
  Sizing, 187
Wound rotor secondary, 343

X/R ratio, 86, 448

Zonal cavity method, 314